METHODS IN
MICROBIOLOGY

METHODS IN
MICROBIOLOGY

Volume 19
Current Methods for Classification and Identification of Microorganisms

Edited by

R. R. COLWELL

*Department of Microbiology, University of Maryland,
Adelphi, USA*

and

R. GRIGOROVA

*Institute of Microbiology, Bulgarian Academy of Sciences,
Sofia, Bulgaria*

1987

ACADEMIC PRESS
Harcourt Brace Jovanovich, Publishers
London   Orlando   San Diego   New York
Austin   Boston   Sydney   Tokyo   Toronto

ACADEMIC PRESS LIMITED
24–28 Oval Road
London NW1

United States Edition published by
ACADEMIC PRESS INC.
Orlando, Florida 32887

British Library Cataloguing in Publication Data
Methods in microbiology.
Vol. 19
1. Microbiology—Technique
I. Colwell, R. R.   II. Grigorova, R.
576'.028   QR65

ISBN 0–12–521519–3

Printed in Great Britain by Galliard (Printers) Ltd, Great Yarmouth, Norfolk

CONTRIBUTORS

A. S. Antonov A. N Belozersky Laboratory of Molecular Biology and Bioorganic Chemistry, Moscow State University, Moscow 119899, USSR

Shoshana Bascomb St Mary's Hospital Medical School, Department of Medical Microbiology, Praed Street, Paddington, London W2 1PG, UK

Shireen Chantler Wellcome Research Laboratories, Langley Court, Beckenham BR3 3BS, UK

Rita Colwell Central Administration, The University of Maryland, Adelphi, Maryland 20783, USA

George E. Fox Department of Biochemical Sciences, University of Houston, University Park, Houston, Texas 77004, USA

Colin S. Gutteridge Cadbury Schweppes plc, Group Research, The Lord Zuckerman Research Centre, The University, Whiteknights, PO Box 234, Reading RG6 2LA, UK

J. N. Hansen Department of Chemistry, Division of Biochemistry, University of Maryland, College Park, Maryland 20742, USA

Peter J. H. Jackman Division of Microbiology, AFRC Institute for Food Research, Colney Lane, Norwich NR4 7UA, UK

Kazuo Komagata Institute of Applied Microbiology, The University of Tokyo, Tokyo 113, Japan

B. Lányí National Institute of Hygiene, Gyali ut 2–6, H-1097 Budapest, Hungary

M. T. MacDonell Center of Marine Biotechnology, University of Maryland, Adelphi, Maryland 20783, USA

M. B. McIllmurray Wellcome Research Laboratories, Langley Court, Beckenham BR3 3BS, UK

Mark O'Brien Department of Microbiology, University of Maryland, College Park, Maryland 20742, USA

B. A. Ortiz-Conde Department of Microbiology, University of Maryland, College Park, Maryland 20742, USA

M. J. Sackin Department of Microbiology, University of Leicester, Leicester LE1 7RH, UK

Erko Stackebrandt Institut für Allegemeine Mikrobiologie, Universität Kiel, 23 Kiel, Federal Republic of Germany

Ken-ichiro Suzuki Japan Collection of Microorganisms, Riken, Wakso-shi, Saitama 351-01, Japan

T. P. Tourova A. N Belozersky Laboratory of Molecular Biology and Bioorganic Chemistry, Moscow State University, Moscow 119899, USSR

PREFACE

The systematics of microorganisms has received a great deal of attention in recent years, particularly with the development of new methods for tracking the evolution of microbial species. The techniques for molecular genetic analysis have advanced substantially from the early work on DNA base composition to DNA/DNA hybridization and the more recent and exciting methodology of DNA and RNA sequencing. Coupled with these biochemical and molecular genetic advances are computer applications in systematics. Software for large scale data handling provides extraordinary opportunities for improved identification and classification of microorganisms.

This volume will provide an excellent means for initiating students into the excitement of microbial systematics, generated by the developments of the last few years. It is hoped that the volume will fill a need for a methodology text dealing with techniques for identification and classification of microorganisms The techniques covered range from those that are relatively simple, including classical and rapid identification methods to those used routinely in molecular biology as, for example, the most recent procedures of DNA and RNA sequencing.

Both the novice and the experienced research worker will be interested in some aspects of the material provided herein, which was intended to provide an "alpha and omega" coverage of the methodology for microbial systematics. Because one must "freeze" the knowledge available in order to review the state of the science at a given time, there is always the danger of the material rapidly becoming dated. In this case, the volume was planned to be both broad in scope and detailed in presentation, so that it will provide a valuable and useful reference, as well as a record of the field at the contemporary stage of development.

We would like to express our appreciation to Academic Press for the care with which they have prepared the material for publication and the high quality they have achieved.

April 1987   R. R. Colwell
                                                               R. Grigorova

CONTENTS

1
Classical and Rapid Identification Methods for Medically Important Bacteria

B. LÁNYI

National Institute of Hygiene, Budapest, Hungary

METHODS IN MICROBIOLOGY
VOLUME 19   ISBN 0–12–521519–3

I. Introduction

A. General considerations

In the early days of bacteriology, obtaining pure cultures of microorganisms from the mixtures in which they generally occur in Nature was the first important advance in distinguishing one kind of organism from the others. Using a solid medium and "streak plate" or "pour plate" methods, investigators were able to isolate and identify many kinds of bacteria. Early taxonomists considered mainly cell shape and staining, cell size, and the form of colonies, type of growth in broth, site of isolation, and pathogenicity. Subsequently, it has been recognized that cultural properties on simple media are too variable to be expressed as positive or negative characters and that habitat and pathogenicity are unsatisfactory features for a systematic classification. Even morphological and staining properties, which remain of great importance in taxonomy, are now regarded, in view of the availability of excellent selective and differential media, as not worthwhile to determine in routine identification of certain organisms, e.g. the Enterobacteriaceae. Early studies on nutritional, growth temperature and atmospheric requirements soon led to the discovery that Nature has produced a wide variety of physiological entities among the bacteria. Transformation of chemical compounds by bacterial enzymes is now recognized as an important tool in classification. Growth inhibitors are also widely used for both isolation and taxonomic characterization.

Thousands of identification methods have been described in the literature. The overwhelming majority represent modifications of tests discovered in the first half of this century, when the foundation of modern taxonomy was laid. Selection of the best of these methods or replacement of an old test with an improved one requires extensive comparative trials. In choosing methods, an enormous number of commercial reagents, dehydrated or complete media and multitest systems also have to be considered. In general, any method is satisfactory that gives accurate and reproducible results. Tests used in routine clinical and public health bacteriology should be suitable for a tolerably rapid and reliable identification.

In this chapter methods are described that may be considered as reference procedures (Kauffmann, 1954; Edwards and Ewing, 1972; Cowan, 1974; Holdeman et al., 1977; Paik, 1980; Sonnenwirth, 1980; Vera and Power, 1980). In Hungary these methods have proved to give consistent results and have been prescribed as standard tests for the Hungarian Public Health Laboratory Service and for Hungarian hospital microbiology laboratories (Lányi, 1980).

Because of the limited space available in this chapter, identification methods for mycobacteria have been omitted. These have been described in detail elsewhere (Vestal, 1975; Runyon *et al.*, 1980; Kubica and David, 1980) and have been used as reference methods all over the world. Determination of antigens and toxins also will not be described here, having been covered in earlier volumes of this series. Bacterial serology, although providing a practical and rapid aid for the identification of many bacteria, serves best for secondary subdivision of taxa.

B. Basic requirements of identification

To determine their characteristics, bacteria must be grown in pure culture, which is a group of organisms that have developed from a single cell or from a single clump of similar cells. In routine diagnostic work it is usually—and, for saving time, it has to be—sufficient to subculture a single colony grown on the primary plate. Taxonomic studies, in contrast, require several replatings from separate colonies, until an undoubtedly pure subculture is secured. Common sources of impure culture are colonies picked from the selective medium, which suppresses growth of most unwanted bacteria but does not kill them. On a selective plate seeded with specimens containing many kinds of microorganisms, inhibited but living cells are scattered throughout the surface of the medium and under the colonies of the non-inhibited organism. For subculturing, the culture that is sought must be picked up by touching only the point of an inoculating needle or loop on to the surface of one well-isolated and seemingly pure colony. It would be a serious mistake to "sweep" two or more colonies and/or to touch the seemingly "sterile" surface of the plate. Another source of impurity is the spreading growth of some bacteria, which can be avoided by using media inhibitory to swarming. A simultaneous subculturing of the colony on a differential plate, other than the primary one, saves time in repeating the purification process. For example, a suspected Salmonella colony from bismuth sulphite agar should be transferred, in addition to triple sugar iron agar and other tubed media, to brilliant green or MacConkey plates. Cultures that are difficult to identify are frequently mixed ones and should be examined for purity by streaking on several kinds of differential and selective media.

A correct incubation temperature is important for obtaining interpretable results. As a rule, tests should be done at the temperature optimal for growth, which may be estimated by observing growth of the culture on media seeded with the specimen. To permit growth of common pathogens and opportunistic pathogens, primary plates are usually incubated first at 35–37 °C overnight, followed by incubation for another day at 22–30 °C. Two temperature ranges are also sufficient for most identification tests: 35–37 °C for most clinically important bacteria and 30 °C for glucose-non-fermenting, Gram-negative bacteria. The incubation temperature will be specified below only if different from that required for optimal growth.

The atmospheric requirement of isolates is evident from their growth on primary plates. Tests, unless otherwise stated, should be carried out under optimal conditions, i.e. in air (aerobes and facultative anaerobes), in air with 10% CO_2 (capnophilic bacteria), in nitrogen with 10% CO_2 and 5% O_2 (campylobacters and other microaerophilic organisms), or in nitrogen with 10% CO_2 and less than 1% O_2 (anaerobes). Tests for anaerobic bacteria include cultivation in anaerobic incubators and in ordinary anaerobe jars; the same media are suitable for pre-reduced preparation and handling (Holdeman et al., 1977), a procedure that cannot be performed in most clinical laboratories because of lack of equipment more elaborate than anaerobe jars.

To obtain reproducible results, the incubation time is of great importance. With tests requiring culturing, a stage of sufficient multiplication, i.e. turbidity or precipitate in liquid media and good surface growth on solid media, should be obtained. To ensure adequate growth, the media should be supplemented with 5% serum and/or growth factors for fastidious bacteria and with 3–7% NaCl for halophilic vibrios. The standard incubation time for rapidly growing bacteria is specified for each test. For a tentative diagnosis in routine work, an incubation period shorter than that prescribed for a standard reading is usually sufficient, especially if the test is positive. For anaerobic bacteria the test should be read when good growth is evident or when no increase of growth occurs after an additional 8 hours of incubation (Holdeman et al., 1977).

Growth is influenced by the size of the inoculum and the volume of the test medium. The inoculum, whenever different from the usual needlepoint amount of solid culture or 0.2–0.3 ml of anaerobic broth culture, is specified. Except when otherwise stated, the volume of the test medium is 2–3 ml for narrow tubes (diameter 10–12 mm) or 5–6 ml for ordinary test tubes (usual diameter 16 mm). For Petri dishes 90 mm in diameter, about 25 ml of medium should be used.

An essential point in identification is biological quality control. All batches of media and reagents must be tested with appropriate cultures before being put into routine use (see interpretation of individual tests). As reference ingredients of media, this chapter specifies commercial products that have been proved suitable from long personal experience. Other products, as far as they give interpretable and reproducible results, can be considered equally good.

II. Morphological characterization

A. Cell morphology

In practical identification of bacteria, cell morphology is determined either in unstained wet preparations examined by phase-contrast microscopy or in stained smears observed with ordinary optics. Wet mounts of young cultures reflect the natural morphology of the organisms, whereas in stained preparations, because of a shrinking of their protoplasm, bacteria appear shorter and thinner than their actual dimensions. Different procedures have been described by Norris and Swain (1971); this chapter presents tests used most frequently in routine identification.

1. Wet mounts

(i) *Procedure.* Mix a needlepoint amount of culture grown on solid medium in a small drop of water placed on an ordinary plain microscope slide and place a coverslip onto it. Cultures grown in liquid medium are suitable without dilution. The film of bacterial suspension should be thin; absorb the excess liquid with a piece of blotting paper so that the coverslip does not float over the slide. Examine immediately under a phase-contrast microscope with a high-power dry or an oil-immersion objective. The preparation, unless sealed with molten vaseline or with nail varnish along the edge of the coverslip, dries rapidly and becomes unsuitable for examination.

(ii) *Interpretation.* Record the shape and approximate size of cells. For motility examination see Section C.

2. Staining procedures

Stains described below are satisfactory for observation of the morphology and staining properties of most bacteria. The methylene blue stain serves for simple examination of cultures and is advantageous for presumptive recognition of bacteria in smears prepared from clinical specimens. The Gram method is the most important differential staining procedure. In young cultures of Gram-positive bacteria, crystal violet and iodine form a complex with cell constituents that is relatively insoluble in ethanol or acetone, whereas Gram-negative bacteria readily lose the violet stain and take the counterstain, which imparts another colour to the cells. Isolates of some taxonomic entities are Gram-variable, but the number of such species is not sufficient to affect the value of the Gram stain. Bacteria having a high concentration of lipids in their cells are difficult to stain by ordinary methods.

They stain readily, however, with hot fuchsin-containing phenol. When once stained, they retain the dye after treatment with acidified ethanol, i.e. "acid-fast bacteria". The Ziehl–Neelsen carbol fuchsin stain diluted 1:3–1:10 may be used for organisms that are not acid-fast but take up other dyes less readily (legionellae, spirochaetes).

To make a stained preparation, the bacterial suspension is smeared thinly on a slide. After allowing it to dry at room temperature for a few minutes, the smear is fixed by passing, specimen side up, through the flame of a Bunsen burner, three or four times in succession. Fixation solidifies the protoplasm of bacteria and causes them to adhere to the slide. The gentle heating of the slide is insufficient to kill some bacteria (spore-formers, mycobacteria), and the slides should be decontaminated after examination. After fixing, the smear is covered with the staining solution, then washed off with water. The smear is dried in air or by blotting it with absorbing paper and examined under oil immersion, with the oil placed directly on the stained smear.

(a) Methylene blue stain

(i) *Reagent.* Saturated alcoholic methylene blue solution (approx. 1.4 g dye in 100 ml 95% ethanol), 30 ml; potassium hydroxide, 1% aqueous solution, 1 ml; distilled water, 100 ml.

(ii) *Procedure.* Stain the fixed smear for 2 min, rinse with water and blot.

(iii) *Interpretation.* Cells stain blue.

(b) Gram stain (Hucker's modification)

(i) *Reagents.* Crystal violet solution: crystal violet, 2 g; ethanol (95%), 10 ml; distilled water, 90 ml. Oxalate solution: Na-, K- or NH_4-oxalate, 1 g; distilled water, 100 ml. Lugol's solution (for Hucker's stain): iodine, 1 g; potassium iodide, 2 g; distilled water, 300 ml; add a few ml of distilled water to the iodine and potassium iodide, mix, add small amounts of water gradually until the substances are dissolved, then bring up the volume to 300 ml; store in a glass stoppered bottle protected from light. Decolourizer: ethanol (95%). Safranin solution: safranin O, 0.25 g; ethanol (95%), 10 ml; distilled water, 90 ml.

(ii) *Procedure.* Suspend the cultures in small drops of water placed on a slide and prepare smears (not more than 5 on one slide 25 mm × 75 mm in size). Make the first smear round and the others oval and record their position. Prepare next to them a control smear consisting of a mixture of known Gram-negative and Gram-positive bacteria. Fix and stain for 1 min with a mixture of 1 volume of crystal violet and 4 volumes of oxalate solution. Wash with water. Apply Lugol's solution for 1 min. Wash with water and blot dry. Decolourize by allowing ethanol to drip onto one end of the inclined slide so as to flow evenly over the smears until the solvent flows colourlessly from the slide. Wash with water, stain with safranin for 2–3 min, blot and examine.

(iii) *Interpretation.* Gram-positive: the bacteria are deep violet (*Staphylococcus aureus*). Gram-negative: the bacteria are pink to red (*Escherichia coli*). Decolourizing time is influenced by the water content of ethanol. Blotting of the slide before decolourization prevents an uncontrollable dilution of ethanol with water remaining on the slide, but prolongs the decolourizing time.

(c) Ziehl–Neelsen stain

(i) *Reagents.* *Carbol fuchsin solution*: basic fuchsin, 10 g; ethanol (95%), 100 ml; add 900 ml of 5% aqueous phenol solution, mix and filter through paper. *Decolourizer*: ethanol (95%), 97 ml; concentrated HCl, 3 ml. *Loeffler's methylene blue solution*: methylene blue, 1 g; ethanol (95%), 100 ml; potassium hydroxide, 0.01% aqueous solution, 100 ml; the stain improves with keeping.

(ii) *Procedure.* Flood the fixed smear with carbol fuchsin and heat with a flame periodically three times in 5 min until steam rises. Wash with running tap water and decolourize by flooding with several successive portions of acid–alcohol until it flows colourlessly from the slide. Wash, counterstain with methylene blue for about 30 s, wash again and air dry. To prevent contamination of acid-fast bacteria from one slide to another, do not immerse the slides in vessels containing the stain or decolourizing agent and do not blot the preparations.

(iii) *Interpretation.* Acid-fast bacteria are red (*Mycobacterium tuberculosis*), and other organisms and background material are blue.

B. Capsules

Some bacteria form a relatively large mass of slime layer around their cells. Owing to a low affinity for dyes, the capsule is usually not visible by ordinary staining. By use of special staining, the capsules and the cells exhibit different colours (Norris and Swain, 1971; Cowan, 1974). For routine use, "negative staining" of live bacteria with India ink is most satisfactory.

(i) *Procedure.* Mix a needlepoint amount of bacteria grown on solid medium in a loopful of India ink placed on a slide. Prepare a thin film by pressing a coverslip on the drop and removing the excess liquid with a piece of blotting paper. Examine immediately under a phase-contrast microscope.

(ii) *Interpretation.* The capsule appears as a bright zone between the dark cells and the grey background (*Klebsiella aerogenes*).

C. Flagella

Flagella are the locomotor organelles of bacteria, consisting of whiplike appendages invisible under an optical microscope. The number, position and arrangement of flagella are fairly constant taxonomic features.

1. Phase-contrast microscopic examination of motility

The procedure described in Section II.A.1. is recommended for examining the motility of bacteria other than Enterobacteriaceae, which should be tested in semisolid agar (Section II.D.). Observation of swimming movement in a wet microscopic preparation is not sufficient to determine the arrangement of flagella, although polar flagellated bacteria show an apparently rapid darting motility, whereas peritrichous cells usually move at a lower speed. True motility should be distinguished from the oscillatory (Brownian) movement due to a continuous jostling of bacteria by molecules of the suspending fluid. Motility is best in young broth cultures incubated at 22–30 °C. Motility must be examined immediately after placing the culture on the slide. Light has an adverse effect, and the number of motile bacteria will decrease rapidly.

2. Leifson's flagella stain

Flagella can be seen under an electron microscope and by special staining in which an opaque substance is precipitated on their surfaces so as to increase their thickness above the resolution of optical microscopes. Staining of flagella requires a very careful and standardized technique, including extremely clean slides and as low amounts of background materials as possible, in order to prevent precipitation of the stain on the surface of the slide.

(i) *Reagents.* *Solution A*: basic fuchsin certified for flagella staining, 0.8 g;

ethanol (95%), 100 ml. *Solution B*: NaCl, 1.4 g; tannic acid, 3.0 g; distilled water, 200 ml. Mix the two solutions by thorough shaking. Allow to settle for 24 h, distribute in convenient amounts and store in the freezing compartment of a refrigerator. Just prior to use, warm the required amount of dye to room temperature and, if necessary, correct the pH by adding 0.1 volume phosphate buffer (0.5 M KH_2PO_4 and 0.5 M K_2HPO_4 mixed to provide a final pH of 6.0–6.2 to the dye solution). *Preparation of slides*: clean slides by boiling in 20% nitric acid for 5–10 min or by immersing them for 24 h in chromic–sulphuric acid (potassium dichromate saturated aqueous solution, 500 ml; concentrated sulphuric acid, 800 ml); wash by rinses of distilled water to remove all traces of acid, and allow to drain; store in a closed container.

(ii) *Procedure.*   Use young cultures grown at 22–30 °C. Add 0.25 ml formalin (commercial preparation containing about 35% formaldehyde) to 4 ml broth culture, allow to stand for 15 min after gentle mixing, add about 4 ml distilled water, mix and centrifuge at 2000 rpm. Decant the supernatant, add about 8 ml distilled water, mix and centrifuge. Decant the supernatant and resuspend the bacteria in distilled water to a slight turbidity. Heat the slide in the blue portion of a Bunsen flame. Place a loopful of bacterial suspension at the end of the cooled slide tilted at about 80° and allow the liquid to flow lengthwise to the opposite end. Remove the excess with a blotting paper and dry at room temperature. Bacteria are fixed by the stain; do not heat the slide. Flood the slide with the stain. Staining lasts for 5–15 min, depending on the temperature and the age of the reagent: the higher the temperature of the laboratory, the more rapidly does ethanol evaporate from the stain and the dye precipitate, whereas an old solution stains less rapidly than a freshly prepared one. When staining is complete, a lighter red precipitate forms in the solution. Gently wash the stain off with water; do not pour the stain off before rinsing. Wipe the back of the slide and allow to dry in air.

(iii) *Interpretation.*   Examine several areas of the slide and many flagellated bacteria for number and arrangement of flagella. Polar flagellated bacteria are regarded as monotrichous if the majority of cells have just one flagellum, and lophotrichous if the majority of cells have two or more flagella.

If the above method fails to give a sufficient number of flagellated bacteria, try to prepare a suspension as follows. Carefully pipette about 3 ml distilled water on nutrient agar slope cultures and allow them to stand until bacteria separate spontaneously from the agar and form a cloudy suspension; do not add formalin and do not centrifuge. Other flagella stains have been suggested by Cowan (1974).

D. Spores

The spore is a stage in the life cycle of certain bacteria, when the cell protoplasm becomes condensed into a small body surrounded by a relatively impervious wall. The spores may be spheroidal or ovoid in shape, and their position within the parent cell may be central, subterminal or terminal; they may or may not swell the organism. Of medical bacteria, *Bacillus* and *Clostridium* produce spores. Since there is a tendency for some species to lose the ability to produce spores, it is often necessary to cultivate suspected spore formers for up to 14 days on media enhancing sporulation (e.g. on garden-soil-infusion nutrient agar). Although ordinary stains do not penetrate the spore wall, the outlines of intracellular and free spores can be seen in stained films under conventional illumination. In wet preparations under a phase-contrast microscope (Section II.A.1.) spores appear as brilliant refractile objects. The use of spore stains (Norris and Swain, 1971; Cowan, 1974) is not necessary in identification.

E.   Intracellular bodies

The presence of cytoplasmic inclusions of reserve material is an aid in the identification of certain kinds of bacteria. In medical bacteriology, the presence of metachromatic granules, also known as Babes–Ernst granules, is characteristic of most corynebacteria.

(i) *Reagents.*   *Neisser's solution A*: methylene blue, 1 g; ethanol (95%), 20 ml; glacial acetic acid, 50 ml; distilled water, 1000 ml. *Neisser's solution B*: crystal violet, 1 g; ethanol (95%), 10 ml; distilled water, 300 ml. *Neisser's solution C*: chrysoidin, 2 g; hot distilled water, 300 ml; cool and filter.

(ii) *Procedure.*   Stain the fixed smear for 5 min with a mixture of 2 volumes solution A and 1 volume solution B. Rinse with distilled water and counterstain with solution C for 10 s. Blot dry without washing. Prolonged counterstaining causes a fading of the metachromatic granules.

(iii) *Interpretation.*   Metachromatic granules are dark violet-brown, cytoplasm is yellow (*Corynebacterium diphtheriae*).

III. Cultural characterization

A. Growth temperature and heat tolerance

As differentiating criteria, identification tables list, as a rule, growth at 4, 20, 30, 37, 41, 45 and/or 65°C. For testing, tubed media known to support the growth of the organism are inoculated lightly and incubated at different temperatures until good growth occurs in one or more of the tubes. For testing above 37°C, water baths should be used. In taxonomic studies the results should be confirmed by serially subculturing the organisms at the given temperatures several times.

Temperature tolerance means survival of the organism on heating. The test is used mainly for the differentiation of streptococci. One millilitre of Todd–Hewitt or other suitable broth is inoculated with a drop of 24 h broth culture, placed in a water bath at 60 °C for 30 min, then incubated at 35–37 °C for 48 h. Growth indicates survival. *Streptococcus faecalis* is a useful reference culture for this test.

B. Oxygen and carbon dioxide requirement

In routine examination, the atmospheric requirement of an isolate can be estimated by considering the mode of incubation of the primary plates. For exact testing, inoculate a series of appropriate plated media and incubate the plates: (1) in an aerobic incubator; (2) in a closed incubator or jar with CO_2 content increased to 10%; (3) in a closed incubator or jar with CO_2 content increased to 10% and oxygen decreased to 5%; and (4) in a closed incubator or jar with anaerobic conditions. For description of anaerobic devices see Holdeman *et al.* (1977), Kaplan (1980) and Allen and Siders (1980). For a simple test of the ability of the culture to grow anaerobically, inoculate a tube of thioglycollate semisolid medium uniformly with a dilute saline suspension; facultative anaerobes grow throughout the medium, anaerobes below its surface and aerobes on its surface.

C. Nutritional requirements and growth factors

Bacteria display a remarkable diversity in the nutrients they can utilize. In systematic studies a wide variety of substances have been examined for utilization and growth-enhancing ability; however, few of these tests have been introduced into routine diagnostic medical bacteriology. Identification tables usually define growth on nutrient agar or in nutrient broth in the absence or in the presence of 5% serum or blood. Of growth factors, the requirement for haemin (X factor) and diphosphopyridine nucleotide (V factor) is of importance.

Haemophilus species require one or both of the two factors X and V, which are practically absent from simple nutrient agar. Blood agar contains the X factor, whereas chocolate agar, in which the V factor has been liberated and V-factor-destroying enzymes have been inactivated by moderate heating, provides both factors. *Staphylococcus aureus* produces the V factor, i.e. if a blood agar is seeded with the organism being tested and a streak of staphylococcal culture is inoculated perpendicularly to the original streak, X + V- and V-factor-requiring *Haemophilus* strains will show satellite growth, a phenomenon rare among the bacteria. For an exact determination of growth factor requirement, discs prepared in the laboratory or purchased from commercial sources are recommended.

(i) *Reagent discs.*   *X-factor stock solution*: dissolve 20 mg Hemin (Serva) in 1 ml 0.1 N NaOH and add distilled water to 10 ml; autoclave at 115 °C for 20 min. *V-factor stock solution*: dissolve 24 mg beta-nicotinamide adenine dinucleotide (Serva) in 10 ml distilled water and sterilize by passing through a glass filter. To make the discs more selective for *Haemophilus*, 10 mg vancomycin may be added to each stock solution. *Preparation of discs*: sterilize filter-paper discs by autoclaving and impregnate each of them with 10 µl amounts of the following solutions: X-factor stock solution diluted with an equal volume of distilled water; V-factor stock solution diluted with an equal volume of distilled water; and X and V stock solutions mixed in equal volumes. Dry quickly at room temperature, distribute in airtight bottles with desiccant, and store in the freezing compartment of a refrigerator.

(ii) *Procedure.*   Inoculate blood-agar base plates (preferably supplemented with 0.02% L-cystine) by streaking a fresh culture evenly over the entire surface. Place X, V- and XV-factor discs near the edge of the plate, about 50 mm apart from one another. Incubate at 35–37 °C for 18–24 h.

(iii) *Interpretation.*   X-factor requirement: organisms requiring only X factor (*Haemophilus aphrophilus*, *Haemophilus ducreyi*) are more fastidious than other *Haemophilus* species, and will grow around the X- and XV-factor discs only if the medium contains serum and is incubated in an atmosphere with increased CO_2. V-factor requirement: growth around V and XV discs (*Haemophilus parainfluenzae*). X + V factor requirement: growth only around XV discs (*Haemophilus influenzae*). If the ingredients of the medium contain traces of X or V factor, *Haemophilus influenzae* may exhibit poor growth around the V or X disc respectively.

D. Demonstration of motility by cultivation

Non-fastidious facultative anaerobes (e.g. Enterobacteriaceae) should be tested by observing their migration through semisolid agar, which is a far more accurate method than microscopic examination (Edwards and Ewing, 1972). Aerobic bacteria cannot be examined in this manner, since they grow only on the surface of the medium; however, the motility of those utilizing nitrate as a terminal hydrogen acceptor, e.g. *Pseudomonas aeruginosa*, may be tested in semisolid agar containing 0.2% potassium nitrate (Lányi and Bergan, 1978).

(i) *Medium.*   Bacto peptone (Difco), 10 g; beef extract (Oxoid), 3 g; NaCl, 5 g; agar (Oxoid No. 1), 1.2 g; distilled water, 1000 ml; pH 7.2–7.4. Dispense in U-tubes or in Craigie tubes (test tubes each containing a piece of glass tubing projecting above the surface of the medium). Sterilize at 121 °C for 20 min.

(ii) *Procedure.*   Inoculate the surface of the medium in one arm of the U-tube or in the central Craigie tube. Incubate at 35–37 °C for 1 day; if negative, follow with further incubation at 22–25 °C for 5 days. Alternatively, inoculate duplicate media and incubate at 35–37 and 22–25 °C.

(iii) *Interpretation.*   Motile: diffuse zone of growth emanating from the site of inoculation and spreading continuously until it reaches the uninoculated surface of the medium, viz *Escherichia coli*. Nonmotile: growth is confined to the inoculated surface, viz *Shigella flexneri*. Stalactite-like streaks of growth below the seeded surface may occur on prolonged incubation as a result of a sinking of the culture into the medium; this should not be interpreted as motility.

E. Pigment production

The intensity of pigmentation is influenced by several factors, varying with the organism tested. As a rule, pigment production is enhanced at temperatures lower than those optimal for growth and by exposure of the culture to light. Nutrient-agar or blood-agar plates and King A slants incubated up to 3 days are generally suitable for pigmentation. For the differentiation of pseudomonads, media A and B of King *et al.* (1954) is recommended.

1. Demonstration of pyocyanin

(i) *Medium A.*   Bacto peptone (Difco), 20 g; glycerol, 10 g; K_2SO_4, 10 g;

MgCl$_2$, 1.4 g; agar (Oxoid No. 1), 9 g; distilled water, 1000 ml; pH 7.2. Distribute in test tubes, sterilize at 115 °C for 20 min, cool as slants.

(ii) *Procedure.*   Incubate at 20–30 °C for up to 3 days. If bluish-green pigment appears, add 3–4 ml chloroform and read the resulting reaction after the culture has been left standing for 2–3 h.

(iii) *Interpretation.*   Record the colour of the pigment (brown, reddish-brown, red, orange, yellow, green, bluish-green, violet) before adding chloroform. Pyocyanin production is indicated by a blue colour after addition of chloroform (*Pseudomonas aeruginosa*).

2. Demonstration of fluorescent pigment

(i) *Medium B.*   Proteose peptone (Difco), 20 g; glycerol, 10 g; K$_2$HPO$_4$, 1.5 g; MgSO$_4$. 7H$_2$O, 1.5 g; agar (Oxoid No. 1), 9 g; distilled water, 1000 ml; pH 7.2. Distribute in test tubes, sterilize at 115 °C for 20 min, cool as slants.

(ii) *Procedure.*   Incubate at 20–30 °C for 1 day (routine identification) and for 3 days (standard identification). Read by daylight or, preferably, under UV light at 254 nm.

(iii) *Interpretation.*   Pyoverdin (fluorescein) production: greenish-yellow fluorescence under daylight and bright-green or yellowish-green fluorescence under UV light, i.e. *Pseudomonas aeruginosa*. Fluorescent pigment not produced: green fluorescence absent; under UV light a faint bluish autofluorescence of the medium (*Pseudomonas maltophilia*). The green colouration read by daylight is not specific for fluorescent pigment, but supports the diagnosis of *Pseudomonas aeruginosa*, established routinely on the basis of OF, nitrate, and other reactions.

F.   Use of selective media in identification

When interpreted by an expert bacteriologist, growth on selective media is excellent not only for presumptive identification, but also for classification. Use of these media is especially recommended for central bacteriology laboratories providing an identification service. The culture to be identified should be streaked on selective plates chosen by considering the primary isolation records received with the strain. For example, a culture suspected as belonging to the Enterobacteriaceae is streaked on bismuth sulphite, deoxycholate–citrate or salmonella–shigella, brilliant green and MacConkey or eosine methylene blue agar plates. If a member of the Vibrionaceae is suspected, a thiosulphate–citrate bile-salts plate is added. Non-fastidious non-fermenters are inoculated, at minimum, on MacConkey or eosin methylene blue and on blood agar. Corynebacteria, in addition to blood agar, are streaked on cysteine–tellurite agar.

Tabulation of the behaviour of different taxonomic entities on selective media presents obvious difficulties. In identification tables for Gram-negative bacteria, the presence or absence of growth on MacConkey and on detergent (e.g. cetrimide) media are usually shown as positive or negative characters.

G.   Growth-inhibition tests

1. Antibiotics

As bacteria easily acquire resistance to antibiotics, the use of these substances in taxonomy is debatable (Cowan, 1974). However, inhibition of some bacterial groups by certain antibiotics is rather constant and may be of importance in identification. Testing of sensitivity for this purpose is usually performed by the agar diffusion technique, using commercial antibiotic discs.

(a) Bacitracin test.   Sensitivity of streptococci to bacitracin is tested on blood agar. It is essential to use adequate control cultures. For example, *Streptococcus pyogenes* usually is sensitive and non-group A beta-haemolytic streptococci are resistant, i.e. not entirely inhibited by bacitracin, e.g. a group L streptococcus.

(b) Other antimicrobial drugs.   The following drugs are of differential value: erythromycin (anaerobes), kanamycin (pseudomonads), metronidazole (anaerobes), nalidixic acid (campylobacters), novobiocin (5 µg discs, staphylococci), penicillin (Gram-negative non-fermenters, streptococci, anaerobes), polymyxin (Gram-negative non-fermenters, Enterobacteriaceae, vibrios, anaerobes), rifampicin (anaerobes) and vancomycin (*Haemophilus*, anaerobes).

2. Bile tolerance

(a) Streptococcus

(i) *Medium.*   Beef extract (Oxoid), 3 g; Bacto peptone (Difco), 5 g; NaCl, 5 g; dehydrated oxgall, 40 g; agar (Oxoid No. 1), 9 g; distilled water, 1000 ml; pH 7.2. Dispense in tubes, autoclave at 121 °C for 20 min and cool as slants.

(ii) *Procedure.*   Inoculate and incubate for 48 h.

(iii) *Interpretation.*   Positive: growth (group D streptococci). Negative: no growth (*Streptococcus mitis*).

(b) Anaerobes

(i) *Medium.*   Add 1 g glucose and 2 g dehydrated oxgall to 100 ml PY basal medium (Section IV.D.1b) before boiling. Distribute and sterilize as in Section IV.D.1b.

(ii) *Procedure.*   Inoculate PY–glucose–bile and PY–glucose medium and incubate as described in Section IV.D.1b. Compare growth in the bile and in the control medium.

(iii) *Interpretation.*   Inhibited: no growth (*Bacteroides melaninogenicus*). Positive: growth (*Bacteroides praeacutus*). Stimulated: growth better than the control (*Bacteroides fragilis*).

3. Cetrimide tolerance

(i) *Medium.*   Nutrient agar plates containing 0.03% (w/v) cetrimide (hexadecyltrimethylammonium bromide).

(ii) *Procedure.*   Inoculate and incubate for 2 days.

(iii) *Interpretation.*   Positive: growth (*Pseudomonas aeruginosa*). Negative: no growth (*Pseudomonas stutzeri*).

4. Dye tolerance

Dyes as selective agents are frequently used in primary isolation media, but in identification procedures they provide less-convincing results. Identification tables provide species differentiation for *Brucella* using basic fuchsin and thionin (1:25 000–1:100 000). The dyes may be incorporated in any medium supporting the growth of *Brucella*. Positive and negative results must be controlled with adequate reference strains.

5. Optochin sensitivity

(i) *Discs.*   Impregnate each autoclaved filter paper disc with 10 μl of an 0.05% aqueous solution of optochin (ethylhydrocuprein HCl). Dry at 37 °C and store at refrigerator temperatures.

(ii) *Procedure.*   Inoculate blood-agar plates as for antibiotic sensitivity testing and place a disc on the surface.

(iii) *Interpretation.*   Positive: zone of inhibition (*Streptococcus pneumoniae*). Negative: inhibition zone absent or narrow (*Streptococcus mitis*).

6. 0/129 sensitivity

(i) *Discs.*   Impregnate sterile filter-paper discs with 10 μl of an 0.1% acetone solution of 0/129 (2,4–diamino-6,7-isopropylpteridine phosphate).

(ii) *Procedure.*   Inoculate nutrient-agar plates as for antibiotic sensitivity testing and place a disc on the agar surface after inoculation.

(iii) *Interpretation.*   Positive: zone of inhibition (*Vibrio cholerae*). Negative: inhibition zone absent or narrow (*Aeromonas hydrophila*).

7. Potassium cyanide test

The cyanide ion produces a complex with heavy-metal ions and inhibits in this manner the iron-containing enzymes involved in the electron-transport system of bacterial respiration. The inhibitory concentration of KCN depends on the ingredients of the medium, but not on the amount of oxygen present. The respiration of KCN-tolerant bacteria is controlled by enzymes less sensitive to the agent (Gunsalus and Stanier, 1961; Stanier *et al.*, 1963).

(i) *Medium.*   Proteose peptone No. 3 (Difco), 3 g; NaCl, 5 g; KH_2PO_4, 0.22 g; K_2HPO_4, 5.64 g; distilled water, 1000 ml; pH 7.6. Sterilize at 115 °C for 20 min. Cool the medium to 4 °C and add 15 ml 0.5% KCN solution, freshly prepared with distilled water cooled to 4 °C. One millilitre of boiled and cooled 1% aqueous TTC (2,3,5-triphenyltetrazolium chloride) solution may be added. Distribute immediately in 2–3 ml amounts in narrow tubes placed in an ice bath. Seal the tubes with corks soaked in hot paraffin wax. Store at 4 °C and use within 2 months.

(ii) *Procedure.*   Inoculate by dipping a needle in the medium and incubate for 4 days.

(iii) *Interpretation.*   Positive: growth, bacteria are stained red (*Citrobacter freundii*). Negative: the medium remains clear and colourless (*Escherichia coli*).

If the KCN medium is supplemented with TTC, the test is easier to read, since growing bacteria reduce the colourless substance to red formazan. The above instructions for preparation of the medium should be carefully followed, as KCN is unstable and readily evaporates as HCN. The substance is highly poisonous: it must be handled with care and *never* pipetted by mouth. Before discarding the tubes, the KCN in the cultures should be destroyed by adding a crystal of ferrous sulphate and 0.1 ml 40% potassium hydroxide per tube (Cowan, 1974). Syringes, pipettes and unused KCN solution should be discarded as described in Section IV.C.2.

8. Salt tolerance and requirement

Usual concentrations for testing growth of different organisms are 0, 3, 6, 6.5, 7 and 10% for *Vibrio*, 1.5 and 3.5% for *Campylobacter*, 6.5% for Gram-negative non-fermenters and streptococci, and 7% for *Bacillus*. Nutrient-agar or blood-agar plates containing the indicated concentrations of NaCl are satisfactory for most bacteria. For streptococci, the salt should be added to tryptose or heart-infusion broth with 0.1% glucose.

9. TTC tolerance

Growth in the presence of TTC (2,3,5-triphenyltetrazolium chloride) is used for the identification of campylobacters (0.4 g TTC per litre of blood agar) and of Gram-negative non-fermenters (10 g TTC per litre of nutrient agar). TTC can be sterilized at 115 °C for 20 min.

IV.   Biochemical characterization

A.   Respiratory-enzyme tests

1. Oxidase test

As a last link in the respiratory chain of oxidase-positive bacteria, oxidized cytochrome *c* takes up electrons and passes them to molecular oxygen, which, being the terminal hydrogen acceptor, is reduced to hydrogen peroxide. The subsequent regeneration of cytochrome *c* to the oxidized form is catalysed by the enzyme cytochrome oxidase. In the oxidase test, *p*-phenylenediamine derivatives used as reagents are oxidized to coloured compounds by oxidized cytochrome *c*, which in turn changes to reduced cytochrome *c*. Accordingly, the test reagent acts as an artificial electron donor and does not react directly with the enzyme. The test proceeds only in the presence of air, since oxygen is necessary for the production of oxidized cytochrome c (Kovács, 1956; Gaby and Hadley, 1957; Gunsalus and Stanier, 1961; Steel, 1961; Harper et al., 1977).

p-Phenylenediamine reagents vary in sensitivity: the tetramethyl compound is highly sensitive, and, in combination with dimethyl sulphoxide, it can be used for the intrageneric differentiation of staphylococci (Faller and Schleifer, 1981), which are oxidase-negative with other reagents. The somewhat less sensitive diethyl-p-phenylenediamine is excellent for differentiation of Gram-negative bacteria by Kovács's method. The dimethyl derivative is the least sensitive, even when combined with α-naphthol, i.e. the indophenol blue reaction (Gaby and Hadley, 1957).

As a standard oxidase test, that described by Kovács (1956) is recommended. Commercial reagent strips are used in a similar way. To select oxidase-positive colonies, the reagent may be added to agar plates dropwise. The oxidase reaction is a basic test for the identification of Gram-negative bacteria since Enterobacteriaceae, Acinetobacter and obligate anaerobes do not produce oxidase.

(i) *Reagent.*   Pick up about 10 mg diethyl- (or tetramethyl-) p-phenylenediamine HCl on the tip of a plastic strip calibrated for this purpose and dissolve in 1 ml distilled water. The solution can be stored, protected from light, for up to 2–3 days.

(ii) *Procedure.*   Make a thin smear of the colonies on a filter-paper strip placed on a slide and impregnate with the reagent. For testing mycoplasma, excise an agar block from the plate and rub it face down on the paper strip.

(iii) *Interpretation.*   Positive: development of dark-purple colour within 10 s (*Pseudomonas aeruginosa*). Delayed positive: purple colour within 30 s (*Haemophilus influenzae*). Negative: pale yellow colour (*Escherichia coli*).

Reagents for the oxidase and for the indole tests, both devised by Kovács, should not be confused. If exposed to light and air, the oxidase reagent rapidly deteriorates: do not use the reagent if it has become purple-coloured. Iron catalyses the oxidation of the reagent, and therefore, instead of a loop made of iron alloy, a platinum wire, glass rod, tip of a pipette or the edge of a glass slide should be used for transferring the culture onto the test paper. Iron released from haemoglobin does not interfere with the oxidase test, if ordinary blood or chocolate agar is used; however, *Bordetella parapertussis* growing on Bordet–Gengou agar containing 20–30% blood, may give a false positive test (Lautrop, 1960). Cultures grown on media containing a compound that is convertible to acid may give a false negative reaction (Havelaar et al., 1980). Traces of oxidative substances (e.g. chromic acid on insufficiently rinsed slides) may give a false, delayed positive reaction. Testing of cultures from media containing dyes or indicators should be avoided. Anaerobically incubated plates should be exposed to air for about 30 min before performing the oxidase test.

2. Catalase test

Hydrogen peroxide, the toxic product of bacterial respiration, is destroyed by catalases or peroxidases:

$$2H_2O_2 \xrightarrow{\text{catalase}} 2H_2O + O_2$$

$$H_2O_2 \xrightarrow{\text{peroxidase}} H_2O + O$$

Catalase activity results in the production of molecular gaseous oxygen, whereas peroxidase decomposes H_2O_2 only in the presence of an organic oxygen acceptor. Catalase production is of great taxonomic importance; in contrast, detection of peroxidase is not significant in identification. Micrococcaceae produce catalase abundantly, and many other bacteria exhibit a weaker activity. For example, Streptococcus, Erysipelothrix, Cardiobacterium, Kingella and Eikenella are characteristically catalase-negative organisms. Strict anaerobes lack catalase; however, most anaerobically growing Propionibacterium isolates produce the enzyme. The following tests are standard procedures (Cowan, 1974; Vera and Power, 1980).

(a) Slide test

(i) Reagent.   Aqueous hydrogen peroxide solution containing about 30% H_2O_2.

(ii) Procedure.   Transfer growth from solid medium to a drop of 30% H_2O_2. For testing mycoplasma, place an excised agar block face down into the H_2O_2 drop.

(iii) Interpretation.   Positive: intensive bubbling (Staphylococcus aureus). Weakly positive: slight bubbling (Aerococcus viridans). Negative: no gas production (Streptococcus faecalis).

(b) Tube test

(i) Reagent.   Aqueous hydrogen peroxide solution containing about 3% H_2O_2.

(ii) *Procedure.* Pour about 1 ml of 3% of H_2O_2 over growth on an agar slant or in broth.

(iii) *Interpretation.* Same as for the slide test.

Use a nichrome wire, glass rod or the edge of a slide for transferring the culture to the H_2O_2 reagent; platinum acts as a powerful catalytic agent, decomposing H_2O_2 immediately. As erythrocytes contain catalase, H_2O_2 must not be poured over a blood-agar culture. Using the slide method, pick up only bacterial culture, as carry-over of small pieces of blood-agar medium may give a false positive result. As heating destroys catalase in erythrocytes, the use of chocolate-agar cultures is advantageous. Anaerobically incubated plates should be exposed to air for about 30 min before testing. Spontaneous deterioration of H_2O_2 to water and oxygen gas takes place fairly rapidly if the reagent is exposed to light: small bubbles may appear in the reagent drop before the addition of the culture. Although H_2O_2 is a disinfectant, more resistant bacteria may remain alive and may be released from the bubbling reagent into the air (MacFaddin, 1980). Concentrated H_2O_2 used for the slide test causes white burns upon contact with the skin.

B. Metabolism of nitrogenous substances

1. Reduction of nitrate

In medical bacteriology, the reduction of nitrate is usually examined in nutrient broth containing the substrate. The main products of nitrate reduction are nitrite (1) or nitrogen gas (2):

$$NO_3^- + 2H^+ \longrightarrow NO_2^- + H_2O \tag{1}$$

$$2\,NO_3^- + 12\,H^+ \longrightarrow N_2 + 6\,H_2O \tag{2}$$

If nitrite reagent (Griess–Ilosvay) is added to a culture decomposing nitrate according to equation (1), a red colour develops (diazonium-compound formation). This reaction may be recorded as "$NO_3 \longrightarrow NO_2$," or "nitrite production".

Nitrogen-gas production according to equation (2) indicates complete nitrate breakdown or denitrification. Nitrogen forms a bubble in a Durham tube that is inserted in the medium, and no colour reaction develops after adding the Griess–Ilosvay reagent. As the absence of colour reaction may be due either to the lack of nitrate-decomposing ability or to the complete breakdown of nitrate, the result should be confirmed by adding powdered zinc to the tube to reduce any nitrate remaining:

$$NO_3^- + 2\,Zn + H_2O \longrightarrow NO_2^- + 2\,ZnO + H_2$$

Consequently, if a nitrite reaction (red colour) develops over the zinc dust in the bottom of the tube, the organism was unable to attack the nitrate (negative nitrate test, NO_3-). Alternatively, if nitrate has been completely decomposed, the red colour fails to appear over the zinc dust ($NO_3 \longrightarrow N_2$ or "nitrogen-gas production").

In the course of denitrification nitrite is formed as an intermediate product: in overnight cultures of denitrifying organisms the nitrite reaction may be positive. In this early stage of denitrification, in the case of non-fermenters (e.g. *Pseudomonas aeruginosa*) gas bubbles in the Durham tube or on the surface of the medium indicate a "$NO_3 \longrightarrow N_2$" reaction, regardless of the presence or absence of nitrite. Certain bacteria decompose nitrate to ammonia, hydroxylamine or nitrous oxide, i.e. nitrate disappears from the medium, but neither nitrite nor molecular nitrogen can be demonstrated (Gunsalus and Stanier, 1961; Stanier *et al.*, 1963; Cowan, 1974; MacFaddin, 1980).

Testing of nitrate decomposition is of great value in identification. *Acinetobacter, Flavobacterium, Alcaligenes odorans* and some other aerobes and many anaerobic bacteria do not attack nitrate. Most bacteria, including Enterobacteriaceae produce nitrite, whereas *Pseudomonas aeruginosa* and some other pseudomonads and *Alcaligenes denitrificans* produce nitrogen gas. Denitrification to substances other than nitrogen gas is not distinguished in practical diagnostic work from nitrogen-gas production. Standard tests for nitrite reduction are described in the following. Commercial strips, discs and spot tests may be used for routine identification (MacFaddin, 1980; Allen and Siders, 1980).

(a) Nitrate test for aerobes and facultative anaerobes

(i) *Medium.*   Beef extract (Oxoid), 3 g; Bacto peptone (Difco), 5 g; KNO_3, 1 g; distilled water, 1000 ml; pH 7.3–7.4. Distribute in about 5 ml portions into test tubes containing inverted Durham tubes and autoclave at 115 °C for 20 min. For fastidious bacteria add aseptically 5% rabbit or ox serum sterilized by filtration.

Reageants.   Solution A: sulphanilic acid, 8 g; 5 N acetic acid (300 ml glacial acetic acid mixed with 700 ml distilled water), 1000 ml; dissolve by gentle heating and store at 4 °C. *Solution B*: α-naphthylamine or dimethyl-α-naphthylamine, 5 g; 5 N acetic acid, 1000 ml. Store at room temperature. The reagents are stable for at least 6 months. *Zinc dust* should be stored in a screw-capped bottle.

(ii) *Procedure.* Inoculate the medium and incubate for up to 3 days; in routine work, the test may be read after incubation overnight. Record gas formation in the Durham tube, then add 0.1 ml reagent A + 0.1 ml reagent B and observe the development of colour reaction within 1 min. If colour is absent, add about 25 mg zinc dust on the tip of a plastic strip calibrated for this purpose. Observe the development of colour reaction within 3 min.

(iii) *Interpretation.* Nitrate reduced to nitrite ($NO_3 \longrightarrow NO_2$): red colour after the addition of reagents A and B (*Escherichia coli*). Nitrate reduced to nitrogen gas ($NO_3 \longrightarrow N_2$): gas production, absence of red colour after the addition of reagents A and B and after the subsequent addition of zinc dust (*Pseudomonas aeruginosa*). Nitrate test negative (NO_3-): no gas in the Durham tube, absence of colour reaction after the addition of reagents A and B, but red colour after the subsequent addition of zinc dust (*Acinetobacter calcoaceticus*).

(b) Nitrate test for anaerobes

(1) *Medium.* Proteose peptone (Difco), 20 g; glucose, 1 g; $Na_2HPO_4.2H_2O$, 2 g; KNO_3, 1 g; agar (Oxoid No. 1), 1 g; distilled water, 1000 ml; pH 7.2–7.4. If necessary for growth, add 10 ml haemin solution and 0.2 ml vitamin K solution (Section IV.D.1b.), but do not add cysteine. Distribute in 6–8 ml portions in test tubes and sterilize at 121 °C for 20 min. Add a layer of sterile paraffin oil immediately after removal from the autoclave. For *reagents* see Section IV.B.1a.

(ii) *Procedure.* See Section IV.B.1a.

(iii) *Interpretation.* See Section IV.B.1a. Control cultures: nitrate reduced to nitrite, *Propionibacterium acnes*; nitrate not attacked, *Propionibacterium granulosum*.

  The colour reaction developing after addition of the nitrite reagent may fade rapidly, especially if peptones rich in sulphur-containing amino acids are used. The nitrite reagent is very sensitive, ingredients of the medium should be free of nitrite. Cultures reducing nitrate vigorously may show a brown precipitation after addition of the nitrite reagent. If zinc dust is added to the medium in amounts higher than recommended, the nitrite that is being produced by zinc from the nitrate left unattacked by the organism is further reduced to ammonia *in statu nascendi*, i.e. instead of an "NO_3 negative" result, a false "$NO_3 \longrightarrow N_2$" result will be recorded. The zinc dust and the acetic-acid part of the nitrite reagent produce hydrogen gas; consequently, after the addition of the zinc, gas in the medium should not be regarded as evidence of nitrogen production.

2. Reduction of nitrite

Some bacteria (e.g. *Alcaligenes odorans* and most *Flavobacterium odoratum* isolates) do not attack nitrate, but produce nitrogen gas if nitrite is used as substrate:

$$2\ NO_2^- + 8\ H^+ \longrightarrow N_2 + 4\ H_2O$$

(i) *Medium.*   Same as in Section IV.B.1a prepared with 1 g $NaNO_2$ instead of KNO_3. For *reagents* see Section IV.B.1a.

(ii) *Procedure.*   Same as for nitrate-reduction test (Section IV.B.1a), but zinc powder need not be added.

(iii) *Interpretation.*   Nitrite reduced to nitrogen gas ($NO_2 \longrightarrow N_2$): gas production, absence of red colour after the addition of reagents A and B (*Alcaligenes odorans*). Nitrite not decomposed ($NO_2 -$): red colour after the addition of reagents A and B (*Acinetobacter calcoaceticus*).

Bacteria decomposing nitrate via nitrite to nitrogen obviously produce gas not only in nitrate but also in nitrite medium. In the literature, different concentrations of nitrite are recommended: 0.001% (Cowan, 1974), 0.01% (Holding and Collee, 1971) and 0.1% (Vera and Power, 1980). For routine use, 0.1% nitrite is the best; on one hand because a minute amount of nitrite may be consumed by bacteria otherwise incapable of total denitrification (e.g. *Escherichia coli*), and, on the other, because gas production is not visible in a medium with low nitrite concentration.

3. Urease test

Urea is hydrolysed by bacterial urease, an amidase enzyme, into ammonia and carbon dioxide, which form ammonium carbonate in the test medium:

$$(NH_2)_2CO + 2\ H_2O \longrightarrow 2\ NH_3 + CO_2 + H_2O \rightleftarrows (NH_4)_2CO_3$$

The standard urease test is carried out using Christensen's agar slant (Christensen, 1946) or Kristensen's liquid medium (Kauffmann, 1954). These media contain a low concentration of peptone and a small amount of glucose. The fermentation of glucose yields acids, which neutralize the alkaline substances produced from peptone but not the abundant amount of ammonia formed when urea is attacked. Glucose serves also as a source of energy enhancing the production of urease (Christensen, 1946).

For screening, the urease test system can be combined with the indole test (Lányi and Ádám, 1960) and with TSI-type media (Nógrády and Rodler, 1954). The method of Stuart *et al.* (1945) detects only the vigorous urease activity of *Proteus* in a highly buffered medium. Urease being a constitutive enzyme, rapid microtests and commercial paper strip procedures give fairly reliable results (Hormaeche and Munilla, 1957; USSR Ministry of Health, 1964; Cowan, 1974; MacFaddin, 1980).

(a) Christensen's urease test

(i) *Basal medium.* Bacto peptone (Difco), 1 g; NaCl, 5 g; KH_2PO_4, 2 g; agar (Oxoid No. 1), 9 g; distilled water, 1000 ml; pH 6.8; phenol red, 0.2% solution, 6 ml; sterilize at 115 °C for 20 min. *Phenol red solution, 0.2%*: phenol red, 2 g; 0.1 N NaOH, 80 ml; distilled water, 920 ml. *Urea + glucose solution*: urea, 20 g; glucose, 1 g; distilled water, 100 ml; sterilize by filtration.

Test medium. Add 100 ml urea + glucose solution to 1000 ml molten base, distribute aseptically into sterile tubes and allow to cool in a slanted position. The liquid medium modified by Kristensen contains the same ingredients except agar and is distributed in narrow tubes in 2 ml portions.

(ii) *Procedure.* Incubate the inoculated media for 1 day (routine test) and for 4 days (standard test).

(iii) *Interpretation.* Rapid positive: intense red-violet colour in 6–24 h (*Proteus mirabilis*). Positive: red-violet in 4 days (*Klebsiella aerogenes*). Negative: yellow (*Escherichia coli*) or orange (*Pseudomonas maltophilia*).

(b) Urease test for anaerobes

(i) *Medium.* Peptone yeast extract basal medium (Section IV.D.1b.), 100 ml; add aseptically 10 ml of a filter-sterilized solution containing KH_2PO_4, 9.1 g; $Na_2HPO_4.2H_2O$, 9.5 g; urea, 20 g; phenol red, 0.2% solution (Section IV.B.3a), 5 ml; distilled water, 60 ml; distribute in 3 ml amounts and add a layer of liquid paraffin immediately after removal from the autoclave.

(ii) *Procedure.* Inoculate the medium and incubate until growth is visible.

(iii) *Interpretation.* Positive: red-violet (*Clostridium sordellii*). Negative: orange (*Clostridium bifermentans*).

In Christensen's and related media, acid (yellow colour) is produced only by urease-negative glucose-fermenters. A negative test with other bacteria is indicated by an intermediate colour (orange). Acid is not produced in the anaerobe test medium, which does not contain glucose. On prolonged incubation, a weak alkaline reaction may be produced owing to peptone metabolism. Variations in the time and strength of positive reaction occur as a result of difference in the size of inoculum. Christensen's medium is too poor in nutrient to support the growth of fastidious organisms. For testing these bacteria, rapid methods are recommended.

(c) Rapid urease test

(i) *Reagent.*   *Solution A*: urea, 2 g; ethanol (95%), 2 ml; distilled water, 4 ml; store in the refrigerator; the solution need not be sterilized. *Solution B*: KH_2PO_4, 0.1 g; K_2HPO_4, 0.1 g; NaCl, 0.5 g; phenol red, 0.2% solution (Section IV.B.3a), 1 ml; distilled water, 100 ml; sterilize at 115 °C for 15 min.

(ii) *Procedure.*   Mix 1 volume of solution A and 19 volumes of solution B. Suspend a loopful of culture in 0.1 ml of the mixture, incubate at 35–37 °C and observe after 1 h.

(iii) *Interpretation.*   Positive: red-violet colour (*Corynebacterium ulcerans*). Negative: orange colour (*Corynebacterium diphtheriae*).

4. Indole test

Tryptophan added as an ingredient of the medium or produced in the course of peptone breakdown is degraded by hydrolysis and deamination:

$$\text{L-tryptophan} + H_2O \longrightarrow \text{indole} + \text{pyruvic acid} + NH_3$$

In the presence of hydrochloric acid, the pyrrole structure in indole forms a red condensation product with *p*-dimethylaminobenzaldehyde (Ehrlich's reagent). To make the reaction more distinct, the red complex is concentrated by extraction with organic solvents so as to form a layer on the surface of the medium (Kovács, 1928).

Being a volatile product, indole can be detected by a filter-paper impregnated with saturated oxalic acid solution and fastened between the plug and the tube containing the medium; a positive reaction is indicated by a pink colour of the strip. Spot tests (Cowan, 1974) allow a rapid detection of indole production. The standard methods are Kovács technique for general use and the ether or xylene-extraction method for non-fermentative bacteria (King, 1967) and for anaerobes (Holdeman *et al.*, 1977).

Indole is produced by fermentative bacteria (several taxons of Enterobacteriaceae, Vibrionaceae, Pasteurella; weak fermenters may produce a small amount of indole (*Flavobacterium* spp.). The test is also of value in differentiating anaerobic bacteria. Strict aerobic bacteria do not form indole, but may split tryptophan into other metabolites (kinurenine and anthranilic acid) giving an orange colour reaction with Kovács's reagent (*Pseudomonas acidovorans*; Hugh and Gilardi, 1980).

(a) Kovács's indole test

(i) *Medium.*   Bacto peptone (Difco), 10 g; NaCl, 5 g; distilled water, 1000 ml; pH 7.2–7.4; sterilize at 121 °C for 20 min after distribution in narrow tubes.

Reagent.   *Solution A*: *p*-dimethylaminobenzaldehyde, 5 g; isoamyl alcohol, 75 ml; dissolve by gentle heating in a water bath and store in the refrigerator. *Solution B*: concentrated hydrochloric acid, analytical grade. Prepare small quantities of Kovács's reagent by mixing 3 volumes of solution A and 1 volume of solution B; it can be stored, protected from light, for up to 2 months.

(ii) *Procedure.*   Add 0.2 ml Kovács's reagent to a 24 h (routine test) or to a 3 day (standard test) culture and shake well.

(iii) *Interpretation.*   Positive: deep-red colour in the reagent layer (*Escherichia coli*). Negative: the reagent remains light yellow (*Citrobacter freundii*).

(b) Xylene-extraction indole test

(i) *Medium.*   Tryptone (L42, Oxoid), 20 g; NaCl, 5 g; distilled water, 1000 ml; pH 7.2–7.4; distribute in 2–3 ml portions and sterilize at 115 °C for 20 min. For anaerobic bacteria, peptone yeast-extract basal medium (Section IV.D.1b) may be used, substituting tryptone for the peptone and adding a layer of paraffin oil after autoclaving.

Ehrlich's reagent.   *p*-Dimethylaminobenzaldehyde, 1g; 95% ethanol, 95 ml; concentrated hydrochloric acid, 20 ml.

(ii) *Procedure.*   Incubate the cultures for up to 3 days. Add 1 ml of xylene, shake vigorously and, after allowing the mixture to stand for about 2 min, add 0.5 ml Ehrlich's reagent slowly down the side of the tube so as to form a layer between the medium and xylene. Do not shake the tube after the addition of Ehrlich's reagent. In the case of anaerobes, pipette the culture from under the paraffin oil into an empty tube and add the xylene and Ehrlich's reagent, as above.

(iii) *Interpretation.*   Positive: pinkish-red ring below the xylene layer (*Flavobacterium meningosepticum* and *Propionibacterium acnes*). Negative: no colour reaction (*Flavobacterium odoratum* and *Peptostreptococcus anaerobius*).

The test medium should be prepared with peptones yielding, on utilization, a sufficient amount of tryptophan, and should not contain fermentable sugars. Cultures of aerobic and facultative anaerobic bacteria should be incubated aerobically. Indole remains stable in the medium for several days; however, clostridia frequently continue to metabolize it further, and may exhibit a false negative reaction. Kovács's reagent should be straw-yellow; a rapid browning indicates impurity of the ingredients.

5. Amino acid-deaminase tests

Amino acids are converted by oxidative deamination to keto acids, e.g.

$$\text{L-phenylaline} + \tfrac{1}{2}\ O_2 \longrightarrow \text{phenylpyruvic acid} + NH_3$$

$$\text{L-tryptophan} + \tfrac{1}{2}\ O_2 \longrightarrow \text{indole-3-pyruvic acid} + NH_3$$

Keto acids form coloured compounds with ferric ions. The most distinct are the green-colour reaction with phenylpyruvic acid (Edwards and Ewing, 1972; Cowan, 1974) and the cherry-red reaction with indole-3-pyruvic acid (Singer and Volcani, 1955; Lányi and Ádám, 1960). As deaminases are preformed enzymes, spot and paper-strip tests are suitable for their rapid detection.

The production of amino acid deaminase is highly specific for the tribe Proteae of the Enterobacteriaceae. *Erwinia herbicola* (syn. *Enterobacter agglomerans*), *Moraxella*, *Pseudomonas* and *Achromobacter* spp. produce smaller amounts of deaminase, detectable usually by growth on phenylalanine agar slants.

(a) Phenylalanine deaminase test

(1) *Medium.* Yeast extract (Oxoid), 3 g; DL-phenylalanine, 2g; $Na_2HPO_4.2H_2O$, 1 g; NaCl, 5 g; agar (Oxoid No. 1), 12 g; distilled water, 1000 ml. Distribute in 3 ml portions in narrow tubes, sterilize at 115 °C for 20 min and cool to produce a long slope.

Reagent. Dissolve 5 g ferric chloride in 10 ml 0.1 N HCl and bring to 100 ml volume with distilled water.

(ii) *Procedure.* Inoculate the slants heavily and incubate them overnight. Place 3–4 drops of reagent onto the culture.

(iii) *Interpretation.* Positive: green colour within 1 min on the slant and in the syneresis fluid (*Proteus mirabilis*). Negative: light-yellow colour of non-reacting ferric ions (*Escherichia coli*).

(b) Rapid tryptophan deaminase test

(i) *Substrate solution.* DL-tryptophan, 0.1 g (or L-tryptophan, 0.05 g); distilled water, 10 ml; dissolve by heating and, after cooling, add 0.5 ml of a 0.2% aqueous merthiolate solution. The *reagent* is the same as above (Section IV.B.5a).

(ii) *Procedure.* Pipette one drop of substrate solution into a narrow tube or into a hollow on a plastic plate and suspend a heavy loopful of culture in it. Incubate at 35–37 °C for 1 h and add a drop of reagent.

(iii) *Interpretation.* Positive: cherry-red colour (*Proteus mirabilis*). Negative: light-yellow colour (*Escherichia coli*).

Both tests require aerobic incubation; if using plastic plates, avoid airtight covering. Read the test within one minute after addition of the reagent because the colour fades rapidly.

6. Amino acid-decarboxylase and dihydrolase tests

Decarboxylases break down amino acids to alkaline amines detectable with pH indicators:

$$\text{L-lysine} \longrightarrow \text{cadaverine} + CO_2$$

$$\text{L-ornithine} \longrightarrow \text{putrescine} + CO_2$$

Arginine may be decomposed via two pathways occurring separately or simultaneously (Møller, 1955):

$$\text{L-arginine} \xrightarrow{\text{decarboxylase}} \text{putrescine} + \text{urea} + CO_2$$

$$\text{L-arginine} \xrightarrow{\text{dihydrolase}} \text{L-ornithine} + 3\,NH_3 + CO_3$$

Ammonia production in arginine medium, which is detectable with Nessler's reagent, indicates a dihydrolase pathway, provided that the organism is unable to split urea. If urea is further decomposed, NH_3 and CO_2 are also formed at the end of the decarboxylation pathway. In practical identification, the two pathways are not distinguished, i.e. an alkaline reaction is interpreted as a positive arginine test.

Decarboxylation proceeds best anaerobically at pH 5.0–6.0. In addition to the amino-acid substrates, the media contain pyridoxal phosphate and glucose. The former enhances decarboxylase activity, the latter serves as a source of energy. Acids produced from glucose by fermentative bacteria maintain a low pH, which is turned alkaline if the amino acid is decomposed. The tests are reliable and essential taxonomic tools for a wide variety of bacteria.

(i) *Basal medium.* Bacto peptone (Difco), 5 g; beef extract (Oxoid), 5 g; pyridoxal, 0.005 g; glucose, 0.5 g; distilled water, 1000 ml; bromocresol purple, 0.2% solution, 5 ml; cresol red, 0.2% solution, 2.5 ml; pH 6.0. If not used immediately, autoclave at 115 °C for 20 min. *Bromocresol purple and cresol red, 0.2%*: dissolve 2 g indicator in 50 ml 0.1 N NaOH and add 950 ml distilled water.

Test medium. Dissolve 1% L-amino acid (arginine, lysine or ornithine hydrocholoride) in the basal medium by gentle heating and readjust to pH 6.0. Distribute the amino-acid media and control basal medium in narrow tubes and sterilize at 115°C for 20 min. Layer the media immediately after removal from the autoclave with liquid paraffin. The colour of the uninoculated medium should be light grey.

(ii) *Procedure.* Lightly inoculate test and control media through the paraffin-oil layer and incubate for up to 4 days.

(iii) *Interpretation.* Positive: violet colour in the test medium (arginine:

Pseudomonas aeruginosa; lysine: *Salmonella paratyphi-B*; ornithine: *Shigella sonnei*). Negative: yellow colour (glucose fermenters) or light grey colour (glucose non-fermenters) in the test medium (arginine: *Proteus vulgaris* and *Pseudomonas maltophilia*; ornithine: *Shigella flexneri* and *Pseudomonas aeruginosa*; lysine: *Citrobacter freundii* and *Pseudomonas aeruginosa*). Colour changes in the control medium without amino acids are identical with those of the negative tests.

As amino acids may alter the pH of the basal medium considerably, an adjustment is essential prior to final distribution and sterilization. D-Isomers of amino acids are not utilized, accordingly, DL-substrates should be added at double concentration. The tubes must be layered with paraffin oil—partly to ensure anaerobic conditions for the test, partly because alkali production from other ingredients of the medium is less intense in the absence of air. The small amount of air that penetrates the oil seal on storage is consumed by the multiplying organism. Inoculation of a control medium without amino acid is important to recognize a weak or delayed positive test: a shift toward alkalinity in the amino acid medium, compared to the control, is interpreted as a positive test (e.g. light grey in the substrate versus yellow in the control).

7. Acetamide hydrolysis

Bacteria producing acylamidase decompose acetamide to acetic acid and ammonia:

$$CH_3CONH_2 + H_2O \longrightarrow CH_3COOH + NH_3$$

Ammonia gives a coloured precipitate with Nessler's reagent. The test is useful for the differentiation of non-fermenting Gram-negative bacteria. A procedure based on the method of Arai *et al.* (1970) is recommended.

(i) *Acetamide solution*: acetamide, 2 g; sterile distilled water, 20 ml; need not be sterilized. *Buffer solution*: K_2HPO_4, 0.4 g; KH_2PO_4, 0.1 g; KCl, 8.0 g; distilled water, 1000 ml; sterilize at 115 °C for 20 min. *Test solution*: dilute 1 part of the acetamide solution with 99 parts of buffer solution. *Nessler's reagent*: potassium iodide, 5 g; distilled water, 5 ml; add cold saturated mercuric chloride solution until a slight precipitate remains after shaking; add 40 ml 9 N NaOH and add distilled water to 100 ml final volume.

(ii) *Procedure.* Suspend a loopful of culture in one drop of test solution pipetted into a narrow tube or into a hollow of a Microtiter plate. Incubate tubes fitted with cotton plugs or with loosened screw caps or plates in a wet chamber at 35–37 °C for 22–24 h. Add one drop of Nessler's reagent and read immediately.

(iii) *Interpretation.* Positive: brownish red or brown precipitate (*Pseudomonas acidovorans*). Negative: yellow colour (*Pseudomonas stutzeri*).

If the test is performed in duplicate, strong acylamidase activity can be detected after incubation for 1–2 h. All reagents must be free of ammonia: use freshly sterilized distilled water. Since Nessler's solution becomes brown if exposed to light, the reagent must be stored in a paraffin-lined dark bottle.

8. Porphyrin test

Haemophilus isolates that are haemin-independent, i.e. that do not require X factor for their growth, produce porphobilinogen and porphyrins from δ-aminolaevulinic acid. These substrates are intermediates in haemin biosynthesis. The test is based on the detection of porphyrins under UV light or porphobilinogen using Kovács's indole reagent (Kilian, 1974).

(i) *Substrate solution.* δ-Aminolaevulinic acid HCl (Sigma), 34 mg; $MgSO_4.7H_2O$, 20 mg; KH_2PO_4, 1.36 g; K_2HPO_4, 1.74 g; sterile distilled water, 100 ml. Dispense in 0.5 ml volumes in narrow tubes and store in the freezing compartment of the refrigerator. For *Kovács's indole reagent* see Section IV.B.4a.

(ii) *Procedure.* Prepare a heavy suspension in the substrate solution and incubate at 35–37 °C for 4 h. Read under UV light at 360 nm and/or add 0.5 ml of indole reagent, shake and allow the phases to separate.

(iii) *Interpretation.* Positive: red fluorescence under UV light; red colour in the lower aqueous phase (*Haemophilus parainfluenzae*). Negative: fluorescence and colour in the aqueous phase absent (*Haemophilus influenzae*). Red colour in the upper amyl alcohol phase after addition of Kovács's reagent is due to indole production, and should therefore not be interpreted as a positive porphyrin test.

9. Hippurate test

Hippuric acid (*N*-benzoylglycine) is hydrolysed to benzoic acid and glycine:

$$C_6H_5CO.NH.CH_2COOH + H_2O \longrightarrow C_6H_5COOH + NH_2.CH_2COOH$$

The reaction can be demonstrated either by showing benzoic acid, which gives an insoluble precipitate with ferric chloride, or by detecting glycine, which forms a blue coloured condensation complex with ninhydrin. The ferric chloride method is more sensitive than the ninhydrin test; however, the result is strongly dependent on the exact concentration of the reagent: at low iron content not only benzoate but also hippurate and glycinate are precipitated (Cowan, 1974). The ninhydrin reagent produces a colour reaction, not only with glycine, but also with all culture-medium ingredients that have free carbonyl groups (proteins, peptones and amino acids). The test can therefore be performed only in a single substrate system (MacFaddin, 1980). The hippurate test is used mainly for identification of *Streptococcus* and *Campylobacter* spp. and *Gardnerella vaginalis*. In view of its rapidity and reliability, the ninhydrin method described by Yong and Thompson (1982) for *Gardnerella*, is recommended for other bacteria, too.

(i) *Substrate solution.*   Sodium hippurate, 0.25 g; distilled water, 25 ml; sterilize by filtration. *Reagent*: ninhydrin, 3.5 g; acetone–butanol mixture (1:1), 100 ml.

(ii) *Procedure.*   Prepare a moderately dense suspension in 2 drops of substrate solution pipetted into a narrow tube. Incubate for 1 h at 35–37 °C and add 2 drops of reagent, reincubate for 15 min.

(iii) *Interpretation.*   Positive: purple colour within 15 min (*Campylobacter jejuni, Gardnerella vaginalis* and *Streptococcus agalactiae*). Negative: colour-less within 15 min (*Campylobacter coli* and *Streptococcus pyogenes*).

The ninhydrin reaction should be carefully standardized; a too heavy suspension and prolonged incubation, either before or after addition of the reagent, may cause a false positive reaction. Store the reagent protected from light.

10. Deoxyribonuclease test

Deoxyribonuclease (DNase) is an extracellular enzyme hydrolysing deoxy-ribonucleic acid to oligonucleotides. Several kinds of deoxyribonuclease are distinguished on the basis of antigenic properties, response to inhibitory substances, hydrolytic end products and activity in the presence of Ca^{2+} and Mg^{2+} ions (MacFaddin, 1980). *Staphylococcus aureus* produces a heat-resistant DNase ("thermonuclease"), whereas the DNase of other bacteria is heat-sensitive. DNase is shown by culturing the organism on agar containing deoxyribonucleic acid (DNA) and then flooding the plates with hydrochloric acid (Jeffries *et al.*, 1957). DNA is precipitated by HCl, but its hydrolytic products are soluble in the acid. The DNase test is useful for intra- and extrageneric differentiation of *Staphylococcus, Serratia, Pseudomonas* and *Flavobacterium*.

(i) *Substrate solution.* Dissolve by heating 2 g DNA in 100 ml distilled water, distribute small portions into tubes, sterilize at 115 °C for 20 min, and store in the freezing compartment of a refrigerator. *Test agar*: to 20 ml molten nutrient agar add 2 ml substrate solution and pour a plate; store the plate in the refrigerator for not more than 3 days.

(ii) *Procedure.* Inoculate the cultures as lines on the surface. Incubate for 1 day (routine test) or for 2 days (standard test). Flood the plates with 1 N HCl.

(iii) *Interpretation.* Positive: clear zone around the growth (*Staphylococcus aureus*) Negative: cloudy precipitate in the surrounding medium (*Staphylococcus saprophyticus*).

The optimal temperature for DNase production is not necessarily the same as the optimum growth temperature. It is recommended that the culture be grown at 25, 30 and 37 °C (Jeffries *et al.*, 1957; Cowan, 1974). For identification tables, it would be advisable to specify the temperature of incubation, e.g. 35–37 °C for *Staphylococcus* and 30 °C for non-fermentative Gram-negative bacteria.

11. Phosphatase test

Detection of the enzyme phosphatase is based on the release of phenolphthalein from phenolphthalein diphosphate. The substrate is colourless, whereas phenolphthalein, an acid–base indicator, is red at alkaline pH. The test serves to differentiate staphylococci.

(i) *Medium.* To 1000 ml of nutrient agar cooled to 45 °C add 10 ml of 1% aqueous phenolphthalein diphosphate solution sterilized by filtration; pour plates. For testing mycoplasma, use heart-infusion agar supplemented with 20% horse serum and 1% yeast extract.

(ii) *Procedure.* Inoculate each plate with a single organism and incubate for 2 days (staphylococci) or 7 and 14 days in a wet chamber (mycoplasma). Pipette 0.1 ml concentrated ammonium hydroxide in the lid of the Petri dish to expose the plate to ammonia vapour. Read after 20–30 s exposure. As ammonia is bactericidal, the exposed plates should not be incubated further.

(iii) *Interpretation.*   Positive: pink colonies (*Staphylococcus aureus*). Negative: no colour reaction (*Staphylococcus cohnii*).

12. Hyaluronidase test

Hyaluronic acid is a mucopolysaccharide present in the intracellular material of body tissues. It is depolymerized by a hyaluronidase, an enzyme called the spreading factor, which facilitates the invasion of tissues by bacteria. The enzyme is produced by *Streptococcus pyogenes, Staphylococcus aureus, Clostridium perfringens* and several other microorganisms. In classical tests the presence or absence of hyaluronidase activity is determined after incubating a mixture of the substrate and bacteria. If hyaluronic acid has not been decomposed, it produces a discrete clot in the acidified ethanol reagent (Holding and Collee, 1971). Using the classical tests, commercial hyaluronic acid gives less satisfactory results than bovine synovial fluid, which contains a sufficient amount of the substrate. The rapid test described here has been elaborated by Smith and Willet (1968). Detection of some other enzymes hydrolysing tissue constituents such as chondroitin sulphate, collagen and fibrin has not so far been used in general classification of bacteria. For details of these tests see Smith and Willet (1968) and Steffen and Hentges (1981).

(i) *Medium.*   Todd–Hewitt broth (Cowan, 1974) or brain–heart-infusion broth solidified with agar to the usual gel strength. Add an aqueous solution of $2 \, \text{mg ml}^{-1}$ sodium hyaluronidate prepared from human umbilical cord (Sigma) sterilized by filtration to the cooled medium to give a final concentration of $400 \, \mu\text{g ml}^{-1}$; add with constant stirring an aqueous solution of 5% bovine albumin fraction V (Sigma) sterilized by filtration to a final concentration of 1%. The final pH should be 6.7–6.9. Pour plates. *Acetic acid reagent*: glacial acetic acid, 120 ml; distilled water, 880 ml.

(ii) *Procedure.*   Spot-inoculate the plates and incubate until good growth is evident. Flood the plates with acetic acid reagent for 10 min. Positive: clear zone around growth (*Streptococcus pyogenes*). Negative: opacity (albumin–hyaluronic acid conjugate around growth and throughout medium: *Staphylococcus epidermidis*).

13. Gelatin hydrolysis

Extracellular proteolytic enzymes of bacteria hydrolyse proteins into polypeptides, peptides and amino acids. Gelatin is an unusual kind of protein, which in aqueous solution forms a solid gel at room temperature but changes to a liquid above 25–28 °C. It tolerates heating at 100–121 °C without being coagulated, and therefore, unlike other proteins, can be sterilized by auto-claving. Upon exposure to formalin, its structure changes such that it remains solid on heating up to 100 °C without losing its sensitivity to gelatinase. Production of the enzyme can be demonstrated in classical nutrient broth solidified with gelatin. As the cultures are usually incubated at a temperature above the melting point of gelatin, 2–3 h prior to reading they should be cooled; the test is positive if the inoculated medium is liquid but the control medium is solid. The classical test, chiefly because it is less sensitive and may require weeks of incubation, has been replaced by rapid methods. Gelatin incorporated into nutrient agar remains solid at 37 °C; if the plate is flooded with acid mercuric chloride solution, the unhydrolysed gelatin is precipitated, whereas a positive test is indicated by a clear zone around the colonies (Frazier, 1926; Whaley et al., 1982).

The light-sensitive layer of a photographic film may be used as a substrate: if a strip of an undeveloped or an exposed and developed film is immersed in the broth culture of a gelatinase-producing organism, the layer is detached from the film (Le Minor and Piéchaud, 1963; Blazevic et al., 1973). The method has the disadvantage that commercial films vary in response to gelatinase. As a standard procedure, the method elaborated by Kohn (1953) is recommended: from formalized gelatin discs containing charcoal powder, gelatinase-producing bacteria release easily detectable charcoal particles.

(i) *Gelatin–charcoal reagent.*   Mix 48 g gelatin powder in 340 ml cold tapwater; allow the gelatin to soak well, then boil the mixture in a water bath, add 14 g powdered charcoal and homogenize by shaking. Cool the mixture to 37 °C and pour into flat glass containers smeared with a thin layer of vaseline to a depth of about 3 mm. Place the containers in the refrigerator; rapid cooling prevents the sedimentation of the charcoal. After solidifying, flood the gelatin–charcoal sheets with an abundant amount of diluted formalin (1 part of commercial formalin containing about 35% formaldehyde and 2 parts of water), and let them stand at room temperature for 24 h. Cut discs with a cork borer (about 10 mm in diameter), or pieces with a knife (about 15 mm × 3 mm), wrap them in gauze and wash under running tap water for 24 h to remove all traces of formalin. Distribute the discs or pieces in small flasks, with 20–30 in each, cover them with water and steam at 100 °C for 20 min. Store in the refrigerator.

(ii) *Procedure.*   Place one piece of gelatin–charcoal in a fresh broth culture or preferably in a heavier suspension prepared from an agar slope or other suitable culture. Incubate for up to 14 days.

(iii) *Interpretation.*   Positive: disintegration of the gelatin–charcoal; free charcoal particles settle to the bottom of the tube (*Pseudomonas aeruginosa*). Negative: the gelatin–charcoal remains intact (*Escherichia coli*).

The heavier the suspension, the quicker is the gelatin–charcoal liquefied. In Kohn's (1953) opinion, nutrient broth, as compared with peptone water, somewhat inhibits gelatinase activity. The test organism may be suspended in saline containing 0.01 M $CaCl_2$, which enhances the action of gelatinases of some bacteria (Lautrop, 1956). The reaction may be accelerated by adding 0.1 ml toluene to each tube (Edwards and Ewing, 1972). However, the gelatinase of many bacteria is inhibited by toluene, and therefore, if it is used, a control tube without toluene should be incubated simultaneously (Lautrop, 1956).

14. Tween 80 test for lipolytic activity

Tween 80 (polyethylene sorbitan monooleate) is a surface-active wetting agent used for emulsifying fats and keeping unstable bacteria in homogeneous suspension. Being soluble in water, Tween 80 is an ideal substrate for showing lipolytic activity (Sierra, 1957). Lipolytic organisms split off oleic acid, the calcium salt of which produces opaque zones around the colonies. The hydrolysis of Tween 80 is used primarily for the differentiation of glucose non-fermenters.

(i) *Basal medium.*   Bacto peptone (Difco), 10 g; NaCl, 5 g; $CaCl_2.H_2O$, 0.1 g; agar (Oxoid No. 1), 9 g; distilled water, 1000 ml; pH 7.4; sterilize at 121 °C for 20 min.

Substrate.   Tween 80 sterilized at 121 °C for 20 min.

Test medium.   Cool the basal medium to 45–50 °C, add Tween 80 to give a final concentration of 1% and pour plates.

(ii) *Procedure.*   Inoculate the cultures as lines on the surface. Incubate for up to 7 days, inspect daily.

(iii) *Interpretation.*   Positive: opaque halo around the growth (*Pseudomonas aeruginosa*). Negative: halo absent (*Bordetella bronchiseptica*).

15. Lecithinase test

Phospholipid complexes are emulsifying agents occurring in tissues, serum and egg yolk. Lecithovitellin is the best known example. As an effect of bacterial lecithinase (phospholipase), the clear emulsion of this substance becomes opalescent due to a release of free fat. Lecithinase activity is used to characterize various Gram-positive and Gram-negative bacteria.

(i) *Basal medium.*   Tryptone (Difco), 40 g; Na_2HPO_4, 5 g; NaCl, 2 g; $MgSO_4.7H_2O$, 0.01 g; glucose, 2 g; agar (Oxoid No. 1), 10 g; distilled water, 1000 ml; pH 7.6; dispense 20 ml per tube and sterilize at 121 °C for 20 min.

Lecithovitellin emulsion.   Scrub and soak antibiotic-free eggs in 95% ethanol for 1 h. Separate the yolks from the whites aseptically and mix the yolks with an equal volume of physiological (0.85%) saline to form a homogeneous emulsion. This can be stored in a refrigerator for up to 3 weeks.

Test medium.   Cool 20 ml of the molten basal medium to 50 °C, add 2 ml egg-yolk emulsion, mix and pour plates.

(ii) *Procedure.*   Inoculate the plates as streaks or spots and incubate for 3 days.

(iii) *Interpretation.*   Positive: zone of turbidity in the medium surrounding the growth (*Clostridium perfringens*). Negative: turbidity absent (*Clostridium septicum*).

Lecithinase activity resulting in the release of fats should not be confused with the action of lipase, liberating free fatty acids from fats. Whereas the recommended substrate for lipase test is Tween 80, lipolysis can also be observed on egg-yolk agar: with oblique lighting an oily iridescent sheen ("pearly layer") appears over the growth and in its close vicinity on the surface of the medium (*Clostridium sporogenes*). Fatty acids responsible for the pearly layer are stained bluish-green if the plate is flooded with saturated copper sulphate solution, the excess solution is removed and the plate is dried at 37 °C for 20 min (Cowan, 1974). Lecithinase and lipase activity may appear simultaneously (*Clostridium novyi* type A). Highly proteolytic bacteria (e.g. *Pseudomonas aeruginosa*) usually produce a wide zone around their growth that is somewhat clearer than the rest of the medium and is not associated with either lecithinase or lipase activity.

C.   Sulphur metabolism

1. Hydrogen sulphide test

The existence of two kinds of H_2S test, giving sharply different results for many bacterial entities, must be taken into consideration in identification, as well as for taxonomy.

The *thiosulphate–iron method* detects H_2S produced abundantly by the reduction of thiosulphate; the H_2S forms a black ferrous sulphide precipitate with the iron–salt indicator:

$$3 S_2O_3^{2-} + 4 H^+ \longrightarrow 2 SO_3^{2-} + 2 H_2S$$

$$H_2S + FeSO_4 \longrightarrow FeS + H_2SO_4$$

Reduction of thiosulphate is an anaerobic process (Stanier *et al.*, 1963). It occurs inside but not on the surface of the standard H_2S stab agar (Rauss and Vörös, 1959; Lányi, 1980). In the butt of TSI-type media, fermentation of glucose creates an oxidation–reduction potential favourable for H_2S production. Similarly, on multitest plates described by Sanders *et al.* (1957) and by Lányi and Ádám (1960), black FeS appears at sites providing suitable conditions for its accumulation (under the carbohydrate discs or tablets or as a band at the edge of acid zones produced around the carbohydrates). The thiosulphate-iron method serves primarily to differentiate Enterobacteriaceae (Edwards and Ewing, 1972). Other bacteria, except *Pseudomonas putrefaciens*, do not attack thiosulphate.

The *lead acetate paper-strip method* shows amino-acid-desulphurase activity, i.e. H_2S production in small amounts from cystine, cysteine and/or methionine which are constituents of peptone or are added to the medium. H_2S is a colourless gas, which can be detected sensitively by inserting into the mouth of the tube a paper strip impregnated with lead acetate. A positive reaction is indicated by the dark-brown colour of lead sulphide.

Bacteria that give a positive thiosulphate–iron test are positive also with the lead acetate paper method. The latter is inadequate for the differentiation of Enterobacteriaceae, since almost all species of the family have the ability to produce H_2S from cysteine (Cowan, 1974). The lead acetate paper-strip method is useful for the characterization of *Pasteurella*, *Haemophilus*, *Brucella*, *Campylobacter* and some anaerobic bacteria.

In describing the characters of a taxon and in constructing identification tables, it is of great importance to specify the kind of H_2S test. The two basic methods must not be combined—i.e. H_2S production from thiosulphate must not be detected with lead acetate, and media without thiosulphate must not contain iron salts as H_2S indicators.

(a) Thiosulphate–iron H_2S test

(i) *Standard medium.* Nutrient agar free from fermentable substances, pH 7.4, 1000 ml; $FeCl_2.7H_2O$, 2% solution, 20 ml (or $FeSO_4.7H_2O$, 2%

solution, 40 ml); $Na_2S_2O_3.5H_2O$, 0.8% solution, 50 ml. Distribute into narrow tubes in 5 ml volumes, sterilize at 115 °C for 20 min and cool in an upright position. Store in the refrigerator for not more than 2 months.

(ii) *Procedure.*   Stab with a needle and incubate for 1 day.

(iii) *Interpretation.*   Positive: black colour (*Proteus mirabilis*). Negative: no colour change (*Escherichia coli*). H_2S production in TSI-type media occasionally differs from the results obtained in the standard thiosulphate–iron medium. Since FeS is unstable at low pH, H_2S production by *Citrobacter freundii* isolates may be masked by an abundant production of acid from lactose.

(b) Lead acetate paper-strip H_2S test

(i) *Medium.*   Chopped-meat broth containing 0.5 g cysteine per litre (Holdeman *et al.*, 1977).

Reagent paper.   Cut filter-paper strips (5 mm × 50 mm) and impregnate them with hot saturated aqueous lead acetate solution; after drying, store in screw-capped glass containers.

(ii) *Procedure.*   Inoculate the medium and insert a reagent-paper strip between the plug or cup and the tube so as not to touch the medium. Incubate and examine daily for 7 days.

(iii) *Interpretation.*   Positive: blackening of the paper (*Actinobacillus equuli*). Negative: no colour change (*Pasteurella ureae*).

2. Rhodanese test

Rhodanese (thiosulphate:cyanide sulphurtransferase) is a constitutive intracellular enzyme that catalyses the formation of thiocyanate from cyanide and thiosulphate. With ferric ions, thiocyanate (syn. rhodanate) produces red ferric thiocyanate:

$$S_2O_3^{2-} + CN^- \longrightarrow SCN^- + SO_3^{2-}$$

$$3\ SCN^- + F_e^{3+} \longrightarrow Fe\ (SCN)_3$$

In the first step of the test, the enzyme is liberated from the cells by exposure to lysozyme and ethylenediaminetetraacetic acid (EDTA). In the second step, the lysozyme-treated bacteria are added to a buffered substrate solution, and, finally, the presence of thiocyanate ions is tested with ferric nitrate reagent.

The test is useful for the differentiation of Gram-negative bacteria (Vandenbergh et al., 1979; Lányi, 1982). Escherichia coli and Pseudomonas spp. are nearly 100% positive, shigellae, with the exception of Shigella flexneri serovars 1–5, are positive, and Citrobacter, Klebsiella and Hafnia are positive in 16–61% of the cases. Other Enterobacteriaceae fail to produce rhodanese.

(i) Lysozyme solution.   Lysozyme, 50 mg; sterile distilled water, 10 ml; store in the refrigerator for not more than 2 days. EDTA solution: disodium ethylenediaminetetraacetate, 7.4 g; distilled water, 1000 ml. Thiosulphate solution: $Na_2S_2O_3.5H_2O$, 31.0 g; distilled water, 1000 ml. Tris solution: 2-amino-2-hydroxymethylpropane-1,3-diol, 12.0 g; distilled water, 1000 ml; adjust with 1 N HCl to pH 8.0. KCN solution: potassium cyanide, 140 mg; distilled water, 10 ml; this can be stored stoppered airtight in the refrigerator for up to a week. Ferric nitrate solution: dissolve 40 g Fe $(NO_3)_3.9H_2O$ in 1000 ml approx. 13% w/v nitric acid (concentrated HNO_3, 100 ml; distilled water, 900 ml). Formalin: commercial formalin containing approx. 35% formaldehyde.

(ii) Procedure.   Mix lysozyme and EDTA solutions in equal parts and dispense 0.5 ml volumes in narrow tubes. Make a heavy suspension from a blood-agar culture corresponding visually to a standard containing ca. 3×10^{10} cells per ml. Incubate the tubes at 25 °C for 60 min. Prepare the substrate solution each day by mixing 2 volumes of thiosulphate, 1 volume Tris and 1 volume potassium cyanide solutions and add 0.5 ml of the mixture to each tube of lysozyme-treated bacteria. Shake and incubate in a water bath at 37 °C for 15 min, shake again. Add 0.5 ml ferric nitrate reagent to each tube and inspect immediately.

(iii) Interpretation.   Positive: slowly fading brownish-red colour (Escherichia coli). Negative: honey yellow or faint yellow colour (Proteus mirabilis).

The number of bacteria is critical; an insufficient amount of culture results in a false negative test. The colour reaction is sensitive to EDTA: at concentrations higher than optimum, the brownish-red colour quickly fades. Many bacteria, especially Proteus, exhibit a honey-yellow colour, which is probably associated with a minor degree of thiocyanate formation. However, in practice, it is more feasible to regard the honey-yellow colour as negative, because it is difficult to distinguish from the pale-yellow colour of a "true negative" test.

TABLE I

Substrates used in carbohydrate metabolism tests

Group	Name	Chemical characterization
Tetrose	D-Erythrose	Aldotetrose
Pentoses	L-Arabinose	Aldopentose
	D(−)-Ribose	Aldopentose
	D-Xylose	Aldopentose
Hexoses	D-Fructose	Ketohexose
	D-Galactose	Aldohexose
	D-Glucose	Aldohexose
	D(+)-Mannose	Aldohexose
	L-Sorbose	Ketohexose
Deoxysugar	L-Rhamnose	6-Deoxy-L-mannose
Disaccharides	Cellobiose	O-β-D-Glucopyranosyl-$(1 \rightarrow 4)$-D-glucopyranoside
	Lactose	O-β-D-Galactopyranosyl-$(1 \rightarrow 4)$-β-D-glucopyranoside
	D(+)-Maltose	O-α-D-Glucopyranosyl-$(1 \rightarrow 4)$-β-D-glucopyranoside
	Melibiose	6-α-D-Galactopyranosyl-D-glucose
	Sucrose	O-β-D-Fructofuranosyl-$(2 \rightarrow 1)$-α-D-glucopyranoside
	Trehalose	O-α-D-Glucopyranosyl-$(1 \rightarrow 1)$-α-D-glucopyranoside
Trisaccharides	Melezitose	O-α-D-Glucopyranosyl-$(1 \rightarrow 3)$-O-β-D-fructofuranosyl-$(2 \rightarrow 1)$-α-D-glucopyranoside
	D(+)-Raffinose	O-α-D-Galactopyranosyl-$(1 \rightarrow 6)$-O-α-D-glucopyranosyl-$(1 \rightarrow 2)$-β-D-fructofuranoside

Polysaccharides	Glycogen	D-Glucose units in (1→4) and (1→6) linkages
	Inulin	D-Fructose units in (2→1) linkage
	Pectin	Methyl-D-galacturonate polymer
	Starch	D-Glucose units in (1→4) and (1→6) linkages
Glycosides	Aesculin	6-β-Glucosido-7-hydroxycoumarin
	Amygdalin	Mandelonitrile-β-gentiobioside
	Arbutin	Hydrochinon glycoside
	Salicin	Saligenin-β-D-glucopyranoside
Sugar alcohols	Adonitol	Reduction product of ribose
	Dulcitol	Reduction product of galactose
	Erythritol	Reduction product of erythrose
	Glycerol	Reduction product of glycerose
	i-Inositol	1, 2, 3, 4, 5, 6-Cyclohexane-hexol
	D-Mannitol	Reduction product of D-mannose
	D-Sorbitol	Reduction product of D-sorbose
Organic-acids, salts of	Potassium gluconate	
	Potassium sodium tartrate, (+), (−) and optically inactive	
	Sodium acetate	
	Sodium citrate	
	Sodium malonate	
	Sodium mucate	

Note. In identification tests, substrates of the specified configuration (D or L) and optical rotation (+ or −) should be used. Isomers of the same compound, such as D-arabinose instead of L-arabinose, may give different results.

Procedures in which KCN is handled are potentially hazardous and should preferably be performed in a cabinet equipped with exhaust ventilation. Pipettes, tubes and flasks containing the remainder of the KCN reagent should be discarded by immersing in potassium permanganate solution (*ca.* 15 g in 3 litres of water).

D.   Carbohydrate metabolism

1. Fermentative and oxidative breakdown of carbohydrates

The ability to attack different substrates consisting of carbon, hydrogen and oxygen (Table I) varies with the battery of enzymes present in the bacteria being identified. Complex carbohydrates are first hydrolysed by extracellular enzymes to molecules of sufficiently small size to enter readily into the cell. Further dissimilation results in end-products that can be detected by various methods. The carbohydrate decomposition spectrum determined by production of acid from substrates is now regarded as a secondary tool in classification, but for the characterization of lower taxa and for epidemiological purposes it is still a valuable feature. Much emphasis is put on the pathways and end-products of glucose metabolism. On this basis, bacteria are divided into three principal groups: fermenters, oxidizers and non-utilizers.

Fermentation is characteristic of most obligate anaerobic and facultative anaerobic bacteria. In the first phase of fermentative degradation, glucose is phosphorylated and decomposed to pyruvic acid, in most bacteria via the Embden–Meyerhof pathway:

glucose ⟶ glucose-6-phosphate ⟶ fructose-6-phosphate ⟶ fructose-1,6-diphosphate ⟶ 2 moles glyceraldehyde-3-phosphate ⟶ 2 moles pyruvic acid

In the second phase of decomposition, different pathways lead to a variety of end-products, the most important examples of which are: (1) lactic acid, acetic acid, formic acid, ethanol, carbon dioxide, and hydrogen gas in *Escherichia coli* and many other enteric bacteria; (2) acetoin and 2,3-butanediol in addition to the above products in *Klebsiella* and *Enterobacter*; (3) organic acids without gas in *Shigella* and *Salmonella typhi*; (4) lactic acid in *Lactobacillus* and *Streptococcus*; and (5) propionic acid and carbon dioxide in *Propionibacterium*. The fermentation products of anaerobic bacteria determined by gas chromatography are key characteristics for their identification (Holdeman *et al.*, 1977). The fermentative pathway requires an organic compound as a terminal electron acceptor (Stanier *et al.*, 1963), i.e. fermentation is an anaerobic process. Facultative anaerobes, however, are able to decompose carbohydrates fermentatively in the presence of air.

The oxidative carbohydrate metabolism is characteristic of many obligate aerobic bacteria. The oxidative pathway requires no initial phosphorylation to produce pyruvic acid:

glucose ———→ gluconic acid ————→ 2-ketogluconic acid ————→
2-keto-6-phosphogluconic acid ————→ 2 moles pyruvic acid

Further breakdown of pyruvic acid occurs by direct oxidation through the tricarboxylic-acid cycle, the final products being carbon dioxide and water. As the terminal electron acceptor is molecular oxygen, the process does not take place in the absence of air. Many facultative anaerobic bacteria split carbohydrates not only fermentatively but also oxidatively; however, in young cultures, fermentative metabolism predominates even when the organisms are grown aerobically. As acids accumulate in the medium transiently, a pure oxidative metabolism produces considerably less acidity than the fermentative process.

The degree of acidity in the culture is also influenced by the buffering capacity of the ingredients and by alkaline substances produced during growth. In nutrient media all bacteria produce alkaline compounds (ammonia and amines) as end-products of peptone utilization; the higher the concentration of peptone, the more alkali accumulates. In peptone water, broth or nutrient agar containing 1% peptone and 1% carbohydrate, prompt fermenters produce acid from the carbohydrate in excess. In the same medium, weak fermenters form small amounts of acid, which are frequently masked by the alkaline products of the peptone. Oxidizers, as a rule, produce even less acid, which is, with few exceptions, neutralized. This is the very reason why the carbohydrate spectrum of oxidizers must not be examined in media rich in peptone.

The substantial amount of acid produced by rapidly fermenting bacteria can be detected with indicators changing colour at pH 5.0–5.5 (Andrade's, bromocresol purple). For showing acid production by weak fermenters and oxidizers, more sensitive indicators with a pH range of 6.0–8.0 (bromothymol blue, phenol red) are used.

The carbohydrate spectrum of fermenters that have no special nutritional requirements (Enterobacteriaceae, Vibrionaceae, Staphylococcus) is usually tested in classical 1% peptone water or broth containing the substrates and the indicator. To show gas production, a Durham tube is placed in the glucose medium. For fastidious fermenters, (*Pasteurella*, *Actinobacillus*, *Streptococcus*, *Corynebacterium*), the medium is supplemented with serum. A suitably enriched peptone water is used for testing anaerobic bacteria. Weak

fermenters (*Haemophilus, Cardiobacterium, Flavobacterium, Kingella*) produce acid slowly and frequently unreliably, even in peptone water supplemented adequately for their growth.

Nutrient agar media containing glucose and lactose or glucose, lactose and
sucrose are widely used in the presumptive identification of fermenters.
Supplied with an acid–base indicator, these media are solidified in tubes so as
to form slopes with deep butts. They usually contain thiosulphate and an
iron salt for the detection of hydrogen sulphide production. These differential media are known as triple-sugar iron (TSI) agar, Kligler's iron agar
(KIA) and Russel's modified thiosulphate–iron agar. The double-layer
medium of Nógrády and Rodler (1954) shows the breakdown of urea, too.

The TSI-type media, inoculated by stabbing the butt and drawing the
needle over the surface of the slope, allow a distinction between the
breakdown of glucose characteristic of all Enterobacteriaceae and Vibrionaceae and of lactose or of lactose + sucrose characteristic of most *Escherichia*,
Klebsiella and *Enterobacter* isolates. The biochemical basis of this test is that
TSI-type media contain about ten times more lactose or lactose + sucrose
than glucose. If the culture attacks only glucose, acids accumulate in the butt
where anaerobic conditions prevail; the slope exhibits an acid reaction
usually at the beginning of multiplication only, then turns neutral or alkaline
as a consequence of an oxidative breakdown of the acids and of their
neutralization by alkaline products from peptone. Glucose fermenters growing less readily on TSI-type media (*Yersinia, Pasteurella* and some *Salmonella typhi* isolates) often show an acid slant even after 24 h incubation.
Owing to a higher concentration of lactose or sucrose, bacteria that attack
these substrates produce acids in amounts sufficient to maintain an acid pH,
not only in the butt, but also in the slope at least for 1 day (*Klebsiella,
Enterobacter*) and even for 2–3 days, in the case of *Escherichia coli*. Gas
produced from the sugars splits the agar or forms bubbles in it.

The carbohydrate spectrum of fermentation bacteria may be examined on
nutrient-agar plates containing an indicator. The substrates are incorporated
in paper discs or in tablets and placed on the inoculated plates. A positive
reaction is indicated by acid zones around the discs or tablets (Sanders *et al.*,
1957; Lányi and Ádám, 1960). Commercial microtube systems are extensively
used for routine determination of the carbohydrate fermentation spectrum.

Standard testing of the carbohydrate spectrum of non-fastidious oxidizers
is performed in the oxidation–fermentation (OF) medium of Hugh and
Leifson (1953). This is a stab agar containing 1% carbohydrate, 0.2%
peptone and bromothymol blue indicator. Owing to a low peptone content,
in OF medium the acid from carbohydrate exceeds the alkali from peptone,
not only in cultures of fermenters, but also in those of oxidizers. Accumulation of the acid in the agar gel at the site of its formation makes the positive

reaction more marked. OF medium is essential for the determination of the type of glucose metabolism. Rapid fermenters produce acid that spreads throughout the medium. Weak fermenters (e.g. *Flavobacterium*), as a rule, show delayed acid production, at first at the surface, then along the site of the stab. Oxidizers produce acid only at the surface, but those attacking glucose more vigorously, viz., *Acinetobacter calcoaceticus* and biovars of *Pseudomonas cepacia* and *Pseudomonas pseudomallei*, produce a strong acid reaction at the surface, which spreads downwards on further incubation. OF medium is unsuitable for testing fastidious bacteria; results with OF supplemented with serum have been disappointing. The use of duplicate OF tubes (one accessible to air and one deaerated by boiling and covered with melted petrolatum or paraffin oil) allows a more definitive distinction of the two types of glucose breakdown: acid production only in the open medium indicates oxidative metabolism.

For determination of the carbohydrate utilization spectrum of *Bacillus* species, some of which are oxidizers and others weak fermenters, the agar slope medium of Smith *et al.* (1952) may be used (Cowan, 1974). The main source of nitrogen in this medium is an ammonium salt, from which ammonia is produced in small amounts, but not enough to mask the acid reaction.

A solution of the carbohydrate, amended only with phosphate salts and an indicator (buffered single substrate, BSS), is suitable for the demonstration of preformed, carbohydrate-decomposing enzymes. Using this method, Pickett and Nelson (1955) were able to show carbohydrate breakdown by *Brucella*, which fail to produce detectable amounts of acid in other media. A BSS test has been elaborated by Kellogg and Turner (1973) for *Neisseria*. A slightly modified Kellogg–Turner test, employing 11 kinds of carbohydrate (see Section IV.D.1f) is used successfully in the Hungarian Public Health Laboratory Service for routine identification of non-fermenters and fastidious fermenters.

(a) Peptone water with carbohydrates for facultative anaerobes

(i) *Basal medium.*   Bacto peptone (Difco), 10 g; NaCl, 5 g; distilled water, 1000 ml; Andrade's indicator, 10 ml or bromocresol purple indicator, 12 ml; pH 7.2; sterilize at 121 °C for 20 min. *Andrade's indicator*: acid fuchsin, 5 g; distilled water, 1000 ml; 1 N NaOH, 150 ml; allow to stand at room temperature with frequent shaking; add more 1 N NaOH until the dye is decolourized from red to straw yellow. *Bromocresol purple indicator*: see Section IV.B.6.

Test medium.   Dissolve 1% w/v substrate (see Table I) in the basal medium, adjust the pH to 7.5–7.6 and sterilize by filtration; dispense 2 ml portions into sterile narrow tubes. Place inverted Durham's tubes in the tubes for glucose and after dispensing the medium, steam for 30 min to remove air from the inserts.

(ii) *Procedure.*   Inoculate the tubes, incubate aerobically and observe for up to 14 days. For testing fastidious fermenters, add 0.1 ml (approx. 5%) of sterile rabbit or sheep serum to each tube of medium. For the demonstration of fermentative glucose breakdown by staphylococci, inoculate duplicate tubes, one of which has been deaerated by boiling and layered with liquid paraffin.

(iii) *Interpretation.*   Positive: red (Andrade's indicator) or yellow (bromocresol purplé). Negative: colourless or faint pink (Andrade's indicator) or purple (bromocresol purple).

(b) Peptone yeast extract (PY) medium with carbohydrates for anaerobes   (Holdeman *et al.*, 1977)

(i) *PY basal medium.*   Proteose peptone (Difco), 20 g; yeast extract (Oxoid), 10 g; resazurin solution, 4 ml; salts solution, 40 ml; distilled water, 1000 ml; boil and add vitamin K_1 solution, 0.2 ml; haemin solution, 10 ml; cysteine HCl, 0.5 g; pH 7.2; distribute in 100 ml portions and sterilize at 121 °C for 20 min. *Resazurin solution*: resazurin, 25 mg; distilled water, 100 ml. *Salts solution*: $CaCl_2$, 0.2 g; $MgSO_4.7H_2O$, 0.5 g; K_2HPO_4, 1.0 g; KH_2PO_4, 1.0 g; $NaHCO_3$, 10.0 g; NaCl, 2.0 g; mix $CaCl_2$ and $MgSO_4$ in 300 ml distilled water until dissolved; add 500 ml distilled water and dissolve the remaining salts; add 200 ml distilled water, mix and store at 4 °C. *Vitamin K_1 solution*: vitamin K_1, 20 mg; ethanol (95%), 20 ml. *Haemin solution*: dissolve 50 mg haemin in 1 ml 1 N NaOH; add distilled water to a final volume of 100 ml; sterilize at 121 °C for 20 min.

Test medium.   Prepare a 20% (w/v) aqueous solution of the carbohydrates (a 5% solution of salicin); sterilize by filtration. Add 5 ml of carbohydrate solution (10 ml of salicin solution) to 100 ml basal medium and dispense 4–5 ml amounts in tubes. Drive off air by boiling until the resazurin indicator changes from pink to colourless, and add a layer of paraffin oil to each tube if tested in an aerobic incubator.

(ii) *Procedure.*   Inject 0.2–0.5 ml chopped meat broth culture in the medium by means of a Pasteur capillary pipette or a suitable syringe. Avoid pumping air bubles into the medium. Incubate until growth is visible. Add 1 drop of neutral (pH 7.0) bromocresol purple indicator solution (Section IV.B.6.) and shake the tube to mix the culture.

(iii) *Interpretation.*   Positive: yellow colour. Negative: purple colour. The pH of cultures incubated without paraffin layer in an anaerobic jar should preferably be determined electrometrically by use of a thin combination electrode; pH < 5.5 is interpreted as strongly positive, pH 5.5–6.0 as weakly positive and pH > 6.0 as negative.

(c) Triple-sugar iron agar   (TSI; Report, 1958)

(i) *Medium.*   Bacto peptone (Difco), 20 g; beef extract (Oxoid), 3 g; yeast extract (Oxoid), 3 g; glucose, 1 g; lactose, 10 g; sucrose, 10 g; NaCl, 5 g; $Na_2S_2O_3.5H_2O$, 0.3 g; agar (Oxoid No. 1), 7.5 g; distilled water, 1000 ml. Dissolve the ingredients by heating, add 12 ml phenol red solution, 0.2% (Section IV.B.3a) and 0.2 g $FeSO_4.7H_2O$ dissolved in a small amount of distilled water. Distribute immediately after the addition of the iron salt into tubes 16 mm in diameter, sterilize at 115 °C for 20 min, cool to form deep (2.5–3 cm) butts and slants (3–3.5 cm).

(ii) *Procedure.*   Inoculate with a wire slightly bent at the end by stabbing into the butt and streaking the slant uniformly without scratching its surface.

(iii) *Interpretation.*   Unchanged butt, unchanged or alkaline slant (*Pseudomonas aeruginosa*). Acid butt, alkaline slant (*Shigella*). Acid butt with gas and with black colour spread throughout the butt and black ring near the top of the butt, alkaline slant (*Salmonella paratyphi-B*). Acid butt with gas and alkaline slant (*Proteus morganii*). Acid butt with gas and acid slant (*Escherichia coli*). For the reactions of other bacteria see Edwards and Ewing (1972), Martin and Washington (1980) and Hugh and Gilardi (1980).

(d) Oxidation-fermentation (OF) medium

(i) *Basal medium.*   Bacto peptone (Difco), 2 g; NaCl, 5 g; K_2HPO_4, 0.3 g; agar (Oxoid No. 1), 3 g; distilled water, 1000 ml; bromothymol blue, 0.2% solution, 15 ml; pH 7.2; sterilize at 121 °C for 20 min. *Bromothymol blue solution, 0.2%:* bromothymol blue, 2 g; 0.1 N NaOH, 50 ml; distilled water, 950 ml.

Test medium.   To the basal medium add carbohydrate solutions (20%; salicin 5%) to give a final concentration of 1% carbohydrate; dispense aseptically in narrow tubes in 4–5 ml amounts and cool in an upright position. Some carbohydrates, including glucose, may be dissolved directly in the molten basal medium, and the tubes may be autoclaved at 115 °C for 20 min. Fructose, maltose and xylose must not be sterilized by heating. However, it is recommended that all carbohydrates be sterilized by filtration. The colour of the uninoculated medium should be light green. Glucose tubes serving to distinguish fermenters and oxidizers should not be stored for more than 14 days. Older media may be used if first boiled for 10 min in a water bath to drive off dissolved air.

(ii) *Procedure.*   Inoculate lightly by stabbing with a straight wire. Observe daily for 3 days (routine diagnosis) and for 14 days (standard procedure). For a more precise distinction between fermentative and oxidative glucose metabolism, inoculate duplicate tubes and cover one of them with sterile paraffin oil or petrolatum (not essential in routine work).

(iii) *Interpretation.*   Fermentative breakdown: yellow colour throughout the medium in open and covered tubes (*Escherichia coli*). Weak fermentative activity: delayed acid production at the surface of the open tube and a delayed, weak acid production appearing as a thin yellow line along the stab in both tubes (*Flavobacterium meningosepticum*). Oxidative glucose breakdown: yellow at the surface in the open tube (*Pseudomonas aeruginosa*). Negative: no colour change (green) or blue colour on the surface of the open tube, indicating alkali production (*Alcaligenes faecalis*).

    In tests for carbohydrate decomposition, whenever growth requirements allow, the media should be incubated in air and not in an atmosphere with increased CO_2 content. CO_2 trapped in the medium causes an acidic shift of the pH, usually to 6.2–6.4. To make aerobic and facultative anaerobic cultures accessible to air, screw-capped tops of the peptone water and OF tubes should be loosened prior to incubation. Many anaerobic bacteria decolourize dyes. Therefore it is more advisable to add a drop of indicator solution to the culture after completion of incubation, rather than incorporate the indicator in the medium.

(e) Ammonium-salt sugars for aerobic spore formers

(i) *Medium.* $(NH_4)_2HPO_4$, 1 g; KCl, 0.2 g; $MgSO_4.7H_2O$, 0.2 g; yeast extract, 0.2 g; agar (Oxoid No. 1), 9 g; distilled water, 1000 ml; bromocresol purple, 0.2% solution (Section IV.B.6.), 4 ml; sterilize at 115 °C for 20 min. Add carbohydrate solutions sterilized by filtration to give a final concentration of carbohydrate of 1%. Dispense aseptically 3 ml per narrow tube and cool as a slope.

(ii) *Procedure.*   Inoculate lightly and observe for 14 days.

(iii) *Interpretation.*   Positive: yellow. Negative: orange or red-violet.

(f) Rapid single-substrate method for testing carbohydrate utilization spectrum (BSS method)

(i) *Buffer.* K_2HPO_4, 0.4 g; KH_2PO_4, 0.1 g; KCl, 8 g; distilled water, 1000 ml; phenol red solution, 1%, 2 ml; distribute in 25 ml amounts and sterilize at 115 °C for 20 min. *Phenol red solution, 1%*: phenol red, 1 g; 0.1 N NaOH, 40 ml; distilled water, 60 ml.

Substrate solutions.   Dissolve 1 g carbohydrate in 25 ml buffer and correct the pH, if necessary, to that of the basal buffer (orange colour). Sterilize by filtration or, with substrates other than fructose, maltose and xylose, heat at 100 °C for 30 min.

(ii) *Procedure.*   Pipette one drop (50 µl) of each substrate solution into wells in Microtiter plates sterilized with ethylene oxide or into sterile narrow tubes. Prepare a heavy suspension of the organism grown on non-selective, carbohydrate-free solid medium in 0.5–1.0 ml substrate-free basal buffer and add one drop to each well or tube. Incubate at 35–37 °C for 24 h. The Microtiter plates should be incubated in a wet chamber.

(iii) *Interpretation.*   Positive: yellow colour. Negative: orange or red-violet colour. The colour of the positive test is influenced by alkali production from residual nutrients: if the suspension in the substrate-free control buffer and in undegraded carbohydrate is red-violet, an orange colour is interpreted as a weak acid production.

To prove, for taxonomic purposes, that an organism is unable to utilize carbohydrates, it should be tested in peptone water supplemented with 5% (v/v) filtered and inactivated serum, in the case of fastidious bacteria, and in OF medium incubated for 14 days and by the BSS method read after 24 h. In addition to glucose, fructose, maltose and xylose should also be used as substrates, since some bacteria may not utilize glucose or may do so only slowly, whereas they may break down other sugars readily, for example fructose (*Pseudomonas acidovorans*), maltose (*Pseudomonas maltophilia*) and xylose (*Achromobacter xylosoxidans*). For routine identification, an organism not producing acid within 1 day in a TSI-type medium and within 3 days in OF tubes containing glucose and maltose may be regarded as a carbohydrate non-utilizer. One should, however be careful to distinguish yellow pigment of surface growth on OF medium from oxidative carbohydrate breakdown.

2. Methyl red test

The methyl red (MR) test is used to distinguish two different pathways of glucose fermentation. In glucose, phosphate, peptone-water medium, MR-positive bacteria produce acid in amounts sufficient to maintain the pH below 4.5 for several days. MR-negative bacteria (most biovars of *Klebsiella*, *Enterobacter* and *Serratia*) continue to metabolize the acids that are produced into neutral substances and cause a reversion of the initial pH to about 6.0. The MR reagent is an ideal indicator to show this difference, being red at pH less than 4.5 and yellow above 6.0. The MR test is performed mainly for the intrageneric differentiation of Enterobacteriaceae.

To decompose the initial acid products of fermentation, MR-negative bacteria require atmospheric oxygen (Barry *et al.*, 1970), i.e. the test is of no value for anaerobic bacteria lacking the oxidative pathway of carbohydrate utilization. Also, it would be superfluous to test carbohydrate non-utilizers or oxidizers that are unable to produce an acid reaction below the pH range of the MR indicator.

(i) *MR–VP test medium.* Bacto peptone (Difco), 7 g; K_2HPO_4, 5 g; glucose, 5 g; distilled water, 1000 ml; pH 7.5; distribute 2–3 ml portions in narrow tubes and sterilize at 115 °C for 20 min.

    MR reagent. Methyl red (Merck), 0.25 g; ethanol, 100 ml.

(ii) *Procedure.* Inoculate the tubes lightly and incubate for 2 days (routine test) and for 4 days (standard test) at 35–37 °C. Add one drop of methyl red reagent. After reading the MR test, the same culture may be examined for the Voges–Proskauer test.

(iii) *Interpretation.* MR-positive: red colour (*Escherichia coli*). MR-negative: yellow colour (*Serratia marcescens*). A sample of the MR culture may be tested after 1 day, especially if the isolate produces abundant gas in the TSI type of media, which is characteristic of *Klebsiella* and *Enterobacter*. If the 24 h culture of a vigorously fermenting organism is yellow when tested with the MR reagent, it can be recorded as MR-negative. A red colour indicates that the isolate may be MR-positive or MR-negative, and the culture must be further incubated. An orange colour is associated with a negative MR-test, i.e. decomposition of the acids is in progress. A MR test carried out in duplicate tubes inoculated at 35–37 °C and at room temperature is useful for the identification of *Hafnia alvei*, which is usually MR-positive at 35–37 °C but MR-negative at 20 °C.

3. Voges–Proskauer test

The Voges–Proskauer (VP) test is based on the detection of acetoin (acetylmethylcarbinol) produced in the course of glucose breakdown by most isolates of *Klebsiella, Enterobacter* and *Serratia*. If potassium hydroxide is added in the presence of air to the culture of VP-positive organisms, acetoin is oxidized to diacetyl, which forms a pink condensation product with guanidine nuclei present in arginine and other peptone constituents (Mac-Faddin, 1980). The colour is intensified if creatine, which contains a guanidine nucleus, is added (O'Meara, 1931). α-Naphthol, acting as a catalyst for diacetyl production, is another colour intensifier (Barritt, 1936). As a standard test, Barritt's method is recommended. The VP test can be used not only for the differentiation of Gram-negative, but also of Gram-positive bacteria.

(i) *MR–VP medium.*   See Section IV.D.2.

   Reagent A.   α-Naphthol, 5 g; absolute ethanol, 100 ml; the reagent must not be darker than straw colour.

   Reagent B.   Potassium hydroxide, 40 g; distilled water, 100 ml.

(ii) *Procedure.*   Incubate the MR–VP cultures for 2 days (routine test) and for 4 days (standard test) at 35–37 °C. After reading the MR test, add 0.6 ml reagent A and 0.2 ml reagent B per ml of culture. Shake well after the addition of each reagent and slope the tube to increase aeration. Read after 15 and 60 min.

(iii) *Interpretation.*   Positive: strong red colour (*Enterobacter cloacae*). Negative: no colour reaction, occasionally faint pink to copper colour (*Escherichia coli*). A duplicate tube incubated at 20 °C is useful for the identification of *Hafnia alvei* (VP-variable at 35–37 °C, but positive at 20 °C).

   α-Naphthol exerts its catalytic effect only if added before the potassium hydroxide. On incubation lasting more than 4 days, acetoin may be degraded to compounds not giving the VP test. If reagent B is added in amounts more than specified, development of a copper colour, which may be misinterpreted as a positive test is more likely to occur.

4. o-Nitrophenyl-β-D-galactopyranoside test (ONPG)

The first step of lactose utilization is controlled by β-galactosidase permease, which is responsible for the transport of the substrate through the cell wall. In the next step another enzyme, β-D-galactosidase, hydrolyses lactose into its monosaccharide constituents. Rapid lactose fermenters, for example most *Escherichia coli* isolates, produce both enzymes. Delayed lactose fermenters such as *Salmonella arizonae*, usually produce intracellular β-D-galactosidase, but are devoid of permease. On prolonged incubation in lactose-containing medium, however, they split off permease-producing mutants, which are able to take up the substrate and hydrolyse it (Le Minor and Ben Hamida, 1962; Cowan, 1974; MacFaddin, 1980). Bacteria are impenetrable to the usual concentration of lactose (1%), but at higher concentrations (5–10%) permeability increases and delayed lactose fermenters produce acid more readily. Acid production in 10% lactose may be used for the differentiation of non-fermenters (Hugh and Gilardi, 1980).

The presence of β-D-galactosidase, independently of the presence or absence of permease, can be demonstrated by the ONPG test. The enzyme hydrolyses *o*-nitrophenyl-β-D-galactopyranoside (colourless) to *o*-nitrophenol (yellow).

(i) *Reagent discs.*   Sterilize small filter-paper discs by autoclaving, and impregnate each of them with 1 drop of substrate solution: *o*-nitrophenyl-β-D-galactopyranoside, 0.06 g; $Na_2HPO_4.2H_2O$, 0.017 g; sterile distilled water, 10 ml. Dry at 37 °C for 24 h and store in screw-capped tubes at room temperature.

(ii) *Procedure.*   Prepare a heavy bacterial suspension in 0.5 ml physiological saline in a narrow tube and add an ONPG disc. Read after incubation at 35–37 °C for 24 h.

(iii) *Interpretation.*   Positive: yellow colour (*Escherichia coli*). Negative: colourless (*Salmonella paratyphi-B*).

Bacteria grown on media containing glucose may give a false negative ONPG test. The release of the enzyme from the cells may be enhanced by adding a drop of toluene at the beginning of incubation. If the test is read after incubation overnight, toluene is not needed.

5. Hydrolysis of starch, glycogen and pectin

Polysaccharides are hydrolysed through a series of breakdown products to their monosaccharide components. In starch peptone water the hydrolysis is indicated by an acid reaction due to the fermentation of the monosaccharide constituent, glucose. This method is inadequate to show starch decomposition by aerobic bacteria, but is applied to differentiate some facultative anaerobes (*Corynebacterium, Listeria*). Glycogen hydrolysis of these bacteria can be examined in a similar manner.

A starch-hydrolysis test, applicable for all kinds of microorganisms, is based on a colour reaction of non-hydrolysed starch with Lugol's iodine. Starch gives a deep-blue colour, whereas its breakdown products, as hydrolysis progresses, gradually become violet, brownish-red and finally colourless. For testing the hydrolysis of pectin, the liquefaction test is recommended (Edwards and Ewing, 1972).

(a) Starch hydrolysis

(i) *Basal medium.*   Nutrient agar, double strength, 500 ml.

Starch solution.   Dissolve 10 g potato starch in 500 ml distilled water by boiling.

Test medium.   Add the hot starch solution to the molten basal medium, mix and autoclave at 115 °C for 20 min; dispense into Petri dishes.

Iodine reagent.   Lugol's solution diluted so as to contain approx. 0.1% iodine and 0.2% potassium iodide, e.g. Hucker's iodine (Section II.A.2b), 1 volume; distilled water, 2 volumes.

(ii) *Procedure.*   Inoculate up to 6 isolates on one plate as spots and incubate for 4 days. Flood with iodine reagent and read immediately, as the blue colour fades rapidly.

(iii) *Interpretation.*   Positive: clear colourless zones around the growth (*Flavobacterium indologenes*). Negative: blue colour throughout the medium and around the growth (*Pseudomonas aeruginosa*).

(b) Pectin hydrolysis

(i) *Medium.*   Yeast extract (Oxoid), 5 g; $CaCl_2.2H_2O$, 0.5 g; agar (Oxoid No. 1), 8 g; sodium polypectate, 10 g; distilled water, 1000 ml; 1 N NaOH, 9 ml;

bromothymol blue, 0.2% solution (Section IV.D.1d), 12.5 ml. Stir thoroughly to wet the pectate, and heat in boiling water to dissolve the ingredients as much as possible. Distribute in 100 ml amounts in flasks and autoclave at 121 °C for not more than 5 min. Pour plates.

(ii) *Procedure.*   Inoculate up to 8 isolates on one plate as spots. Incubate for 3 days.

(iii) *Interpretation.*   Positive: depression in the medium surrounding growth (*Erwinia carotovora*). Negative: depression absent (*Erwinia herbicola* syn *Enterobacter agglomerans*).

6. Aesculin hydrolysis

The hydrolysis of aesculin yields aesculetin (6,7-dihydroxycoumarin) and glucose. Aesculetin, depending on the concentration, forms a dark-brown to black complex with ferric ions. The test is carried out in peptone water or on peptone-agar slants. The most important bacteria of medical significance capable of splitting aesculin are *Klebsiella aerogenes, Enterobacter aerogenes, Flavobacterium meningosepticum* and D-group streptococci. For a selective differentiation of streptococci, the aesculin medium may be supplemented with bile (Cowan,1974). For streptococci, use the following liquid medium, which, for Gram-negative bacteria, may be solidified with agar to provide slants.

(i) *Medium.*   Bacto peptone (Difco), 15 g; aesculin, 1 g; ferric ammonium citrate or ferric citrate, 0.5 g; distilled water, 1000 ml; pH 7.0; distribute into narrow tubes and sterilize at 115 °C for 20 min.

(ii) *Procedure.*   Inoculate and incubate for up to 7 days.

(iii) *Interpretation.*   Positive: black or dark-brown (*Streptococcus faecalis*). Negative: no blackening (*Streptococcus pyogenes*).

7. Production of dextran and levan

Dextran is a gummy water-soluble glucose polymer produced by bacteria from sucrose. Levan consists of the fructose units of sucrose. Polymerization proceeds directly from sucrose; neither dextran nor levan can be produced from its monosaccharide components. In medical bacteriology the test is used for the differentiation of streptococci; *Leuconostoc mesenteroides* is a classical dextran-producing organism.

(i) *Medium.*   Trypticase peptone (BBL), 15 g; thioton peptone (BBL), 5 g; sucrose, 50 g; K_2HPO_4, 4 g; agar (Oxoid No. 1), 10 g; distilled water, 1000 ml pH 7.0; trypan blue, 1% aqueous solution, 7.5 ml; crystal violet, 1% aqueous solution, 0.1 ml; sterilize at 115 °C for 20 min. Cool to 50 °C and add 1 ml of 1% potassium tellurite aqueous solution sterilized by filtration. Pour plates.

(ii) *Procedure.*   Streak so as to obtain well-isolated colonies. Incubate at 37 °C for 24 h, then at room temperature for another 24 h.

(iii) *Interpretation.*   Dextran production: small, dark-blue colonies pitting the agar and adhering to the surface (*Streptococcus sanguis*). Levan production: large, mucoid, confluent growth blue or pink in colour (*Streptococcus salivarius*). Negative: faint or dark blue minute, easily emulsifyable colonies (*Streptococcus mitis*).

8. 2-Ketogluconate test

Gluconic acid, an intermediate product of oxidative glucose breakdown (Section IV.D.1.) is further degraded to 2-ketogluconic acid by *Klebsiella*, *Enterobacter*, *Pseudomonas aeruginosa* and some other bacteria of medical importance. The test is carried out in liquid peptone medium containing gluconate as substrate. Gluconate is not a reducing agent, but 2-ketogluconate reduces cupric hydroxide, which is present in Benedict's reagent as a blue citrate complex, into orange-red cuprous oxide. The test is used mainly for the identification of Gram negative non-fermenters (Hugh and Gilardi, 1980).

(i) *Medium.*   Bacto peptone (Difco), 1.5 g; yeast extract (Oxoid), 1 g; potassium gluconate, 40 g; distilled water, 1000 ml; pH 7.0. Filter, distribute into narrow tubes in 2.5 ml portions, sterilize at 115 °C for 20 min.

Benedict's reagent.   Sodium citrate, 17.3 g; Na_2CO_3, 10 g; $CuSO_4.5H_2O$, 1.73 g; distilled water to make 100 ml. First dissolve citrate and carbonate in about 60 ml water; dissolve copper sulphate separately in about 20 ml water. Add the latter solution to the former with constant stirring and add distilled water to 100 ml. Store at room temperature.

(ii) *Procedure.*   Inoculate the tubes and incubate for 2 days. Add $\frac{1}{5}$ part (about 0.5 ml) of Benedict's reagent, shake and place in boiling water for 10 min.

(iii) *Interpretation.*   Positive: orange or orange-red precipitation (*Pseudomonas aeruginosa*). Negative: blue or greenish-blue (*Flavobacterium meningosepticum*).

9. Decomposition of organic acids

Organic acids are decomposed first to different lower acids and carbon dioxide. Subsequently, if the medium is incubated aerobically, the intermediary acids are oxidized and more CO_2 is formed (Gunsalus and Stanier, 1961). The organic acids are added to the medium as alkali salts. In the course of breakdown by bacteria, alteration of the pH depends on the mode of incubation (aerobic or anaerobic) and on the kind of nitrogen source (peptone or ammonium salt).

During aerobic incubation and rapid growth in an organic-acids–peptone-water medium, fermentative bacteria produce, initially, an oxidation–reduction potential favourable for accumulation of lower acids; later, however, as oxidation of the acids and ammonia formation from the peptone proceeds, the pH changes to alkaline. This kind of reaction takes place in organic-acids–peptone-water media, described by Kauffmann (1954), and also in Jordan–Harmon tartrate agar (Edwards and Ewing, 1972). Consequently, anaerobic incubation results in a more rapid and persistent acid production.

If an ammonium salt is the sole or main source of nitrogen, and the organic acid is the source of carbon, then energy for growth is obtained oxidatively. The end product is carbon dioxide, which forms carbonates with residual alkali ions. Acids do not accumulate, and, as multiplication proceeds, the pH shifts to alkaline. This type of reaction occurs in Simmons' and Christensen's citrate media, in Ewing's acetate medium and in Leifson's malonate medium (Kauffmann, 1954; Edwards and Ewing, 1972; Cowan, 1974).

(a) Decomposition of organic acids in peptone water

(i) *Medium.*   Bacto peptone (Difco), 10 g; NaCl, 5 g; distilled water, 1000 ml; bromothymol blue, 0.2% solution (Section IV.D.1d), 12.5 ml. Add 10 g of sodium potassium tartrate, dextrorotary ("*d*-tartrate"), laevorotatory ("*l*-tartrate") or optically inactive ("*i*-tartrate") sodium alginate or sodium citrate. Adjust the pH to 7.4, dispense in 3 ml amounts in narrow tubes with inverted Durham vials and sterilize at 115 °C for 20 min. For mucic acid, sterilize the basal medium in bulk, add 1% mucic acid and sufficient amount of 1 N NaOH to dissolve it while the base is hot, adjust the pH to 7.4, distribute in sterile tubes with Durham vials and steam without pressure for 30 min.

Reagent.   Dissolve lead acetate in distilled water to give a neutral saturated solution.

(ii) *Procedure.*   Inoculate media that have been stored for not more than 14 days. After a longer storage, boil the tubes in a water bath for 10 min to drive off air. The tests may be carried out in tubes layered with paraffin oil after steaming. Read daily for colour change. After incubation for 14 days, add an equal volume of lead acetate reagent to tartrate and citrate cultures and to uninoculated control media.

(iii) *Interpretation.*   *d*-Tartrate positive: gas production, greenish yellow colour, small volume of precipitate with lead acetate (*Salmonella java*). *d*-Tartrate negative: blue colour, large volume of precipitation with lead acetate (*Salmonella paratyphi-B*). For examination of other organic-acid tests, which are infrequently used in identification, see Edwards and Ewing (1972) and Martin and Washington (1980). In aerobically incubated cultures the acid reaction appears earlier and lasts longer inside the Durham vials. If the medium is layered with paraffin oil, a blue colour fails to develop, since alkali is not produced from peptone. Negative cultures show a neutral green colour, while positive cultures cause, initially, a yellow colour reaction then a decolourization of the indicator.

(b) Utilization of ammonium citrate (Simmons' test) and ammonium acetate

(i) *Medium.*   NaCl, 5 g; $NH_4H_2PO_4$, 1 g; K_2HPO_4, 1 g; $MgSO_4.7H_2O$, 0.2 g; sodium citrate, 2 g, or sodium acetate, 2.5 g; agar (Oxoid No. 1), 9 g; distilled water, 1000 ml; bromothymol blue, 0.2% solution (Section IV.D.1d), 40 ml; pH 6.8. Dispense, sterilize at 115 °C for 20 min, and cool so as to obtain a short butt and long slope.

(ii) *Procedure.*   Inoculate lightly and incubate aerobically for up to 4 days.

(iii) *Interpretation.*   Ammonium citrate positive: multiplication and blue colour (*Citrobacter freundii*). Ammonium citrate negative: no multiplication and original green colour (*Escherichia coli*). Ammonium acetate positive: multiplication and blue colour (*Escherichia coli*). Ammonium acetate negative: no multiplication and original green colour (*Shigella flexneri*). If liquid media are used instead of slopes, the positive test appears somewhat later. Unlike Simmons' citrate, Christensen's citrate medium is supplemented with glucose and yeast extract; an organism positive in Simmons' will be positive in Christensen's; however, some bacteria negative with Simmons' are positive with Christensen's method (Cowan, 1974). Accordingly, in identification tables, the medium used for organic-acid tests should be specified. A carry-over of nutrients with a too heavy inoculum from the original culture may give a false positive result. When inoculating a series of biochemical tests, inoculate utilization media first.

(c) Malonate utilization

(i) *Medium.* $(NH_4)_2SO_4$, 2 g; K_2HPO_4, 0.4 g; NaCl, 2 g; beef extract (Oxoid), 0.5 g, or yeast extract (Oxoid), 1 g; sodium malonate, 3 g; distilled water, 1000 ml; bromothymol blue, 0.2% solution (Section IV.D.1d), 12.5 ml; pH 6.8. Distribute in narrow tubes in 2–3 ml amounts and sterilize at 115 °C for 20 min.

(ii) *Procedure.* Inoculate lightly and incubate for 48 h.

(iii) *Interpretation.* Positive: blue colour (*Salmonella arizonae*). Negative: original green colour (*Salmonella paratyphi-B*). For malonate utilization, certain bacteria require a small amount of organic nitrogen source (beef or yeast extract). Some authors prefer to add glucose as a further supplement for growth (MacFaddin, 1980).

E. Miscellaneous tests

1. Haemolysis

Haemolysis is a useful characteristic for identifying a wide variety of bacteria. The chemical structure and properties of bacterial products causing haemolysis vary with different taxa. In practical identification, two main types of haemolysis, originally described for streptococci, are distinguished. On blood-agar alpha-haemolysis is characterized by a greenish zone around the colonies; the envelope of erythrocytes is intact or partially destroyed. Beta-haemolysis appears as a clear colourless zone around the colonies in which the envelope of erythrocytes has been destroyed.

Beta-haemolytic streptococci produce oxygen-labile streptolysin O and oxygen-stable streptolysin S. In aerobic surface cultures, streptolysin S activity is demonstrated. As streptolysin S production may vary from strain to strain, it is advisable to test the isolate also by anaerobic incubation on carbohydrate-free blood-agar plates. However, many strains of streptococci that are beta-haemolytic, when incubated aerobically, produce alpha-haemolytic zones when grown anaerobically or in an atmosphere with increased CO_2 content.

The cytolytic toxins of staphylococci act differently on the erythrocytes of various species. The name of these toxins, or haemolysins (alpha, beta and delta), must not be confused with the type of haemolysis described above (alpha or beta). Alpha-toxin, the most important staphylococcal haemolysin, causes a beta-type, complete haemolysis on sheep-blood agar. Staphylococcal beta-toxin usually causes a wide band of incomplete haemolysis, and is characterized by the ability to produce hot–cold lysis, i.e. haemolysis is enhanced if incubation at 35–37 °C is continued in the refrigerator or at room temperature. Delta-toxin produces a complete haemolysis of human erythrocytes.

The presence or absence of haemolytic toxins in *Clostridium* is of intrageneric differential value. These toxins usually cause a beta-type haemolysis, which may be surrounded by a wider zone of incomplete haemolysis. For Gram-negative bacteria, haemolysis is also an important taxonomic tool. Some produce changes around the colony that correspond neither to alpha- nor to beta-haemolysis, for example the lavender-green discolouration associated with proteolysis around *Flavobacterium* colonies.

For general use, ox or sheep blood (5%) in a suitable nutrient-agar base may be recommended. Glucose inhibits haemolysin production by streptococci and therefore should not be incorporated. Cysteine blood agar used for anaerobes may contain 0.2% glucose. Haemolysis of some bacteria can be detected with erythrocytes of other species, for example *Gemella haemolysans* on rabbit and horse erythrocytes, *Gardnerella vaginalis* on human and usually on rabbit-blood-agar.

2. *CAMP test*

CAMP is an acronym for Christie, Atkins and Munch-Petersen (1944), who developed the test for the differentiation of group B streptococci. (CAMP should not be confused with cAMP, which stands for cyclic adenosine 5′-monophosphate.) If a beta-toxin-producing *Staphylococcus aureus* and a CAMP-factor-producing organism are streaked on a blood-agar plate as straight lines at right-angles to one another then, after incubation, the incomplete haemolysis of the staphylococcus changes to complete haemolysis at the site where the products of the two organisms have converged. A reverse CAMP reaction is characterized by an inhibition of staphylococcal haemolysis by the test organism (Záhorová and Kubelka, 1960). Instead of growing staphylococci on the plate, staphylococcal beta-toxin (10 units per ml) may be dropped on colonies of the test organism (Cowan, 1974), or paper discs containing beta-toxin may be placed on the plate (MacFaddin, 1980).

The CAMP reaction takes place only on blood agar made with sheep or ox blood. A high anti-beta-haemolysin titre in some batches of blood may inhibit the development of a positive test. It is essential to use a *Staphylococcus aureus* strain that produces a wide band of incomplete haemolysis; a narrow zone of complete haemolysis within the band does not interfere with the test.

(i) *Medium.*   Blood agar giving satisfactory results with the control strains.

(ii) *Procedure.*   Inoculate *Staphylococcus aureus* on the plate so as to produce a diametrical line of growth. Streak the organisms under examination as straight lines at right-angles on one side, or preferably on both sides, of the staphylococcal inoculum, without touching the latter. Incubate for 24 h aerobically.

(iii) *Interpretation.*   Positive: arrowhead-, flame- or crescent-shaped clear zone located around the growth of the tested organism within the incomplete (dark) staphylococcal haemolytic zone (*Streptococcus agalactiae*). Reverse: lack of staphylococcal incomplete haemolysis at the juncture of the two organisms (*Corynebacterium pyogenes*). Negative: neither stimulation nor inhibition of staphylococcal haemolysis (*Streptococcus pyogenes*). In the case of a doubtful positive reaction, the test should be repeated by first culturing the organism undergoing identification overnight, and then by inoculating the staphylococcus and reincubating the plate for another day.

3. Chicken erythrocyte agglutination

Chicken erythrocytes are agglutinated by about 90% of *Vibrio cholerae* var. *el-tor* isolates, but only by about 20% of classical *Vibrio cholerae* strains.

(i) *Erythrocytes.*   Collect 4 volumes of chicken blood in 1 volume of 3.8% sterile sodium citrate solution. Wash four times in saline (0.85%) and use the deposit.

(ii) *Procedure.*   Prepare a moderately heavy suspension of the organism grown on nutrient agar in a drop of saline placed on a slide. Add a loopful of chicken erythrocytes, mix with the loop and tilt the slide.

(iii) *Interpretation.*   Positive: haemagglutination in 5 s (*Vibrio cholerae* var. *el-tor*). Negative: haemagglutination absent (*Vibrio cholerae*).

4. Coagulase test

Staphylococcal coagulase clots plasma, probably by activating prothrombin, which, as in physiological clotting of blood, converts fibrinogen to fibrin. In contrast with physiological clotting, coagulase activity is not dependent on calcium ions. To avoid spontaneous clotting, the plasma used as a reagent must contain anticoagulants (citrate, heparin or EDTA). The plasma should not be filtered, since this procedure decreases its ability to form a coagulum. Human, rabbit and swine plasma are suitable reagents.

Staphylococcus aureus produces a coagulase bound to the bacterial cells and a free coagulase released to the liquid medium. Most *Staphylococcus intermedius* strains produce only free coagulase, whereas other staphylococci fail to form either type of the enzyme. Bound coagulase can be detected by the slide method. The tube test does not distinguish between bound and free coagulase.

(a) Slide test

(i) *Plasma.*   Collect aseptically 4 volumes of human or rabbit blood into 1 volume of 3.8% sterile sodium citrate solution. Centrifuge and mix 19 volumes of supernatant with 1 volume of 0.2% aqueous merthiolate solution. The plasma may be diluted with 0.01% merthiolate solution so that it continues to give a strong reaction with positive strains. Store in a refrigerator at 4 °C.

(ii) *Procedure.*   On a slide, mix a loopful of culture grown on nutrient agar in a drop of plasma. The growth may be first mixed in saline and the plasma added with a loop.

(iii) *Interpretation.*   Positive: immediate coarse clumping (*Staphylococcus aureus*). Negative: homogeneous suspension or slight granulation (*Staphylococcus epidermidis*).

(b) Tube test

(i) *Plasma.*   Prepare plasma as described for the slide test, but do not add merthiolate. Store in the freezing compartment of a refrigerator.

(ii) *Procedure.*   Pipette 0.5 ml plasma in a narrow tube and add 0.5 ml 18–24 h broth culture or suspend a loopful of growth from solid medium in it. Mix by rotating the tube; do not shake. Incubate at 35–37 °C and examine by slanting but not shaking the tube after 1, 4 and 18–20 h.

(iii) *Interpretation.*   Positive: complete or partial clot (*Staphylococcus aureus*). Negative: homogeneous suspension (*Staphylococcus epidermidis*).

For a slide test use fresh cultures. Growth from ordinary nutrient agar or chocolate agar gives the best results: blood-agar cultures may react somewhat less strongly. Do not use a culture grown on hypertonic salt agar. Contamination of citrated plasma with citrate-utilizing bacteria may result in a false positive tube test: after binding the citrate, calcium ions are released, and a physiological clotting occurs. Some *Staphylococcus aureus* strains produce high amounts of fibrinolysin, which lyses the clot or inhibits clotting; frequent observation of the tube in the first hours of incubation help to avoid this kind of false negative test.

5. String test

Bile salts may cause a mucous alteration of cell-wall constituents. The string test is specific for vibrios; some *Aeromonas* isolates may give a weak delayed reaction (Smith, 1970).

(i) *Reagent.*   Sodium deoxycholate, 0.5 g; distilled water, 100 ml. Adjust the pH with 1 N NaOH to 8.2.

(ii) *Procedure.*   Mix a small amount of growth from an 18–24 h nutrient-agar culture in a drop of the reagent placed on a slide. Lift the loop and look for a mucus-like string extending from the drop to the loop. Repeat at intervals of about 10 s.

(iii) *Interpretation.*   Positive: string formation occurs immediately and lasts for 50 s or longer; the delayed string is even more mucous than the initial one (*Vibrio cholerae*) or weaker than that observed initially or absent after 50 s (most other *Vibrio* spp.). Negative: initial or delayed string absent (*Escherichia coli*).

6. Bile solubility test

Streptococcus pneumoniae, unlike other streptococci, produces a rapidly acting autolytic enzyme, clearing the turbid broth culture of the organism after incubation for a few days. It is assumed that bile salts accelerate lysis by activating the autolytic enzyme (Cowan, 1974; MacFaddin, 1980). The classical crude bile reagent has long been replaced by chemically controlled sodium deoxycholate. The tube method is regarded as a standard test. The plate method gives, as a rule, identical results.

(a) Tube test

(i) *Reagent.*   Sodium deoxycholate, 1 g; distilled water, 10 ml. After adding a drop of phenolphthalein indicator (0.1% in ethanol), the solution must be colourless (pH < 7.8).

(ii) *Procedure.* To a 24 h serum broth culture add one tenth volume of reagent. Incubate at 35–37 °C for 15 min.

(iii) *Interpretation.* Positive: clearing of the suspension with an increase of viscosity (*Streptococcus pneumoniae*). Negative: no lysis (*Streptococcus mitis*). The tube test must be carried out in a neutral or slightly alkaline medium, since at pH less than 6.8, the reagent forms an inactive gel. If the medium contains a fermentable substance (e.g. glucose in Todd–Hewitt broth), the culture should be neutralized prior to testing (green with bromothymol blue indicator).

(b) Plate test

(i) *Reagent.* Same as for the tube test.

(ii) *Procedure.* Pipette a small drop of reagent onto an 18–24 h confluent growth on blood-agar plate. Incubate the plate "face-up" (lid on top) at 35–37 °C for 30–45 min. Observe the site on the plate where the reagent caused haemolysis.

(iii) *Interpretation.* Positive: growth lysed (*Streptococcus pneumoniae*). Negative: growth intact (*Streptococcus mitis*).

References

Allen, S. D. and Siders, J. A. (1980). In *Manual of Clinical Microbiology* (E. H. Lennette, A. Balows, W. J. Hausler, and J. P. Truant, eds.), 3rd edn, pp. 397–417. American Society for Microbiology, Washington, D.C.
Arai, T., Otake, M. and Enomoto, S. (1970). *Japan. J. Microbiol.* **14,** 279–284.
Barritt, M. M. (1936). *J. Pathol. Bacteriol.* **42,** 441–454.
Barry, A. L., Bernsohn, K. L., Adams, A. P. and Thrupp, L. D. (1970). *Appl. Microbiol.* **20,** 866–870.
Blazevic, D. J., Koepke, M. H. and Matsen, J. M. (1973). *Appl. Microbiol.* **25,** 107–110.
Christensen, W. B. (1946). *J. Bacteriol.* **52,** 461–466.
Christie, R., Atkins, N. E. and Munch-Petersen, E. (1944). *Aust. J. Exp. Biol. Med. Sci.* **22,** 197–200.
Cowan, S. T. (1974). *Manual for the Identification of Medical Bacteria*, 2nd edn. Cambridge University Press, London.
Edwards, P. R. and Ewing, W. H. (1972). *Identification of Enterobacteriaceae*, 3rd edn. Burgess, Minneapolis, Minnesota.
Faller, A. and Schleifer, K. H. (1981). *J. Clin. Microbiol.* **13,** 1031–1035.
Frazier, W. C. (1926). *J. Infect. Dis.* **39,** 302–309.
Gaby, W. L. and Hadley, C. (1957). *J. Bacteriol.* **74,** 356–358.

Gunsalus, I. C. and Stanier, R. Y. (1961). *The Bacteria*, Vol. 2. Academic Press, New York.

Harper, H. A., Rodwell, V. W. and Mayes, P. A. (1977). *A Review of Physiological Chemistry*, 16th edn. Lange Medical Publications, Los Altos, California.

Havelaar, A. H., Hoogendorp, C. J., Wesdorp, A. J. and Scheffers, W. A. (1980). *Antonie van Leeuwenhoek* **46**, 301–312.

Holdeman, L. V., Cato, E. P. and Moore, W. E. C. (1977). *Anaerobe Laboratory Manual*, 4th edn. Virginia Polytechnic Institute and State University, Blacksburg, Virginia.

Holding, A. J. and Collee, J. G. (1971). In *Methods in Microbiology* (J. R. Norris and D. W. Ribbons, eds.), Vol. 6A, pp. 1–32. Academic Press, London and New York.

Hormaeche, E. and Munilla, M. (1957). *Int. Bull. Bacteriol. Nomencl. Taxon.* **7**, 1–20.

Hugh, R., and Gilardi, G. L. (1980). In *Manual of Clinical Microbiology* (E. H. Lennette, A. Balows, W. J. Hausler and J. P. Truant, eds.), 3rd edn, pp. 288–317. American Society for Microbiology, Washington, D.C.

Hugh, R. and Leifson, E. (1953). *J. Bacteriol.* **66**, 24–26.

Jeffries, C. D., Holtman, D. F. and Guse, D. G. (1957). *J. Bacteriol.* **73**, 590–591.

Kaplan, R. L. (1980). In *Manual of Clinical Microbiology* (E. H. Lennette, A. Balows, W. J. Hausler and J. P. Truant, eds.), 3rd edn, pp. 235–241. American Society for Microbiology, Washington, D.C.

Kauffmann, F. (1954). *Enterobacteriaceae*, 2nd edn. Munksgaard, Copenhagen.

Kellogg, D. S. and Turner, E. M. (1973). *Appl. Microbiol.* **25**, 550–552.

Kilian, M. (1974). *Acta Pathol. Microbiol. Scand.* **B82**, 835–842.

King, E. O. (1967). *The Identification of Unusual Pathogenic Gram Negative Bacteria.* Center for Disease Control, Atlanta, Georgia.

King, E. O., Ward, M. K. and Raney, D. E. (1954). *J. Lab. Clin. Med.* **44**, 301–307.

Kohn, J. (1953). *J. Clin. Pathol.* **6**, 249.

Kovács, N. (1928). *Z. ImmunForsch. Exp. Ther.* **55**, 311–315.

Kovács, N. (1956). *Nature (London)* **178**, 703.

Kubica, G. P. and David, H. L. (1980). In *Gradwohl's Clinical Laboratory Methods and Diagnosis* (A. C. Sonnenwirth and L. Jarett, eds.), 8th edn, pp. 1693–1730. Mosby, St. Louis, Missouri.

Lányi, B. (1980). *Public Health and Clinical Bacteriology. Standard Methods* (Hung.). National Institute of Hygiene, Budapest.

Lányi, B. (1982). *J. Med. Microbiol.* **15**, 263–266.

Lányi, B. and Ádám, M. M. (1960). *Acta Microbiol. Acad. Sci. Hung.* **7**, 313–328.

Lányi, B. and Bergan, T. (1978). In *Methods in Microbiology* (T. Bergan and J. R. Norris, eds.). Vol. 10, pp. 93–168. Academic Press, London and New York.

Lautrop, H. (1956). *Acta Pathol. Microbiol. Scand.* **39**, 357–369.

Lautrop, H. (1960). *Bull. World Health Org.* **23**, 15–35.

Le Minor, L. and Ben Hamida, F. (1962). *Ann. Inst. Pasteur* **102**, 267–277.

Le Minor, L. and Piéchaud, M. (1963). *Ann. Inst. Pasteur* **105**, 792–794.

MacFaddin, J. F. (1980). *Biochemical Tests for Identification of Medical Bacteria*, 2nd edn. Williams and Wilkins, Baltimore, Maryland.

Martin, W. J. and Washington, J. A. (1980). In *Manual of Clinical Microbiology* (E. H. Lennette, A. Balows, W. J. Hausler and J. P. Truant, eds.), 3rd edn, pp. 195–219. American Society for Microbiology, Washington, D.C.

Møller, V. (1955). *Acta Pathol. Microbiol. Scand.* **36**, 158–172.

Nógrády, G. and Rodler, M. (1954). *Acta Microbiol. Acad. Sci. Hung.* **1**, 437–443.

Norris, J. R. and Swain, H. (1971). In *Methods in Microbiology* (J. R. Norris and D. W. Ribbons, eds.), Vol. 5A, pp. 105–134. Academic Press, London and New York.

O'Meara, R. A. Q. (1931). *J. Pathol. Bacteriol.* **34**, 401–406.
Paik, G. (1980). In *Manual of Clinical Microbiology* (E. H. Lennette, A. Balows, W. J. Hausler and J. P. Truant, eds.), 3rd edn, pp. 1000–1024. American Society for Microbiology, Washington, D.C.
Pickett, M. J. and Nelson, E. L. (1955). *J. Bacteriol.* **69**, 333–336.
Rauss, K. and Vörös, S. (1959). *Acta Microbiol. Acad. Sci. Hung.* **6**, 233–248.
Report (1958). *Int. Bull. Bacteriol. Nomencl. Taxon.* **8**, 25–70.
Runyon, E. H., Karlson, A. G., Kubica, G. P. and Wayne, L. G. (1980). In *Manual of Clinical Microbiology* (E. H. Lennette, A. Balows, W. J. Hausler and J. P. Truant, eds.), 3rd edn, pp. 150–179. American Society for Microbiology, Washington, D.C.
Sanders, A. C., Faber, J. R. and Cook, T. M. (1957). *Appl. Microbiol.* **5**, 36–40.
Sierra, G. (1957). *Antonie van Leeuwenhoek* **23**, 15–22.
Singer, J. and Volcani, B. E. (1955). *J. Bacteriol.* **69**, 303–306.
Smith, H. L. (1970). *Bull. World Health Org.* **42**, 817–818.
Smith, R. F. and Willett, N. P. (1968). *Appl. Microbiol.* **16**, 1434–1436.
Smith, N. R., Gordon, R. E. and Clark, F. E. (1952). *US Dept of Agriculture Monograph* No. 16.
Sonnenwirth, A. C. (1980). In *Gradwohl's Clinical Laboratory Methods and Diagnosis* (A. C. Sonnenwirth and L. Jarett, eds.), 8th edn, pp. 1391–1450, 1731–1852. Mosby, St. Louis, Missouri.
Stanier, R. Y., Doudoroff, M. and Adelberg, E. A. (1963). *The Microbial World*, 2nd edn. Prentice-Hall, Englewood Cliffs, New Jersey.
Steel, K. J. (1961). *J. Gen. Microbiol.* **25**, 297–306.
Steffen, E. K. and Hentges, D. J. (1981). *J. Clin. Microbiol.* **14**, 153–156.
Stuart, C. A., van Stratum, E. and Rustigian, R. (1945). *J. Bacteriol.* **49**, 437–444.
USSR Ministry of Health (1964). *Prophylaxis of Diphtheria* (Russ.). Medical Bulletin, Moscow.
Vandenbergh, P. A., Bawdon, R. E. and Berk, R. S. (1979). *Int. J. Syst. Bacteriol.* **29**, 339–344.
Vera, H. D. and Power, D. A. (1980). In *Manual of Clinical Microbiology* (E. H. Lennette, A. Balows, W. J. Hausler and J. P. Truant, eds.), 3rd edn, pp. 965–999. American Society for Microbiology, Washington, D.C.
Vestal, A. L. (1975). *Procedures for the Isolation and Identification of Mycobacteria.* U.S. Public Health Service Publication 75–8230. Center for Disease Control, Atlanta, Georgia.
Whaley, D. N., Dowell, V. R., Wanderlinder, L. M. and Lombard, G. L. (1982). *J. Clin. Microbiol.* **16**, 224–229.
Yong, D. C. T. and Thompson, J. S. (1982). *J. Clin. Microbiol.* **16**, 30–33.
Záhorová, L. and Kubelka, V. (1960). *Folia Microbiol. (Prague)* **5**, 57–59.

2
Characterization Tests for Numerical Taxonomy Studies

MARK O'BRIEN and RITA COLWELL

Department of Microbiology, University of Maryland, College Park, Maryland 20742, USA

I. Introduction

The selection of characterization tests for a numerical taxonomy (NT) study presents the novice, and on occasion even the more experienced, numerical taxonomist with a dilemma. Which tests to choose? Are some tests more reliable than others? How many tests should be done, i.e. should a lower and/or upper limit on the number of tests be set? How important these considerations are, is implicit from the overall objective of numerical taxonomy enunciated by Sneath and Sokal (1973), i.e. that numerical methods will lead different scientists employing the same data base and working independently to obtain comparable estimates of resemblance among any group of organisms. However, even a cursory review of the literature illustrates why such a dilemma arises. Not only is the number and

METHODS IN MICROBIOLOGY
VOLUME 19 ISBN 0–12–521519–3

diversity of characterization tests very large, but frequently the variety of test methods for a particular characteristic is almost bewildering. Although relatively little attention has been given to the problem of general test selection in NT, the contributions of the Pseudomonas Working Party (Sneath and Collins, 1974), the International Working Group on Mycobacterial Taxonomy (see Wayne et al., 1974, 1976), the International Streptomyces Project (see Williams and Wellington, 1980) and others (Lockhart, 1967; Colwell and Wiebe, 1970) for specific bacterial groups, have been significant.

The following is an attempt to clarify and resolve some of the problems encountered in selecting characterization tests for NT studies. Our aim is to emphasize the importance of test selection in NT and to draw attention to those areas in need of future work.

II.   Numerical taxonomy: concepts and terminologies

Rather than provide an exhaustive listing of the theories and language of NT, instead an overview, albeit brief, is provided of those key concepts and terminologies of NT applied to bacteriology and that are relevant to the topics of discussion to follow. More complete and comprehensive treatments of NT theory and its application to bacteriology are given by Sneath (1957a, b, 1958, 1962, 1964a,b,c, 1965, 1968a, b, 1969, 1971, 1972, 1978), Sneath and Cowan (1958), Floodgate (1962a, b), Leifson (1966), Lockhart and Liston (1970), Colwell (1970a, b) and Clifford and Stephenson (1975). In particular, the rigorous treatises of Sokal and Sneath (1963) and Sneath and Sokal (1973) provide invaluable information on the theories and practice of NT, in general, and should be mandatory reading. Articles by Skerman (1967) and more recently Jones and Sackin (1980), Colwell and Austin (1981), Holmberg and Nord (1984), Chaika and Nikonova (1984), Sneath (1984), MacDonell and Colwell (1985) and Russek-Cohen and Colwell (1986) also provide general but informative discussions on NT, together with guidelines for planning and designing of NT analyses.

Many definitions of NT have been offered. Numerical taxonomy may be simply viewed as the grouping of organisms by statistical methods. A more descriptive definition would be that NT is the collection and computer-aided evaluation of data on a large number of observable properties of each organism under study in order to determine, quantitatively, the similarity of each organism to all others and thereby allow for the arrangement or sorting of every organism into a group or cluster based on these similarities. However NT is defined, the aim is the same; that is, to generate classification constructs based on such groupings and that reflect these similarities. Usual, and fundamental to those classifications, is that the within-group variance in properties of the organisms will be less than the between-group variance (Hill, 1974). NT expresses phenetic relationships between organisms, i.e. proportions of similarities (and differences) in existing properties or traits, as distinct from phylogenetic relationships, i.e. measuring changes due to evolutionary lineage (Sneath and Sokal, 1973; Sneath, 1984). It should be clearly understood that phenetic relationships measured in NT include similarities (and differences) in both phenotype and genotype. The main focus of NT is not on individual properties, but rather stability and frequency of occurrence in the group (Krichevsky and Norton, 1974). The advantage of NT is that, at best, it should yield stable, precise taxonomies based on objective criteria (Sneath, 1962). At the very least, the planned approach of NT can lead to improved efficiency in classifications (Sokal and Sneath, 1963).

The principles of NT are based on concepts first enunciated by Adanson (1763) and later refined for bacterial taxonomy by Sneath (1957a, b). In practice the key principles may be summarized as follows:

(i)   Maximize the information content, i.e. all possible tests should be studied for all the strains.
(ii) Ideally, data collection and analysis should be objective and empirical, for example *a priori* every test (and consequently every test character) is considered to be of equal importance.
(iii) Taxa (i.e. groupings) should be defined on the basis of overall similarity according to the results of phenetic analysis.

It is generally agreed that the protocol for a NT study should involve at least, the following five key steps (Sneath, 1971, 1978; Colwell and Austin, 1981; Sneath, 1984).

Step 1.   *Collection of data:*
(i)   Choice of strains (i.e. operational taxonomic units or OTUs).
(ii) Choice of tests (i.e. measure observable properties or traits).

Step 2.   *Coding data:*
Coding and scaling (arraying) test results in a format suitable for computer analysis. Commonly in bacteriology the characters are presence-absence ones, but quantitative characters can also be used (see Sneath and Sokal, 1973; Holmberg and Nord, 1984; Russek-Cohen and Colwell, 1986).

Step 3.   *Computer analysis of data:*
Similarity or resemblance between strains (OTUs) is calculated, yielding a table of similarities (so-called similarity matrix) based on the chosen set of characters.

Step 4. Presentation and interpretation of the results:
Similarities are analysed for taxonomic structure, to yield the groups or clusters that are present, and the strains are arranged into phenons (i.e. phenetic groups), which are broadly equated with taxonomic groups (i.e. taxa).

Step 5. Description of taxa:
The results of the computation require evaluation, both by statistical methods and by comparison with other kinds of available information, ultimately providing a formal description of the taxa (either the establishment of new taxa or the revision of existing classifications).

While this chapter focuses on the second component of the first step, i.e. selection of characterization tests, it should be emphasized that the other four steps are no less important, and, as such, deserve equal attention when planning a NT analysis. These aspects are examined in greater detail elsewhere (see the general references given above).

III. Test selection: a review

A. Types of tests and test characters

A test character is simply any property or attribute that can vary between strains (OTUs), and the possible values we can assign to it are called "character states", each of unit weight and, ideally, each mutally exclusive. Each character state should contribute one new piece of information (Sneath, 1962). Thus "decarboxylation of lysine" is a character, with the states "positive" and "negative" usually coded numerically as 1 (or +) and 0 (or −) respectively. A "two-state" or "binary" character such as this is the most common kind used in bacteriological NT studies. "Multistate" characters, which are less commonly employed, include qualitative (e.g. pigmentation and colony elevation) and quantitative (e.g. absorbance readings, antimicrobial sensitivity, enzymatic activity) features. Qualitative multistate characters are usually scored as plus for the character state exhibited and minus for the alternatives, while quantitative multistate characters may be scored using the additive method of Sneath and Sokal (1973). To prevent any single character assuming excessive weight in an analysis, it is wise to restrict the character states on any one property to 10 or less and in most cases only two or three states will be justified (Sneath, 1962). For further discussion on coding and scaling of characters see Sneath (1962), Silvestri *et al.* (1962), Sneath and

Sokal (1973), Krichevsky and Norton (1974), Jones and Sackin (1980). Sackin (1981) and Holmberg and Nord (1984).

Tests for bacteriological NT studies may be categorized as follows (examples of tests are given in parentheses): (1) cytological (cell dimensions, flagella number, spore shape); (2) cultural (colonial morphology); (3) physiological (pH or temperature growth range); (4) biochemical (decarboxylation of lysine, arylamidase activity); (5) nutritional (utilization of acetate as sole source of carbon and energy for growth); (6) chemical constituents (presence of lysine in cell wall); (7) antimicrobic susceptibility (sensitivity to benzy-*o*-penicillin); (8) tolerance to dyes, heavy metals etc. (safranin, cadmium); (9) serological (agglutination by an antiserum to a reference culture); and (10) molecular genetic (%GC).

Serological and genetic data may be of two kinds (Sneath, 1978): (a) the reaction indicates the presence or absence of some defined property (e.g. an antigen or a phage receptor). These are scored like any other character; (b) the cross-reaction between organisms is measured, and this is analogous to a similarity value (see Sneath (1978) and Hubalek (1982) for further discussion).

The most frequently used tests for NT analyses fall into one or more of the above categories. Other "special" test categories less frequently used include ecological (habitats, hosts, parasites) and behavioural (chemotactic responses to nutrient). Additional examples are given by Skerman (1967), Lockhart and Liston (1970) and Sneath (1978).

B. Number of tests

Sneath and Sokal (1973) addressed the problem of the number of tests that should be used in NT analyses, presenting arguments that served to highlight the complexities of the problem. Even a cursory inspection of the problem raises considerable experimental and computational difficulties. Unfortunately, one cannot reduce the problem to a simple statistical evaluation, for example to obtain an estimate of similarity with desired confidence limits and a desired probability level, since the appropriate number of tests (or test characters) is related to the problem of the congruence of classifications based on different character sets, i.e. different sets of tests yield different phenetic data (Sneath and Sokal, 1973). There are also problems associated with similarity measurements between OTUs, the complexity of the interactions between genome and expression of the phenome, as well as test and investigator biases. These are dealt with more fully by Sneath and Sokal (1973).

The consensus is that, as yet, a definitive answer as to the number of tests (or test characters) to use in an NT analysis is not possible. However, for practical purposes some recommendations can be made. There can be little dispute, and logic would seem to dictate, that the larger the number of tests (or test characters) the better, since a better measure of the phenome (and presumably the genome) would be obtained with a larger number of tests employed. Such a statement should not belie the importance of test-character diversity, which is also intimately associated with expression of the phenome. The assumption is that any adequately large sample of the total properties of two strains will yield an estimate of their phenetic similarity that closely approaches the true value attainable if *all* their properties were compared (Lockhart, 1967). Another argument in favour of using large numbers of tests is provided by Harwood (1980), who claims that in NT studies where a large number of independent characters are employed the effect of a plasmid-borne trait would normally be expected to be small. An upper limit of 200 characters (i.e. ≤ 200 tests) has been recommended.

It must be emphasized, however, that while theoretically there is no real upper limit to the number of tests that can be used, in practice, with higher numbers the gain in information falls off disproportionately with the effort involved in obtaining the data (Sneath, 1984). Other problems associated with the use of large (> 100) numbers of tests include either an over-representation of some classes of tests (*vide infra*) or large gaps in the data due to the fact that not all tests are applicable to all strains (Russek-Cohen and Colwell, 1986).

A lower limit on the number of tests in an NT analysis is more difficult to rationalize. Some numerical taxonomists claim that 40 test characters are sufficient (Lockhart, 1967) while others recommend a minimum of 50–60 test characters (Sokal and Sneath, 1963; Sneath, 1964a; Skerman, 1967). According to Jones and Sackin (1980) with less than 50 tests not enough information is obtained to be discriminatory. A lower limit on the number of tests to be included in an NT analysis may be dictated, at least in part, by sampling error which is significant when the number of tests is low (Sneath and Johnson, 1972) (see Section III.C.). In addition, many multivariate statistical analyses, such as factor analyses, cannot be performed if the number of strains does not significantly exceed the number of tests employed (Rosswall and Kvillner, 1981).

Most laboratories can effectively manage 50–200 tests, especially with the development of rapid screening procedures, such as multipoint inoculating devices for test tubes and plates (Fung and Hartman, 1972, 1975; Lovelace and Colwell, 1968; Neal *et al.*, 1966; Wilkins *et al.*, 1975; Wilkins and Walker, 1975) and replica plating techniques (Stanier *et al.*, 1966).

C. Choice of tests

1. General considerations

Since NT is based on phenetic comparisons, ideally tests that represent a broad range of the biological properties of the organism, i.e. those that reflect as much information as possible about the phenome and the genome, should be chosen and should be representative of the categories outlined in Section III.A. above. In the past, any test providing quantitative and/or qualitative information about an organism under study was considered to be suitable for inclusion in an NT analysis. Such an ill-defined criterion for test selection really is no longer tenable for several reasons.

(a) Certain tests and test characters are, by their very nature, inadmissible in NT studies. Those test characters that do not reflect the inherent nature of the organism (e.g. strain names or code numbers) are meaningless and should obviously be excluded. Diagnostic tests are usually constant within a given taxon (Sneath and Sokal, 1973). Sneath (1978) warns about the use of tests previously described in the literature, since there has been a historical bias in favour of diagnostic tests. Any property of an organism that is a logical consequence of another should be omitted from analysis (Lapage, 1974). Both Russek-Cohen and Colwell (1986) and MacDonell and Colwell (1985) cite examples from the literature to illustrate this important point. Russek-Cohen and Colwell (1986) suggest that many catabolic properties may be involved in only a limited number of biochemical pathways. They recommend that the statistical examination of such properties to eliminate those apparently measuring the same metabolic event may be useful, and in fact may also offer insight into how mutations affecting a given pathway may also affect tests employed for phenetic analysis. At the very least, the use of many highly correlated properties may allow for only a small measure of the genome (Russek-Cohen and Colwell, 1986). Sneath and Sokal (1973) give several examples of inadmissible test characters.

(b) A test may be inapplicable; that is, under certain conditions a result cannot be determined (for example the oxidase reaction of *Chromobacterium* may be confused with the violet pigment) (Lapage, 1974).

(c) A test may be meaningless; that is, a result is required for a test that cannot be determined (for example motility at 37 °C when all or some of the strains being tested cannot grow at this temperature). (Lapage, 1974).

(d) There are many factors, both intrinsic and extrinsic, that significantly affect characterization tests, and the data therefrom, in bacteriological NT analyses. These are discussed in greater detail in Section III.C.2. below.

(e) The objective of the study, in many cases, will or should dictate which tests can be used. Russek-Cohen and Colwell (1986) argue that some tests may be suitable for differentiating families, but may not be sufficient to distinguish amongst genera within families. They recommend a two-stage approach to NT analyses. The first stage would employ tests selected for the purpose of clustering strains within families. The next stage would be carried out separately and within each family for the purpose of distinguishing genera. They concede that, whilst such an approach unfortunately implies an element of character weighting, it may offer some computational advantages, since larger data sets can be processed using a set of tests that will be useful to separate out strains into families.

Each of the above points illustrates an important paradox in that, while we need to be more judicious in our choice of tests for bacteriological NT studies, we cannot, or should not, prejudice the analysis by selecting one test over another, lest we compromise one of the fundamental principles of NT (i.e. equal weighting of tests). This aspect is discussed further in Section IV.C.

2. Factors influencing test selection

(a) Character weighting

While the consideration that all characterization tests should be of equal importance in NT has attracted much criticism, most numerical taxonomists, at least the workers in bacterial taxonomy, agree that, at present, it is not possible, objectively, to assign a weighting value to each test (or each test character). It is important here to distinguish the biased weighting of tests in routine diagnostic identification, where the weighting of one test over another improves the overall identification, and the *a priori* equal weighting of tests in classification. Sneath and Sokal (1973) and others (Michener and Sokal, 1957; Sneath, 1957a, 1958; Cain and Harrison, 1958) have all addressed the question of character weighting in taxonomy. Many of the arguments lack firm supportive evidence, statistically or otherwise. Nevertheless, overall there is a strong case in favour of equal weighting of tests in NT. Some of the key arguments are as follows.

(i)   If it cannot be decided how to weight tests then logically they must be assigned equal weight.

(ii) If differential weighting is used, there must be exact criteria for estimating, which at present is not possible.

(iii) To create taxonomic groups, it must first be decided how to weight the tests to be used in the classification. Therefore no criterion can be used that presupposes the existence of these taxa. For example, constant features cannot be chosen, since to know if they are constant requires the presupposing of taxonomic groups before they have been established.

(iv) The use of many characters greatly evens out the effective weight that each character contributes to the similarity coefficient. Unless highly unequal weights are given to some characters, the use of many characters tends to make the taxonomy equally weighted.

(b) Test error and test reproducibility

The extent of error in characterization tests is much greater than previously thought (Lockhart and Liston, 1970; Sneath, 1971; Sneath and Johnson, 1972). Errors may be divided in two types (Lapage, 1974): (a) Mistakes (e.g. misnumbering, cross-contamination of cultures or wrong cultures); this type of error is definite and additional to that due to lack of test reproducibility (see below), and such errors are obviously not inherent in the tests themselves; (b) those due to failure of test reproducibility (which are deviations from a statistical norm), whether between laboratories or within a laboratory. Under most circumstances (and optimistically) the contributions of mistakes to test error is much less than that due to the lack of test reproducibility (Lapage, 1974). Variations in either inter- or intralaboratory test reproducibility may be due to (a) investigator inexperience with the test procedure or careless errors in performance; (b) variability in certain strains or species, which may reflect, for example, different degrees of uniformity in permeability and/or rates and conditions of enzyme induction; or (c) variability inherent in the techniques due to unknown and uncontrolled factors that affect test responses of most or all organisms (Wayne *et al.*, 1974). Despite the apparent widespread awareness of the influence of test error on NT analyses, surprisingly few studies have focused on this aspect. A very good statistical treatment of test errors in bacteriological NT is given by Sneath and Johnson (1972). They outline in some detail formulae for estimating test error and provide recommendations for improving test reproducibility based on their own findings and those from the literature. Some of their key points are discussed below.

There is general agreement that test error can be significantly high even when the test methods are standardized (Sneath and Johnson, 1972; Lapage, 1974). With almost all tests the sensitivity of the technique has a pronounced influence on the results, and, furthermore, in practice it is weakly reacting strains that often give trouble, rather than the complete failure of the method (Sneath, 1974). Test errors in NT have the general effect of lowering similarities between phenetically similar strains, increasing the scatter and uncertainty of similarity values, and making clusters less compact (Sneath and Johnson, 1972; Holmberg and Nord, 1984). The overall effect is to degrade taxonomic structure (Sneath, 1974).

For statistical purposes, test error p may be defined as the probability that a test is erroneous, averaged over n tests, taking it as equally probable that a negative will be misread as a positive and vice versa, and also assuming that the probabilities are the same for both strains (Sneath and Johnson, 1972). Such assumptions, while generally true, are not without their exceptions (Sneath and Johnson, 1972). Values for test error p can range from less than 4% within one laboratory to as high as 20% for results between laboratories (Taylor et al., 1970; Lapage et al., 1970, 1973; Ericsson and Sherris, 1971; Bergan and Lystad, 1972; Sneath and Johnson, 1972; Snell and Lapage, 1973; Sneath, 1974). In estimating test error, care must be taken to make an unbiased selection of strains and tests, since there may be a tendency toward choosing the more difficult tests and the more troublesome strains when performing checks and replicates, and this makes the average discrepancies apparently much greater (Sneath, 1974). Sneath and Johnson (1972) recommend that tests with > 10–15% error should be rejected. This accords with the recommendations of other workers. Sneath (1974) argues that if the average test error is greater than 10% then the taxonomic structure is severely damaged, and when p is over 20% little of the original structure is recoverable, even if the OTUs were in tight clusters. Paradoxically, the upper limit to the permissible error on any one test is not yet clear, because a few unreliable tests can evidently be tolerated (Sneath and Johnson, 1972). Furthermore, this sort of taxonomic distortion must be judged against that due to sampling error, which predominates when the number of tests is small (Sneath and Johnson, 1972). Hence NT analyses should employ as many tests as possible, provided that the test error for any one test is not too high. According to Jones and Sackin (1980), it is usual practice to repeat the tests on at least 25% of the strains in the study to assess which tests are particularly unreliable.

Test reproducibility is affected by the following factors, which may act singly or in combination. Unfortunately, test errors tend to accumulate rather than cancel one another (Sneath and Johnson, 1972).

(i) *Time of reading of tests.*   For most tests different results will be obtained if the tests are read at different times. Studies by Sneath and Collins (1974) and others (Sneath and Johnson, 1972; Wayne et al., 1974, 1976) on test reproducibility provide many examples to support this claim. Indeed some tests are very sensitive to length of incubation (Sneath, 1974). Results will vary depending on (i) the organism (e.g. fast growers versus slow growers),

(ii) the test (e.g. amylase activity versus decarboxylase activity), (iii) the test method (e.g. gelatinase activity as determined by the plate method versus the X-ray film method, see Blazevic and Ederer, 1975). The influence of the time of reading of tests would be, according to Sneath (1974), particularly pronounced for tests that are read at a time when the proportion of positive results is increasing swiftly; under such conditions, small changes in temperature, aeration, etc., by affecting growth rate, could well account for many of the discrepancies observed. This makes standardization of the time of reading of tests a real problem. Despite this drawback, two recommendations can be made: (i) specified times for the reading of test results should be clearly given for each test; and (ii) particular care should be taken to read tests at the specified times, for example at exactly 24 h and not at "one" day, which may mean 20 h or 26 h.

It is important to bear in mind that the time of reading that gives the most reproducible results may not be the most appropriate time for taxonomic purposes (for example if all organisms are uniformly negative this is not very useful) (Sneath and Johnson, 1972).

(ii) *Incubation temperatures.*   Growth rates and metabolic activities can be significantly affected by even small fluctuations in incubator temperature or differences in temperature in different parts of the same incubator (Sneath and Johnson, 1972; Lapage, 1974). The effect of deliberately changing temperatures (or times of reading of tests) is not the same as error in the usual sense for it involves moving the strains systematically into another portion of taxonomic space (this aspect is discussed in greater detail by Sneath and Sokal, 1973). Again, like (i) above, the temperature of incubation that gives the most reproducible results is not necessarily the optimum temperature for taxonomic purposes.

(iii) *Culture media.*   The batch or brand of culture media used may seriously affect the results obtained (Sneath and Johnson, 1972; Lapage, 1974). Even the origin of the distilled water used to prepare test media may be a potential source of test error (Leifson, 1966).

(iv) *Mutations.*   Failure of test reproducibility may be due to an unstable gene (Lapage, 1974). Both Audureau (1942) and Baumann *et al.* (1968) in their studies on the *Moraxella* group found evidence that a single mutation may cause a significant modification of the nutritional spectrum of a strain, and therefore poses another problem in the evaluation of physiological data for the purposes of NT.

The source and size of the inoculum (Al-Hiti and Gilbert, 1983; Lapage,

1974) and substrate concentration (Sneath and Collins, 1974) may also be significant factors in reducing test reproducibility. This list is by no means comprehensive, one can easily think of other potential sources of test error (e.g. inoculation technique, experimenter bias, growth conditions).

Other factors, very different from those described above, may also significantly affect test results. For example, different laboratories may obtain identical results, but score them differently (Sneath and Collins, 1974). Such discrepancies can be reduced if the source of error is recognized (see Sneath and Collins, 1974, p. 519).

Test reproducibility between laboratories is usually much worse than between replicates within laboratories, and this appears to be a direct result of the interactive effect of the sources of variability listed above (Sneath and Johnson, 1972). Eliminating test error would obviously be one way of improving taxonomic structure, and thereby allow for independent comparable estimates of resemblance among OTUs. This is difficult with certain tests. Many tests are reliable with some groups of bacteria but not with others (Jones and Sackin, 1980). Furthermore, some tests are "plagued" by an inherent degree of variability, due to unknown factors, which are difficult to reduce despite standardization of the test method (Sneath and Collins, 1974). However, we can at least provide guidelines that should lead to a substantial reduction in test error and therefore a substantial increase in test reproducibility in general (see Section IV.A.).

D.   Further considerations

Controls are an integral factor in any properly designed NT analysis, serving as a verification of theory and methods. They also improve test reproducibility by improving standardization. The following are recommended by Colwell and Austin (1981).

(i)   Type and/or reference strains, for which test results are known, should be included in every set of strains as a means of verification of media and methods. Randomized duplicate sets of strains whose identities are not revealed until the completion of work should be included to avoid subjective factors creeping in and thereby giving an unbiased estimate of reliability. Uninoculated controls serve to detect accidental contamination.

(ii)   For improved standardization of methods, inoculation loops of known diameter or Pasteur pipettes (or micropipettes) delivering inocula of known volume for transferring cultures should be used.

(iii)   Cultures in the logarithmic growth phase should be used. Incubation times are governed by growth rates of the strains being examined, so allow an adequate time of incubation for slow-growing strains, since a negative result for a test may be wrongly concluded if insufficient incubation time has been allowed. Usually, examine and record results after incubation for 1, 2, 3, 7, 14, 21, and 28 days. Provide incubation temperatures that are optimum for the strains being examined.

(iv) Standardize the treatment of all strains in a test set whenever possible. For example, if one strain in a set of strains requires 0.5% (w/v) sodium chloride, media for all strains in the set should contain this concentration of NaCl, provided it is not inhibitory for the other strains.

IV.   Guidelines

A.   General recommendations and precautions

1. Select tests that represent a broad range of the biological attributes of the organism, i.e. reflect as much phenetic information as possible, and that provide information about a single property, i.e. a unit character.

2. Choose tests that are repeatable and easily standardized. Reject tests with > 10–15% error.

3. The number of tests should be kept to between 50 and 200.

4. Obtain complete sets of data (i.e. ideally one should carry out all tests on all strains).

5. If possible, agreement should be reached in advance on the quantity of data needed to evaluate a test; exact criteria should be given for interpreting and scoring test results, and these should be rigidly adhered to.

6. Wherever possible, standardize the treatment of all strains in a test, as well as the inoculation and incubation procedures. Describe in detail the test methodology.

7. Include type or reference strains, for which test results are known, in every set of strains as a means of verification of media and methods. Use randomized duplicate sets of strains whose identities are not revealed until the completion of work. Include uninoculated controls in testing.

8. In constructing data sets, do not use inadmissible tests, such as tests for redundant characters or for characters positive or negative in all the strains of the set (i.e. cases where such characters provide no useful discriminatory information).

9. Do not consider the relative importance of one test over another. However, avoid those tests that are not highly reliable (i.e. the experimental error of determining them must not be so great as to render the result more a matter of chance than of the properties of the strain) or that are subject to errors of interpretation (see discussion on test reproducibility above).

B. Characterization tests for NT studies

The following is merely a guide, and does not claim to be complete. As stated above, the final choice of tests will depend on the individual investigator, the objective of the study, and the bacteria under investigation.

1. Classical approaches

The following is a list of characterization tests that have been used in bacteriological NT studies. Since there are well over 300 tests that have been described in the literature, all are not included here; instead only selected representative ones are considered, namely those commonly employed in NT analyses and/or where at least some data on test reproducibility is available. Some investigators will no doubt disagree with some of the tests (or test methods) that we have included (or excluded). For brevity and to avoid unnecessary duplication, descriptions of methods for most tests have been excluded but may be found elsewhere in this volume (see Chapters 1 and 3). For additional tests and descriptions of test methods the following general references are recommended: Skerman (1967, 1969); Colwell and Wiebe (1970); Holding and Collee (1971); Blazevic and Ederer (1975); Gerhardt et al. (1981); Clarke (1984).

It is important to note that data given below on test reproducibility by Sneath and Collins (1974), Wayne et al. (1974, 1976) and Sneath and Johnson (1972) are drawn from specific studies on Pseudomonas, Mycobacterium and Bordetella and related genera respectively. We remind the reader that some tests (or test methods) that are unreliable for some bacteria may not be so for others (see discussion above).

(a) Phenotypic

(i) *Cytological*
(1) *Cell micromorphology.*   Cytological features can be determined by (i) phase-contrast microscopy (wet mounts), (ii) high-resolution microscopy (cytological staining) or (iii) electron microscopy (negative shadowing). Methods for (i) and (ii) are given in Chapter 1. Electron-microscopy techniques are described by Cole and Popkin (1981) and in Volume 17 of this series. A good discussion on micromorphology and fine structure of bacteria, with special reference to Actinomycetes is given by Williams and Wellington (1980).

Features include cell shape (including the formation of coccoid bodies, cysts and microcysts), dimensions and arrangement, flagellation, spores, capsules, metachromatic granules, poly-β-hydroxybutyrate inclusions, acid-fast reaction, Gram reaction.

Sneath and Collins (1974) reported rather poor interlaboratory reproducibility in determining cell shape, dimensions and arrangement. Variability in results was attributed to investigator bias (e.g. unconscious bias toward scoring cells as rods) and procedural errors (e.g. incorrect calibration of eyepiece micrometers).

(2) *Motility.*   Motility may be determined by (i) the hanging-drop method, (ii) Craigie tubes and (iii) migration through semisolid agar. All three methods have been criticized (Cowan and Steel, 1965; Sneath and Collins, 1974; see also Chapter 1 of this volume). Test results may be significantly affected by a number of variables including incubation temperature and the glucose concentration of the growth medium (Cowan and Steel, 1965; Sneath and Collins, 1974; Smibert and Krieg 1981; see also Chapter 1 of this volume).

Sneath and Collins (1974) reported reasonably good interlaboratory reproducibility in determining motility by Craigie tube, according to the method of Cruickshank (1965). Motility detected by Craigie tube may be confirmed by the hanging-drop method. Some organisms (e.g. *Cytophaga, Flexibacter, Beggiatoa*) are motile by a gliding movement, and for them to be observed, special media and techniques are necessary (Smibert and Krieg, 1981). This type of movement is not only affected by the concentration of agar in the medium, but also by the peptone concentration (Cowan and Steel, 1965). Further discussion and examples are given by Gerhardt *et al.* (1981).

(ii) *Morphological*

(1) *Colonial morphology.*   The following features may be determined:

colony size (diameter), form, elevation, surface appearance, opacity, texture, margin. The medium, age of culture, gaseous conditions, exposure to illumination, and other cultural conditions may affect the colonial morphology (Smibert and Krieg, 1981). This character has been criticized (Lockhart, 1967; see Williams and Wellington, 1980).

(2) *Pigment production.* Pigment production is generally considered to be an unreliable characteristic since it is significantly affected by a variety of factors, including investigator bias (e.g. subjective scoring), medium composition, incubation temperature and time of reading (Lockhart, 1967; Sneath and Collins, 1974).

Sneath and Collins (1974) report good interlaboratory reproducibility for fluorescein pigment production using medium B, as described by King, Ward and Raney (1954). Wayne *et al.* (1974) claim that pigment production on Lowenstein-Jensen medium is a highly reproducible test for mycobacteria, but noted that the production of pigment is affected by factors such as those given above.

(iii) *Physiological*

(1) *Growth temperature and heat tolerance.* For NT studies, growth temperatures ranging from 0–45 °C have been employed; the most frequently used temperatures being 4, 10, 15, 30, 37, 42 and 44 °C. Tolerance to temperatures as high as 65 °C has been found.

The reliability of this test has been questioned (Leifson, 1966; Goodfellow and Pirouz, 1982). Sneath and Collins (1974) reported good interlaboratory reproducibility for growth at 4 °C. Less satisfactory results were obtained for growth at 42 °C, and poor interlaboratory reproducibility was observed for growth at 37 °C. Test results are significantly affected by the amount of inoculum used (Klinge, 1960; Jessen, 1965), and time of reading of results (Sneath and Collins, 1974). According to Sneath and Collins (1974), more consistent results may be obtained with short incubation times at 37 and 42 °C (i.e. one and three days respectively). The importance of using accurately regulated water baths versus convection-type air- or water-jacketed incubators and subculturing to fresh media for confirmation of growth has been stressed (Sneath and Collins 1974; Costilow, 1981). The latter should reduce the subjective nature of test interpretation, particularly with broth cultures. Growth should be recorded as present or absent.

(2) *Salt tolerance and requirement.* Details of the method are given in Chapter 1. For NT studies, sodium chloride (NaCl) concentrations ranging

from 0% (w/v) to 20% (w/v) have been used. Colwell (1970c) tested for seawater and specific salt requirement in vibrios by spot-drop inoculation with washed cells of a basal medium with (i) 2.4% NaCl, (ii) 2.4% NaCl and 0.07% KCl, (iii) 2.4% NaCl and 0.53% $MgCl_2$ (iv) 0.07% KCl, 0.53% $MgCl_2$ and 0.7% $MgSO_4$, (v) 0.6 M NaCl and (vi) aged seawater. The basal medium consisted of 0.1% Trypticase (BBL), 2.0% Ionagar (Difco) and distilled water. Other basal media have been described.

(iv) *Biochemical*

(1) *Acetic acid from ethanol.* Sneath and Collins (1974) reported reasonably good interlaboratory reproducibility for this test using the medium and method recommended by Carr (see Sneath and Collins, 1974). This test is affected by variables such as the growth medium employed, amount of inoculum used and length of incubation (i.e. time of reading of test).

(2) *Acid production from carbohydrates.*   A detailed description of media and methods is given in Chapter 1. Table I is a partial list of carbohydrates that have been used in NT studies.

Using dehydrated O/F medium (Difco) with carbohydrates at a final concentration of 1.0% (w/v) Sneath and Collins (1974) found good interlaboratory reproducibility in tests for glucose and sucrose oxidation, but results were less consistent for acid production from lactose. In all three cases the time of reading of results was found to be critical.

TABLE I
Partial list of carbohydrates used in NT studies

Amygdalin, arbutin, arabitol, adonitol, arabinose, cellobiose, dextrin, dulcitol, erythritol, ethanol, fructose, galactose, glucose, glycerol, glycogen, inositol, inulin, lactose, maltose, mannitol, mannose, melibiose, melezitose, mucate, *N*-acetylglucosamine, raffinose, rhamnose, ribose, salicin, sorbitol, sorbose, sucrose, trehalose, xylose

---

(3) *Aesculinase activity.*   Aesculinase (esculinase) activity may be determined using any appropriate nutrient medium (agar or broth) supplemented with 0.1% aesculin. Aesculinase activity can be detected by a variety of methods (see general references above); the most common detection method used in NT studies is observation of the black colour formed with ferric iron (see Chapter 1). Sneath and Collins (1974) report good interlaboratory reproducibility with this method. Interlaboratory test differences were due to differences in technique, reading of results, or medium pH and composition.

(4) *Amino-acid decarboxylases.*   A number of test methodologies are available, including some rapid micromethods (see general references). The classical method devised by Møller (1955) is described in detail in Chapter 1. Amino-acid decarboxylases include lysine, ornithine, histidine, glutamic acid, glutamine, asparagine and malate. However, theoretically, any single amino acid is suitable as a substrate for this test.

(5) *Arginine dihydrolase.*   The method of Thornley (1960), which is the most frequently used method for this test in NT studies, gave excellent results for test reproducibility (both intra- and interlaboratory), according to Sneath and Collins (1974). In fact, they reported this as the most reproducible test of all the tests examined. However, the pH of the medium is important (Sneath and Collins, 1974).

(6) *Casein hydrolysis.*   Good inter- and intralaboratory reproducibility has been reported for this test (Sneath and Collins, 1974). The method of Smith *et al.* (1952) is recommended. Time of reading of results was found to be an important variable in this test. Sneath and Collins (1974) also found a strong correlation between gelatinase and caseinase activities with the strains they examined and suggest that the same proteolytic enzyme may be involved.

(7) *Egg-yolk reaction.*   Reactions on egg-yolk media can be both varied and difficult to interpret, since egg yolk is a heterogeneous mixture of many water soluble and water-insoluble components (proteins, lipoproteins, etc.) (White *et al.*, 1973). Many different enzymes (e.g. lipases, phospholipases, proteases) are involved (Shah and Wilson, 1963, 1965; Baird-Parker, 1963; Willis, 1960a, b; Marinetti, 1965), some of which may be linked. Problems in scoring the reactions may also be encountered. Results obtained by Sneath and Collins (1974) on test reproducibility for this character were less than satisfactory.

(8) *Esterase and lipase activities.*   Media and methods for determining esterase activity using Tween 80 as substrate are given in Chapter 1. For NT studies, esterification of Tweens 20, 40, 60 and 80 substrates have been tested for. Smibert and Krieg (1981) give methods for determining lipase activity.

(9) *Gelatin hydrolysis.*   A variety of methods have been described for the gelatin hydrolysis test. Reproducibility is variable and test-method-dependent. Sneath and Collins (1974) reported reasonably good interlaboratory reproducibility with the nutrient gelatin stab method depending on the scoring criteria. Poor growth of some strains and the need for incubation at 22 °C is a disadvantage of the stab test. Interlaboratory test reproducibility

for gelatin hydrolysis by the plate method is generally poor and subject to factors such as gelatin concentration, time of reading of the test and strain mutation (e.g. cultures with mixed populations of gelatinolytic and non-gelatinolytic cells) (Sneath and Collins, 1974). This test is not generally recommended for NT studies (Colwell and Austin, 1981).

(10) *Gluconate oxidation.*   The method of Haynes (1951) showed good interlaboratory reproducibility according to Sneath and Collins (1974). They found the time of reading of this test to be very important.

(11) *Haemolytic activity.*   Details of this test are given in Chapter 1 and by Smibert and Krieg (1981). A variety of blood types (e.g. human, bovine (ox), equine (horse), ovine (sheep), caprine (goat) and porcine (pig), have been used.

Sneath and Johnson (1972) reported rather poor intralaboratory reproducibility for haemolysis of horse blood. Haemolytic activity is affected by temperature of incubation, gaseous conditions and the species of blood used (Smibert and Krieg, 1981; O'Brien and Davis, 1982).

(12) *Hydrogen sulphide production.*   There are a variety of methods for determining hydrogen sulphide (H_2S) production. Because different enzymes are involved, the results of tests for H_2S may vary depending on the type of medium or substrate or the type of indicator used (Blazevic and Ederer, 1975). A detailed description of test methodologies is given in Chapter 1. For NT studies, H_2S production from sodium thiosulphate (e.g. TSI, Difco) is commonly used. It is important to note that the results of tests for H_2S can be compared only if the basal media are similar. It should also be stressed that detection of H_2S production is not an absolute; many organisms produce H_2S if a very sensitive detection method is used (Blazevic and Ederer, 1975).

(13) *Indole production.*   Several different methods for determining production of indole have been described (see general references). According to West and Colwell (1984), the test is dependent on the method and medium employed. The method of Kovács (1928) is given in Chapter 1. Kovács' (1928) procedure has been the method of choice in most NT studies. However, many workers consider the method of Böhme (1905) to be more sensitive (Blazevic and Ederer, 1975).

(14) *Levan production.*   Details of the method are given in Chapter 1. An appropriate basal nutrient agar medium containing 5% (w/v) sucrose is commonly used.

(15) *Methyl red test.*   Details of the method are given in Chapter 1 and by Smibert and Krieg (1981).

(16) *Nitrate reduction.   Nitrite production.* Many types of growth media for the detection of nitrite production have been described (Skerman, 1967, 1969; West and Colwell, 1984; see also Chapter 1 of this volume). Sneath and Collins (1974) recommend BBL-nitrate medium. The choice of medium will depend on the physiology of the organism (i.e. aerobe versus anaerobe) (see Chapter 1). In most NT studies a commercial nitrate broth or appropriate nitrite-free basal nutrient broth containing 0.1% (w/v) KNO_3 has been used (see West and Colwell, 1984). Sulphanilic acid and α-naphthylamine have been the reagents of choice for detection of nitrite production in most NT studies. West and Colwell (1984) recommend using 1-naphthylamine-7-suphonic acid, described by Crosby (1967), since α-naphthylamine is a potentially carcinogenic compound. To determine nitrite reduction, the zinc-dust method described by Sneath and Collins (1974) is recommended. Sneath and Collins (1974) reported that interlaboratory reproducibility for this test was satisfactory, but time of reading may affect test results, depending on the test method employed.

Denitrification. Sneath and Collins (1974) found that both growth and gas production in the denitrification test of Stanier *et al.* (1966) were erratic with the strains they examined. The complexity of medium preparation and variations in the effectiveness of the agar seal were given as reasons for the poor results obtained. Furthermore, the time of reading may affect the results, depending on the test method employed. A nitrite reduction medium containing 0.1% $NaNO_2$ is described in Chapter 1.

(17) *Oxidase activity.*   Despite its value as a diagnostic test, this feature is not highly recommended for NT studies. There are a variety of test methods (see general references above) to determine oxidase activity, each of which is subject to a number of factors that influence the test result, including medium composition, type and age of the test reagents, time of reading and the criteria of scoring the reaction (Colwell and Austin, 1981).

Sneath and Collins (1974) reported good intralaboratory reproducibility but poor interlaboratory reproducibility in determining oxidase activity by the filter paper method employing the tetramethyl-*p*-phenylenediamine dihydrochloride reagent, according to the method of Kovács (1956).

(18) *Pectinase activity.*   Details of the method are given in Chapter 1.

(19) *Urea hydrolysis.*   According to Sneath and Collins (1974) who compared the methods of Christensen (1946) and Stewart (1965), this test was

one of the least satisfactory because of poor interlaboratory reproducibility. The test was affected by factors such as the concentration of urea and time of reading. Sneath and Collins (1974) also found considerable variation in test sensitivities between laboratories. Conversely, Wayne *et al.* (1974), in their studies on mycobacteria, reported high interlaboratory reproducibility for the urease test using their own urea medium.

(20) *Voges–Proskauer reaction.* Several methods have been described for detection of acetoin from glucose fermentation (see Skerman, 1967, 1969; Smibert and Krieg, 1981; West and Colwell, 1984). Barritt's (1936) method is outlined in Chapter 1. Incubation time, rather than type of method, and temperature influence the production of acetoin (West and Colwell, 1984). The use of this test has been criticized (Colwell and Austin, 1981).

(v) *Nutritional*

Sources of carbon and/or nitrogen for growth and energy. A very large and diverse range of compounds have been used to determine nutritional patterns of bacteria in NT studies. For a list of these compounds see Stanier *et al.* (1966) and Snell and Lapage (1973). This test is affected by a variety of factors, including investigator bias (e.g. inoculation technique, subjective scoring), time of reading of test, concentration of compound, toxicity of the compound for some or all of the strains being studied, and temperature of incubation (Snell and Lapage, 1973). Snell and Lapage (1973) give a good account of test variability and reproducibility in their carbon-source utilization study on non-fermenting bacteria. The test should be standardized (Smibert and Krieg, 1981; West and Colwell, 1984).

(vi) *Antimicrobial susceptibility*

Susceptibility to antimicrobials has been used in many NT studies. A range of antimicrobials and suggested concentrations are given in Table II. The disc diffusion method (Bauer *et al.*, 1966) has been the method of choice in NT analyses.

(vii) *Phytopathogenicity*

Kersters *et al.* (1973) cite references for determining phytopathogenicity of *Agrobacterium*.

(viii) *Miscellaneous*

(1) *Sensitivity to 0/129.* A variety of methods have been described since the

TABLE II
List of antimicrobial agents used in bacterial NT studies

Antimicrobial	Conc.[a]	Antimicrobial	Conc.
Ampicillin	10 μg	Neomycin	10 μg
Aureomycin	30 μg	Nitrofurantoin	50 μg
Chloramphenicol	10 μg, 30 μg	Novobiocin	5 μg, 30 μg
Chlortetracycline	30 μg	Oleandomycin	10 μg
Dihydrostreptomycin	2.5 μg, 10 μg	Penicillin G	10 U
Erthromycin	15 μg, 30 μg	Polymyxin B	10 U, 300 U
Ethambutol	5 μg	Streptomycin	10 μg, 25 μg
Furazolidone	50 μg	Terramycin	2.5 μg, 30 μg
Gentamicin	10 μg	Tetracycline	10 μg, 30 μg
Kanamycin	15 μg		
Nalidixic acid	30 μg		

[a]Suggested concentration.

original procedure for detecting sensitivity to the vibriostatic agent 0/129 (2,4-diamino-6,7-diisopropylpteridine) was reported by Shewan *et al.* (1954). For NT studies, sensitivity to the phosphate derivative (Sigma) of 0/129 at concentrations of 150 μg/ml and 10 μg/ml is usually employed (West and Colwell, 1984).

(2) *Tolerance tests.*   *(a) Tolerance to dyes.* The following dyes have been used in NT studies: brilliant green; pyronin B, G, and Y; neutral red; crystal violet; methyl violet; methylene blue and safranin. Concentrations of dyes range from 0.00001% to 1.0% (w/v) (Grimont and de Rosnay, 1972; Mallory *et al.*, 1977; Austin *et al.*, 1977; Goodfellow *et al.*, 1978).

(b) Tolerance to heavy metals. A few NT studies have included tolerance to heavy metals as part of their characterization criteria. Heavy metals that have been used include cadmium, chromium, cobalt, iron, lead, manganese, mercury, molybdenum and tin (Mallory *et al.*, 1977; Austin *et al.*, 1977).

(3) *Growth on selective media.*   The list of selective media used in NT include: MacConkey agar (MCA), thiosulphate-citrate-bile salts-sucrose agar (TCBS), Salmonella-Shigella (SS) agar, eosin methylene blue agar (EMB), brilliant green agar (BG), desoxycholate citrate (DCC) agar, sodium selenite agar, enterococci presumptive broth, ethyl violet azide broth (EVA), Brucella agar, cysteine heart agar.

(b) Genotypic

(i) *DNA base composition*

Base composition can be determined directly by hydrolysis and subsequent separation of the nucleotides or the purine and pyrimidine bases by chromatography or electrophoresis, or indirectly by calculating the mole percent guanine plus cytosine (%G + C) from (i) the hyperchromic shift accompanying thermal denaturation of DNA (the T_m or melting point of DNA), (ii) bouyant density centrifugation in caesium chloride, (iii) bromination, (iv) depurination, (v) the ratio of absorbancies at 260 and 280 nm in low-ionic pH 3 buffer and (vi) high-pressure liquid chromatography of nucleotides or free bases. Contaminating RNA will interfere with all of the above methods except for (i) and (ii). These two are the methods of choice. A brief review on the value of DNA base composition for taxonomy is given by Bradley (1980). Techniques and references for determining DNA base composition are outlined in detail by Johnson (1981) and Owen and Pitcher (1985).

2. New approaches

A major impetus for applying new methods and new approaches to bacterial taxonomy has been the need to discover criteria that reveal biologically significant relatedness (Bradley, 1965).

(a) Chemotaxonomic

Chemical methods are becoming well-established in taxonomy (see Goodfellow and Minnikin, 1985). Although they may pose certain problems in coding, chemical characters are just as valid for NT analyses as any others (Sneath and Sokal, 1973). The contribution of chemotaxonomic analyses to taxonomy in general, and NT in particular, is now becoming more fully realized, especially in bacterial groups where an over-reliance on classical features, such as form and function, have not yielded satisfactory classifications (Keddie and Bousfield, 1980). The confusion in classification of coryneform and nocardioform bacteria based primarily on morphological considerations provides a case in point (see Keddie and Bousfield, 1980; Minnikin and Goodfellow, 1980).

(i) *Microbial metabolites and cellular constituents*

Results from studies of microbial metabolites, cellular constituents (including amino acids, fatty acids, respiratory quinones, lipids and peptidoglycan), and products from pyrolysis of whole bacterial cells have demonstrated the value of this approach for taxonomy (Holdeman *et al.*, 1977; Moss, 1981; Minnikin and Goodfellow, 1980; Keddie and Bousfield, 1980; Werner and Hammann, 1980; Moss, 1984; Collins, 1985; Ross *et al.*, 1985). Whilst somewhat sophisticated techniques [e.g., gas liquid chromatography (GLC), high performance liquid chromatography (HPLC), mass spectrometry (MS), nuclear magnetic resonance spectroscopy (MS), and, more recently pyrolysis mass spectrometry (PMS)] are used, there are the advantages of reliability, precision and accuracy. Details of the methodologies involved are given by Moss, 1981 and Shute et al., (1985).

(ii) *Enzymes*

(1) *Enzyme activity assays.*   Enzymatic characterization tests have been used extensively in bacteriological NT studies. Usually these tests are based on conventional identification methodology, where the substrate is incorporated into an agar or broth medium (see (*a*) above). Enzymatic activities determined by such methods are: (1) often non-specific, (2) the same enzyme may catalyse a variety of reactions; a serious problem discussed earlier (see Section III.C.), and (3) such tests (depending on the test method) are usually very insensitive (for example, only high concentrations of enzyme can be detected).

The recent development of growth-independent enzyme assays (GIEAs or so-called "rapid enzyme tests") may be useful for NT studies. The potential of GIEA for bacterial identification and characterization is already being exploited. A most comprehensive review of these aspects is given in Chapter 3 of this book. One advantage of GIEAs is that they can be, and usually are, significantly more specific and sensitive in detecting enzyme activities compared with their "conventional counterparts".

The value of "rapid" enzyme test methodologies for bacteriological NT analyses is now being better appreciated. The GIEA test kits developed by API Products (including API ZYM, API Peptidase, API 50) may be particularly useful. A few NT studies have used API enzyme test kits as part of their characterization criteria (Holmes *et al.*, 1981; Mergaert *et al.*, 1984). The advantages of these kits for NT studies are that they are (i) available commercially, (ii) easy to use, (iii) easily standardized, (iv) mostly quantifiable and (v) reproducible. However, for environmental isolates, results can be less reproducible than for clinical isolates, and are not recommended.

There are, however, limitations with GIEAs that need to be identified: (i) many enzymes cannot be determined with this methodology, and still require conventional testing methods; (ii) the problem of linked enzymes (see Section III.C. above) is still apparent; (iii) some assays are more specific and/or sensitive than others (see Chapter 3); (iv) there may be problems with fastidious organisms; and (v) exact criteria for scoring results are needed.

(2) *Electrophoretic enzyme patterns.*   A biochemical test that depends on the presence of an enzyme has no taxonomic value within a group of organisms that all have the same enzyme (Norris, 1968). The molecular properties of such an enzyme may be different, however, and these differences may have considerable taxonomic value (Williams and Shah, 1980). Furthermore, although the electrophoretic pattern of an enzyme is as likely to be changed by mutation as is the rest of a fermentation test, it seems likely that the interlaboratory reproducibility of enzyme patterns should be higher, as is the case with other chemotaxonomic tests (Williams and Shah, 1980). Thus in fermentation tests a faint positive result may be incorrectly regarded as negative, but with enzyme electrophoresis differences in electrophoretic mobility can hardly be confused (Williams and Shah, 1980). A recent review on the use of enzyme patterns in bacterial classification is given by Williams and Shah (1980).

(3) *Enzyme structure and function.*   Weitzman (1980) discusses the applications of enzyme characterization based on structure (e.g. subunit composition of polymeric enzymes) and function (e.g. catalytic and regulatory behaviour) to bacterial classification. There may be applications of this approach to NT analyses, provided that criteria for scoring and coding results can be defined.

(iii) *Proteins*

Relationships based on NT analyses of electrophoretic whole-cell protein patterns have shown a very good correlation with those derived from DNA:DNA hybridization or from NT analyses based on classical tests. P. Jackman has described in detail the theory and methodologies of this approach (see Chapter 6). A list of bacterial genera examined by protein gel electrophoresis is given in Table III.

C.   Concluding remarks

Problems of test error and test reproducibility are not new in taxonomy. Numerical taxonomists did not invent these limitations they simply made them painfully obvious by quantitating them (Lockhart, 1967). Basic studies are needed into the mechanisms of many of the tests in use to provide an understanding of the reasons for the variability recorded for some strains or species. Some simple measures may be immediately adopted to address the reproducibility problem. In any case, the overall objective must be to improve interlaboratory reproducibility, thus enabling collective analysis of data from different NT studies, i.e. the so-called "interlocking NT" approach

TABLE III
Bacterial genera examined by polyacrylamide gel electrophoresis of proteins[a]

A. Soluble proteins; alkaline gel and buffer system

Acetobacter, Gluconobacter (200)*[b]	Kersters and De Ley, unpublished
Actinoplanaceae (31) 10 genera	Davies and Gottlieb (1973)
Agrobacterium (250)*	Kersters and De Ley (1975) and unpublished
Alcaligenes, Achromobacter (200)*	Kersters and De Ley (1980)
Arthrobacter (44)*	Rouatt *et al.* (1970)
Campylobacter (40)	Morris and Park (1973)
Enterobacteriaceae (40)*	Feltham (1975)
Enterobacteriaceae from breweries (60)*	van Vuuren, Kersters and De Ley (to be published); Kersters and De Ley (1980)
Mycobacterium (55)	Haas *et al.* (1972, 1974)
Pseudomonas plant pathogenic (38)	Palmer and Cameron (1971)
Xanthomonas (70)	El-Sharkway and Huisingh (1971)
Yersinia pestis (160)*	Hudson *et al.* (1973, 1976)
Zymomonas (43)*	Swings *et al.* (1976)

B. Proteins soluble in phenol–acetic acid–water (4:2:1 w/v/v):
    acid- and urea-containing gel and buffer system

Brucella (38)	Morris (1973): Balke *et al.* (1977)
Campylobacter (40)	Morris and Park (1973)
Corynebacterium (38)	Larsen *et al.* (1971)
Corynebacterium (38)	Larsen *et al.* (1971)
Enterobacteriaceae (84) 9 genera	Sacks *et al.* (1969)
Mycoplasma (28)	Razin and Rottem (1967), Rottem and Razin (1967)
Mycoplasma, porcine (30)	Ross and Karmon (1970)
Mycoplasma, canine (53)	Rosendale (1973)
Mycoplasma, avian (45)	Mullegger *et al.* (1973); Mullegger and Gerlach (1974)
Mycoplasma, bovine, equine (34)	Dellinger and Jasper (1972)

C. Cell-envelope proteins
Neutral, SDS-containing gel and buffer system:

Bordetella pertussis (13)	Parton and Wardlaw (1975), McDonald (1976)
Salmonella (8)	Parton (1975)

Urea-containing gel and buffer system; isoelectric focusing:

Streptococcus, cariogenic (7)	Hamada and Mizuno (1974)

D. Ribosomal proteins
Neutral and SDS-containing gel and buffer system:

Bacillus (2), *Escherichia*, *Proteus, Salmonella* (3)	Sun *et al.* (1972)

Acid- and urea-containing gel and buffer system:
Enterobacteriaceae

(Escherichia, Enterobacter, Erwinia, Klebsiella, Salmonella)	Schaad (1974)
Erwinia	Kado *et al.* (1972)

---

[a]From Kersters and De Ley (1980)
[b]The numbers of the strains investigated are shown in parentheses. An asterisk (*) indicates that the electrophoretograms were compared and grouped by numerical analysis

proposed by Hill (1975). The simplest and most effective way to maximize test reproducibility and minimize test error is to standardize tests and document in careful detail the methods employed (MacDonell and Colwell, 1985). The idea of "core characteristics" put forward by Colwell and Wiebe (1970) is a step towards achieving that goal. In this respect, the value of working parties and international committees in establishing standard procedures should be emphasized. Furthermore, the centralized collection of NT data, advocated by Skerman (1973) and Hill (1984) merits serious consideration.

This should not draw attention away from the importance of rigidly adhering to the principles of NT set forth at the beginning of this chapter. Indeed, as MacDonell and Colwell (1985) point out, poor correlation between results of NT analysis and nucleic-acid homology studies frequently can be traced to significant departure from established Adansonian practice.

Finally, despite mechanization and the concurrent development of sophisticated characterization methods, which have led to significant improvements in the efficiency and accuracy of NT data collection, taxonomists cannot study as many strains and or as many tests as they would wish. Therefore, as Hill (1975) points out, limitations are set on the number and choice of strains to be studied and, in turn, the kinds of tests to be used. We agree with Hill that, within these limitations, the practice of NT may well be "objective", but the limitations themselves prevent complete objectivity. We therefore propose that for improved taxonomic structure a "degree of bias" arising from choice of tests will have to be tolerated within the present limitations set by NT theory. As Hill (1974) emphasizes, NT theory should be regarded like any other theory, and as such should be refined by further testing and modification based on new evidence, including nucleic-acid sequencing and other phylogenetically rooted approaches. These are discussed in greater detail by MacDonell and Colwell (1985) and elsewhere in this volume (Chapter 11).

Appendix

The following is a brief list of representative NT studies published since 1980. This list is by no means complete, since well over 300 such studies have been published over this period (MacDonell and Colwell, 1985).

General studies

Food. Lee *et al.* (1982)
Environmental. Tabor *et al.* (1981)

Bacterial groups

Actinomycetaceae. Goodfellow and Pirouz (1982), Bianchi and Bianchi (1982)
Enterobaceriaceae. Austin *et al.* (1981)
Coryneform/Nocardioform. Bousfield *et al.* (1983). Seiler and Hennlich (1983)
Lactic acid bacteria. Shaw and Harding (1984)
Methanotrophs. Gal'chenko and Nesterov (1981). Green and Bousfield (1982)

Bacterial genera

Alteronomas. Gray and Stewart (1980)
Acetobacter. Gosselé *et al* (1983b)
Actinobacillus. Bercouvier *et al.* (1984), O'Reilley *et al.* (1984), Sneath and Stevens (1985)
Actinomadura. Athalye *et al.* (1985)
Actinomyces. Collins and Jones (1982), Ellen and Grove (1985)
Aeromonas. Allen *et al.* (1983), Kalina *et al.* (1984)
Agrobacterium. Holmes and Roberts (1981), Du Plessis *et al.* (1984)
Allomonas. Kalina *et al.* (1980)
Archanobacterium. Collins *et al.* (1982)
Bacillus. De Barjac *et al.* (1980), Garcia *et al.* (1982), Baumann *et al.* (1984)
Brevibacterium. Collins *et al.* (1980)
Campylobacter. Neill *et al.* (1985)
Cellulomonas. Hervera and Francisco (1984)
Corynebacterium. Jackman (1982), Collins and Jones (1982), Goodfellow *et al.* (1982a, Elia *et al.* (1984).
Cytophaga. Jooste *et al.* (1985)
Deleya. Quesada *et al.* (1984)
Enterobacter. Izard *et al.* (1980)
Erwinia. Dye (1981), Mergaert *et al.* (1984)
Escherichia. Dott *et al.* (1981)
Flavobacterium. Holmes *et al.* (1981), Jooste *et al.* (1985)
Gluconobacter. Gosselé *et al.* (1983a)
Haemophilus. Broom and Sneath (1981)
Hafnia. Greipsson and Priest (1983)
Klebsiella. Izard *et al.* (1981), Seal *et al.* (1981), Ferragut *et al.* (1983)
Kurthia. Shaw and Keddie (1983)
Mycobacterium. Wayne (1981), Weiten *et al.* (1981), Mezensky and Slosarek (1981, 1986), Tsukamura *et al.* (1981, 1983), Ridell and Goodfellow (1983), Tsukamura (1983)
Nocardia. Goodfellow *et al.* (1982b), Ridell and Goodfellow (1983), Minnikin (1981), Orchard and Goodfellow (1980)
Nocardiopsis. Athalye *et al.* (1985)
Paracoccus. Nokhal and Schlegel (1983)
Pasteurella. Erasmus (1983a), Sneath and Stevens (1985)
Plesiomonas. Kalina *et al.* (1984)
Pseudomonas. Garcia *et al.* (1981), Sneath *et al.* (1981), Kiprianova *et al.* (1981), Gillespie (1981), Molin and Ternstrom (1982), Shaw and Latty (1982), Rosenberg (1983), Ercolani (1983), Pavlenko and Ivechenko (1984)
Rhizobium. Jordan (1982)
Rhodococcus. Panichev *et al.* (1979), Goodfellow *et al.* (1982)

Shigella. Dodd and Jones (1982)
Staphylococcus. Schumacher-Perdreau *et al.* (1983), Gunn and Colwell (1983), Goodfellow *et al.* (1983) Erasmus (1983b), O'Donnell *et al.* (1985)
Streptobacteria. Dainty *et al.* (1984)
Streptococcus. Bridge and Sneath (1983), Sedov and Shumilo (1983)
Streptomyces. Williams *et al.* (1983)
Thermoactinomyces. Panichev *et al.* (1984)
Vibrio. Agarwal *et al.* (1980). Lee *et al* (1981), Parija *et al.* (1982), Hada *et al.* (1983), West *et al.* (1984), Kalina *et al.* (1984)
Xanthomonas. Vera Cruz *et al.* (1984)
Yersinia. Zaremba (1981), Kapperud *et al.* (1981), Kaneko and Hashimoto (1982) Sneath and Stevens (1985)

References

Adanson, M. (1763). *Familles des plants.* Vincent, Paris.
Agarwal, R. K., Parija, S. C. and Sanyal, S. C. (1980). *Indian J. Med. Res.* **71,** 340–353.
Al-Hiti, M. M. A. and Gilbert, P. (1983). *J. Appl. Bacteriol.* **55,** 173–175.
Allen, D. A., Austin, B. and Colwell, R. R. (1983). *Int. J. Syst. Bacteriol.* **33,** 599–604.
Athalye, M., Goodfellow, M., Lacey, J. and White, R. P. (1985). *Int. J. Syst. Bacteriol.* **35,** 86–98.
Audureau, A. (1942). *Ann. Inst. Pasteur.* **68,** 528–537.
Austin, B., Allen, D. A., Mills, A. L. and Colwell, R. R. (1977). *Can. J. Microbiol.* **23,** 1433–1447.
Austin, B., Hussong, D., Weiner, R. M. and Colwell, R. R. (1981). *J. Appl. Bacteriol.* **51,** 101–112.
Baird-Parker, A. C. (1963). *J. Gen. Microbiol.* **30,** 409–427.
Barritt, M. M. (1936). *J. Pathol. Bacteriol.* **42,** 441–454.
Bauer, A. W., Kirby, W. M. M., Sherris, J. C. and Turck, M. (1966). *Am. J. Clin. Pathol.* **45,** 493–496.
Baumann, P., Doudoroff, M. and Stanier, R. Y. (1968). *J. Bacteriol.* **95,** 1520–1541.
Baumann, L., Okamoto, K., Unterman, B. M., Lynch, M. J. and Baumann, P. (1984). *J. Invertebr. Pathol.* **44,** 329–341.
Bercouvier, H., Escande, F. and Grimont, P. A. D. (1984). *Ann. Microbiol.* **135A,** 203–218.
Bergan, T. and Lystad, A. (1972). *Acta. Pathol. Microbiol. Scand.* **B80,** 345–350.
Bianchi, M. A. G. and Bianchi, A. J. M. (1982). *Microb. Ecol.* **8,** 61–70.
Blazevic, D. J. and Ederer, G. M. (1975). *Principles of Biochemical Tests in Diagnostic Microbiology.* Wiley, New York.
Böhme, A. (1905). *Centr. Bacteriol. I. Abt. Orig.* **40,** 129–133.
Bousfield, I. J., Smith, G. L., Dando, T. R. and Hobbs, G. (1983). *J. Gen. Microbiol.* **129,** 375–394.
Bradley, S. G. (1965). *Int. Bull. Bacteriol. Nomen. Taxon.* **15,** 239–241.
Bradley, S. G. (1980) In *Microbiological Classification and Identification* (M. Goodfellow and R. G. Board, eds.). pp. 11–26. Academic Press, New York.
Bridge, P. D. and Sneath, P. H. A. (1983). *J. Gen. Microbiol.* **129,** 565–598.
Broom, A. K. and Sneath, P. H. A. (1981). *J. Gen. Microbiol.* **126,** 123–150.
Cain, A. J. and Harrison, G. A. (1958). *Proc. Zool. Soc. Lond.* **131,** 85.

Chaika, N. A. and Nikonova, V. A. (1984). *Zh. Microbiol. Epidemiol. Immunobiol.* **1,** 7–14.

Christensen, W. B. (1946). *J. Bacteriol.* **52,** 461–466.

Clarke, G. (1984). *Staining Procedures.* Williams and Wilkins, Baltimore.

Clifford, H. T. and Stephenson, W. (1975). *An Introduction to Numerical Classification.* Academic Press, New York.

Cole, R. M. and Popkin, T. G. (1981). In *Manual of Methods for General Bacteriology* (P. Gerhardt, R. G. E. Murray, R. N. Costilow, E. W. Nester, W. A. Wood, N. R. Krieg and G. B. Phillips, eds.), pp. 34–51. American Society for Microbiology, Washington, D.C.

Collins, M. D. (1985). In *Chemical Methods in Bacterial Systematics* (M. Goodfellows and D. E. Minnikin, eds.), pp. 267–288. Academic Press, New York.

Collins, M. D. and Jones, D. (1982). *J. Gen. Microbiol.* **128,** 901–904.

Collins, M. D., Jones, D., Keddie, R. M. and Sneath, P. H. A. (1980). *J. Gen. Microbiol.* **120,** 1–10.

Collins, M. D., Jones, D. and Schofield, G. M. (1982). *J. Gen. Microbiol.* **128,** 1279–1282.

Colwell, R. R. (1970a). *Dev. Ind. Microbiol.* **11,** 154–160.

Colwell, R. R. (1970b). In *Culture Collections of Microorganisms* (H. Iizuka and T. Hasegawa, eds.), pp. 421–436. University Park Press, Baltimore.

Colwell, R. R. (1970c). *J. Bacteriol.* **104,** 410–433.

Colwell, R. R. and Austin, B. (1981). In *Manual of Methods for General Bacteriology* (P. Gerhardt, R. G. E. Murray, R. N. Costilow, E. W. Nester, W. A. Wood, N. R. Krieg and G. B. Phillips, eds.), pp. 444–449. American Society for Microbiology, Washington, D.C.

Colwell, R. R. and Wiebe, W. J. (1970). *Bull. Ga. Acad. Sci.* **28,** 165–185.

Costilow, R. N. (1981) In *Manuals of Methods for General Bacteriology* (P. Gerhardt, R. G. E. Murray, R. N. Costilow, E. W. Nestor, W. A. Wood, N. R. Krieg and G. B. Phillips, eds.), pp. 66–78. American Society for Microbiology, Washington, D.C.

Cowan, S. T. (1974). *Cowan and Steel's Manual for the Identification of Medical Bacteria.* Cambridge University Press.

Cowan, S. T. and Steel, K. J. (1965). *Manual for the Indentification of Medical Bacteria.* Cambridge University Press.

Crosby, N. T. (1967). *Proc. Soc. for Water Treatment and Examination* **16,** 51–55.

Cruickshank, R. (1965). *Medical Microbiology.* Livingstone, Edinburgh.

Dainty, R. H., Hibbard, C. M. and Edwards, R. A. (1984). *Syst. Appl. Microbiol.* **5,** 233–240.

De Barjac, H., Veron, M. and Dumanoir, V. C. (1980). *Ann. Microbiol.* **131,** 191–202.

Dodd, C. E. R. and Jones, D. (1982). *J. Gen Microbiol.* **128,** 1933–1958.

Dott, W., Wolff, H. J. and Botzenhart, K. (1981). *Zentralblt. Bakteriol. Microbiol. Hyg. Abt. I. Orig. B. Hyg. Umwelthyg. Krankkerhaushyg. Arbeitshyg. Praev. Med.* **173,** 233–241.

Du Plessis, H. J., van Vuuren, H. J. J. and Hattingh, M. J. (1984). *Phytopathol.* **74,** 524–529.

Dye, D. W. (1981). *N.Z. J. Agric. Res.* **24,** 223–232.

Elia, S, Gosselé, F., Vantomme, R., Swings, J. and De Ley, J. (1984). *Phytopathol. Z.* **110,** 89–105.

Ellen, R. P. and Grove, D. A. (1985). *J. Clin. Microbiol.* **21,** 850–853.

Erasmus, J. A. (1983a). *Onderstepoort, J. Vet. Res.* **50,** 97–100.

Erasmus, J. A. (1983b). *Onderstepoort, J. Vet. Res.* **50,** 291–294.

Ercolani, G. L. (1983). *J. Gen. Microbiol.* **129**, 901–916.
Ericcson, H. M. and Sherris, J. C. (1971). *Acta. Pathol. Microbiol. Scand.* **B217**, S1–90.
Ferragut, C., Izard, D., Gavini, F., Kersters, K., De Ley, J. and Leclerc, H. (1983). *Int. J. Syst. Bacteriol.* **33**, 133–142.
Floodgate, G. D. (1962a). *Bact. Rev.* **26**, 277–291.
Floodgate, G. D. (1962b). In *Bull Bacteriol. Nomen Taxon.* **12**, 171–179.
Fung, D. Y. C. and Hartman, P. A. (1972). *Can. J. Microbiol.* **18**, 1623–1627.
Fung, D. Y. C. and Hartman, P. A. (1975) In *New Approaches to the Identification of Microorganisms* (C. G. Hedén and T. Illéni, eds.), pp. 385–392, Wiley, New York.
Gal'chenko, V. F. and Nesterov, A. I. (1981). *Mikrobiologiya* **50**, 725–730.
Garcia, J. L., Roussos, S. and Bensoussan, M. (1981). *Cah. Or. Stom. Ser. Biol.* **43**, 13–26.
Garcia, J. L., Roussos, S., Bensoussan, M., Bianchi, A. and Mandel, M. (1982). *Ann. Microbiol.* **133**, 471–488.
Gerhardt, P., Murray, R. G. E., Costilov, R. N., Nester, E. W., Wood, W. A., Krieg, N. R. and Phillips, G. B. (1981). *Manual of Methods for General Bacteriology.* American Society for Microbiology, Washington, D.C.
Gillespie, N. C. (1981). *J. Appl. Bacteriol.* **50**, 29–44.
Goodfellow, M. and Minnikin, D. E. (1985). In *Chemical Methods in Bacterial Systematics* (M. Goodfellow and D. E. Minnikin, eds.), pp. 1–15. Academic Press, New York.
Goodfellow, M. and Pirouz, T. (1982). *J. Gen. Microbiol.* **128**, 503–528.
Goodfellow, M., Orlean, P. A. B., Collins, M. D., Alshamaony, L. and Minniken, D. E. (1978). *J. Gen. Microbiol.* **109**, 57–68.
Goodfellow, M., Beckham, A. R. and Barton, M. D. (1982a). *J. Appl. Bacteriol.* **53**, 199–208.
Goodfellow, M., Minnikin, D. E., Todd, C., Alderson, G., Minnikin, S. M. and Collins, M. D. (1982b). *J. Gen. Microbiol.* **128**, 1283–1298.
Goodfellow, M., Alderson, G., Nahaie, M. R., Peters, G., Schumacher-Pedreau, F., Pulverer, G., Heczko, P. B. and Mordarski, M. (1983). *Zentralblt. Bakteriol. Mikrobiol. Hyg. Abt. I. Orig A.* **256**, 7–24.
Gosselé, F., Swings, J., Kersters, K. and De Ley, J. (1983a). *Int. J. Syst. Bacteriol.* **33**, 65–81.
Gosselé, F., Swings, J., Kersters, K., Pauwels, P. and De Ley, J. (1983b). *Syst. Appl. Microbiol.* **4**, 338–368.
Gray, P. A. and Stewart, D. J. (1980). *J. Appl. Bacteriol.* **49**, 375–384.
Green, P. N. and Bousfield, I. J. (1982). *J. Gen. Microbiol.* **128**, 623–638.
Greippson, S. and Priest, F. G. (1983). *Int. J. Syst. Bacteriol.* **33**, 470–475.
Grimont, P. A. D. and de Rosnay, H. L. C. D. (1972). *J. Gen. Microbiol.* **72**, 259–268.
Gunn, B. A. and Colwell, R. R. (1983). *Int. J. Syst. Bacteriol.* **33**, 751–759.
Hada, H. S., Krichevsky, M. I. and Sizemore, R. K. (1983). *J. Microbiol. Methods* **1**, 229–238.
Harwood, C. R. (1980) In *Microbiological Classification and Identification* (M. Goodfellow and R. G. Board, eds.), pp. 27–53. Academic Press, New York.
Haynes, W. C. (1951). *J. Gen. Microbiol.* **5**, 939–950.
Hervera, A. and Francisco, G. (1984). *Rev. Cienc. Biol.* **15**, 1–16.
Hill, L. R. (1974). *Int. J. Syst. Bacteriol.* **24**, 494–499.
Hill, L. R. (1975). *Int. J. Syst. Bacteriol.* **25**, 245–251.
Hill, L. R. (1984). In *New Horizons in Microbiology* (A. Sanna and G. Morace, eds.), pp. 325–333. Elsevier, New York.

Holdeman, L. V., Cato, E. P. and Moore, W. E. C. (1977). *Anaerobe Laboratory Manual*. Virginia Polytechnic Institute and State University, Anaerobe Laboratory, Blacksburg.

Holding, A. J. and Collee, J. G. (1971). In *Methods in Microbiology*, Vol. 6A (J. R. Norris and D. W. Ribbons, eds.), pp. 1–32. Academic Press, New York.

Holmberg, K. and Nord, C. E. (1984) In *Methods in Microbiology*, Vol. 16 (T. Bergan, ed.), pp. 341–360. Academic Press, New York.

Holmes, B., and Roberts, P. (1981). *J. Appl. Bacteriol.* **50**, 443–468.

Holmes, B., Owen, R. J. and Weaver, R. E. (1981). *Int. J. Syst. Bacteriol.* **31**, 21–34.

Hubalek, Z. (1982). *J. Appl. Bacteriol.* **52**, 307–318.

Izard, D., Gavini, F. and Leclerc, H. (1980). *Zentralblt. Bakteriol. Mikrobiol. Hyg. I. Abt. Orig. C.* **1**, 51–60.

Izard, D., Ferragut, C., Gavini, F., Kersters, K., De Ley, J. and Leclerc, H. (1981). *Int. J. Syst. Bacteriol.* **31**, 116–127.

Jackman, P. J. H. (1982). *J. Med. Microbiol.* **15**, 485–492.

Jessen, O. (1965). *Pseudomonas aeruginosa and Other Green Fluorescent Pseudomonads. A Taxonomic Study*. Munksgaard, Copenhagen.

Johnson, J. L. (1981) In *Manual of Methods for General Bacteriology* (P. Gerhardt, R. G. E. Murray, R. N. Costilow, E. W. Nester, W. A. Wood, N. R. Krieg and G. B. Phillips, eds.), pp. 450–472. American Society for Microbiology, Bethesda.

Jones, D. and Sackin, M. J. (1980). In *Microbiological Classification and Identification* (M. Goodfellow and R. G. Board, eds.), pp. 73–106. Academic Press, New York.

Jooste, P. J., Britze, T. J. and De Haast, J. (1985). *J. Appl. Bacteriol.* **59**, 311–324.

Jordan, D. C. (1982). *Int. J. Syst. Bacteriol.* **32**, 136–139.

Kalina, G. P., Nikonova, V. A., Grafova, T. I., Podosinnikova, L. S., Somova, A. G. and Lapenkov, M. I. (1980). *Zh. Mikrobiol. Epidemiol. Immunobiol.* 16–21.

Kalina, G. P., Antonov, A. S., Turova, T. P. and Grafova, T. I. (1984). *Int. J. Syst. Bacteriol.* **34**, 150–154.

Kaneko, K. I. and Hashimoto, N. (1982). *Int. J. Syst. Bacteriol.* **32**, 275–287.

Kapperud, G., Bergan, T. and Lassen, J. (1981). *Int. J. Syst. Bacteriol.* **31**, 401–419.

Keddie, R. M. and Bousfield, I. J. (1980). In *Microbiological Classification and Identification* (M. Goodfellow and R. G. Board, eds.), pp. 167–188. Academic Press, New York.

Kersters, K. and Deley, J. (1980). In *Microbiological Classification and Identification* (M. Goodfellow and R. G. Board, eds.), pp. 273–297. Academic Press, New York.

Kersters, K., De Ley, J., Sneath, P. H. A. and Sackin, M. (1973). *J. Gen. Microbiol.* **78**, 227–239.

King, E. O., Ward, M. K. and Raney, D. E. (1954). *J. Lab. Clin. Med.* **44**, 301–307.

Kiprianova, E. A., Levanova, G. F., Panichev, A. V. and Garagulga, A. D. (1981). *Microbial. Zh. (Kiev)* **43**, 411–416.

Klinge, K. (1960). *J. Appl. Bacteriol.* **23**, 442–462.

Kovács, N. (1928). *Z. ImmunForsch. Exp. Ther.* **55**, 311–315.

Kovács, N. (1956). *Nature (London)* **178**, 703.

Krichevsky, M. I. and Norton, L. M. (1974). *Int. J. Syst. Bacteriol.* **24**, 524–531.

Lapage, S. P. (1974). *Int. J. Syst. Bacteriol.* **24**, 500–507.

Lapage, S. P., Bascomb, S., Willcox, W. R. and Curtis, M. A. (1970). In *Automation, Mechanization and Data Handling in Microbiology*. Academic Press, London.

Lapage, S. P., Bascomb, S., Willcox, W. R. and Curtis, M. A. (1973). *J. Gen. Microbiol.* **77**, 273–290.

Lee, C. Y., Fung, D. Y. C. and Kastner, C. L. (1982). *J. Food Sci.* **47**, 363–367, 373.

Lee, J. V., Shread, P., Furniss, A. L. and Bryant, T. N. (1981). *J. Appl. Bacteriol.* **50**, 73–94.

Leifson, E. (1966). *Bacteriol. Rev.* **30**, 257–266.

Lockhart, W. R. (1967). *J. Bacteriol.* **94**, 826–831.

Lockhart, W. R. and Liston, J. (1970) *Methods for Numerical Taxonomy*. American Society for Microbiology, Bethesda, MD.

Lovelace, T. E. and Colwell, R. R. (1968). *Appl. Microbiol.* **16**, 944–945.

MacDonell, M. and Colwell, R. R. (1985). In *Computer Assisted Bacterial Systematics* (M. Goodfellow, D. Jones and F. G. Priest, eds.), pp. 107–135. Academic Press, London.

Mallory, L. M., Austin, B. and Colwell, R. R. (1977). *Can. J. Microbiol.* **23**, 733–750.

Marinetti, G. V. (1965). *Biochim. Biophys. Acta* **98**, 554–565.

Mergaert, J. Verdonck, L., Kersters, K., Swings, J. Boeufgrass, J. M. and De Ley, J. (1984). *J. Gen. Microbiol.* 130, 1893–1910.

Mezensky, L. and Slosarek, M. (1981). *Cesk. Epidemiol. Mikrobiol. Immunol.* **30**, 36–48.

Mezensky, L. and Slosarek, M. (1986). *Česk. Epidemiol. Mikrobiol. Immunol.* **35**, 113–123.

Michener, C. D. and Sokal, R. R. (1957). *Evolution.* **11**, 130.

Minnikin, D. E. (1981). *Zentralblt. Bakteriol. Mikrobiol. Hyg. I. Abt.* **S11**, 39–46.

Minnikin, D. E. and Goodfellow, M. (1980) In *Microbiological Classification and Identification* (M. Goodfellow and R. G. Board, eds.), pp. 189–256. Academic Press, New York.

Molin, G. and Ternstrom, A. (1982). *J. Gen. Microbiol.* **128**, 1249–1264.

Møller, V. (1955). *Acta. Pathol. Microbiol. Scand.* **36**, 158–172.

Moss, C. W. J. (1981). *Chromatogr.* **203**, 307.

Moss, C. W. (1984) In *New Horizons in Microbiology* (A. Sanna and G. Morace, eds.). pp. 63–70.

Neal, J. L., Lu, K. C., Bollen, W. B. and Trappe, J. M. (1966). *Appl. Microbiol.* **14**, 695–696.

Neill, S. D., Campbell, J. N., O'Brien, J. J., Weatherup, S. T. C. and Ellis, W. A. (1985). *Int. J. Syst. Bacteriol.* **35**, 342–356.

Nokhal, T. H. and Schlegel, H. G. (1983). *Int. J. Syst. Bacteriol.* **33**, 26–37.

Norris, J. R. (1968). In *Chemotaxonomy and Serotaxonomy* (J. G. Hawkes, ed.), pp. 49–56. Academic Press, London.

O'Brien, M. and Davis, G. H. G. (1982). *J. Clin. Microbiol.* **16**, 417–421.

O'Donnell, A. G., Nahaie, M. R., Goodfellow, M., Minnikin, D. E. and Hajek, V. (1985). *J. Gen. Microbiol.* **131**, 2023–2033.

Orchard, V. A. and Goodfellow, M. (1980). *J. Gen. Microbiol.* **118**, 295–312.

O'Reilly, T., Rosendal, S. and Niven, D. F. (1984). *Can. J. Micriobiol.* **30**, 1229–1238.

Owen, R. J. and Pitcher, D. (1985). In *Chemical Methods in Bacterial Systematics* (M. Goodfellow and D. E. Minnikin, eds.), pp. 67–93. Academic Press, New York.

Panichev, A. V., Nesterenko, O. A. and T. M. (1979). *Mikrobiol. Zh. (Kiev).* **41**, 593–602.

Panichev, A. V., Kokina, V. A. and Agre, N. S. (1984). *Biol. Nauki*, 67–71.

Parija, S. C., Agarwal, R. G. and Sanyal, S. C. (1982). *Indian J. Med. Res.* **75**, 638–642.

Pavlenko, G. V. and Ivchenko, A. I. (1984). *Vest. Leningr. Univ. Biol.*, 82–88.

Quesada, E., Ventosa, A., Ruiz-Berraquero, F. and Ramos-Cormenzana, A. (1984). *Int. J. Syst. Bactenoi.* **34**, 287–292.

Ridell, M. and Goodfellow, M. (1983). *J. Gen. Microbiol.* **129**, 599–612.

Rosenberg, A. (1983). *Arch. Microbiol.* **136**, 117–123.

Ross, H. N. M., Grant, W. D. and Harris, J. E. (1985). In *Chemical Methods in Bacterial Systematics* (M. Goodfellow and D. E. Minnikin, eds.), pp. 289–300. Academic Press, New York.

Rosswall, T. and Kvillner, E. (1981) In *Advances in Microbial Ecology* (M. Alexander, ed.). Plenum Press.

Russek-Cohen, E. and Colwell, R. R. (1986) In *Microbial Autecology* (R. L. Tate, ed.). Wiley, New York.

Sackin, M. J. (1981). *J. Gen. Microbiol.* **122**, 247–254.

Schumacher-Perdreau, F., Rotering, H. and Pulverer, G. (1983). *Zentralbl. Bakteriol. Mikrobiol. Hyg. Ser. A.* **256**, 25–36.

Seal, D. V., McSwiggan, D. A., Datta, N. and Feltham, R. K. A. (1981). *J. Med. Microbiol.* **14**, 295–306.

Sedov, V. I. and Shumilo, O. M. (1983). *Zh. Mikrobiol. Epidemiol. Immunobiol,* 24–28.

Seiler, H. and Hennlich, W. (1983). *Syst. Appl. Microbiol.* **4**, 132–140.

Shah, D. B. and Wilson, J. B. (1963). *J. Bacteriol.* **85**, 516–521.

Shah, D. B. and Wilson, J. B. (1965). *J. Bacteriol.* **89**, 949–953.

Shaw, B. G. and Harding, C. D. (1984). *J. Appl. Bacteriol.* **56**, 25–40.

Shaw, B. G. and Latty, J. B. (1982). *J. Appl. Bacteriol.* **52**, 219–228.

Shaw, S. and Keddie, R. M. (1983). *Syst. Appl. Microbiol.* **4**, 253–276.

Shewan, J. M., Hodgkiss, W. and Liston, J. (1954). *Nature (London)* **173**, 208–209.

Shute, L. A., Berkeley, R. C. W., Norris, J. R. and Gutteridge, C. S. (1985). In *Chemical Methods in Bacterial Systematics* (M. Goodfellow and D. E. Minnikin, eds.), pp. 95–114. Academic Press, New York.

Silvestri, L., Turri, M., Hill, L. R. and Gilardi, E. (1962). In *Microbial Classifications: 12th Symp. Soc. General Microbiology* (G. C. Ainsworth and P. H. A. Sneath, eds.). pp. 333–360. Cambridge University Press.

Skerman, V. B. D. (1967). *A Guide to the Identification of the Genera of Bacteria.* Williams and Wilkins, Baltimore.

Skerman, V. B. D. (1969). *Abstracts of Microbiological Methods.* Wiley-Interscience. New York.

Skerman, V. B. D. (1973). *Int. J. Syst. Bacteriol.* **23**, 477–479.

Smibert, R. M. and Krieg, N. R. (1981). In *Manual of Methods for General Bacteriology* (P. Gerhardt, R. G. E. Murray, R. N. Costilow, E. W. Nester, W. A. Wood, N. R. Krieg and G. B. Phillips, eds.), pp. 409–443. American Society for Microbiology, Washington, D.C.

Smith, N. R., Gordon, R. E. and Clark, F. E. (1952). *Aerobic Spore-Forming Bacteria.* US Dept. Agriculture Monograph No. 16., Washington, D.C.

Sneath, P. H. A. (1957a). *J. Gen. Microbiol.* **17**, 184–200.

Sneath, P. H. A. (1957b). *J. Gen. Microbiol.* **17**, 201–226.

Sneath, P. H. A. (1958). *Ann. Microbiol. Enzymol.* **8**, 261–268.

Sneath, P. H. A. (1962) In *Microbiol Classification: 12th Symp. Soc. General Microbiology* (G. C. Ainsworth and P. H. A. Sneath, eds.), pp. 289–332. Cambridge University Press.

Sneath, P. H. A. (1964a). *Ann. Rev. Microbiol.* **18**, 335–346.

Sneath, P. H. A. (1964b). *Adv. Sci.* **20**, 572–582.

Sneath, P. H. A. (1964c) In *Taxonomic Biochemistry and Serology* (C. A. Leone, ed.), pp. 565–583. Ronald Press, New York.

Sneath, P. H. A. (1965) In *Mathematics and Computer Science in Biology and Medicine*, pp. 81–91. Her Majesty's Stationery Office, London.

Sneath, P. H. A. (1968a). *Classification Soc. Bull.* **1**, 28–45.
Sneath, P. H. A. (1968b). *J. Gen. Microbiol.* **54**, 1–11.
Sneath, P. H. A. (1969). *J. Clin. Pathol.* **22**, 87–92.
Sneath, P. H. A. (1971) In *Recent Advances in Microbiology* (A. Perez-Miravete and D. Palaez, eds.), pp. 581–586. Associacion Mexicana de Microbiologia, Mexico City.
Sneath, P. H. A. (1972). In *Methods in Microbiology*, Vol. 7A (J. R. Norris and D. W. Ribbons, eds.), pp. 29–98. Academic Press, London.
Sneath, P. H. A. (1974). *Int. J. Syst. Bacteriol.* **24**, 508–523.
Sneath, P. H. A. (1978) In *Essays in Microbiology* (J. R. Norris and M. H. Richmond, eds.), pp. 9/1–9/31. Wiley, Chichester.
Sneath, P. H. A. (1984) In *Bergey's Manual of Systematic Bacteriology* (N. R. Krieg and J. G. Holt, eds.), pp. 5–7. Williams and Wilkins, Baltimore.
Sneath, P. H. A. and Collins, V. G. (1974). *Antonie van Leeuwenhoek J. Microbiol.* **40**, 481–527.
Sneath, P. H. A. and Cowan, S. T. (1958). *J. Gen. Microbiol.* **19**, 551–565.
Sneath, P. H. A. and Johnson, R. (1972). *J. Gen. Microbiol.* **72**, 377–392.
Sneath, P. H. A. and Sokal, R. R. (1973) *Numerical Taxonomy: The Principles and Practice of Numerical Classification.* Freeman, San Francisco.
Sneath, P. H. A. and Stevens, M. (1985). *J. Gen Microbiol.* **131**, 2711–2738.
Sneath, P. H. A., Stevens, M. and Sackin, M. J. (1981). *Antonie van Leeuwenhoek J. Microbiol.* **47**, 423–448.
Snell, J. J. S. and Lapage, S. P. (1973). *J. Gen. Microbiol.* **74**, 9–20.
Sokal, R. R. and Sneath, P. H. A. (1963) *Principles of Numerical Taxonomy.* Freeman, San Francisco.
Stanier, R. Y., Palleroni, N. J. and Doudoroff, M. (1966). *J. Gen. Microbiol.* **43**, 159–271.
Stewart, D. J. (1965). *J. Gen. Micriobol.* **41**, 169–174.
Tabor, P. S., Ohwada, K. and Colwell, R. R. (1981). *Microb. Ecol.* **7**, 67–84.
Taylor, G. R., Guthrie, R. K. and Shirling, E. B. (1970). *Can. J. Microbiol.* **16**, 107–115.
Thornley, M. J. (1960). *J. Appl. Bacteriol.* **23**, 37–52.
Tsukamura, M. (1983). *Microbiol. Immunol.* **27**, 315–334.
Tsukamura, M., Mizuno, S. and Tsukamura, S. (1981). *Int. J. Syst. Bacteriol.* **31**, 263–275.
Tsukamura, M., Kita, N., Otsuka, W. and Shimode, H. (1983). *Microbiol. Immunol.* **27**, 219–236.
Vera-Cruz, C. M., Gosselé, F., Kersters, K., Segers, P., Van Den Mooter, M., Swings, J. and De Ley, J. (1984). *J. Gen. Microbiol.* **130**, 2983–3000.
Wayne, L. G. (1981). *Rev. Inf. Dis.* **3**, 822–828.
Wayne, L. G., Engbaek, H. C., Engel, H. W. B., Froman, S., Gross, W., Hawkins, J., Kappler, W., Karlsson, A. G., Kleeberg, H. H., Krasnow, I., Kubica, G. P., McDurmont, C., Nel, E. E., Pattyn, S. R., Schroder, K. H., Showalter, S., Tarnok, I., Tsukamura, M., Vergmann, B. and Wolinsky, E. (1974). *Int. J. Syst. Bacteriol.* **24**, 412–419.
Wayne, L. G., Engel, W. H. B., Grassi, C., Gross, W., Hawkins, J., Jenkins, P. A., Kappler, W., Kleeberg, H. H., Krasnow, I., Nel, E. E., Pattyn, S. R., Richards, P. A. Showalter, S., Slosarek, M., Szabo, I., Tarnok, I., Tsukamura, M., Vergmann, B. and Wolinsky, E. (1976). *Int. J. Syst. Bacteriol.* **26**, 311–318.
Weiten, G., Haverkamp, J., Engel, H. W. B. and Berwald, L. G. (1981). *Rev. Inf. Dis.* **3**, 871–877.

Weitzman, P. D. J. (1980) In *Microbial Classification and Identification* (M. Goodfellow and R. G. Board, eds.), pp. 107–124. Academic Press, New York.

Werner, H. and Hammann, H. (1980) In *Microbial Classification and Identification* (M. Goodfellow and R. G. Board, eds.), pp. 257–271. Academic Press, New York.

West, P. A. and Colwell, R. R. (1984) In *Vibrios in the Environment* (R. R. Colwell, ed.), pp. 285–363. Wiley-Interscience, New York.

West, P. A., Okpokwasili, G. C., Brayton, P. B., Grimes, D. J. and Colwell, R. R. (1984). *Appl. Environ. Microbiol.* **48,** 988–993.

White, A., Handler, P. and Smith, E. L. (1973). *Principles of Biochemistry.* McGraw-Hill, New York.

Wilkins, T. D. and Walker, C. B (1975). *Appl. Microbiol.* **30,** 825–830.

Wilkins, T. D., Walker, C. B. and Moore, W. E. C. (1975). *Appl. Microbiol.* **30,** 831–837.

Wilkinson, C. R., Nowak, M., Austin, B. and Colwell, R. R. (1981). *Microbial Ecol.* **7,** 13–22.

Williams, R. A. D. and Shah, H. N. (1980). In *Microbiological Classification and Identification* (M. Goodfellow and R. G. Board, eds.), pp. 299–318. Academic Press, New York.

Williams, S. T. and Wellington, E. M. H. (1980). In *Microbiological Classification and Identification* (M. Goodfellow and R. G. Board, eds.), pp. 139–165. Academic Press, New York.

Williams, S. T., Goodfellow, M., Alderson, G., Wellington, E. M. H., Sneath, P. H. A. and Sackin, M. J. (1983). *J. Gen. Microbiol.* **129,** 1743–1814.

Willis, A. T. (1960a). *Nature (London)* **185,** 943–944.

Willis, A. T. (1960b). *J. Pathol Bacteriol.* **80,** 379–390.

Zaremba, M. (1981). *Med. Dosw. Microbiol.* **33,** 197–205.

3
Enzyme Tests in Bacterial Identification

SHOSHANA BASCOMB

*St. Mary's Hospital Medical School, Department of Medical Microbiology,
London W2 1PG, UK*

I. Introduction

Identification of bacteria is based on results of characterization tests, which place the unknown organism in a defined group. The results of conventional tests applied to clinical isolates are usually not available in less than 2 days

METHODS IN MICROBIOLOGY
VOLUME 19   ISBN 0–12–521519–3

from receipt of specimen (Bascomb, 1984, 1985a). A meaningful decrease in completion time will be obtained with systems able to perform all tests with bacteria from a single colony, taken from the primary isolation plate, and requiring not more than 3 h for completion. These requirements preclude growth-dependent tests (Kersters and De Ley, 1971; Bascomb, 1980a). On the other hand, growth-independent enzyme tests applied to non-proliferating cells would be most suitable for rapid characterization of bacteria (Kersters and De Ley, 1971; Bascomb, 1980a, 1983b, 1984, 1985a).

Methods of testing for bacterial enzymes have been previously reviewed in this series (Kersters and De Ley, 1971; Watson, 1976). Descriptions of a number of enzyme tests can also be found in monographs dealing with general tests for bacterial identifications (Holding and Collee, 1971; Cowan, 1974; Richard, 1978).

A large number of enzyme classes have been studied in bacteria. Each class will be dealt with briefly, followed by the results of application of batteries of enzyme tests to characterization and identification of various bacterial taxa, and problems of handling quantitative enzyme data.

A.   Application of enzyme tests to characterization of bacteria

Type of enzyme tests.   Methods of application of enzyme tests to classification or identification of bacteria can be divided into 4 categories:

(1) Qualitative tests in which the presence of an enzyme is detected subjectively by observation of a change in the appearance (e.g. gas bubbles as an indication of catalase activity), a change in colour (Gordon and McCleod, 1928; Le Minor and Ben Hamida, 1962), or a change in the fluorescence (Maddocks and Greenan, 1975) of bacteria–substrate mixture.

(2) Study of iso-enzymes using electrophoretic techniques, in which enzymes performing the same catalytic activities are compared with regard to their electrophoretic mobility, as well as their substrate, cofactor and inhibitor specificities (Stewart and Stewart, 1971; Goullet, 1978; Williams and Shah, 1980).

(3) Quantitative tests in which the activity of the enzyme is measured and expressed in terms of the quantity or rate of formation of reaction product (Leclerc, 1967; Roodyn and Maroudas, 1968; Bascomb and Spencer, 1980; Godsey et al., 1981).

(4) Qualitative or quantitative tests for detection of activities of enzymes conjugated to antibodies or antigens as used in enzyme-linked immunoassay techniques.

B. Effect of enzyme localization on ability to detect activity

Bacterial enzymes may be situated within the cell or secreted into the growth medium. Extracellular enzymes can be measured around bacterial growth on solid medium or in the supernatant of spent liquid medium. Within the prokaryotic cell three different localities have been defined namely, the periplasm, the cytoplasmic membrane and the cytoplasm.

1. Periplasmic enzymes

Enzymes of the periplasm can easily be released into the supernatant using methods for producing sphaeroplasts, for example osmosis and cold shock, or hydrolysis of cell wall using lysozyme + EDTA (Malmy and Horecker, 1964; Neu and Heppel, 1965; Cheng et al., 1971; MacAlister et al., 1972).

Between 50 and 93% of the activity of such enzymes can be detected in intact cells (Neu and Heppel, 1965; Heppel, 1967; Lazdunski et al., 1975b). The proportion of activity obtained with intact cells increases with substrate concentration, 1×10^{-2} M giving highest activities (Heppel, 1967).

2. Membrane enzymes

Enzymes of the cytoplasmic membrane can usually be detected in intact cells, for example oxidase (Jurtshuk et al., 1975). Activities of some depend on the organization within the membranes, and may be decreased by methods that affect the permeability barrier of the cell (Wade et al., 1971; Pelmont et al., 1972; Bascomb and Grantham, 1975; Bascomb, 1980a). Examples of the effect of cell disruption treatments, on the membrane enzyme phenylalanine amino oxidase (Pelmont et al., 1972) and on the cytoplasmic enzyme NADH oxidase, are shown in Fig. 1.

3. Cytoplasmic enzymes

Cytoplasmic enzymes are usually detected in cells after disruption of the permeability barrier by treatment with ultrasonic waves or various chemicals (Bascomb, 1980a). However, if the substrate molecule can enter the cell as a result of the activity of the appropriate permease or other processes, enzyme activity can be detected in intact cells also. This is particularly true when very sensitive detection methods are employed. Thus Maddocks and Greenan (1975) showed that, using the 4-methylumbelliferone (4-MU) derivatives of β-galactopyranoside, β-galactosidase activity of intact MacConkey-grown E. coli cells could be detected in a few minutes. Similar results were obtained with other 4-MU derivatives using quantitative enzyme methods (Bascomb, 1980b; Godsey et al., 1981).

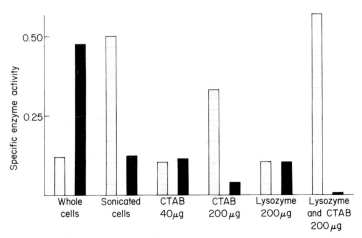

Fig. 1. Effect of interference with bacterial permeability barrier on activity of L-amino-oxidase and NADH oxidase. CTAB, cetyltrimethylammonium bromide; ▦, NADH oxidase; ■ L-amino-oxidase. (Bascomb, unpublished).

The detection of dehydrogenase activities is of interest. Methods of detection that depend on measurement of reduction of NAD to NADH or of NADP to NADPH are usually applied to cell extracts (Kersters and De Ley, 1971), but those that rely on reduction of tetrazolium dye can be performed with intact cells. This could be related to the inability of the NAD molecule to penetrate the cell, or to the fact that reduction of the tetrazolium dye results in its precipitation as formazan, thus moving the reaction of equilibrium towards complete reduction.

C.   Use of synthetic substrates

Enzymes can usually act on more than one substrate. This allows the use of synthetic substrates for detection and measurement of enzyme activities; provided that the affinity of the enzyme towards the synthetic substrate is at least as high as it is towards the natural substrate. Synthetic substrates contain a metabolic moiety attached to a chromatic or fluorescent moiety. The conjugated molecule usually has a different absorption and/or emission spectrum from the unconjugated form. Moreover, the unconjugated chromatic or fluorescent moiety shows a considerably higher absorption or fluorescence coefficient than that of the conjugated molecule (Zimmerman *et al.*, 1976). This allows the measurement of small amounts of reaction product in the presence of the large amounts of conjugated substrate required for maximal enzyme activity. Chromatic or fluorescent moieties are frequently simple or complicated phenol derivatives. In substrates used for the study of hydrolytic enzymes the chromatic moieties contain an hydroxyl (OH) group, which is utilized in the formation of ester bonds. Amino (NH_2) and carboxyl (COOH) groups are utilized for formation of peptide bonds.

Moieties used for detection of enzymes hydrolysing ester bonds include: phenol, α- or β-naphthol, o- or p-nitrophenol, indoxyl, phenolphthalein, 4-MU and fluorescein. Moieties used for detection of peptide bonds include α-or β-naphthylamine (NAP), p-nitroaniline (pNA), 7-methylcoumarin amide (7MCA) and hippurate.

Lists of chromatic and fluorescent moieties of synthetic substrates and some details of their detection are given in Tables I and II respectively.

The choice of chromatic or synthetic moieties depends on the affinity of the enzyme towards the different synthetic moieties, and the sensitivity of the detection procedure. Thus Moss (1966) states that the alkaline phosphatase from human small intestine showed a lower K_m for α-naphthyl phosphate but, as β-naphthol is twice as fluorescent as α-naphthol, the β-naphthyl phosphate is preferred for routine fluorimetric assay. On the other hand, when detecting enzyme activities by measurement of absorbance α-naphthyl phosphate is the preferred substrate, because α-naphthol (Abs 335 nm) absorbs light relatively more strongly than β-naphthol (Abs 345 nm). For detection of enzyme activities on gels by observation of fluorescence under UV light, the α-naphthyl substrate is preferred because α-naphthol fluoresces at a slightly longer wavelength than β-naphthol (455 and 410 nm respectively), and is therefore easier to discern by eye (Moss et al., 1961).

Naphthol (NA) and naphthylamine (NAP) can also be detected by reacting with diazonium dyes as described by Gomori (1954) for detection of peptidases in mammalian tissue and by Muftić (1967) in mycobacteria. The most sensitive method is diazotization in situ (Appel, 1974). However, this method requires addition of 3 or 4 reagents in the correct sequence; the first two (KNO_2 and H_2SO_4 or HCl) produce the diazo compound; sulphamate is then added to neutralize the excess NO_2, and, after this has been achieved naphthylethylenediamine is added to produce colour. This procedure is too cumbersome for routine daily measurements. To simplify the procedure, a number of methods have been developed using preformed diazo dyes to combine with the released naphthol or naphthylamine. The problem encountered with such methods is formation of aggregates of the products (Muftić, 1967).

For systems requiring localization of enzyme activity, i.e. locating enzymes on gels, or in tissues and cells for microscopic examination, the formation of precipitate with the reaction product is advantageous, as it prevents the diffusion of the product, ensuring correct localization; conditions encouraging precipitation without diffusion are therefore sought (McCabe and Chayen, 1965).

TABLE I (a)

Chromatic compounds used in synthetic substrates for forming ester bonds

Compound	Structure	Detection			
		pH	Reagents	Absorbance (nm) (colour)	References
Phenol	OH (phenol ring)	10 9.8 5.6	Fast Red B 4-Aminoantipyrin 2,6-Dibromo-N-chloro-p-quinone-imine and butanol	490 505 (Blue)	Fishman and Gosh, 1967 Fishman and Gosh, 1967 White and Pickett, 1953
o-Nitrophenol	OH, NO_2 (benzene ring)	7.6	—	414	Wallenfels and Malhotra, 1961
p-Nitrophenol	OH, NO_2 (benzene ring)	7.6–8.5 >10	— NaOH	405–420 405	Torriani, 1960; Heppel, 1967 Bascomb and Spencer, 1980
Indoxyl	OH, N–H (indole ring)		KOH, air —	(Blue) (Blue)	Bürger, 1967b; Eriquez and Hodinka, 1983
α-Naphthol	OH (naphthalene ring)	 4.0–9.0 5.0 7.6–7.8	Diazo dye Diazo dye Diazo dye Diazo dye Diazo dye Diazo dye	(red) 590 (Red-violet) (Pink-red) 585; (Green-cara-mel)	Norris and Burges, 1963 Buissière et al., 1967; Stewart and Stewart, 1971; Saito and Masai, 1980; Tierno and Milstoc, 1981 Muamba, 1982

	pH	Reaction	Color / wavelength	Reference
β-Naphthol		Diazo dye	(Violet)	McCoy et al., 1965;
		Diazo dye	585;	Buissière et al., 1967;
	7.4–7.6	Diazo dye	(Pink-caramel)	API ZYM
	7.4–7.6	Diazo dye		Muamba, 1982
6-Bromo-2-naphthol	6.0	Diazo dye	(Pink-red)	Rissler, 1983
	8.5	Aminoantipyrin	(Green)	Bürger, 1967b
Naphthol-AS-BI	7.4–7.6	Diazo dye	(Blue)	API ZYM; D'Amato et al., 1978
Phenolphthalein	> 9	Alkali	(Red)	Bray and King, 1942; Barber and Kuper, 1951; Bürger, 1967b
Fluorescein	7.6	—	490	Schnürer and Rosswall, 1982

TABLE I (b)

Chromatic compounds used in synthetic substrates for forming peptide bonds

Compound	Structure	Detection		Absorbance (nm)(colour)	References
		Reagents			
p-Nitroaniline	NH$_2$ —〈benzene ring〉— NO$_2$	—		405–410	Erlanger *et al.*, 1961; Claeson *et al.*, 1978; Lazdunski *et al.*, 1975a, b; Bascomb, 1980b
		HNO$_2$, HCl, sulphamate, naphthylethylenediamine		546	Appel, 1974; Ison *et al.*, 1982; Berdal and Olsvik, 1983
		p-Dimethylamino-cinnamaldehyde		565	Uete *et al.*, 1981
		3-Phenyl-4-dimethyl-aminoacrolein		(Blue to dark-purple)	RapID/NH[a]
β-Naphthylamine	〈naphthalene ring〉 NH$_2$	H$_2$SO$_4$, NaNo$_2$, KOH, β-naphthol		350 (Orange-red)	Machuga, 1982; Bürger, 1967b; Kersters and DeLey, 1971

	Reagent	λ (nm) / (colour)	References
	HNO$_2$, HCl, sulphamate, naphthylethylenediamine	575–578	Appel, 1974; Linder et al., 1974; Ison et al., 1982
	p-Dimethylamino-cinnamaldehyde	540 (Deep-red)	Uete et al., 1981; Bosley et al., 1983
	Azo dyes Azo dyes Azo dyes Azo dyes	540 (Red) (Red)	Gomori, 1954; Nachlas et al., 1962; McCabe and Chayen, 1965; Muftić, 1967; API ZYM[b]
	3-Phenyl-4-dimethyl-aminoacrolein	(Dark-pink to purple)	RapID/ANA[a]
4-Methoxy-naphthylamine	HNO$_2$, HCl, sulphamate, naphthylethylenediamine	574	Bascomb, unpublished
(4-methoxynaphthylamine structure: NH$_2$, OCH$_3$)	Azo dyes	(Orange)	ZYM AP[b]
Hippuric acid (structure: CO–NH–CH$_2$–COOH)	—	254	Appel, 1974

[a] Innovative Diagnostic Systems, Atlanta, Georgia 30340, USA.
[b] API-System SA, La Balme les Grottes, 38390 Montalieu Vercieu, France.

TABLE II
Fluorescent compounds of synthetic substrates

Compounds	Structure	Optimum pH for measurement	Wavelength Exc	Wavelength Em	References
o-Carboxyphenol		4.0–9.5	300	410	Brandenberger et al., 1967
α-Naphthol		10.4	335	455	Moss, 1960; Campbell and Moss, 1961; Greenberg, 1962
β-Napthol		10.4	350	410	Moss et al., 1961; Greenberg, 1962
β-Napthylamine		10.4	335	410	Greenberg, 1962; Westley et al., 1967; Behal and Cox, 1968
			365	415	Peterson and Hsu, 1978
			360	450	Uglem and Beck, 1972
4-Methylumbelliferone		10.3	360	457	Chen, 1968
			325	448	Stead, 1983
		10.3	364	448	Dahlén and Linde, 1973
		< 7.0	320	474	Chen, 1968
Methylcoumarinamide		7.5–8.0	383	454	Zimmerman et al., 1978
Fluorescein		7.3–7.6	470	510	Guilbault and Kramer, 1964

On the other hand, for detection of enzyme activity by measurement of light absorption or deflection, or fluorescence of a known volume of liquid, it is essential that the product should be completely soluble, as any formation of aggregates might distort the light measurement. Although Muftić (1967) has tried both α- and β-NAP derivatives, most of the other studies used the latter. Diazotization of β-NAP can be achieved by using diazonium salts like Fast Blue BB (API ZYM), Fast Garnet (F0875, Sigma; Ball et al., 1982), Fast Garnet GBC (Sigma; Miller and Mackinnon, 1974), or reaction with dimethylaminocinnamaldehyde reagent (Uete et al., 1981; Bosley et al., 1983).

Gomori (1954) observed that azo dyes can form a collodial suspension. Muftić (1967) showed the effect of different emulsifiers on the solubilization of colloids formed from Echtrotsaltz B (Fast Red salt B) with β-NAP and recommended the use of 10–20% Tween 80 in the dye solution. A 10% solution of lauryl sulphate is included in the API ZYM reagent A.

Choice of azo-dye depends on the type of enzyme reaction product (α- and β-naphthol or naphthylamine) and the pH of the reaction.

A list of azo dyes in use and some characteristics of coupling reactions are given in Table III.

Gurr (1971) emphasized that diazonium salts are unstable and explosive in the dry form. The stabilized diazonium salts are not pure compounds, since they contain, of necessity, stabilizers, buffers and other "necessary substances", the actual diazonium salt content is about 20–25%. It is therefore important to establish the commercial source of any dye used.

The problems involved in use of such dyes for detection of the released β-NAP were studied by Muftić (1967). The carcinogenicity of β-NAP and many of the azo dyes has led us to search for other substrates. Erlanger et al., described in 1961 the synthesis of p-nitroaniline (pNA) derivatives, and Buissière et al. (1967) and Bürger (1967b) included pNA derivatives in their studies of bacterial enzymes. The cleavage of the peptide bond of the pNA derivatives is detected by measurement of absorbance of the released pNA at 405–410 nm or by diazotization of the released pNA, (Appel, 1974; Uete et al., 1981; Ison et al., 1982; Berdal and Olsvik, 1983).

Zimmerman et al. (1976) reported the synthesis of 7-aminomethylcoumarin (7AMC) derivatives for the more sensitive fluorescent assay of the aryl amidase activity of chymotrypsin, and Godsey et al. (1981) were the first to use 7AMC derivatives for measurement of bacterial peptidases.

D. Measurement of enzyme activities

Bascomb (1980a, 1983b, 1984, 1985a) reviewed the methods available for quantitative measurements of enzyme activities covering continuous-flow

TABLE III

Azo dyes for coupling reactions

Azo dye	Structure	Solubility in water (%)	Coupling rate	Colour/wavelength	References
Fast Red B	OCH$_3$, NH$_2$, O$_2$N	20	Very rapid	Deep-red[a] Blue, 590 nm[b]	Muftić, 1967 Stewart and Stewart, 1971
Fast Blue B	CH$_3$O, OCH$_3$, H$_2$N, NH$_2$	10	Very rapid	Deep red[a] 540 nm[a] Red[b] Deep blue[c] Violet[d]	Mulczyk and Szewczuk, 1970 Nachlas et al., 1962 Taylor and Bettelheim, 1966 Lillie, 1977 Bürger, 1967a
Fast Blue BB	CO—NH, OC$_2$H$_5$, NH$_2$, H$_5$C$_2$O	4	Slow	Black[a] Orange[a] Violet[c] Blue[c] Violet[d]	Lillie, 1977 API ZYM API ZYM API ZYM API ZYM
Fast Garnet GBC	CH$_3$, N=N, CH$_3$, NH$_2$	5	Very rapid	Deep-red[a,e] Pink-red[d] Red[e] Red-brown[b]	Miller and MacKinnon, 1974 Rissler, 1983 Lillie, 1977 Lillie, 1977
Fast Violet B	CO—NH, OCH$_3$, NH$_2$, H$_3$C	10	Slow	Pink-red[e]	API Z[f]
Fast Red TR	CH$_3$, Cl, NH$_2$.HCl	20	Rapid	405 nm[b] Brown[b] Deep-red[a]	Hillmann, 1971 Lillie, 1977 Lillie, 1977

Notes: Colour developed with: [a]β-naphthylamine; [b]α-naphthol; [c]naphthol AS-BI; [d]6-bromo-β-naphthol; [e]β-naphthol; [f]API, address as Table Ib.

systems and discrete analysis. In recent years a great increase in the use of multiwell plates for identification of bacteria and determination of susceptibility to antimicrobial agents has occurred; Ison *et al.* (1982) and Berdal *et al.* (1982) advocated their use for enzyme tests. Advantages of multiwell plates are: (1) only small volumes of reagents and bacterial suspensions are required; (2) availability of mechanical pipetting devices enables rapid distribution of a large number of solutions; (3) the plates are disposable; and (4) they occupy only a small space. Moreover, the availability of instruments for reading both absorbance and fluorescence of well contents at the rate of > 100 wells min^{-1} makes them suitable for rapid measurement of large numbers of tests.

Obviously multiwell plates cannot be read using a horizontal light beam. The available vertical-beam photometers differ in the position of the detecting device, the number of wells read simultaneously and whether absorbances or fluorescence is measured. A number of photometric scanning devices have also been adapted for reading multiwell plates (Labrousse *et al.*, 1982). Accuracy and reproducibility of both the Dynatech Autoreader and Flow Titerek Multiskan readers have been compared (Genta and Bowdre, 1982). Technical details for some multiwell plate readers are available in a survey of immunoassay hardware (*Lab. Practice*, March 1984, pp. 27–35). The disadvantage of multiwell plates is the inability to measure light of < 300 nm through them and their vulnerability to organic solvents, thus restricting the scope of chemical reactions.

II. Enzyme classes

A. Enzymes metabolizing single amino acids

1. L-*amino-oxidase (deaminase)*

Phenylalanine deaminase has been used for the specific recognition of members of the tribe Proteae (Bernheim *et al.*, 1935; Singer and Volcani, 1955). The enzyme is present in all species of *Proteus* and *Providencia* as a constitutive enzyme, and can be detected in 1 min using test papers (Pathotec, General Diagnostics; Narayan *et al.*, 1967). It is also present in *Moraxella phenylpyruvica* and a few pseudomonads. The basic reaction involves an L-amino acid and oxygen, and results in the formation of an α-keto acid and ammonia:

$$RCHNH_2COOH + 1/2\ O_2 \longrightarrow RCOCOOH + NH_3$$

Detection of activity by conventional methods is based on reaction of the keto group, formed by deamination of phenylalanine or tryptophan, with ferric chloride ($FeCl_3$) in acid conditions to give a green colour (Singer and Volcani, 1955).

Detection can also be achieved by measuring the consumption of oxygen (using Clark oxygen electrode) or the reduction of dichlorophenolindophenol (Pelmont et al., 1972) or the released ammonia (Bascomb and Grantham, 1975; Bascomb and Spencer, 1980).

Pelmont et al. (1972) studied the enzyme of a strain of P. mirabilis. The enzyme is situated in the cell membrane and is closely bound to the cytochromes of the respiratory chain; disruption of this link, by treatment with phospholipase or detergents, caused decrease in activity, suggesting that this close link is essential for enzyme function. They also showed that the optimum pH for activity is 7.6 and that the enzyme showed activity (measured as increase in oxygen consumption in the presence of amino acid) towards a variety of amino acids. High activities were obtained with histidine, phenylalanine, leucine, norleucine, methionine and ornithine. Activity with tryptophan, which is used in the API 20E kit for detection of the L-amino oxidase, was about $\frac{1}{3}$ of that with phenylalanine, the substrate used in conventional tests. Sphaeroplasts and cell envelopes differed slightly in their affinities toward different amino acids. Bascomb and Grantham (1975) measured ammonia released from a number of amino acids and other amino-containing metabolites. They found that all members of the tribe Proteae released ammonia from phenylalanine and methionine, as well as asparagine and cytidine. As cytidine deaminase was also found in Klebsiella (S. Bascomb, unpublished) and in Serratia marcescens (Sakai et al., 1975) and asparaginase has been found in E. coli (Mashburn and Wriston, 1964), Citrobacter (Bascomb et al., 1975) and many other bacteria (Wade et al., 1971) the deamination of these compounds is probably performed by enzymes other than the Proteae-specific L-amino-acid oxidase. Bascomb and Grantham (1975) also showed that the ammonia-releasing activity of P. morganii was much higher in cells grown in corn-steep liquor medium than in nutrient broth. Bascomb and Spencer (1980) used the continuous-flow Nessler assay for measurement of ammonia released from leucine for the detection of Proteae-specific L-amino-acid oxidase. Their results also show that leucine ammonia-lyase activity was mirrored by the production of a change in β-p-nitrophenylalanine-containing medium. This change was manifested, after addition of 2 N NaOH, by the appearance of a brownish colour (maximum absorbance at 492 nm; S. Bascomb, unpublished). The nature of the product has not been established, but it was assumed that p-nitrophenylalanine was deaminated by the L-amino-acid oxidase to produce p-nitrophenylpyruvic acid. The fact that fluorophenylalanine derivatives were oxidized at almost twice the rate of phenylalanine by the L-amino-acid oxidase of *P. mirabilis* (Pelmont *et al.*, 1972) supports this assumption. Details of the *p*-nitrophenylalanine test in micromethod are given below.

Schofield and Schaal (1980) described a micromethod for detection of deaminase of amino acids by facultative anaerobic actinomycetes using Nessler reagent; they found deamination of ornithine, serine and alanine by strains of *Arachnia* but of serine only by those of *Rothia*. Sereny described, in a series of papers, (for references see Sereny, 1966) alkalinization of media containing a variety of amino acids as a means of detection of deamination. However, it is not clear if these observed changes in pH were really due to specific deamination of the amino acids, as alkalinization of media also occurred in control broth devoid of amino acids.

Rapid micromethod for detection of L-amino-acid oxidase

Reagents. (A) 10 mM *p*-nitrophenylalanine stock solution: DL-β-(*p*-nitrophenyl)alanine (Koch Light Laboratories), 52.3 mg; DW, 25 ml. Dissolve and store 5 ml aliquots in screwcapped bottles frozen at $-20\,^{\circ}$C. (B) Tris phosphate buffer pH 8.0: 0.2 M tris(hydroxymethyl)methylamine (24.2 g l^{-1}); 0.2 M KH_2PO_4 (27.2 g l^{-1}). Mix equal volumes, adjust pH to 8.0, store at 3–8 $^{\circ}$C. (C) Substrate working solution: dilute stock substrate solution (A) with buffer (B) in 1:3 ratio. Distribute 25 µl aliquots into multiwell plates. (D) 2 N NaOH.

Test procedure. Inoculate each well with 25 µl of a suspension of one colony, taken from a primary isolation medium, in 0.8 ml sterile saline. After 2 h incubation at 37 $^{\circ}$C, add 25 µl of 2 N NaOH. A positive reaction is indicated by the appearance of orange brown colour, negative wells appear clear or pale yellow. Measure absorbance at 492 nm.

2. Arginine deaminating enzymes

Particular interest is shown in the deamination of arginine, which can proceed through 3 different pathways:

(1) arginine dihydrolase system; arginine desiminidase producing citrulline + NH_3, with further breakdown of citrulline by ornithine transcarbamylase and carbamate kinase to ornithine + CO_2 + NH_3;

(2) arginase; producing ornithine and urea with further release of $2NH_3 + CO_2$ from urea by urease;

(3) L-amino-acid oxidase.

The only method for determining which enzyme has been active is by analysis of the breakdown products using gas chromatography (Fugate *et al.*, 1977) or thin-layer chromatography (Chen *et al.*, 1982).

The first pathway, termed arginine dihydrolase (Møller, 1955; Thornley, 1960), is found mainly in pseudomonads (Fugate *et al.*, 1977) and *Streptococcus faecalis* (Sokatch, 1969) and other Gram-positive organisms (Chen *et al.*, 1982). On the basis of this enzymatic activity, a strain of *St. faecalis* was used in a bioselective membrane electrode for measuring arginine by coupling resting cells to an ammonia-sensing electrode (Rechnitz *et al.*, 1977). Krasuski (1981a, b) has measured ammonia released from arginine or urea by strains of *S. aureus*, and found that the ratio between the two was correlated to the phage type.

3. Urease

Urease activity has been used in bacterial identification since 1941 (Rustigian and Stuart, 1941; Stuart *et al.*, 1945; Christensen, 1946). Usually the activity is indicated by increase in the pH of a growth medium containing less than normal amounts of peptone or yeast extract, urea and a pH indicator. Some non-growth tests based on a buffered solution of urea and a coloured pH indicator are also available (Stuart *et al.*, 1945; MacFaddin, 1980). Godsey *et al.* (1981) included 4-methylumbelliferone as a fluorescent pH indicator in their quantitative test system. However, increase in pH can be caused by a number of reactions, and more specific methods are desirable. Bascomb and Grantham (1975) and Bascomb and Spencer (1980) measured urease activity using Nessler reagent in a continuous flow system to assay released ammonia. MacFaddin (1980) states that urease is a constitutive enzyme; however, Kaltwasser *et al.* (1972) showed that during nitrogen starvation a 20–250-fold increase in urease specific activity was observed in *Ps. aeruginosa* extract. Bascomb and Grantham (1975) found that when cells were grown in corn-steep liquor medium only *P. rettgeri* and *P. morganii* showed urease activity, while *P. mirabilis* and *P. vulgaris* did not show any activity. Bascomb and Spencer (1980), who tested activity of MacConkey-grown cells, found that 75% and 62% of *Proteus* and *Klebsiella* strains respectively, were positive in the automated urease test (18 min incubation period, detection of ammonia by Nessler reagent), while all gave positive results with the conventional 24 h test. Bascomb (1980a) showed that the time needed for appearance of induced urease in MacConkey-grown cells of *Klebsiella* spp. and *Proteus* spp. incubated with urea varied from 14 min to more than 3 h. Godsey *et al.* (1981) found that the urease test was specific to *M. morganii* only, while *P. mirabilis*, *P. vulgaris* and *P. rettgeri* showed insignificant activity in their 30 min tests. Krasuski (1981b) has shown that, in resting cells of some phage types of *S. aureus*, a lag period of 24–48 h was needed before release of ammonia by urease could be measured, regardless of the presence of urea in the growth medium from which the cells were harvested. Generally speaking, some of the primary isolation media, particularly those containing high concentrations of sugars, tend to repress the synthesis of a number of enzymes, urease included.

4. Decarboxylases

Decarboxylation of arginine, lysine and ornithine (Møller, 1955) has been used extensively for identification of enterobacteria. Most conventional tests are based on detection of increase in pH of the growth medium (caused by appearance of primary amine after decarboxylation) as evidenced by the colour change of the pH indicator. These enzymes are inducible by the presence of the substrate at an acid pH, usually under anaerobic conditions. Unlike L-amino-acid oxidase, substrate specificity of most decarboxylases is very high. Increase in pH of a medium containing amino acids could be caused either by decarboxylation, resulting in appearance of primary amines, or by deamination resulting in appearance of NH_3; methods have been sought to differentiate between these two possibilities. Schofield and Schaal (1980) described a micromethod for detection of deamination and/or decarboxylation of amino acids by actinomycetes using triplicate compartments for each amino acid. After 24 h incubation, the first compartment was tested for a decrease in pH, using bromocresol purple as indicator (pH range 5.2–6.8). After an additional 48 h, the second compartment was tested for an increase in pH, using phenol red (pH range 6.8–8.4). The third compartment was used for detection of ammonia, after 72 h incubation, using the Nessler reagent. Increase in pH, without release of ammonia, was taken as evidence of decarboxylation. Leucine decarboxylation activity was found in 3 out of 6 strains of *Rothia*.

Hartman and Bast (1969) showed that acetone powder of *P. vulgaris* and *B. sphaericus* decarboxylated L-methionine; they assumed that this was done by substrate-unspecific decarboxylase of neutral amino acids described by Ekladius *et al.* (1957). They also showed that activity towards valine was 10-fold higher than that towards methionine. Fugate *et al.* (1977) recommended the use of gas–liquid chromatography for determination of decarboxylation production of arginine, lysine and ornithine. They showed that different strains yielded various amounts of citrulline, ornithine and agmatine as metabolic products of arginine; cadaverine and putrescine were the only metabolic products of lysine and ornithine respectively. This procedure may help to differentiate between the different pseudomonads. Chen *et al.* (1982) developed a method incorporating induction of decarboxylases for arg, glu, his, lys, orn, phe, try and tyr by growth on special medium, followed by transfer to 3 different test broths for detection of enzyme activities. After 1 h incubation, the test broths were centrifuged to remove bacterial cells. Determination of results was achieved by dansylation of products in the supernatants and separation of the fluorescent amino-acid–dansyl derivatives by TLC.

5. Glutamic acid decarboxylase

Glutamic acid decarboxylase from *E. coli* was purified and characterized by Shukuya and Schwert (1960). Leclerc (1967) described a continuous flow technique for measuring its activity and showed the usefulness of the test in taxonomy. Measurement of the enzyme has been used for enumeration of *E. coli* in water (Trinel and Leclerc, 1977; Trinel *et al.*, 1980) and in milk (Moran and Witter, 1976). The test was also included by Bascomb (1980b) and Bascomb and Spencer (1980) in schemes for identification of bacteria of clinical importance. Shah *et al.* (1981) isolated and characterized a glutamate decarboxylase from *Listeria monocytogenes*. The enzyme was also found useful in differentiation of anaerobic Gram-negative bacteria. Prabhakaran *et al.* (1983) isolated this enzyme from *Mycobacterium leprae*, and pointed out the connection between its presence in *M. leprae*, the unusual affinity of the organism for peripheral nerve tissue and the fact that glutamic acid is the most abundant amino acid in the nerve tissue.

6. Tryptophanase

The indole-producing enzyme tryptophanase was one of the first enzyme tests for identification of *E. coli*. The various conventional tests differ in source of tryptophan (whether in a protein or protein hydrolysate, or added separately) as well as in reagents used to demonstrate the presence of indole. The original Kovacs and Ehrlich reagents both use *p*-dimethylaminobenzaldehyde (DMBA) and rely on extraction of the indole from the aqueous substrate solution into a solvent layer (ether, xylene or amyl alcohol) during mixing with the reagent. Harley-Mason and Archer (1958) described a new reagent using *p*-dimethylaminocinnamaldehyde (DMCA) for detection of indole derivatives on paper chromatograms. Effect of acid and DMCA concentration on the rate of development of colour, final intensity and colour stability were determined by Turner (1961). A DMCA reagent was applied to bacterial colonies by Vracko and Sherris (1963); a 0.5 N HCl reagent produced colour which was stable. Development of other dyes was described by James and Yeoman (1984).

A spot test using filter paper impregnated with a DMBA reagent was described by Vracko and Sherris (1963). Miller and Wright (1982) compared the use of 4 reagents in spot indole tests, and found that the DMCA reagent gave best correlation with the conventional test. Tryptophanase is uniquely synthesized by bacteria, and the ability to form the enzyme appears to be closely related to ability to grow in animal intestinal tracts (DeMoss and Moser, 1969; Whitt *et al.*, 1979). Tryptophanase is inducible by tryptophan and its analogues and partially repressed by glucose in the medium. MacConkey-grown cells show significantly lower activity than those grown on BA (Miller and Wright, 1982). An improved medium for detection of indole production by *Pasteurella* was described by Clemons and Gadberry (1982). Induction of enzyme synthesis in log-phase cells is very quick; synthesis of tryptophanase-specific messenger RNA may be completed within one minute after addition of inducer (Bilezikian *et al.*, 1967). However, with cells taken from an overnight MacConkey culture, about 2 h must elapse before enzyme activity can be detected (Bascomb, 1980b). Bascomb (1980b) described a 2 h microtest using DMCA reagent and the Kem-O-Mat (Coulter Electronics) discrete analyser. A micromethod based on multiwell plates is described here.

Rapid micromethod for detection of indole produced by colonies taken from lactose-containing primary isolation medium

Reagents. (A) Peptone water: peptone-water-medium powder (Oxoid), 1.5 g; DW, 100 ml. Dissolve powder in water, distribute 5 ml aliquots into screwcapped bottles and autoclave at 121 °C for 15 min. Store at room temperature. (B) 2 mM tryptophan: tryptophan, 10.2 mg; DW, 25 ml. Dissolve the tryptophan, distribute 2.5 ml aliquots into screwcapped bottles. Store at −20 °C. (C) Substrate working solution: Dilute (A) 1:100 in sterile distilled water. Mix diluted (A) and (B) in 1:2 ratio and distribute 25 μl aliquots into multiwell plates, just prior to inoculation. (D) *p*-Dimethylcinnamaldehyde (*p*DMCA): *p*DMCA, 0.237 g; concentrated HCl, 10 ml; absolute ethanol, 78 ml. Store at 3–8 °C.

Test procedure. Inoculate each well with 25 μl of a suspension made of one colony, taken from a primary isolation medium, in 0.8 ml sterile saline. After 2 h incubation at 37 °C add 150 μl of DMCA solution, incubate for 20 min at RT for development of maximum colour (blue green for positive, yellow for negative). Measure absorbance at 635 nm.

Alternatively, add 50 μl of a 1% solution of *p*-dimethylbenzaldehyde (DMBA) in 10% HCl (red colour). Measure absorbance at 550 nm. The reaction with DMBA is immediate, but the DMCA reagent is more sensitive, detecting smaller amounts of indole, and is more useful for detection of indole production by"weak positives".

B.   Enzymes producing acetoin/diacetyl

Ability of organisms to produce acetoin (acetylmethylcarbinol, 3-oxobutan-2-ol) and/or diacetyl (butanedione) demonstrated by the VP reaction was detected by Voges and Proskauer as early as 1898. Eddy (1961) reviewed the literature relating to the conditions for their formation and the methods for their detection. Qadri *et al.* (1978) described a 4–8 h test using a MacFarland No. 3 standard cell suspension; the Micro-ID (General Diagnostics) system offers a 4 h test using a slightly less concentrated suspension. Bascomb and Spencer (1980) described a 50 min continuous-flow test using pyruvate at pH 4.5 instead of glucose as substrate, and creatinine, α-naphthol and KOH for the detection. The effect of pH on formation of acetoin in such a system was discussed by Bascomb (1980a). A modification of the test using the Kem-O-Mat was described by Bascomb (1980b). The Flow Titertek–Enterobac™ scheme detects VP-positive organisms by observing an increase in the pH of the test medium. Holländer *et al.* (1982) showed that VP medium (Oxoid), in the presence of 0.03 M glucose and 0.05 M fumarate, provides the conditions for maximum production of acetoin. Höhn-Bentz and Radler (1978) further investigated the enzymes involved in butanediol metabolism of bacteria and found different pH optima for activity of *Bacillus polymyxa* and *Serratia marcescens*. A micromethod based on multiwell plates is described below.

Rapid micro method for the detection of diacetyl/acetoin-producing enzymes (VP)

Reagents.   (A) Acetate buffer pH4.5: 0.2 M acetic acid (11.5 ml l^{-1}), 56 ml; 0.2 M sodium acetate (16.4 g l^{-1}), 44 ml; DW up to 200 ml. Add the first two solutions to 50 ml DW, adjust pH to 4.5 and make up volume to 200 ml. Store at 3–8 °C. (B) 0.3 M sodium pyruvate containing 0.2% creatine: sodium pyruvate, 3.305 g; creatine, 0.2 g. Dissolve the above in 100 ml of acetate buffer pH 4.5 (reagent A). Store refrigerated at 3–8 °C. (C) 0.4 mM thiamine pyrophosphate (cocarboxylase): thiamine pyrophosphate, 42.9 mg; DW, 25 ml. Dissolve and store at −20 °C in 5 ml aliquots. (D) Substrate working solution: mix (B) and (C) above in 1:2 ratio just prior to testing. Distribute 25 μl aliquots into multiwell plates. (E) 2.5% α-naphthol in 1 N NaOH: α-naphthol, 0.125 g; 1 N NaOH, 5 ml. Dissolve α-naphthol just prior to use, as the reagent deteriorates on exposure to air.

Test procedure.   Inoculate each well with 25 μl of a suspension made of one colony, taken from a primary isolation medium, in 0.8 ml sterile saline. After 2 h incubation at 37 °C add 25 μl of α-naphthol (reagent E), leave on the bench for 20 min for development of colour (positive: red; negative: straw colour). Measure absorbance at 520 nm.

C. Esterases and lipases

A number of synthetic esters of organic acids are available for the study of esterases and lipases. The demarcation line between these types of enzymes is not clear; generally speaking, esterases can hydrolyse molecules with the smaller-chained organic acids C_2,C_3,C_4, while lipases are capable of acting on derivatives of longer-chain acids. Esterases are found in all living organisms, and the diacetate ester of fluorescein has been used to detect viability, for example microbial activity of soil samples (Schnürer and Rosswall, 1982). Demonstration of various esterases by electrophoretic separation was described by Norris and Burges (1963) for *Bacillus* and by Stewart and Stewart (1971) for *E. coli*. Goullet, in a series of papers (for references see Goullet, 1978), has studied esterases of a number of genera of the Enterobacteriaceae. The enzymes were separated by their relative mobilities as well as affinity toward the α- or β-naphthol derivatives of acetate or butyrate. Bürger (1967b) lists 8 different substrates, which vary in both the metabolic and synthetic moieties. Guibault and Kramer (1964) described fluorescent tests for esterases and lipases using fluorescein derivatives.

The API esterases strip contains 10 different derivatives of β- or α-naphthol, the release of which is detectable using Fast Blue BB. Derivatives of 4-MU were used by Grange (1977), Bascomb (1980b) and Godsey *et al.* (1981).

Lipase synthetic substrates are only slightly soluble in aqueous solutions, and their tests are often done either with $< 10^{-6}$ M substrate concentrations or with the substrate provided as an emulsion and not as a true solution. Solubility in aqueous reagents is even more of a problem with natural lipase substrates. Hydrolysis of natural substrates is detected, either by observation of clearing of agar medium containing emulsion of the substrates, or by following decrease in the pH of the reaction mixture brought about by the released carboxylic groups of the organic acids.

D. Glycosidases

These enzymes are important because they are involved in breakdown of exogenous natural products for the supply of carbon and energy. Such enzymes are probably also involved in synthesis and breakdown of cell-wall polysaccharides, and synthesis of nucleosides. Ability to ferment lactose was used by MacConkey as early as 1908 for differentiation between the lactose fermenting, generally non-pathogenic, bacteria of the gut flora and the pathogenic non-lactose-fermenting *Salmonella* and *Shigella*. The first enzyme in the catabolism of lactose, β-galactosidase, has been studied extensively ever since, often with synthetic substrates, derivatives of *p*-nitrophenol (*p*NP).

Kilian and Bülow (1976) extended the range of nitrophenyl derivatives used for enzyme assay and established the pH optima for the various substrates. D'Amato *et al.* (1978) used β-naphthylglycosides; activity being detected using Fast Blue BB.

Synthetic derivatives of *p* nitrophenol are available with different metabolic moieties. These include α, β, D or L isomers of the monosaccharides glucose, galactose, glucuronic acid, mannose, fucose and xylose; the disaccharides lactose and maltose (API osidase strip) as well as the penta-, hexa- or heptamaltosides (Calbiochem-Behring). Derivatives of *N*-acetyldeoxyglucosamine and *N*-acetyldeoxygalactosamine are also available. With the exception of the oligosaccharides, 4-MU derivatives of most of these saccharides are available for more sensitive fluorogenic detection.

Marin and Marshall (1983a) studied glycosidases of psycotrophic bacteria isolated from milk by observing release of *p*-NP from 11 glycosidic derivatives. The β-D-galactoside derivative was hydrolysed by the largest number of strains. The same authors studied the glycosidase of a strain of *Ps. fluorescens* in more detail (Marin and Marshall, 1983b). The pH and temperature optima and V_{max} obtained with six *p*NP derivatives were compared. On the basis of these comparisons they concluded that the activities towards the various substrates are probably due to different enzymes. Highest activity was obtained with *N*-acetyl-β-galactosamide-*p*-NP. Rissler (1983) describes a net replication method for demonstrating glycosidic activity of individual colonies. A sterile nylon net is placed over the agar surface of an inoculated plate. After growth of colonies, the net is removed and sprayed with a substrate–reagent solution. The β-D-glucosidase activities of colonies of *E. coli* were shown by this method; 6-bromo-2-naphthyl derivative and Fast Garnet GBC were used as detecting reagent. Rissler also suggested that the enzyme is induced by the polysaccharide linamarin, though it is not clear if the inducer can be hydrolysed directly by the β-D-glucosidase.

1. β-Galactosidase

The best-characterized oligosaccharide-hydrolysing enzyme is probably the inducible enzyme β-galactosidase (Lederberg, 1950; Cohn, 1957). The substrate specificities of the enzyme were studied by Wallenfels and Malhotra (1961), who showed the relative rates for substrate hydrolysis towards β-galactose derivatives of *o*- and *p*-nitrophenol-β-D-galactopyranoside (ONPG and PNPG respectively) and other glycosides. Activity towards the *o*- and *p*-nitrophenol derivatives was respectively between 20- and 3-fold more than that towards the natural substrate lactose. Activities towards nitrophenyl derivatives of L-arabinoside at about $\frac{1}{2}$ of that towards PNPG were also noticed. Le Minor and Ben Hamida (1962) were the first to recommend the use of the synthetic substrate ONPG for differentiation of delayed lactose-fermenting organisms like *Escherichia* A-D group, *Citrobacter* and *Arizona*, from lactose-negative organisms of the *Salmonella* and *Shigella* genera. Bürger (1967a) described detection methods based on ONPG, PNPG and 6-bromo-2-naphthyl-β-galactopyranoside. Activity toward the latter substrate can be detected by coupling with *o*-dianisidine (Fast Blue B), or as a colour reaction with 4-aminoantipyrin. Use of the fluorogenic substrate 4-MU-β-D-galactopyranoside was suggested by Dyer (1970). A 10 min qualitative test was described by Maddocks and Greenan (1975) using 4-MU-β-D-galacto-pyranoside and 4 other derivatives. Quantitative fluorimetric tests were described by Grange (1978), Grange and McIntyre (1979) and Godsey *et al.* (1981). Quantitative automated methods using PNPG were described by Bascomb and Spencer (1980) and Bascomb (1980b). An ingenious droplet method (Rotman, 1961) was utilized by Cundell *et al.* (1979) with fluores-cein-β-D-galactopyranoside for detection and enumeration of *E. coli* in water. The β-galactosidase of lactic streptococci is able to hydrolyse only the phosphorylated β-galactosides (Heller and Röschenthaler, 1978).

2. *β-D-Glucuronidase*

The enzyme β-glucuronidase was shown by Williams (1954) and by Röd *et al.* (1974) to be of value in streptococci characterization. Kilian and Bülow (1976) showed it to be present in *E. coli* and *Shigella* species, and Le Minor *et al.* (1978, 1982, 1983) showed its value in identification of certain species of *Salmonella*. Derivatives of phenolphthalein (Bürger, 1967a), nitrophenol (Kilian and Bülow, 1976; Le Minor *et al.*, 1978; Kilian, 1978; Massenti *et al.*, 1981; Edberg and Trepeta, 1983), umbelliferone (Dyer, 1970), 4-MU (Grange, 1978; Bascomb, 1980b; Godsey *et al.*, 1981; Trepeta and Edberg, 1984b) have been used to assay the enzyme. The enzyme was used as one of 4 tests in a rapid economic scheme for identification of urinary-tract pathogens using the *p*-NP (Edberg and Trepeta, 1983) and 4-MU (Trepeta and Edberg, 1984b) glucuronic acid derivatives. The test (4-MU-β-glucuronate) is also included as one of 3 tests in the RIM (rapid identification method; Austin Biological Laboratories) *E. coli* kit, which consists of a single swab saturated with substrates for all 3 enzymes.

Though detection of β-glucuronidase activity is supposed to be very useful for identification of *E. coli*, the absence of the enzyme in a small proportion of faecal and environmental strains (Nastasi *et al.*, 1982), its presence in some *Salmonella* species (Le Minor *et al.*, 1978, 1982, 1983; Massenti *et al.*, 1981) and the fact that MacConkey-grown cells do not show enzyme activity necessitates inclusion of other tests for a definite identification of *E. coli*. Trepeta and Edberg (1984b) found that addition of 4-MU-glucuronide to a

MacConkey agar medium did not interfere with the expression of lactose
fermentation and enabled detection of both β-galactosidase (lactose fermentation indicated by the pink appearance of colonies) and β-D-glucuronidase
(blue fluorescence of the colonies) on the same medium.

Feng and Hartman (1982) described a rapid assay for *E. coli* in food
samples, using a medium containing 4-MU-glucuronide in a multiwell plate.
Fluorescence was observed after 4–20 h incubation.

3. β-D-Glucosidase

The enzyme that splits di- and oligosaccharides with β 1–4-linked glucose, is
probably involved in hydrolysis of a number of natural substrates like
cellobiose (Kilian and Bülow, 1976), salicin, arbutin and aesculin (Bürger,
1967a). The conventional test for acid production from salicin and cellobiose
probably indicates the presence of such an enzyme. Other enzymes, such as a
suitable permease and those involved in glycolysis, are also needed for
production of acid. The aesculin test, based on production of brown/black
colour in the presence of ferric citrate or detection of disappearance of
fluorescence in a spot test (see reviewed literature, Edberg *et al.*, 1977; Qadri
et al., 1981; Qadri and Smith, 1982), probably also involves β-D-glucosidase.
Edberg *et al.* (1984) showed that pNP-β-glucopyranoside in the presence of
sodium deoxycholate could replace the bile aesculin test used in characterization of enterobacteria and streptococci. Bürger (1967a) also described use of
indoxyl-β-D-glucoside as a synthetic substrate for the enzyme. Bascomb
(1980b) and Godsey *et al.* (1981) used 4-MU derivatives. Positive results are
obtained with members of the tribe Klebsiellae (Kilian and Bülow, 1976;
Edberg *et al.*, 1976). The test is also useful in identification of group D
streptococci (Rochaix, 1924; Qadri *et al.*, 1980).

4. α-Amylase

Very few synthetic substrates are available for detection of enzymes that
hydrolyse polysaccharides. Trepeta and Edberg (1984a) described the use of
Calbiochem-Behring amylase kit for detection of bacterial amylases. The kit
contains a mixture of p-nitrophenol(maltose)$_n$ derivatives ($n = 5,6,7$) as well
as the enzyme α-glucosidase. The α-glucosidase was originally added to the
mixture to ensure that the hydrolysis would proceed to completion as
evidenced by release of p-NP. For the bacterial testing, maltose in high
concentration is also added to the reaction mixture. This is done so as to
avoid hydrolysis of the p-NP-(maltose)$_n$ derivative by the bacterial α-
glucosidase. This suggests a broad substrate specificity of bacterial α-
glucosidase.

It is quite likely that α-glucosidase is one of the enzymes involved in production of acid from sucrose, maltose and trehalose.

The API ZYM strip contains 8 different glycosidase substrates. The API ZYM osidase strip contains p-NP derivatives of 12 sugars, 2 uronic acids, 2 acetyl sugar-aminides, 3 oligosaccharides and 1 phosphate sugar.

E. Nucleases

Nucleases are essential to nucleic-acid metabolism, and must therefore be present in every living cell. Although many enzymes can be demonstrated in cell extracts, only a few organisms show extracellular enzymes (Rothberg and Schwartz, 1965). The first enzyme used for identification purposes was the extracellular DNase of *Staphylococcus aureus* (Cunningham *et al.*, 1956; Weckman and Catlin, 1957). Although a number of staphylococci strains show DNase activity, including those of *S. epidermis*, *S. intermedium* and *S. hyicus* subspecies *hyicus* (Gudding, 1983), *S. aureus* excretes the enzyme in greater quantities (Zierdt and Golde, 1970). The test is used for differentiation of *S. aureus* from other staphylococci. Extracellular DNase is also produced by streptococci (Jeffries *et al.*, 1957), *Serratia marcescens* (Eaves and Jeffries, 1963), and *Corynebacterium diphtheriae* (Messinova *et al.*, 1963).

Enzymes can be differentiated by their substrate specificities: some can hydrolyse both DNA and RNA, others act on one type of nucleic acid only (Eaves and Jeffries, 1963; von Tigerstrom, 1981). Enzymes also differ in the position of the bond cleaved i.e. endo- or exonucleases, the ion and pH requirements, and the resistance to heat treatment. The *S. aureus* DNase is heat-stable, and this characteristic is used for differentiating the species from other staphylococci and for detection of staphylococcal contamination in foods (Ibrahim, 1981; Ackerman and Chesbro, 1981). This enzyme is also different from other nucleases in the requirement for Ca^{2+} and not Mg^{2+} for activity.

Commonly used tests for characterization of isolates are based on hydrolysis of natural DNA.

(i) *DNase medium* (Jeffries *et al.*, 1957).   DNA (0.2%, w/v) is added to agar growth medium containing peptone and NaCl before sterilization and distributed into plates. Plates are inoculated, often as spot inocula to enable testing of a number of strains in the same plate, and incubated overnight. Hydrolysis of the DNA can be detected by flooding the plates with 1 M HCl. DNA precipitates, resulting in a cloudy appearance. Clearing zones around inoculation spots indicate hydrolysis of DNA and presence of DNase.

Methods that do not require addition of reagent after incubation have also been devised.

(ii) *Toluidine blue modifications* (Schrier, 1969). Toluidine blue is added to DNase medium to give a final dye concentration of 0.01%. The dye complexes with the DNA, producing a clear blue medium. Inoculation and incubation is as above. DNase activity is shown by appearance of a rose-pink zone, indicating hydrolysis of DNA and breakdown of the toluidine blue DNA complex.

(iii) *Methyl green modification* (Smith *et al.*, 1969). Methyl green is added to DNase agar to a final concentration of 0.05% (Smith *et al.*, 1969) or 0.02% (Black *et al.*, 1971). At pH 7.5, the dye combines with DNA, forming a green complex. Hydrolysis of the complex releases the methyl green, which becomes colourless. Fading is not instantaneous, and may take 4–6 h (Kurnick, 1950).

(iv) *Acridine orange modification* (Lachica and Deibel, 1969). Cultures are overlayed with sterile acridine orange DNA agar consisting of: DNA, 150 mg; acridine orange, 10 mg; K_2HPO_4, 0.5 g; Agar, 1 g; DW up to 100 ml; pH adjusted to 9.0. The acridine is a basic fluorophore, which intercalates in double-stranded nucleic acids and fluoresces green (Exc 488 nm, Em 515–575 nm; Burns, 1980). Hydrolysis of DNA will cause appearance of non-fluorescent halos around colonies or discs, as opposed to the green fluorescence of the intact DNA.

The method can also utilize small paper discs impregnated with culture broths placed on agar plates and overlayed with the acridine orange DNA agar. This modification enables testing of broth that has been heat-treated prior to the assay, and can thus differentiate between heat-labile and heat-stable (*S. aureus* only) nucleases.

Two types of spectrophotometric tests have also been described. In the Erickson and Deibel (1973) test DNA-containing liquid growth medium is inoculated and incubated overnight. DNA is then denatured by heat and precipitated by addition of acid. The turbidity is measured at 600 nm. DNase activity is indicated by a decrease in turbidity as compared with the uninoculated control broth.

In the Ackerman and Chesbro (1981) method boiled food samples are incubated with heat-denatured calf-thymus DNA (final concentration 1 mg ml^{-1}) for 30 min at 50 °C. The reaction is stopped by the addition of cold 7% perchloric acid (0.5 ml to 0.4 ml enzyme–substrate mixture) and 3.0 ml of cold distilled water. The mixture is centrifuged at 1100g for 10 min at 4 °C, and the increase in absorbance of the supernatant at 260 nm indicates the presence of nucleotides, i.e. DNase activity.

In these tests natural substances are used as substrates. The ability of the DNA molecule to form complexes with certain dyes, thereby altering their absorption (toluidine blue, methyl green) or fluorescence (acridine orange) characteristics, has been utilized to detect hydrolysis of the DNA molecules. Three synthetic molecules have been used for detection of nuclease activities. Hydrolysis of thymidine 5'-monophosphate p-nitrophenyl ester ammonium salt by a purified extracellular nuclease from a *Bacillus* sp. was measured by monitoring the release of p-nitrophenol, as indicated by increase in absorbance at 410 nm (Onishi *et al.*, 1983). Hydrolysis of 5-bromo-4-chloro-3-indolyl-thymidine-3'-phosphate or of indolyl phosphate at acid pH has also been used. DNase or phosphodiesterase will cause the release of indoxyl, which, upon autooxidation, will produce a blue-green indigo colour. The method was described by Wolf *et al.* (1969). An indoxyl derivative is used in the Flow Laboratories NF-Tek kit for identification of non-fermentative Gram-negative bacteria.

Austin Biological laboratories provide a rapid microtest based on detection of acidification of a DNA medium; detection of DNase activity of *Branhamella* and *Serratia* can be achieved in 15 min and 2 h respectively.

A number of dyes have been used for fluorimetric determination of DNA and for detection of aquatic microflora. They include 4',6-diamidino-2-phenylindole (DAPI; Exc 365 nm, Em 390 nm; Kapuściński and Skoczylas, 1977; Porter and Feig, 1980), ethidium bromide (Exc 525 nm, Em 600 nm; Morgan *et al.*, 1979) and the Hoechst dye 33258 (Exc 352 nm, Em 448 nm; Paul and Myers, 1982) of Calbiochem-Behring. These compounds are weakly fluorescent at neutral pH but strongly fluorescent when bound to DNA. The increase in fluorescence intensity of the Hoechst dye 33258 on complexing to calf thymus DNA is about 40-fold (Burns, 1980). Paul and Myers (1982) showed that treatment of aquatic extracts with DNase I (bovine pancreas) completely removed the fluorescence of the sample. Lee *et al.* (1983) have described a method for detection of thermonuclease in food samples using an overlay of DNA (0.45 g l^{-1}) and ethidium bromide (100 μg l^{-1}) in an agar medium designed to inhibit bacterial growth. DNase activity is detected after 24–48 h incubation by examination under UV light.

F. Oxidases

The oxidase test was originally described for differentiating *Neisseria* on primary isolation plates (Schultze, 1910; Gordon and McLeod, 1928). It has since been used for differentiating *Aeromonas*, *Vibrio*, *Plesiomonas* and *Pasteurella* from enterobacteria and other fermentative Gram-negative bacteria and for identification of non-fermentative Gram-negatives (Steel, 1961), particularly species of *Pseudomonas* (Kovács, 1956) and *Neisseria*. Various reagents have been used, they differ in the nature of the electron donor (i.e. p-phenylenediamine and its mono-, di- or tetramethyl derivatives; Ellingworth *et al.*, 1929), the addition of other ingredients—e.g. α-naphthol (Schultze, 1910; Gaby and Hadley, 1957), ascorbate (Steel, 1962; Jurtshuk and McQuitty, 1976; Bascomb and Spencer, 1980)—and in the anionic salt configuration of the electron donor. Carpenter *et al.* (1947) showed that the oxalate salts of dimethyl-*p*-phenylenediamine or *p*-amino-*N*,*N*-dimethylaniline were more resistant to oxidation by air than their hydrochloric salts. The oxalate salts are less soluble, but this can be overcome in the preparation of the reagent by gentle heating. Ellingworth *et al.* (1929) and Kersters and De Ley (1971) show the molecular structure of the oxidized and reduced forms of the various redox dyes.

The oxidase tests detect ability of the organisms to oxidize the redox dyes in the presence of atmospheric oxygen. The identity of the enzyme responsible for this colour change is unclear (Gaby and Hadley, 1957). Cytochrome oxidase *a*, *aa* or *o* and the presence of cytochrome *c* are obligatory prerequisites for the oxidase reaction (Jurtshuk *et al.*, 1975; Jones, 1977 and 1980). Jurtshuk and McQuitty (1976) used manometric methods to measure the amount of atmospheric O_2 consumed by cells in the presence of N,N,N′,N′–tetramethyl-*p*-phenylenediamine (TMPD) and ascorbate (TMPD rate), and compared it with the amounts consumed without the redox molecule (endogenous rate). Using the difference and the ratio of the two measurements, they divided the strains tested into 4 groups. Species found positive by the Kovács oxidase test were found amongst the first two groups, showing high values for both parameters. Most of the enterobacteria belonged to group 3, showing fairly low but significantly measurable values, while truly anaerobic organisms and lactic acid bacteria belonged to group 4, showing very low values for both parameters. They concluded that high TMPD rate and oxidase activity will be found in bacteria that possess an integrated terminal or cytochrome oxidase enzyme complex consisting of both a *c*-type cytochrome and a terminal oxidase component such as cytochrome *o* and/or $a + a_3$. Cytochromes and their structure have been reviewed by Kamen (1983). Bacterial oxidases have been reviewed by Poole (1983).

Steel (1962) recommended addition of 0.1% (w/v) ascorbate to a 1% (w/v) aqueous TMPD solution, thus increasing the reagent "shelf life". Bascomb and Spencer (1980) described an automated quantitative assay based on estimation of the oxidized TMPD by measurement of absorbance at 550 nm.

The test is now often performed on paper strips, impregnated with the reagent(s), rather than directly on the agar medium itself. A number of commercial reagents are available, on paper strips or discs (General Diagnostics, BBL, Difco), or as a stable liquid reagent (API, Marion Scientific), or on a swab (EY Laboratories).

The *N*,*N*-dimethyl derivative of *p*-phenylenediamine is used in the commercially available preparations PathoTec cytochrome oxidase (General Diagnostics), Bacto differentiation oxidase disc (Difco) and Taxo N disc (BBL). Probably the oxalate, not the hydrochloride salt, is used in the above preparations. The Marion Scientific liquid reagent contains TMPD at pH 2.1 (Tarrand and Gröschal, 1982). The API OX reagent is a 1% solution of TMPD in isoamyl alcohol. Faller and Schleifer (1981) and Tarrand and Gröschal (1982) have shown that dissolving TMPD in dimethyl sulphoxide provides a more stable reagent; 6% and 1% solutions (w/v) were recommended as giving the best results. The effects of pH on response of *Aeromonas* strains revealed the importance of neutral to alkaline pH for detection of activity and could explain negative oxidase test results with MacConkey-grown cells (Hunt *et al.*, 1981). Suitability of commercially available reagents for testing *Pasteurella* strains has been examined by Tarrand and Gröschal (1982), Blackall (1982) and Gadberry *et al.* (1980). All agree that 1% aqueous TMPD appears to be the best reagent, giving positive results with all species of *Pasteurella*. Blackall (1982) also found that the Taxo N discs detected activity in 97% of the isolates found positive by the aqueous 1% TMPD test.

The benzidine test (Deibel and Evans 1960) is sometimes confused with the cytochrome oxidase test. The former is specific for iron–porphyrin compounds, and will therefore detect respiratory systems that contain the haem group, namely all cytochromes as well as catalase and nitrate reductase. Deibel and Evans (1960) claim that, as such, it is probably more suitable than the catalase test for the recognition of lactic acid bacteria, which are negative for the benzidine test. Faller and Schleifer (1981) described a modification of this test where the non-covalently bound haems are removed by extraction; the test is then applicable to detection of cytochrome *c*. The results of this modified test, when applied to micrococci, show correlation with TMPD oxidase.

G.   Peptidases and proteases

Peptidases and proteases are important for utilization of peptides as sources of extraneous individual amino acids for protein synthesis, or as sources of carbon and nitrogen. They must also be involved in the process by which intracellular peptides and proteins are degraded to amino acids. Proteases are considered to be involved in the pathogenicity of the organism (Lyerly and Kreger, 1983). The knowledge of the activities and physiological significance of many of these enzymes is still scant. However, it is well established that the bacterial cells contain several peptidases whose substrate specificities overlap.

The classification of enzymes that metabolize amino-acid chains can be related to the length of the chain (short chains by peptidases, long chains by proteases), the position of the cleaved bond (in the middle of the chain, endopeptidases; at the end, exopeptidases), the requirement for an amino acid at the *N*-terminal or *C*-terminal end of the peptide (amino- or carboxy-peptidases), and specificity for the amino acids at the cleaved bond. Enzymes are sometimes named after the amino acid for which they are specific (leucine aminopeptidase); those hydrolysing synthetic derivatives of amino acids are called arylamidases.

Peptidases are also classified according to components essential for their activity. Hartley (1960) classified bacterial proteases into 4 groups: serine proteases, thiol proteases, metal-chelation-sensitive proteases and acid proteases.

Substrate specificities of peptidases have been demonstrated by comparing activities towards the following.

(a) Amides of amino acids (e.g. leucinamide) (amidase activity): activity is demonstrated by measurement of the released ammonia.

(b) Different di- or tri- or other oligopeptides (peptidase activity): the enzymatic activity can then be demonstrated by revealing the released amino acids by ninhydrin or dansyl reactions, often following some form of separation using paper, column or thin layer chromatography.

(c) Different synthetic amino-acid esters of alcohols or phenols (e.g. ethyl or methyl or *p*-nitrophenol (*p*NP) derivatives) (esterase activity), such as tosylarginine methyl ester (TAME, Laskowski, 1955) and carboxy-benzoyltyrosine *p*-nitrophenyl ester (cbz-L-tyrosine-*p*-NP ester) are examples of such substrates: activity is demonstrated by measuring the released synthetic moiety of the substrate.

(d) Different synthetic amino-acid derivatives of β-NAP, *p*NA or 7AMC (arylamidase activity): activity is demonstrated by the colour or fluorescence of the released synthetic substrate moiety (see further Tables I–III).

(e) Synthetic derivatives of benzoylglycine (hippurate) or of carbobenzoxyglycine (carboxypeptidase activity): activity is demonstrated by measurement of absorbance of the released synthetic substrate moiety.

The affinity of the enzyme towards the synthetic moieties has been less frequently studied. Some studies suggest that activity with β-NAP derivatives is higher than with those of *p*NA (Muller, 1981) but Lazdunski *et al.* (1975a) and Machuga (1982) suggest the opposite. Differentiation of microorganisms by the substrate specificities of the aminopeptidases, as indicated by the measurement of the fluorescence of the β-NAP released from the non-fluorescent synthetic substrates of L-amino-acid β-naphthylamides, was reviewed by Watson (1976). Buissière *et al.* (1967) included some β-NAP derivatives in their testing for bacterial enzymes. Five such derivatives are included in the API ZYM kit, and 60 derivatives are provided by AP 1–6 of API (see below). The detection of activity in these kits was achieved by reacting the products with diazonium dyes.

Detection of peptidase activity by gel staining can be achieved by demonstration of the following.

(1) Cleavage of natural peptides: the assay mixture includes a peptide, L-amino-acid-oxidase and a peroxidase in an enzyme cascade system for the detection of released free amino acids (Miller and MacKinnon, 1974).

(2) Cleavage of β-NAP derivatives and detection of the released β-NAP by diazotization with Fast Garnet GBC (Miller and MacKinnon,1974).

(3) Cleavage of *p*NA derivatives and its detection by appearance of yellow colouring (Miller and Mackinnon, 1974; Murgier *et al.*, 1976).

When a crude extract of a bacterial strain is shown to have activities towards a variety of amino-acid derivatives it is not possible to decide *a priori* whether these activities are due to a single enzyme with broad but varying specificity to the various derivatives, or to a number of enzymes with narrow specificity towards the individual derivatives. This is because peptidases tend to show a broad spectrum of activity. Many bacterial enzymes with activity towards alanyl derivatives have been described (Behal and Folds, 1967; Behal and Carter, 1970). Enzymes that hydrolyse ala-β-NAP were found in a large number of bacterial species (Murgier *et al.*, 1976). A number of alanyl-specific peptidases were purified and their substrate specificities examined (Riley and Behal, 1971; Behal and Carter, 1970; Behal and Folds, 1967). Eriquez and Knight (1980) showed that enzymatic activities of a crude extract of *Neisseria meningitidis* showed a wider activity profile than that from *Moraxella urethritis*. The former showed highest activity towards ala-β-NAP, between 25 and 50% activity towards leu, lys, arg, gly, N-γ-glut, met and gly-gly β-NAP derivatives; the crude extract of the latter showed activity towards N-γ-glut, less with α-glut, and near 10% activity towards leu, ala, and arg, β-NAP derivatives. Moreover gel staining suggested that the activity towards α-glut-β-NAP could be separated from that towards the N-γ-glut derivative.

Behal and Folds (1967) purified 3 different peptidases from *N. catarrhalis*, a dipeptidase acting on ala-gly peptide, an arylamidase acting on ala-β-NAP, and a leucineaminopeptidase hydrolysing the leu-gly-gly tripeptide. The 3 enzymes differed in their optimal pH for activity, their metal-ion requirements, and their sensitivity to EDTA and other protease–peptidase inhibitors. The relative affinity of the enzymes towards peptide or arlypeptide derivatives also differed. An *N. catarrhalis* enzyme (Behal and Cox, 1968) showed twice as much activity towards ala-β-NAP than towards ala-ala peptide. However, crude extracts of *Streptococcus durans* yielded two enzymes (Machuga, 1982), an arylaminopeptidase with preference towards amino-acid-*p*NA derivatives (leu-*p*NA being the preferred substrate) with no activity towards any of the di- or tripeptides tested and an *N*-terminal exopeptidase active on di- or tripeptides and the B chain of insulin. This enzyme was 10-fold more active towards a dipeptide than the corresponding amino-acid-*p*NA derivatives.

When the peptidase activities of whole cells are investigated the results obtained must depend on the cumulative effect of the various peptidolytic enzymes as well as the cells' permeases, which themselves show marked specificities towards the size and composition of the peptides.

The first studies of bacterial peptidases for taxonomic purposes were by Muftić (1967) with mycobacteria, Westley *et al.* (1967) with bacilli, and Peterson and Hsu (1978) with *Aeromonas liquifaciens* and 14 species and serotypes of Enterobacteriaceae.

Usefulness of one specific peptidase activity for classification and identification was described using ala-*p*NA; activity was detected in significant amounts in Gram-negative bacteria but not in Gram-positive species (Teuber and Cerny, 1973; Murgier *et al.*, 1976; Cerny, 1978). This distinction reflects a quantitative rather than a definite qualitative difference, for example activity was detected in 5 min in Gram-negative strains but required 15–30 min with some Gram-positive species (Cerny, 1978).

Lack of activity of intact cells of Gram-positive bacteria can be because their permeability barriers differ from those of Gram-negative cells, or because of lower specific activity of the enzyme. The presence of ala-*p*NA activity in Gram-positive bacteria, particularly streptococci, can be correlated with the presence of L-alanine in position 1 of the interpeptide bridges of their cell-wall peptidoglycans (Cerny, 1978). Activity towards ala-β-NAP was shown in cell extracts of oral viridans streptococci separated by isoelectric focusing in thin-layer polyacrylamide gels (Linder *et al.*, 1981). Hydrolysis of L-ala-β-NAP was useful in differentiating between *Bacteroides* and *Clostridium*, but did not enable the separation of *Bacteroides* from Gram-positive non-sporing bacilli (Baranowski *et al.*, 1984). Kit tests using ala-*p*NA for rapid differentiation between Gram-negative and Gram-positive bacteria are now available commercially as paper strips or as test swabs (Bactident aminopeptidase, Merck; RIM™ Gram Reaction, Austin Biological Laboratories respectively).

Besides presence of ala-specific aminopeptidase, two other tests have been suggested for distinguishing between Gram-negative and Gram-positive bacteria: (i) the ability of a 3% solution of KOH to lyse only cells of Gram-negative bacteria and liberate the cell DNA as indicated by the viscosity of the suspension; the method was originally described by Ryu (1940) and reintroduced by Gregersen (1978); (ii) susceptibility to vancomycin (5 µg disc)—only Gram-positive bacteria are inhibited. Von Graevenitz and Bucher (1983) showed that KOH or vancomycin tests on their own yielded false results, mainly with non-fermenting Gram-negative bacteria. Carlone *et al.* (1982) applied the KOH and ala-*p*NA tests to 129 organisms with a preponderance of non-fermentative Gram-negative bacteria. The pattern of positive results for both KOH and ala-*p*NA tests obtained with Gram-negative bacteria and negative results for both tests with Gram-positive strains was generally held, but all strains of *Campylobacter* showed positive results with the KOH test and negative results with the ala-*p*NA test.

Aminopeptidase patterns were used to differentiate between *Neisseria* species, meningococci showing N-γ-glutamyl-specific aminopeptidase, and gonococci showing L-hydroxyproline-specific activity (D'Amato *et al.*, 1978; Watson and Perrine, 1978; Ison *et al.*, 1982).

Hydrolysis of pyrollydinyl-β-NAP (PYR) was used in combination with serological techniques (detection of Lancfield group D antigen using Phade-bact group D coagglutination test; Pharmacia) for differentiation and rapid identification of enterococci and Group D streptococci. *S. faecalis*, *S. faecium*, *S. avium* and *S. durans* were PYR and Phadebact D positive; *S. bovis* being PYR negative and Phadebact D positive, while *S. equis* and the viridans streptococci were negative in both tests (Bosley *et al.*, 1983).

Protease activities are usually detected by demonstration of single amino acids or oligopeptides released from specific protein molecules. Detection of products can be done by separating the large protein molecules from their smaller breakdown products by acid precipitation (TCA or perchloric acid) and centrifugation, and detection of free amino groups in the supernatant (Chien, 1978). Another approach is by binding dye molecules to the protein and estimating the amount of dye released into the supernatant. Proteolytic activities of bacterial strains have also been demonstrated by growing them on agar media containing different proteins in an emulsified form and observing the cleared zone around the bacterial growth (Anagnostakis and Hankin, 1975). Generally speaking, denatured proteins are better substrates than the natural ones. Different proteases show specificity towards certain natural proteins like albumin, casein, globulin, elastin, insulin etc.

To avoid the tedious procedures of precipitation and centrifugation, methods able to detect free amino acids in the presence of polypeptides have been devised. They include reacting with TNBS or fluorescamine (Chien, 1978). Synthetic derivatives are also used for detection of protease activity.

Such derivatives can be described as having the general formula Z-A-B-X-Y, where Z represents a non-L-amino-acid compound like acyl, succinyl or benzoyl, or a D-amino acid; A, B, and X represent L-amino acids, and Y a chromatic (pNA or β-NAP) or fluorescent (β-NAP or 7-AMC) molecule. In the case of chymotrypsin-like activity, it was shown that at least 3 or 4 peptide bonds are required for enzymatic hydrolysis (Claeson, et al., 1977, 1978).

Different proteases show high specificity towards the amino acid in position X and less to those in positions A and B. Higher activities are shown towards derivatives where Z is a non-amino-acid group. Trypsin is specific for arg in position X, while chymotrypsin is specific towards phe in that position. Bacteria contain a number of enzymes specific to pro in position X, (Berdal et al., 1983).

Many proteolytic enzymes are excreted by the bacterial cell and can be detected in spent culture broth (Muamba, 1982). Legionella pneumophilla was differentiated from other Legionella species by qualitative and quantitative differences in extracellular protease activity towards 4 oligopeptide derivatives of pNA (Berdal et al., 1982). Certain Shigella serotypes were characterized by their activity towards tosyl-gly-pro-lys-pNA (Chromozym PL of Boehringer Mannheim; Giammanco et al., 1982).

H. Phosphatases

Phosphatases are clearly very important enzymes, as they are involved in such processes as the transport of metabolites into the cell (kinases), glycolysis (phosphorylation of glucose or fructose to 1,6-fructose-diphosphate), and energy metabolism (AMP,ADP,ATP), as well as nucleic-acid metabolism. However, most phosphatase studies have utilized the hydrolysis of phosphate esters, rather than their synthesis, for the measurement and characterization of these enzymes. The phosphatases have been divided, according to their pH optimum, into alkaline and acid phosphatases. They are also divided, to some extent, on the basis of their substrate specificities, for example cyclic phosphodiesterase, nucleotidase (Neu and Heppel, 1965).

Alkaline phosphatase activity of Gram-negative bacteria was studied extensively in the sixties and seventies. In E. coli, enzyme synthesis is induced when inorganic phosphate becomes limiting in the medium (Torriani, 1960). The enzyme has been shown to be located in the periplasm, and can be released from the cell by osmotic shock treatment (Neu and Heppel, 1965). They also showed that 50–70% of the total activity could be measured with intact cells. The optimal conditions for its assay were studied by Wilson et al. (1964), who showed that the enzyme can perform hydrolysis of the phosphate ester bond as well as transphosphorylation. The acceptor molecules for the phosphate ion have been characterized as hydroxyl compounds containing a second hydroxyl or amino group at a distance of not more than one or three atoms from the terminal hydroxyl group. Tris, ethanolamine and glycerol were typical acceptors. The presence of acceptors in the reaction mixture results in a significant increase in measured activity. Similar effects of the buffer ion were shown for mammalian alkaline phosphatase where ethylaminoethanol, diethanolamine and 2-amino-2-methyl-1-propanol proved to be the most suitable buffer systems (McComb and Bowers, 1972). With bacterial enzymes the concentration of the Tris buffer affects the magnitude of activity as well as response to pH, a 1 M concentration being optimal for activity.

Many organisms also produce acid phosphatases, again probably located in the periplasm. The enzymes differ in the optimal pH for their activity as well as in substrate specificities. The acid phosphatase (pH optimum 4–5) displays specificities for hexose phosphates while the alkaline enzyme (pH optimum 8.5–9.5) hydrolyses all phosphomonoesters. Synthesis of acid phosphatase is less affected by the concentration of inorganic phosphate in the medium (Torriani, 1960).

Estimation of activity can be performed by measurement of the released phosphate ion or by measurement of the carboxylic moiety of the substrate. The method that relies on measurement of phosphate is universally applicable to all substrates, but is more tedious because it involves centrifugation and addition of a number of reagents. Alternative synthetic substrates, where enzyme activity can be detected in the reaction mixture without centrifugation, have been sought. Synthetic moieties used in phosphatase substrates include phenolphthalein (Bray and King, 1942; Barber and Kuper, 1951; Páčová and Kocur, 1978); phenol (Bürger, 1967b), α-naphthol (Stewart and Stewart, 1971; Saito and Masai, 1980), β-naphthol (API ZYM), p-nitrophenol (pNP) (Torriani, 1960; Bascomb and Spencer, 1980), indoxyl (Eriquez and Hodinka, 1983) and 4-methylumbelliferone (Grange, 1978; Godsey et al., 1981). Heppel (1967) compared the activity of intact cells with that of sonic extracts towards phosphate monoesters, and found that with high substrate concentration (10^{-2} M) intact cells showed 93% and 80% of activity of the sonic extract when tested with p-NP phosphate and α-naphthyl phosphate respectively, while with adenosine-2-phosphate only 19% of sonic extract activity could be detected with whole cells.

Phosphatase activity, as detected in nutrient agar plates containing phenolphthalein phosphate, was used for detection of coagulase positive staphylococci (Barber and Kuper, 1951). Páčová and Kocur (1978) applied a 4 h test at pH 7.4 to 1115 cultures of Gram-positive and Gram-negative bacteria. They found activity in 5 out of 12 species of *Staphylococcus* and in many *Bacillus* species. Among Gram-negative bacteria, all species of facultative non-enterobacteria and anaerobes tested were positive. Amongst the aerobic Gram-negative species, only 4 *Pseudomonas* species were positive. *Proteus* and *Serratia marcescens* were the only positive strains amongst the enterobacteria. Studies using the API ZYM kit showed that most of the anaerobic Gram-negative strains tested by Tharagonnet *et al.* (1977) possessed both acid and alkaline phosphatase activities. Studying α- and non-haemolytic streptococci, both alkaline and acid phosphatase activities were useful for separating closely related species (Waitkins *et al.*, 1980). Different patterns of activity were found for streptococci species studied by Humble *et al.* (1977). *Haemophilus ducreyi* exhibited strong phosphatase activity over a broad pH range (Casin *et al.*, 1982). Acid, but not alkaline phosphatase, was found in species of *Veillonella* (Kelley, 1982). Both acid and alkaline phosphatase activities were found in all strains of *Corynebacterium equi* (Mutimer and Woolcock, 1982) and in *Mycobacterium fortuitum* and *M. chelonei* (Garcia-Rodriguez *et al.*, 1982). Acid, but not alkaline, phosphatase activities were demonstrated with all strains of Actinomycetaceae (Kilian, 1978). Bascomb and Spencer (1980) found acid phosphatase activities in all *Klebsiella* and *Proteus* strains, tested after growth on MacConkey agar, but not in those of *E. coli* or *Pseudomonas*. Acid phosphatase was also used in differentiation of *Neisseria* species (D'Amato *et al.*, 1978; Eriquez and Hodinka, 1983). Grange (1978) found that acid phosphatase activity varied in magnitude and in pH dependence between the different species of mycobacteria. Stewart and Stewart (1971) used gel electrophoresis for detection of acid and alkaline phosphatases of *E. coli* and found great variability in the number of isoenzymes present. The antigenic relationship between alkaline phosphatases of various Gram-negative bacteria was studied by Cocks and Wilson (1972).

Choice of synthetic substrate depends on the desired pH and sensitivity. Thus Eriquez and Hodinka (1983) chose indoxyl phosphate in their system for differentiation of *Neisseria* and *Haemophilus* species because the *p*NP derivative was too sensitive.

III. Enzyme test kits

The API ZYM kits (API Laboratories, and Analytab Products) contain β-NAP peptides of leu, val and cys for detecting arylamidases, benzoyl-arg-β-NAP and *N*-glutaryl-phe-β-NAP for detecting trypsin- and chymotrypsin-like activities respectively; β-NA phosphate ester in alkaline and in acid buffers to detect phosphatases; C_4, C_8 and C_{14} ester derivatives of β-NA for showing esterase, esterase–lipase and lipase activities respectively. The substrates for detection of glycosidase activities contain three β-NA, three

Br-β-NA and one α-NA as synthetic moieties. The kit also contains α-NA AS-BI-phosphodiamide for the detection of phosphoamidase. The activity of all enzymes is detected by incubation with a heavy bacterial suspension. (MacFarland No. 3–6) and by the addition, after 4 h incubation at 37 °C, of 2 reagents. Reagent A contains a 10% solution of lauryl sulphate in Tris HCl buffer, pH 7.6–7.8, to facilitate the dispersion of the micelles formed after addition of the diazonium dye. Reagent B contains a 0.35% solution of Fast Blue BB azo dye in methoxyethanol. Colour reaction is allowed to develop for 10 min and the strip is exposed to the light of a strong lamp (100 W) for 10 s to eliminate the yellow base colour, due to excess Fast Blue BB, thus rendering negative compartments colourless. The kits have been used for the differentiation of Gram-negative anaerobes (Tharagonnet et al., 1977; Hofstad, 1980; Slots, 1981), various bacteria of clinical importance (Humble et al., 1977), Bacteroides (Laughon et al., 1982) and non-haemolytic streptococci (Waitkins et al., 1980), two species of Mycobacterium (Garcia-Rodriguez et al., 1982), Actinomycetaceae (Kilian, 1978), Moraxella (Frank and Gerber, 1981), Alteromonas (Gauthier, 1976), Fusobacterium (Guillermet, 1980), Flavobacterium (Holmes et al., 1981, 1982), Corynebacteria (Mutimer and Woolcock, 1982), species of Veillonella (Kelley, 1982) and of Campylobacter (Ferguson and Lambe, 1983). The kit was used, in combination with other substrates, to study the exoenzymes of Propionibacterium acne (Muamba, 1982) and enzymes of Bacillus (O'Donell et al., 1980), and of Legionella pneumophila (Muller, 1981).

API Systems, France, provide additional kits. Their esterases kit contains 10 organic acid ($C_{4,5,6,8,9,10,12,14,16,18}$) derivatives of β-NA. API ZYM osidases kit contains 17 pNP (p-nitrophenol) derivatives of α, β, D and L monosaccharides, and three pNP derivatives of disaccharides. The aminopeptidase tests are in 6 strips of 10 tests each (AP 1,2,3,4,5,6 respectively). The distribution of chromogenic and metabolic moieties is shown in Table IV. Such kits have been applied to the study of the enzymatic profile of Haemophilus ducreyi (Casin et al., 1982), Flavobacterium (Holmes, 1983), Serratia (Feltham and Stevens, 1983) and Erwinia (Mergaert et al., 1984).

API systems and Analytab Laboratories also produce strips for identification of staphylococci and streptococci, which contain a mixture of enzyme and conventional tests. A combined 5-enzyme medium (API Z; Rapid SST, dms laboratories) for detection of the enteric pathogens Salmonella, Shigella and Yersinia enterocolitica by observation of β-galactosidase, β-xylosidase, phenylalanine deaminase, esterase and cytochrome oxidase activities in 2 h is also available.

A number of kits are available for the identification of Neisseria and related species. The API NeIdent kit (Analytab Products) for identification of Neisseria and Branhamella contains substrates for the following 11 tests:

TABLE IV

Aminopeptidase substrates of API ZYM AP 1–6 (figures refer to the number of substrates in each category)

Number of amino acids	Group at the N-terminal end	Group at the C-terminal end	
		β-NAP[a]	4-methoxy-β-NAP
1	H	21	—
2	H	22	1
3	H	7	—
4	H	1	—
5	H	1	—
1	Benzoyl[b]	1	1
1	Benzyl[c]	1	—
1	cbz[d]	—	1[e]
3	cbz	1[e]	—
2	Acetyl	1	—

[a]β-Naphthylamido: [structure] NH—   [b]Benzoyl: [structure] —CO—

[c]Benzyl: [structure] —CH—   [d]Carbobenzoxy: [structure] —CH₂—O—C—

[e]Compound appears in two different cupules.

β-galactosidase;
phosphatase;
proline aminopeptidase (= iminopeptidase);
hydroxyproline peptidase;
glycyl phenylpeptidase;
glycyl-prolyl peptidase;
γ-glutamyl aminopeptidase;
catalase;
production of acid from fructose;
reduction of resazurin in presence of pyruvate or glucose.

Bohnhoff *et al.* (1983) reported correct identification of nearly 100% for *N. gonorrhoeae*. Using the same kit 90, 71, and 63% agreements with conventional identification of *N. gonorrhoeae*, *N. meningitidis* and *N. lactamica* respectively, were observed; *B. catarrhalis* strains were not identified (Janda *et al.*, 1984).

The development of the RapID/NH System produced by Innovative Diagnostic Systems for identification of *Neisseria* and *Haemophilus* has been described by Eriquez and Hodinka (1983). The dried test substrates are contained in 10 compartments of a disposable plastic panel designed to allow simultaneous inoculation of test cavities, with a suspension of organisms, by a double tilting action. Inoculation suspension is prepared in a special fluid to a MacFarland No. 2 turbidity. After 4 h incubation the changes in colour of each compartment before and after addition of reagents are observed. The following tests are included:

indoxyl phosphatase;
nitrate reductase;
β-galactosidase;
proline iminopeptidase;
γ-glutamyl aminopeptidase;
tryptophanase;
urease;
acid production from glucose;
acid production from sucrose;
ornithine decarboxylase;
reduction of resazurin.

If the results of the tests identify the isolate as *N. gonorrhoeae* or *H. influenza*, a test for β-lactamase is performed additionally by placing a β-lactamase disc in the control compartment.

Robinson and Oberhofer (1983) reported correct identification for *N. gonorrhoeae*, *N. meningitidis* and *N. lactamica* and misidentification of *N. subflava*, using the NH System.

Although these systems provide identifications after 4 h incubation, they require a large inoculum (MacFarland No. 2–3). One way of decreasing the size of the inoculum is by performing more than one test in the same compartment. Chu *et al.* (1984) described the use of a mixed chromogenic substrate combination giving different colour reactions for detection of β-galactosidase, γ-glutamyl aminopeptidase and prolyl aminopeptidase (Gonocheck kit). The nature of the chromogenic moieties was not specified. The colours indicating positive reactions were blue and yellow for β-galactosidase and γ-glutamylaminopeptidase respectively. A diazo reagent is added to detect prolylaminopeptidase, giving a red colour. These colours suggest indoxyl, *p*NA and β-NAP respectively as the chromogenic moieties for the substrates. The authors state that agglutination reactions with antibodies or lectins can also be performed in the same well. Results were available in 30 min, but 10 colonies were still required to perform the test.

The RapID/ANA System (Innovative Diagnostics Inc.) is another example of a combined test system. The panel contains 10 reaction cavities that provide 18 test results; 8 cavities each contain substrates for two tests. The results for esterases and glycosidases are first scored without reagent addition by observing release of nitrophenol, as indicated by development of yellow colour. The results of amino peptidase tests are detected after the addition of

3-phenyl-4-dimethylaminoacrolein for diazotization of the released β-NA. The tests are as follows:

hydrolases—tested with nitrophenol derivatives of
    phosphate,
    β-galactoside,
    α-glucoside,
    β-glucoside,
    α-galactoside,
    α-fucoside,
    N-acetylglucosaminide;
aminopeptidases—tested with β-NAP derivatives of
    leucylglycyl-,
    glycyl-,
    prolyl-,
    phenylalanyl-,
    arginyl-,
    seryl-,
    pyrrolidonyl-;
reduction of triphenyl tetrazolium chloride;
arginine dihydrolase;
acid production from trehalose;
tryptophanase.

Evaluation of the system suggests that agreement with conventional identification varies from 29% for lactobacilli (Ristow et al., 1984) to 90% for Bacteroides (Appelbaum et al., 1984).

RIM Neisseria kit (Austin Biological Laboratories) is based on rapid detection of acid production from glucose, lactose, maltose and sucrose. The media for these tests are provided in dropper-top vials. Tests are performed by placing drops of each substrate in "buffered tubes", inoculation of tubes using a disposable loop for each test, incubation for 30 min and observation of change of the pH indicator in the medium.

IV.   Speed and sensitivity of analyses

Although these kit tests require relatively short periods for completion (30 min–4 h), they all require a "heavy" inoculum of 10 colonies or all the growth from one or two plates (Hofstad, 1980). Such inocula are rarely available from the primary isolation plate and an overnight incubation is necessary to obtain pure cultures. Thus completion times for these so-called "rapid tests" are in practice 23–28 h, almost the same as required for conventional tests. Only tests that can be completed within 3 h, with bacteria from a single colony taken from a primary isolation plate, are truly rapid (see further Bascomb, 1984). This can be achieved if detection of enzyme is not by observation of change of colour in the substrate–bacteria mixture but by measurement of change using sensitive equipment. Bascomb and Spencer (1980) described a continuous-flow method, for identification of urinary pathogens, based on measurement of activity of 8 enzymes. A 100% agreement with conventional identification was obtained with 96 suspensions each of a single colony taken from the primary isolation plates. Godsey et al. (1981) described a fluorocolorimeter (Aminco, American Instrument Co.) method for identification of enterobacteria. Bascomb (1983b, 1984, 1985a) described multiwell plate systems for identification of bacteria of clinical importance including enterobacteria, non-fermenting Gram-negative as well as Gram-positive cocci, based on measurement of absorption (1983b) and fluorescence (1984, 1985a) of bacteria–substrate mixture after addition of colour-developing reagents.

Mattio et al. (1984) described the use of an experimental incubator/ fluorimeter for detection of activities on 4-MU and 7-AMC derivatives in microdilution trays. Fluorescence measurements were taken at 5 min intervals, giving both kinetic and endpoint data.

Enzyme assays can be performed in kinetic or endpoint modes. The first mode requires frequent measurements of reaction in each vessel. Godsey et al. (1981) measured each tube 30 times (5 readings every 5 min over a 30 min assay period). The second mode requires one (continuous-flow methods, Bascomb and Spencer, 1980; semicontinuous-flow methods, Bascomb, 1980b; Multiskan–microtitration plate method, Bascomb, unpublished), or a maximum of 2 readings, one at the beginning and one at the end of the reaction (Kem-O-Mat method, Bascomb, 1980b). The kinetic mode might prove slightly more sensitive, and could be completed in shorter incubation periods than the endpoint mode (30 and 90–120 min respectively). On the other hand, it requires a heavier inoculum and more complicated instrumentation, as the measuring device must provide suitable temperature control during the incubation period as well as fairly sophisticated data-acquisition and processing facilities to cope with the large amount of information generated. These requirements are bound to increase the cost of a tailormade instrument. Moreover, as each organism profile requires a 30 min incubation period, the number of identifications possible on each instrument during a working day is limited to 14–16 strains, and more than one instrument would be needed to cope with the identification load of a medium-sized hospital laboratory.

Furthermore, kinetic-mode methods are only applicable to tests where conditions optimal for enzyme activity are also suitable for measurement of enzyme activity product, accumulation of which can be monitored by repeated measurements. When these sets of conditions differ, enzyme activity is stopped after a definite incubation period by addition of reagents that will reveal the presence of the reaction product. Measurement of activity in such cases is only possible using the endpoint mode.

In the endpoint method described by Bascomb (1984, 1985a), identification of bacterial suspension was completed $2\frac{1}{2}$ h after receipt of primary isolation plate, involving 2 h incubation, 2 min for reading fluorescence, the remaining time being required for inoculation, addition of reagents and computer calculations.

The number of tests required for bacterial identification is related to the number of bacterial taxa considered (Gyllenberg, 1963; Rypka et al., 1967). For clinical isolates the matrix will probably include 50–100 bacterial taxa, requiring perhaps 15–45 enzyme tests. For so many tests to be performed on bacteria from a single colony, very sensitive methods are required. Performance of tests with such small amounts of bacterial protein (< 1 μg test^{-1}) can only be achieved by increasing the ratio of bacterial suspension to total reaction mixture while at the same time decreasing the total reaction volume. In a fully automated continuous-flow mode (Bascomb and Spencer, 1980) it was possible to perform 9 tests on bacteria from a single colony. Any further increase in the number of tests would have decreased the sample throughput to an unacceptable level. In the semiautomated continuous-flow technique bacteria from a single colony sufficed for the performance of 4 tests (Bascomb, 1980b). In the fluorimetric method used by Godsey et al. (1981) a total volume of 2 ml, containing c. 5×10^7 cfu ml^{-1}, was used for each assay. Assuming that the number of cfu in an overnight colony is 2×10^8, then bacteria from a single colony sufficed for performance of only 4 tests; at least 5 colonies would be needed for the 18 tests used in their system.

In the Multiskan tests (Bascomb, 1983b) a total volume of 75 μl containing $c\ 6 \times 10^6$ cfu was used for each assay, and bacteria from a single colony were used to inoculate 30 tests. The activity of some enzymes was very prominent, even with such a small inoculum. Activity of others was rather low and almost within the standard deviation of reagent blank. Measurement of the latter was more reliable if a single colony was used to inoculate 24 instead of 30 tests, or if absorbance was replaced by fluorescence for measurement.

Thus an identification method based on measurement of 24 tests by the Multiskan–microtitration plate method or 31 tests by measurement of fluorescence could be performed on bacteria from a single colony, and would therefore be completed a whole day earlier than with the kinetic mode, using the Aminco Fluorocolorimeter method, which required an overnight incubation to provide sufficient suitable inoculum.

V. Data-handling system

With the large number of individual measurements involved in bacterial identification, automated data-handling techniques are required for performance of 3 tasks:

A. Data acquisition;
B. Data processing;
C. Identification of individual isolates.

A. Data acquisition

Most modern colourimeters or fluorimeters provide an output port which can be connected to a microprocessor for accumulation of data. Data acquisition from continuous measurements (e.g. gel scanner) requires a peak-picking program, while information from a multiwell plate reader is available for each individual compartment immediately. A PDP/11 (Digital Equipment) minicomputer has been used with the Aminco instrument, measuring activity in the kinetic mode (Godsey *et al.*, 1981) and a Commodore PET microcomputer with the multiwell plate reader (Bascomb 1983a, 1984).

B. Data processing

Data transformation is required to convert absorbance or fluorescence data to acceptable units of product concentration and to remove from the data the extraneous variability that is unconnected with the interisolate variability. Bascomb discussed the sources of extraneous variability and methods of diminishing their effect on identification (1983a) and classification (1985b).

C. Identification of individual isolates

Numerical identification systems require a matrix containing the expected results for each taxon in each test, and a suitable mathematical identification model to assign individuals to one of the taxa in the matrix. Formulation of an identification matrix requires prior definition of each taxon, judicious choice of characters, and testing of a sufficient number of individuals in each taxon, so that the matrix data will be statistically significant.

Numerical identification of isolates on the basis of qualitative data, as practised in the various identification kits, has followed the approach of Lapage *et al.* (1970), using percentage of positive results for each taxon in each test in the data matrix, and application of a form of the Bayes probability model to calculate normalized likelihood and assign an unknown individual to a taxon within defined confidence levels. Choice of taxa for inclusion in such a matrix table, and definition of each taxon, were based on numerical taxonomy studies, which included the types of test used in the matrix. Identification of isolates on the basis of quantitative data requires establishment of clusters that will represent the variability of quantitative data. Construction of such clusters is necessary, as the clusters may not coincide with those constructed on the basis of conventional identification tests. As the standard deviation commonly encountered with quantitative data may approach 100% of the mean for each taxon (see e.g. Table 3 of Godsey *et al.* 1981), the intrataxon variability is often very high, and similar in magnitude to the intertaxa variability (see e.g. Table 2 of MacFie *et al.*, 1978). Under such circumstances the choice of type of similarity coefficient used for calculating the taxonomic distances between two individuals is very important. Effect of choice of method of calculation of similarity on classification based on quantitative data only, has been discussed (Bascomb 1985b).

A number of mathematical models are available for identification based on quantitative data. They include the Bayesian classification rule (available in the ARTHUR statistical package, Duewer *et al.*, 1975, 1981; Infometrix) where identification is determined by calculating the probability of an individual belonging to each of the clusters, included in the matrix, on the basis of frequency of occurrence of each test result in each of the clusters. The cluster with the highest probability is chosen.

In both the canonical variate method (available in GENSTAT, Alvey *et al.*, 1977) and discriminant function analysis (available in SPSS, Nie *et al.*, 1975; BMDP, Dixon and Brown, 1979), the position of the unknown organism in a multidimensional space is calculated. In the latter an unknown strain is assigned to the cluster to which centroid the individual is nearest.

In the K-nearest-neighbour method (available in ARTHUR) an unknown is assigned to the cluster to which most of its nearest neighbours belong.

Identification based on linear learning machines (available in ARTHUR) is achieved by assignment of an individual to one of two groups separated from each other by a line, sometimes termed a hyperplane, arrived at by iteration (Nilsson, 1965). As the program separates each taxon in turn from *all* the remaining groups in the whole training set, this procedure is probably too cumbersome for a matrix containing a large number of taxa.

Finally, using the Soft Independent Modelling Cluster Analysis (SIMCA; Wold, 1976) identification model (available in ARTHUR) in which the first principal component and the confidence level for each cluster are determined, an individual is assigned to the cluster to which it is nearest, provided that it is within the confidence limits of the cluster. Facilities exist for indicating if the individual is within the confidence limits of two clusters or if the individual is outside the confidence limits of all clusters included in the analysis. Thus SIMCA is the only technique that does not insist on assignment of an organism to a group regardless of its distance from the "ideal" or "median" organism, and provides categories of individuals that cannot be assigned to any of the clusters unequivocally.

Each of these identification models has merits and drawbacks, and the one most suited to any particular sort of data must be established empirically (Sjöström and Kowalski, 1979; Bascomb, 1983a). In testing the suitability of a mathematical model, it is imperative to use both a training and a test set. The training set, used to form the matrix, should be comprehensive as regards the number of taxa it includes. Also, the number of individuals in each taxon should be sufficiently large so that the standard deviation for each character in each cluster will be statistically meaningful.

In the examples given above, of identification using enzyme assay, a Bayes probability model was used by Godsey et al. (1981), and a discriminant function analysis by Bascomb (1980a, 1983a, b, 1984, 1985a). Identifications by a two-stage quadratic discriminant stepwise discriminant analysis model are used in the Autobac IDX System (General Diagnostics) for identification of Gram-negative bacteria on the basis of measurements of growth in the presence of growth promoters and inhibitors (Sielaff et al., 1982).

Bascomb (1983a, b) described the use of an identification program based on a discriminant analysis model implemented on a Commodore PET microcomputer capable of identification of 63 species, belonging to 24 genera of both Gram-positive and Gram-negative bacteria, without primary categorization tests. In this procedure identification is performed in 2 steps, the unknown is first assigned to one of two groups (basically Gram-positive or Gram-negative) of 11 and 55 species respectively. In the next step the unknown is identified to species level. The reliability of the identification is indicated by 3 parameters: $P(G/X)$, the probability of the group chosen given the results of the unknown strain X; Mahalanobis D^2 distance of the strain X from the centroid of the chosen group; and $P(X/G)$, the probability of the results obtained by strain X given the group chosen. The calculation of the last parameter is very dependent on the number of groups present in the matrix. Thus a smaller D^2 is required to give a high $P(X/G)$ with the Gram-positive group, which contains only 11 taxa. An example of identification obtained using three groups is given in Fig 2.

The agreement between enzyme identification, obtained using the various measuring techniques, and conventional identification varied from 73–99%. It would thus appear that, with the appropriate number of tests and division into groups, identification based on enzyme assay only, as described by Bascomb (1983b, 1985a), would be sufficiently accurate to be used routinely

**IDENTIFICATION OF STRAINS
TESTED ON 2408 623X D1**

GROUP 1

STRAIN NUMBER	FIRST GROUP	D↑2	P (X/G)	P (G/X)	SECOND GROUP	P (X/G)	P (G/X)
010B2227	E. coli I	21.3	.879	.996	Shi. sonnei	.293	.002
023B2234	K. pneumoniae	17.0	.977	.394	K. oxytocum	.965	.255
031B2250	Pro. mirabilis I	16.1	.987	.999	Pro. vulgaris	.171	.000

GROUP 2

STRAIN NUMBER	FIRST GROUP	D↑2	P (X/G)	P (G/X)	SECOND GROUP	P (X/G)	P (G/X)
301B1883	UNIDENTIFIABLE						
041B2288	P. aeruginosa I	34.7	.526	.995	P. stutzeri	.113	.003

GROUP 3

STRAIN NUMBER	FIRST GROUP	D↑2	P (X/G)	P (G/X)	SECOND GROUP	P (X/G)	P (G/X)
066B2187	Strep. group d	13.4	.338	.967	Strep. faecalis	.040	.015
052B2283	Staph. epidermidis	15.1	.235	.991	Staph. saprophyticus	.015	.007

Fig. 2. Example of Commodore PET identification, based on enzyme activity measurements (Bascomb, unpublished).

in the clinical laboratory, thus providing results at least 24 h before those obtained using other methods.

Acknowledgement

I thank Mrs. Anne Chibah for skilful secretarial help.

Appendix: List of suppliers' addresses

1. American Instrument Co., Silver Spring, MD, USA.

2. Analytab Products, Plainview, NY 11803, USA.

3. API System, La Balme-les-grottes, 38390 Montalieu-Vercieu, France.

4. Austin Biological Labs., 6620, Manor Road, Austin, TX 78723, USA

5. BBL (Baltimore Biological Laboratories), P.O. Box 243, Cockeysville, MD 21030, USA.

6. BMDP (Biomedical Computer Programs), Health Sciences Computing Facility, Department of Biomathematics, School of Medicine, University of California, Los Angeles, USA.

7. Boehringer Mannheim, BCL: The Boehringer Corporation (London), Bell Lane, Lewes, East Sussex BN7 1LG, UK.

8. Calibiochem-Behring, 10933 North Torrey Pines Road, La Jolla, CA 92037, USA.

9. Commodore, Commodore Business Machines Inc., 3330 Scott Boulevard, Santa Carla, CA 95051, USA.

10. Coulter Electronics, Luton, Beds. LU3 3RH, UK.

11. Difco Laboratories, P.O. Box 1058A, Detroit, MI 48232, USA.

12. Digital Equipment Corp., Maynard, MA, USA.

13. dms Laboratories, Darts Mill, Flemington, NJ 08822, USA.

14. Dynatech Laboratories, Daux Road, Billinghurst, Sussex, RH14 9SJ, UK.

15. E-Y Laboratories Inc., San Mateo, CA 94401, USA.

16. Flow Laboratories Ltd, Woodcock Hill, Harefield Road, Rickmansworth, Herts, WD3 1PQ, UK.

17. General Diagnostics, Warner-Chilcott, 201 Taber Road, Morris Plains, NJ 07950, USA.

18. Infometrix Inc., P.O. Box 25808, Seattle, WA 98125, USA.

19. Innovative Diagnostic System, 3404 Oakcliff Road, Suite C-1, Atlanta, GA 30340, USA.

20. Koch Light Ltd, 37 Hollands Road, Haverhill, Suffolk CB9 8PU, UK.

21. Marion Scientific, 9233 Ward Parkway, Suite 240, Kansas City, MO 64114, USA.

22. E. Merck, Frankfurter Str. 250, D-6100, Darmstadt 1, FDR.

23. Oxoid, Wade Road, Basingstoke RG24 0PW, Hampshire, UK.

24. Pharmacia Fine Chemicals, Pharmacia House, Midsummer Boulevard, Milton Keynes MK9 3HP, UK.

25. Sigma London Chemical Companies, Fancy Road, Poole, Dorset BH17 7NH, UK.

26. SPSS Inc., Suite 3300, 444 North Michigan Avenue, Chicago, IL 60611, USA.

References

Ackerman, J. I. and Chesbro. W. (1981). *J. Food Safety* **3**, 15–25.

Alvey, N. G., Banfield, D. F., Baxter, R. I., Gower, J. C., Krzanowski, W. J., Lane, P. W., Leech, P. K., Nelder, J. A., Payne, R. W., Phelps, K. M., Rogers, C. E., Ross, G. J. S., Simpson, H. R., Todd, A. D., Wedderburn, R. W. M. and Wilkinson, G. N. (1977). *GENSTAT: A General Statistical Program*. Statistics Department, Rothamsted Experimental Station, Harpenden.

Anagnostakis, S. L. and Hankin, L. (1975). *J. Milk Food Technol.* **38**, 570–572.

Appel, W. (1974). In *Methods of Enzymatic Analysis* 2nd (English) edn, Vol. 2 (H. U. Bergmeyer, ed.), pp. 949–999. Academic Press, New York.

Appelbaum, P. C., Depenbusch, J. W. and Kaufmann, C. S. (1984). In *Abstr. Annu. Meet. Am. Soc. Microbiol.*, C153, p. 262.

Ball, H. J., Neill, S. D. and Reid, L. R. (1982). *J. Clin. Microbiol.* **15**, 28–34.

Baranowski, J., McKinley, G. A., Murray, J. and Pasciuti, M. (1984). In *Abstr. Annu. Meet. Soc. Microbiol.*, C140, p. 260.

Barber, M. and Kuper, S. W. A. (1951). *J. Pathol. Bacteriol.* **63**, 65–68.

Bascomb, S. (1980a) In *Microbiological Classification and Identification* (M. Goodfellow and R. G. Board, eds.), pp. 359–373. Academic Press, New York.

Bascomb, S. (1980b). The Identification of Bacteria. *UK Patent Application* 2 048 302B.

Bascomb, S. (1983a). *INSERM* **114**, 423–430.

Bascomb, S. (1983b). *INSERM* **114**, 471–476.

Bascomb, S. (1984). In *Proc. European Symp. on New Horizons in Microbiology, Rome*, (A. Sanna and G. Morace, eds.), pp. 241–250. Elsevier, Amsterdam.

Bascomb, S. (1985a). In *Proc. 4th Int. Symp. on Rapid Methods and Automation in Microbiology and Immunology, Berlin*. (K.-O. Habermahl, ed.), pp. 367–376. Springer-Verlag, Berlin.

Bascomb, S. (1985b). In *Computer-assisted Bacterial Systematics* (M. Goodfellow, D. Jones and F. G. Priest, eds.), pp. 37–60. Academic Press, London.

Bascomb, S. and Grantham, C. A. (1975). In *Some Methods for Microbiological Assay* (R. G. Board and D. W. Lovelock, eds.), pp. 29–54. Academic Press, New York.

Bascomb, S. and Spencer, R. C. (1980). *J. Clin. Pathol.* **33**, 36–46.

Bascomb, S., Banks, G. T., Skarstedt, M. T., Fleming, A. and Bettelheim, K. A. (1975). *J. Gen. Microbiol.* **91**, 1–16.

Behal, F. J. and Carter, R. T. (1970). *Can. J. Microbiol.* **17**, 39–45.

Behal, F. J. and Cox, S. T. (1968). *J. Bacteriol.* **96**, 1240–1248.

Behal, F. J. and Folds, J. D. (1967). *Biochem. Biophys. Res. Commun.* **27**, 344–349.

Berdal, B. P. and Olsvik, Ø. (1983). *Acta Pathol. Microbiol. Immunol. Scand.* **B91**, 89–91.

Berdal, B. P., Hushovd, O., Olsvik, Ø, Ødegad, O. R. and Bergan, T. (1982). *Acta Pathol. Microbiol. Immunol. Scand.* **B90**, 119–123.

Berdal, B. P., Bøvre, K., Olsvik, Ø. and Omland, T. (1983). *J. Clin. Microbiol.* **17**, 970–974.

Bernheim, F., Bernheim, M. L. C. and Webster, M. D. (1935). *J. Biol. Chem.* **110**, 165–172.

Bilezikian, J. P., Kaempfer, R. O. R. and Magasanik, B. (1967). *J. Mol. Biol.* **27**, 495–506.

Black, W. A., Hodgson, R. and McKechnie, A. (1971). *J. Clin. Pathol.*, **24**, 313–316.

Blackall, P. J. (1982). *Antonie van Leeuwenhoek* **48**, 461–464.

Bohnhoff, M., Janda, W. M., and Morello, J. A. (1983). In *Abst. Annu. Meet. Am. Soc. Microbiol.*, C17, p. 314.

Bosley, G. S., Facklam, R. R. and Grossman, D. (1983). *J. Clin. Microbiol.* **18**, 1275–1277.

Brandenberger, H., Shimizu, M. and Winkler-Keller, H. (1967) *Chimia* **21**, 598.

Bray, J. and King, E. J. (1942). *J. Pathol. Bacteriol.* **54**, 287.

Buissière, J., Fourcard, A. and Colobert, L. (1967). *C. R. Acad. Sci. Paris* **D264**, 415–417.

Bürger, H. (1967a). *Zbl. Bakt. (Naturwiss) I. Abt. Orig.* **202**, 97–109.

Bürger, H. (1967b). *Zbl. Bakt. (Naturwiss) I. Abt. Orig.* **202**, 395–401.

Burns, V. W. (1980). In *Photochemical and Photobiological Reviews*, Vol. 5 (K. C. Smith, ed.), pp. 87–103. Plenum Press, New York.

Campbell, D. M. and Moss, D. W. (1961). *Clin. Chim. Acta* **6**, 307–315.

Carlone, G. M., Valadez, M. J. and Picket, M. J. (1982). *J. Clin. Microbiol.* **16**, 1157–1159.

Carpenter, C. M., Suhrland, L. G. and Morrison, M. (1947), *Science* **105**, 649–650.

Casin, I. M., Sanson-LePors, M. J., Gorce, M. F., Ortenberg, M. and Pérol, Y. (1982). *Ann. Microbiol. (Inst. Pasteur)* **133B**, 379–388.

Cerny, G. (1978). *Eur. J. Appl. Microbiol. Biotechnol.* **5**, 113–122.

Chen, R. F. (1968). *Anal. Lett.* **1**, 423–428.

Chen, K. C. S., Culbertson, N. J., Knapp, J. S., Kenny, G. E. and Holmes, K. K. (1982). *J. Clin. Microbiol.* **16**, 909–919.

Cheng, K. J., Ingram, J. M. and Costerton, J. W. (1971). *J. Bacteriol.* **107**, 325–336.

Chien, P. T. (1978). *Am. Ind. Hyg. Assoc. J.* **39**, 808–816.

Christensen, W. B. (1946). *J. Bacteriol.* **52**, 461–466.

Chu, A. E., Chun, P. K. and Yajko, D. M. (1984). In *Abstr. Annu. Meet. Am. Soc. Microbiol.* C257, p. 279.

Claeson, G., Aurell, L., Karlsson, G. and Friberger, P. (1977). In *New Methods for the Analysis of Coagulation using Chromogenic Substrates* (I. Witt, ed.), pp. 37–54. de Gruyter, Berlin.

Claeson, G., Aurell, L., Friberger, P., Gustavsson, S. and Karlsson, G. (1978). *Haemostasis* **7**, 62–68.

Clemons, K. V. and Gadberry, J. L. (1982). *J. Clin. Microbiol.* **15**, 731–732.

Cocks, G. T. and Wilson, A. C. (1972). *J. Bacteriol.* **110**, 793–802.

Cohn, M. (1957). *Bacteriol. Rev.* **21**, 140–168.

Cowan, S. T. (1974). *Cowan and Steel's Manual for the Identification of Medical Bacteria*, 2nd edn. Cambridge University Press.

Cundell, A. M., Pisani, A. M., and Findl, E. (1979). *Dev. Ind. Microbiol.* **20**, 571–577.

Cunningham, L., Catlin, B. W. and Privat de Garilhe, M. (1956). *J. Am. Chem. Soc.* **78**, 4642–4645.

Dahlén, G. and Linde, A. (1973). *Appl. Microbiol.* **26**, 863–866.

D'Amato, R. F., Eriquez, L. A., Tomfohrde, K. M. and Singerman, E. (1978). *J. Clin. Microbiol.* **7**, 77–81.

Darland, G. (1975). *J. Clin. Microbiol.* **2**, 391–396.

Deibel, R. H. and Evans, J. B. (1960). *J. Bacteriol.* **79**, 356–360.

DeMoss, R. D., and Moser, K. (1969). *J. Bacteriol.* **98**, 167–171.

Dixon, W. J. and Brown, M. B. (eds.) (1979). *BDMP-79, Biomedical Computer Programs P-Series*, 2nd Printing. University of California Press, Berkeley.

Duewer, D. L., Koskinen, J. R. and Kowalski, B. R. (1975). *Documentation for ARTHUR.* Chemometrics Society Report No. 2, Updated (1981) version. Infometrix Inc., Seattle.

Dyer, D. L. (1970). *US Patent* 3 551 295.

Eaves, G. N. and Jefferies, C. D. (1963). *J. Bacteriol.* **85**, 273–278.

Edberg, S. C. and Trepeta, R. W. (1983). *J. Clin. Microbiol.* **18**, 1287–1291.

Edberg, S. C., Pittman, S. and Singer, J. M. (1977). *J. Clin. Microbiol.* **6**, 111–116.

Edberg, S. C., Gam, K., Bottenbley, C. J. and Singer, J. M. (1976). *J. Clin. Microbiol.* **4**, 180–184.

Edberg, S. C., Trepeta, R. W., Kontnick, C. and Torres, A. R. (1984). In *Abstr. Annu. Meet. Am. Soc. Microbiol.* C214, p. 272.

Eddy, B. P. (1961). *J. Appl. Bacteriol.* **24**, 27–41.

Ekladius, L., King, H. K. and Sutton, C. R. (1957). *J. Gen. Microbiol.* **17**, 602–619.

Ellingworth, S., McLeod, J. W. and Gordon, J. (1929). *J. Pathol. Bacteriol.* **32**, 173–183.

Erickson, A. and Deibel, R. H. (1973). *Appl. Microbiol.* **25**, 337–341.

Eriquez, L. A. and Hodinka, N. E. (1983). *J. Clin. Microbial.* **18**, 1032–1039.

Eriquez, L. A. and Knight, G. B. (1980). *J. Clin. Microbial.* **12**, 667–671.

Erlanger, B. F., Kokowsky, N. and Cohen, W. (1961). *Arch. Biochem. Biophys.* **95**, 271–278.

Faller, A. and Schleifer, K. H. (1981). *J. Clin. Microbiol.* **13**, 1031–1035.

Feltham, R. K. A. and Stevens, M. (1983). *INSERM* **114**, 143–155.

Feng, P. C. S. and Hartman, P. A. (1982). *Appl. Environ. Microbiol.* **43**, 1320–1329.

Ferguson, D. A. and Lambe, D. W. (1983). In *Abstr. Annu. Meet. Am. Soc. Microbiol.* C276, p. 357.

Fishman, W. H. and Gosh, N. K. (1967). *Adv. Clin. Chem.* **10**, 255–370.

Frank, S. and Gerber, J. D. (1981). *J. Clin. Microbiol.* **13**, 269–271.

Fugate, K. J., Hanson, L. B. and Evans, J. E. (1977). *Int. J. Syst. Bacteriol.* **27**, 179–184.

Gaby, W. L. and Hadley, C. (1957). *J. Bacteriol.* **74**, 356–358.

Gadberry, J. L., Clemmons, K. V. and Drumm, K. (1980). *J. Clin. Microbiol.* **12**, 220–225.

Garcia-Rodriguez, J. A., Gomez-Garcia, A. C., Iglesias-Garcia J. and Martin-Luengo, F. (1982). *Tubercle* **63**, 209–211.

Gauthier, M. J. (1976). *Int. J. Syst. Bacteriol.* **26**, 459–466.

Genta, V. M. and Bowdre, J. H. (1982). *J. Clin. Microbiol.* **16**, 168–173.
Giammanco, G., Pignato, S., Agodi, A., Toncas, M. and d'Hauteville, H. (1982). *Ann. Microbiol. (Inst. Pasteur)* **133B**, 343–346.
Godsey, J. H., Matteo, M. R., Shen, D., Tolman, G. and Gohlke, J. R. (1981). *J. Clin. Microbiol.* **13**, 483–490.
Gomori, G. (1954). *Proc. Soc. Exp. Biol. Med.* **87**, 559–561.
Gordon, J. and McLeod, J. W. (1928). *J. Pathol. Bacteriol.* **31**, 185–190.
Goullet, Ph. (1973). *J. Gen. Microbiol.* **77**, 27–35.
Goullet, Ph. (1975). *J. Gen. Microbiol.* **87**, 97–106.
Goullet, Ph. (1977). *J. Gen. Microbiol.* **98**, 535–542.
Goullet, Ph. (1978). *J. Gen. Microbiol.* **108**, 275–281.
Goullet, Ph. and Richard, C. (1977). *J. Gen. Microbiol.* **98**, 543–549.
Grange, J. M. (1977). *Tubercle* **58**, 147–150.
Grange, J. M. (1978). *J. Clin. Pathol.* **31**, 378–381.
Grange, J. M. and McIntyre, G. (1979). *J. Appl. Bacteriol.* **47**, 285–288.
Greenberg, L. J. (1962). *Biochem. Biophys. Res. Commun.* **9**, 430–435.
Gregersen, T. (1978). *Eur. J. Appl. Microbiol. Biotechnol.* **5**, 123–127.
Gudding, R. (1983). *J. Clin. Microbiol.* **18**, 1098–1111.
Guilbault, G. G. and Kramer, D. N. (1964). *Anal. Chem.* **36**, 409–412.
Guillermet, F. (1980). *Ann. Microbiol. (Inst. Pasteur)* **131**, 95–96.
Gurr, E. (1971). *Synthetic Dyes in Biology, Medicine and Chemistry*, p. 745. Academic Press, London.
Gyllenberg, H. G. (1963). *Ann. Acad. Sci. Fennicae* A, IV, **69**, 1–23.
Harley-Mason, J. and Archer, A. A. P. G. (1958). *Biochem. J.* **69**, 60P.
Hartley, B. S. (1960). *Ann. Rev. Biochem.* **29**, 45–72.
Hartman, T.and Bast, E.(1969). *Arch. Mikrobiol.* **64**, 239–243.
Heller, K. and Röschenthaler, R. (1978). *Can. J. Microbiol.* **24**, 512–519.
Heppel, L. A. (1967). *Science* **156**, 1451–1455.
Hillmann, G. (1971). *Z. Klin. Chem. Klin. Biochem.* **9**, 273–274.
Hofstad, T. (1980). *Med. Microbiol. Immunol.* **168**, 173–177.
Höhn-Bentz, H. and Radler, F. (1978). *Arch. Microbiol.* **116**, 197–203.
Holding, A. J. and Collee, J. G. (1971). In *Methods in Microbiology*, Vol. 6A (J. R. Norris and D. W. Ribbons, eds.), pp. 1–32. Academic Press, London.
Holländer, R., Böhmann, J. and Grewing, B. (1982). *Zbl. Bakt. Hyg. I. Abt. Orig.* **A.252**, 316–323.
Holmes, B. (1983). *INSERM* **114**, 273–294.
Holmes, B., Owen, R. J. and Weaver, R. E. (1981). *Int. J. Syst. Bacteriol.* **31**, 21–34.
Holmes, B., Owen, R. J. and Hollis, D. G. (1982). *Inst. J. Syst. Bacteriol.* **32**, 157–165.
Humble, M. W., King, A. and Phillips, I. (1977). *J. Clin. Pathol.* **30**, 275–277.
Hunt, L. K., Overman, T. L. and Otero, R. B. (1981). *J. Clin. Microbiol.* **13**, 1054–1059.
Ibrahim, G. F. (1981). *J. Appl. Bacteriol.* **51**, 307–312.
Ison, C., Glynn, A. A. and Bascomb, S. (1982). *J. Clin. Pathol.* **35**, 1153–1157.
James, A. L. and Yeoman, P. (1984). In *Abstr. 4th Int. Symp. on Rapid Methods and Automation in Microbiology and Immunology, Berlin*, Abstr. No. P98.
Janda, W. M., Morello, J. A. and Bohnhoff, M. (1984). *J. Clin. Microbiol.* **19**, 338–341.
Jeffries, C. D., Holtman, D. F. and Guse, D. G. (1957). *J. Bacteriol.* **73**, 590–591.
Jones, C. W. (1977). In *Microbiol Energetics, SGM Symp.* No. 27 (B. A. Haddock and W. A. Hamilton, eds.), pp. 23–59. Cambridge University Press.

Jones, C. W. (1980). In *Microbiological Classification and Identification, Soc. Appl. Bacteriol. Symp.* No. 8 (M. Goodfellow and R. G. Board, eds.), pp. 127–138. Academic Press, London.

Jurtshuk, P. and McQuitty, D. N. (1976). *J. Syst. Bacteriol.* **26**, 127–135.

Jurtshuk, P., Mueller, T. J. and Accord, W. C. (1975). *CRC Crit. Rev. Microbiol.* **3**, 399–468.

Kaltwasser, H., Krämer, J. and Conger, W. R. (1972). *Arch. Mikrobiol.* **81**, 178 196.

Kamen, M. D. (1983). *Fed. Proc.* **42**, 2815–2824.

Kapuściński, J. and Skoczylas, B. (1977). *Anal. Biochem.* **83**, 252–257.

Kelley, R. W. (1982). *Can. J. Microbiol.* **28**, 703–705.

Kersters, K. and De Ley, J. (1971). In *Methods in Microbiology*, Vol 6A (J. R. Norris and D. W. Ribbons, eds.), Academic Press, London.

Kilian, M. (1978). *J. Clin. Microbiol.* **8**, 127–133.

Kilian, M. and Bülow, P. (1976). *Acta. Pathol. Microbiol. Scand.* **B84**, 245–251.

Kovács, N. (1956). *Nature (London)* **178**, 703.

Krasuski, A. (1981a). In *Staphylococci and Staphylococcal Infections* (J. Jeljaszewicz, ed.). *Zbl. Bakt. Suppl.* **10**, 413–416. Gustav Fischer, Stuttgart and New York.

Krasuski, A. (1981b). In *Staphylococci and Staphylococcal Infections* (J. Jeljaszewicz, ed.). *Zbl. Bakt. Suppl.* **10**, 417–423. Gustav Fischer, Stuttgart and New York.

Kurnick, N. B. (1950). *Arch. Biochem.* **29**, 41–53.

Labrousse, H., Guesdon, J.-L., Raginbeau, J. and Avrameas, S. (1982). *J. Immunol. Meth.* **48**, 133–147.

Lachica, R. V. F. and Deibel, R. H. (1969). *Appl. Microbiol.* **18**, 174–176.

Lapage, S. P., Bascomb, S., Willcox, W. R. and Curtis, M. A. (1970). In *Automation, Mechanization and Data Handling in Microbiology* (A. Baillie and R. J. Gilbert, eds.) pp. 1–22. Academic Press, London.

Laskowski, M. (1955). In *Methods in Enzymology*, Vol. 2 (S. P. Colowick and N. O. Keplan, eds.), p. 36. Academic Press, New York.

Laughon, B. E., Syed, S. A. and Loesche, W. J. (1982). *J. Clin. Microbiol.* **15**, 97–102.

Lazdunski, C., Busuttil, J. and Lazdunski, A. (1975a). *Eur. J. Biochem.* **60**, 363–369.

Lazdunski, A., Murgier, M. and Lazdunski, C. (1975b). *Eur. J. Biochem.* **60**, 349–355.

Leclerc, H. (1967). *Ann. Inst. Pasteur Lille* **112**, 713–731.

Lederberg, J. (1950). *J. Bact.* **60**, 381–392.

Lee, W. H., McClain, D., Szymanski, C., Moran, A. and Johnston, R. W. (1983). In *Abstr. Annu. Meet. Am. Soc. Microbiol.* P31, p. 259.

Le Minor, L. and Ben Hamida, F. (1962). *Ann. Inst. Pasteur* **102**, 267–277.

Le Minor, L., Buissière J., Novel, G. and Novel, M. (1978). *Ann. Microbiol. (Inst. Pasteur)* **129B**, 155–165.

Le Minor, L., Veron, M. and Popoff, M. (1982). *Ann. Microbiol. (Inst. Pasteur)* **133B**, 223–243 and 245–254.

Le Minor, L., Veron, M. and Popoff, M. (1983). *INSERM* **114**, 111–118.

Lillie, R. D. (1977). *H. J. Conn's Biological Stains*, 9th edn Williams and Wilkins, Baltimore.

Linder, E. A., Anderson, C. and Sund, M. L. (1981). In *Abstr. Annu. Meet. Am. Soc. Microbiol.*, K23, p. 141.

Linder, L., Lindquist, L., Soder, P.-O. and Holmes, T. (1974). *Acta Pathol. Microbiol. Scand.* **B82**, 602–607.

Lyerly, D. M. and Kreger, A. S. (1983). *Infec. Immun.* **40**, 113–119.

MacAlister, T. J., Costerton, J. W., Thompson, L., Thompson, J. and Ingram, J. M. (1972). *J. Bacteriol.* **111**, 827–832.

McCabe, M. and Chayen, J. (1965). *J. R. Microscop. Soc.* **84**, 361–371.
McComb, R. B. and Bowers, G. N. (1972). *Clin. Chem.* **18**, 97–104.
MacConkey, A. T. (1908). *J. Hyg. Camb.* **8**, 322–341.
McCoy, E. E., Park, J. and England, J. (1965). *Clin. Chim. Acta* **12**, 453–461.
MacFaddin, J. F. (1980). *Biochemical Tests for Indentification of Medical Bacteria*, 2nd edn. Williams and Wilkins, Baltimore and London.
MacFie, H. J. H., Gutteridge, C. S. and Norris, J. R. (1978). *J. Gen. Microbiol.* **104**, 67–74.
Machuga, E. J. (1982). *J. Bacteriol.* **150**, 747–754.
Maddocks, J. L. and Greenan, M. J. (1975). *J. Clin. Pathol.* **28**, 686–687.
Malmy, M. H. and Horecker, B. L. (1964). *Biochemistry* **3**, 1889–1893.
Marin, A. and Marshall, R. T. (1983a). *J. Food Sci.* **48**, 570–573.
Marin, A. and Marshall, R. T. (1983b). *J. Food Protection* **46**, 676–680.
Mashburn, L. T. and Wriston, J. C. (1964). *Arch. Biochem. Biophys.* **105**, 450–452.
Massenti, M. F., Scarlata, G. and Nastasi, A. (1981). *Boll. Ist. Sieroter. Milan* **60**, 1.
Mattio, N. M. Shinn, S. and Goldstein, J. (1984). In *Abstr. 4th Int. Symp. on Rapid Methods and Automation in Microbiology and Immunology, Berlin*, p. 73.
Mergaert, J., Verdonck, L., Kersters, K., Swings, J., Boeufgras, J.-M. and De Ley, J. (1984). *J. Gen. Microbiol.* **130**, 1893–1910.
Messinova, O. V., Yusupova, D. V. and Shamutdimov, N. S. (1963). *Fed. Proc.* **22**, T1033–T1035.
Miller, C. G. and Mackinnon, K. (1974). *J. Bacteriol.* **120**, 355–363.
Miller, J. M. and Wright, J. W. (1982). *J. Clin. Microbiol.* **15**, 589–592.
Møller, V. (1955). *Acta Pathol. Microbiol. Scand.* **36**, 158–172.
Moran, J. W. and Witter, L. D. (1976). *J. Food Sci.* **41**, 165–167.
Morgan, A. R., Evans, D. H., Lee, J. S. and Pulleyblank, D. E. (1979). *Nucleic Acids Res.* **7**, 571–594.
Moss, D. W. (1960). *Clin. Chim. Acta* **5**, 283–288.
Moss, D. W. (1966). *Enzymologia* **31**, 191–202.
Moss, D. W., Campbell, D. M., Anagnostou-Kakaras, E. and King, E. J. (1961). *Biochem. J.* **81**, 441–447.
Muamba, M. L. K. (1982). *Can. J. Microbiol.* **28**, 758–761.
Muftić, M. (1967). *Folia Microbiol. (Praha)* **12**, 500–507.
Mulczyk, M. and Szewczuk, A. (1970). *J. Gen. Microbiol.* **61**, 9–13.
Muller, H. E. (1981). *J. Clin. Microbiol.* **13**, 423–426.
Murgier, M., Pelissier, C., Lazdunski, A. and Lazdunski, C. (1976). *Eur. J. Biochem.* **65**, 517–520.
Mutimer, M. D. and Woolcock, J. B. (1982). *Zbl. Bakt. Hyg. I. Abt. Orig.* **C3**, 410–415.
Nachlas, M. M., Goldstein, T. P. and Seligman, A. M. (1962). *Arch. Biochem. Biophys.* **97**, 223–231.
Narayan, K. G., Guinée, P. A. M. and Mossel, D. A. A. (1967). *Antonie van Leeuwenhoek* **33**, 184–188.
Nastasi, A., Massenti, M. F. and Scarlata, G. (1982). *Boll. Ist. Sieroter. Milan* **61**, 441.
Neu, H. C. and Heppel, L. A. (1965). *J. Biol. Chem.* **240**, 3685–3692.
Nie, N. H., Hull, C. H., Jenkins, J. G., Stenbrenner, K. and Brent, D. H. (1975). *SPSS: Statistical Package for Social Sciences*. McGraw-Hill, New York.
Nilsson, N. B. (1965). *Learning Machines*. McGraw-Hill, New York.
Norris, J. R. and Burges, H. D. (1963). *J. Insect. Pathol.* **5**, 460–472.

O'Donnell, A. G., Norris, J. R., Berkely, R. C. W., Claus, D., Kaneko, T., Logan, N. A. and Nazaki, R. (1980). *Int. J. Syst. Bacteriol.* **30**, 448–459.

Onishi, H., Mori, T., Takeuchi, S., Tani, K., Kobayashi, T. and Kamekura, M. (1983). *Appl. Environ. Microbiol.* **45**, 24–30.

Páčová, Z. and Kocur, M. (1978). *Zbl. Bakt. Hyg. I. Abt. Orig.* **A241**, 481–487.

Paul, J. H. and Myers, B. (1982). *Appl. Environ. Microbiol.* **43**, 1393–1399.

Pelmont, J., Arlaud, G. and Rossat, A. (1972). *Biochimie* **54**, 1359–1374.

Peterson, E. H. and Hsu, E. J. (1978). *J. Food Sci.* **43**, 1853–1856.

Poole, R. K. (1983). *Biochim. Biophys. Acta* **726**, 205–243.

Porter, K. G. and Feig, Y. S. (1980). *Limnol. Oceanogr.* **25**, 943–948.

Prabhakaran, K., Harris, E. B. and Kirchheimer, W. F. (1983). In *Abstr. Annu. Meet. Am. Soc. Microbiol.* D29, p. 63.

Qadri, S. M. H. and Smith, J. C. (1982). *Public Health Lab.* **40**, 27–33.

Qadri, S. M. H., Nichols, C. W., Qadri, S. G. M. and Villarreal, A. (1978). *J. Clin. Microbiol.* **8**, 463–464.

Qadri, S. M. H., DeSilva, M. I. and Zubairi, S. (1980). *J. Clin. Microbiol.* **12**, 472–474.

Qadri, S. M. H., Johnson, S., Smith, J. C., Zubairi, S. and Gillum, R. L. (1981). *J. Clin. Microbiol.* **13**, 459–462.

Rechnitz, G. A., Kobos, R. K., Riechel, S. J. and Gebauer, C. R. (1977). *Anal. Chim. Acta* **94**, 357–365.

Richard, C. (1978). *Ann. Biol. Clin.* **36**, 407–424.

Riley, P. S. and Behal, F. J. (1971). *J. Bacteriol.* **108**, 809–816.

Rissler, J. F. (1983). *Appl. Environ. Microbiol.* **45**, 315–316.

Ristow, K. L., Schreckenberger, P. C., Celig, D. M., Ulanday, M. A. and Lebeau, L. J. (1984). In *Abstr. Annu. Meet. Am. Soc. Microbiol.* C151, p. 261.

Robinson, M. J. and Oberhofer, T. R. (1983). *J. Clin. Microbiol.* **17**, 400–404.

Rochaix, A. (1924). *C. R. Soc. Biol.* **90**, 771–772.

Röd, T. O., Haug, R. H. and Midtvedt, T. (1974). *Acta. Pathol. Microbiol. Scand.* **B82**, 533–536.

Roodyn, D. B. and Maroudas, N. G. (1968). *Anal. Biochem.* **24**, 496–505.

Rothberg, N. W. and Schwartz, M. N. (1965). *J. Bacteriol.* **90**, 294–295.

Rotman, B. (1961). *Proc. Natl. Acad. Sci. USA* **47**, 1981–1991.

Rustigian, R. and Stuart, C. A. (1941). *Proc. Soc. Exp. Biol. Med.* **47**, 108–112.

Rypka, E. W., Clapper, W. E., Bowen, I. G. and Babb, R. (1967). *J. Gen. Microbiol.* **46**, 407–424.

Ryu, E. (1940). *Kitasato Arch. Exp. Med.* **17**, 58–63.

Saito, H. and Masai, H. (1980). *J. Clin. Microbiol.* **11**, 97–98. ·

Sakai, T., Yu, T., Tabe, H. and Omata, S. (1975). *Agr. Biol. Chem.* **39**, 1623–1629.

Schnürer, J. and Rosswall, T. (1982). *Appl. Environ. Microbiol.* **43**, 1256–1261.

Schofield, G. M. and Schaal, K. P. (1980). *Zbl. Bakt. Hyg. I. Abt. Orig.* **A247**, 383–391.

Schrier, J. B. (1969). *Am. J. Clin. Pathol.* **51**, 711–716.

Schultze, W. H. (1910). *Central. f. Bakt. Abt. I. Orig.* **56**, 544–551.

Sereny, B. (1963/1964). *Acta Microbiol. Acad. Sci. Hung.* **10**, 403–407.

Sereny, B. (1964). *Acta Microbiol. Acad. Sci. Hung.* **11**, 131–137.

Sereny, B. (1966). *Acta Microbiol. Acad. Sci. Hung.* **13**, 25–28.

Sereny, B. (1966). *Acta Microbiol. Acad. Sci. Hung.* **13**, 167–170.

Shah, M. S., Siddique, I. H. and Dalvi, R. R. (1981). *Can. J. Comp. Med.* **45**, 196–198.

Shukuya, R. and Schwert, G. W. (1960). *J. Biol. Chem.* **235**, 1649–1652.

Sielaff, B. H., Matsen, J. M. and McKie, J. E. (1982). *J. Clin. Microbiol.* **15**, 1103–1110.

Singer, J. and Volcani, B. E. (1955). *J. Bacteriol.* **69**, 303–306.
Sjöström, M. and Kowalski, B. R. (1979). *Anal. Chim. Acta* **112**, 11–30.
Slots, J. (1981). *J. Clin. Microbiol.* **14**, 288–294.
Smith, P. B., Hancock, G. A. and Rhoden, D. L. (1969). *Appl. Microbiol.* **18**, 991–993.
Sokatch, J. R. (1969). *Bacterial Physiology and Metabolism*, pp. 169–170. Academic Press, London and New York.
Stead, D. (1983). *J. Dairy Res.* **50**, 491–502.
Steel, K. J. (1961). *J. Gen. Microbiol.* **25**, 297–306.
Steel, K. J. (1962). *J. Appl. Bacteriol.* **25**, 445–447.
Stewart, D. B. and Stewart, D. J. (1971). *J. Gen. Microbiol.* **65**, 175–184.
Stuart, C. A., Stratum, E. V. and Rustigian, R. (1945). *J. Bacteriol.* **49**, 437.
Tarrand, J. J. and Gröschal,D. H. M. (1982). *J. Clin. Microbiol.* **16**, 772–774.
Taylor, J. and Bettelheim, K. A. (1966). *J. Gen. Microbiol.* **42**, 309–313.
Teuber, M. and Cerny, G. (1973). *Arch. Mikrobiol.* **91**, 235–240.
Tharagonnet, D., Sisson, P. R., Roxby, C. M., Ingham, H. R. and Selkon, J. B. (1977). *J. Clin. Pathol.* **30**, 505–509.
Thornley, M. J. (1960). *J. Appl. Bacteriol.* **23**, 37–52.
Tierno, P. M. and Milstoc, M. (1981). *J. Clin. Microbiol.* **13**, 998–999.
Torriani, A. (1960). *Biochim. Biophys. Acta* **38**, 460–479.
Trepeta, R. W. and Edberg, S. C. (1984a). *J. Clin. Microbiol.* **19**, 60–62.
Trepeta, R. W. and Edberg, S. C. (1984b). *J. Clin. Microbiol.* **19**,172–174.
Trinel, P. A. and Leclerc, H. (1977). *Ann. Microbiol. (Inst. Pasteur)* **128A**, 419–432.
Trinel, P. A., Hanoune, N. and Leclerc, H. (1980). *Appl. Environ. Microbiol.* **39**, 976–982.
Turner, J. M. (1961). *Biochem. J.* **78**, 790–792.
Uete, T., Motokura, H., Kitano, Y., Fukutani, C., Uenishi, N. and Ando, N. (1981). *J. Clin. Chem. Clin. Biochem.* **19**, 145–154.
Uglem, G. L. and Beck, S. M. (1972). *J. Parasitol.* **58**, 911–920.
von Graevenitz, A. and Bucher, C. (1983). *J. Clin. Microbiol.* **18**, 983–985.
Voges, O, and Proskauer, B. (1898). *Z. Hyg. Infekt. Kr.* **28**, 20–32.
von Tigerstrom, R. G. (1981). *Can. J. Microbiol.* **27**, 1080–1086.
Vracko, R. and Sherris, J. C. (1963). *Am. J. Clin. Pathol.* **39**, 429–432.
Wade, H. E., Robinson, H. K. and Phillips, B. W. (1971). *J. Gen. Microbiol.* **69**, 299–312.
Waitkins, S. A., Ball, L. C. and Fraser, C. A. M. (1980). *J. Clin. Pathol.* **33**, 53–57.
Wallenfels, K. and Malhotra, O. P. (1961). *Adv. Carbohyd. Chem.* **16**, 239–298.
Watson, R. R. (1976). In *Methods in Microbiology*, Vol. 9 (J. R. Norris and D. W. Ribbons, eds.), pp. 1–14. Academic Press, London.
Watson, R. R. and Perrine, S. (1978). In *Immunobiology of* Neisseria gonnorrhoeae (G. F. Brooks, E. C. Gotschild, K. K. Holmes, W. D. Sawyer and F. E. Young, eds.), pp. 35–37. American Society of Microbiology, Washington, D.C.
Weckman, B. G. and Catlin, B. W. (1957). *J. Bacteriol.* **73**, 747–753.
Westley, J. W., Anderson, J., Close, V. A., Halpern, B. and Lederberg, E. M. (1967). *Appl. Microbiol.* **15**, 822–825.
White, M. L. and Pickett, M. J. (1953). *J. Clin. Pathol.* **23**, 1181–1183.
Whitt, D. D., Klug, M. J. and De Moss, R. D. (1979). *Arch. Microbiol.* **122**, 169–175.
Williams, R. A. D. and Shah, H. N. (1980). In *Microbiological Classification and Identification* (M. Goodfellow and R. G. Board, eds.), pp. 299–318. Academic Press, London.
Williams, R. E. O. (1954). *J. Gen. Microbiol.* **10**, 337–341.

Wilson, I. B., Dayan, J. and Cyr, K. (1964). *J. Biol. Chem.* **239,** 4182–4185.

Wold, S. (1976). *Pattern Recogn.* **8,** 127–139.

Wolf, P. L., Horintz, J., Manderville, R., Vaquez, J. and von der Muehll, E. (1969). *Technol. Bull. Reg. Med. Techn.* **39,** 83–86.

Zierdt, C. H. and Golde, D. W. (1970). *Appl. Microbiol.* **20,** 54–57.

Zimmerman, M., Yurewicz, E. and Patel, G. (1976). *Anal. Biochem.* **70,** 258–262.

Zimmerman, M., Quigley, J. P., Ashe, B., Dorn, C., Goldfarb, R. and Troll, W. (1978). *Proc. Natl. Acad. Sci. USA* **75,** 750–753.

4
Lipid and Cell-Wall Analysis in Bacterial Systematics

KAZUO KOMAGATA

Institute of Applied Microbiology, The University of Tokyo, Tokyo 113, Japan

KEN-ICHIRO SUZUKI

Japan Collection of Microorganisms, RIKEN, Wako-shi, Saitama 351-01, Japan

I. Introduction

Recent advances in the biochemistry of microorganisms have revealed that cell-component analysis can be effectively applied to bacterial systematics, providing the basis of chemotaxonomy. Morphology of bacteria does not provide quantitative information at the same level as chemotaxonomy. In addition molecular-genetic data make it clear that morphological resemblance does not always imply phylogenetic relationship. Analyses of cell components are coming to be essential tools not only for bacterial classification but also for identification.

Chemical components that satisfy the following conditions have signifi-

METHODS IN MICROBIOLOGY
VOLUME 19 ISBN 0–12–521519–3

cant meaning in bacterial systematics: (i) they should be distributed universally among the microorganisms to be studied; (ii) the data are homologous among the strains within a taxon, while significant differences exist between the taxa to be differentiated; (iii) analysis is easily carried out for a large number of samples.

One of the reasons for the usefulness of chemotaxonomy is the progress in the development of analytical instruments that enable accurate and reproducible data to be rapidly obtained. They minimize the error or differences between individual research workers or between laboratories. It is important for microbial systematists to remove subjective judgements from data.

Another characteristic of chemotaxonomy is the fact that the microbial cell is considered as a collection of chemical substances. The classical (orthodox) biochemical and physiological tests (e.g. the catalase test and the acid production pattern from various carbohydrates) can be considerably affected by the growth conditions of microorganisms. Therefore, physiological tests often give variable or unstable data. A negative reaction does not always mean the absence of the activity. Sometimes it is the result of weak growth of a microorganism.

A significant merit of chemotaxonomy is the fact that chemical analysis makes it possible to compare microorganisms grown under quite different conditions. For example, cellular fatty-acid composition data can be employed for the comparison of obligate methylotrophs with some heterotrophic bacteria, while sugar-assimilation patterns cannot be employed for an examination of the relationship of the two groups of bacteria. Various kinds of cellular components are common to many bacteria.

The sequence of chromosomal DNA holds the essential genetic information for an organism. Phylogenetic relationships are often examined using data on nucleotide sequences of ribosomal RNA. However, it is still impossible to determine the sequences of large polynucleotides for the number of organisms sufficient for taxonomic purposes. DNA (RNA) homologies, which have been applied to various kinds of bacteria, present useful information on bacterial systematics. Homology indices are the relative values used in comparing microorganisms. DNA homology data contribute to the clarification, not only of the relatedness of two organisms, but also of the evaluation of phenotypic characteristics.

The taxonomic concept of a taxon should be based on absolute data, not on relative data. Therefore, in addition to the usual phenotypic characteristics such as morphological and physiological features, chemical data, including the base composition of DNA, can be applied to the "description". However, the data on DNA (RNA) homologies are not appropriate for the "description", because they show only relative values among the bacteria used in the study. Nucleotide sequences will satisfy the condition of "description" items, because they have absolute meaning. Such data will be widely used in the near future, but it is impossible at present to add the sequence data to the "descriptions".

Lipid and cell-wall components are important components of cells for systematic purposes. In addition to the fact that they are suitable materials for instrumental analysis, they are synthesized by highly regulated enzyme systems and are stable enough to use as taxonomic criteria. The chemical composition sometimes changes in response to culture conditions and culture period. Such changes should be taken into account when employing chemical data for bacterial systematics.

II. Lipid analysis for bacterial systematics

Lipids are structural units with strong hydrophobic components and play various important roles in cells. Various kinds of lipids have been studied by biochemists and physiologists. Results of studies employing lipid analysis provide strong support for taxonomy. Fatty acids, mycolic acids, polar lipids, and isoprenoid quinones are lipids that have been widely studied and proved useful for bacterial systematics. Several reviews on lipids from the viewpoint of bacterial systematics have been published (e.g. Kates, 1964; Shaw, 1974). However, in recent years technical improvements in analytical instrumentation and progress in bacterial systematics have brought changes that must be incorporated into taxonomic evaluation, especially the application of lipid analysis to systematics.

A.   Cellular fatty acids

Fatty acids comprise one of the most essential components of cellular lipids. Some methanogenic bacteria and halophilic bacteria, i.e. the recently named archaebacteria, contain isoprenyl glyceroether taking the place of glycero-esters of fatty acids found in most bacteria (Langworthy, 1982; Langworthy *et al.*, 1982). The major proportion of the fatty acids are located in the cell membrane as components of polar lipids and glycolipids. Gram-negative bacteria generally contain fatty acids as constituents of lipopolysaccharides. Although bacteria have various kinds of fatty acids in their cells, these are produced through highly regulated synthetic pathways (Lennarz, 1966). Further, taxonomic usefulness of the fatty acids has been shown for various kinds of bacteria.

1. Cultivation of bacteria

Cellular fatty-acid components of a bacterium essentially are not changed by cultural conditions, but the composition of cellular fatty acids is affected by culture conditions, cultivation period, temperature, media, etc. To compare the fatty acid composition within a group of bacteria, culture conditions must be standardized for all strains to be analysed. Data on the changing pattern of the composition of some representative strains are helpful in discussions related to taxonomic analysis. Changing patterns of the cellular fatty-acid composition have been studied for some methanol-utilizing bacteria (Urakami and Komagata, 1979) and coryneform bacteria (Suzuki and Komagata, 1983).

2. Preparation of fatty-acid methyl esters (FAMEs)

Several methods can be used for preparations of methyl esters of cellular fatty acids. The following is a simple method found to be suitable for bacterial systematics. It should be noted that this method partly decomposes cyclopropane acids. Alkaline hydrolysis and methylation by diazomethane are required for complete recovery of cyclopropane acids (Katayama-Fujimura et al., 1982). But, considering the time involved in carrying out the method and the danger associated with the use of diazomethane, alkaline hydrolysis followed by diazomethane is usually not necessary for taxonomic purposes. Approximately 20 mg of freeze-dried cells are placed in a Teflon-lined, screw-capped tube with 2 ml of anhydrous methanolic HCl at 100 °C for 3 h. After cooling, 1 ml of water is added, and fatty-acid methyl esters are extracted three times with 3 ml of n-hexane. The n-hexane fraction is washed with an equal volume of water, transferred to a dry test tube and dehydrated with anhydrous Na_2SO_4. Fatty-acid methyl esters are concentrated and stored in a glass microtube for subsequent analysis. The sample can be injected into a gas–liquid chromatograph directly. However, if necessary, the sample is developed on a thin-layer chromatograph for fractionation and purification.

3. Thin-layer chromatography (TLC)

Polar and non-polar fatty-acid methyl esters are separated and determined by TLC. Samples are applied to a silica-gel plate (Kieselgel 60, Merck, Darmstadt, FRG) and developed by n-hexane-diethyl ether (4:1, v/v). Spots are visualized by spraying with 0.02% Rhodamine 6G ethanol solution. The R_f values of non-polar, 2-OH and 3-OH fatty acids are 0.48, 0.10 and 0.06 respectively. For good separation between 2- and 3-hydroxy fatty acids, the solvent system of n-hexane-diethyl ether (1:1, v/v) is employed ($R_f = 0.95$, 0.71 and 0.60 respectively). Iodine also can be used to visualize the spots. Corresponding spots are scraped off and extracted by diethyl ether.

Fractionation, according to polarity, helps separation and identification by gas–liquid chromatography.

4. Gas–liquid chromatography (GLC)

GLC is an essential tool for analysis of FAMEs. Carrier gas and detector are N_2 and the flame ionization detector (FID) respectively. The cellular fatty acid profiles of bacteria are, in general, not too complicated for separation of peaks. However, in some cases, peaks overlap, when viewed on a chart recorder. Therefore, it is recommended that two or more kinds of columns be used for analysis of polar and non-polar fatty acids. The present authors employ three columns, 5% OV-1 (2 m) and 10% DEGS (diethyleneglycol succinate) (2 m and 5 m) at 180 °C for standard analysis, with a temperature of injection set at 220 °C. Examples of chromatograms are shown in Figs. 1 and 2. A capillary column provides high resolution.

Non-polar packing material (e.g. OV-1) yields low recovery and tailing of the hydroxy-fatty-acid peaks. However, trimethylsilylation of hydroxy fatty acids solves the problem. Preparation of Trimethylsilyl (TMS) derivatives is described in Section II.B.2 below.

5. Identification of fatty acids

In GLC analysis, identification of peaks refers to comparison of retention times with those of standard, i.e. reference, materials. Typical fatty acids found in bacterial cells are shown in Table I. Most authentic standards can be obtained from Applied Sciences Laboratories (State College, PA., USA). Fatty acids extracted from bacterial cells are also useful as references. Bacterial fatty acids are synthesized by the cell with biochemical regulation and never contain a large amount of exceptional compounds. Among the fatty-acid homologues, logarithmic values of retention times are linear functions of the carbon number, as shown in Fig. 3. It is recommended that peak identification be confirmed by GLC-mass spectrometry.

6. Application to bacterial systematics

Bacteria can be divided into two large groups, based on cellular fatty-acid composition. One group contains iso- and/or anteiso-branched fatty acids as the major component. The fatty acids of the other group are mainly composed of straight-chain acids, including mono-unsaturated acids.

Many of the aerobic, Gram-positive bacteria—for example *Bacillus* (Kaneda, 1977), *Micrococcus* (Ishizuka *et al.*, 1966; Girard, 1971), *Staphylococcus* (Durham and Kloos, 1978) and *Arthrobacter* (Bowie *et al.*, 1972;

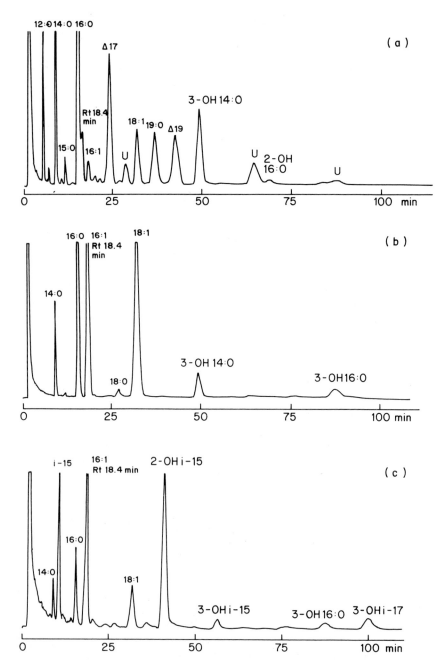

Fig. 1. Gas chromatograms of cellular fatty acids of some Gram-negative bacteria: (a) *Escherichia coli* IAM 1268; (b) *Pseudomonas cepacia* KS 0233; (c) *Cytophaga heparina* KS 0418 (10% DEGS, 5 m) (Oyaizu *et al.*, 1982).

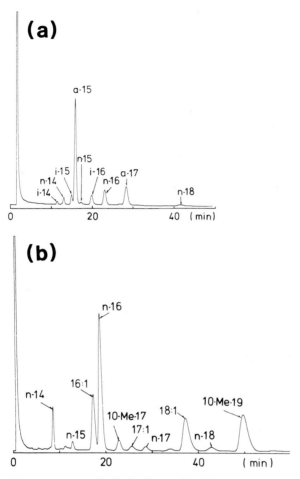

Fig. 2. Gas chromatograms of cellular fatty acids of some Gram-positive bacteria: (a) *Arthrobacter grobiformis* CNF 022 (10% DEGS, 5m); (b) *Rhodococcus equi* CNF 002 (5% OV-1, 2 m) (Suzuki and Komagata, 1983).

Suzuki and Komagata, 1983)—contain branched acids (Fig. 2a), especially anteiso-acids of $C_{15:0}$ and $C_{17:0}$, as major components. This pattern of composition is not found among the Gram-negative bacteria. Therefore results of fatty-acid analysis support the identification of Gram-positive bacteria; for example *Arthrobacter*, which can lose Gram-positivity, i.e., is Gram-variable. On the other hand, the Gram-negative bacteria, which contain branched fatty acids as major components, include *Xanthomonas maltophilia* and other *Xanthomonas* strains (Moss *et al.*, 1973; Ikemoto *et al.*,

TABLE I
Examples of fatty acids found in bacterial cells

n: Straight-chain acid

$$CH_3-(CH_2)_{14}-COOH$$

n-hexadecanoic acid ($C_{16:0}$)
(Palmitic acid)

i: Iso-branched acid

$$CH_3-CH-(CH_2)_{12}-COOH$$
$$|$$
$$CH_3$$

14-methyl pentadecanoic acid
($i-C_{16:0}$)

a: Anteiso-branched acid

$$CH_3-CH_2-CH-(CH_2)_{12}-COOH$$
$$|$$
$$CH_3$$

12-Methyl tetradecanoic acid
($a-C_{15:0}$)

n:1: Monounsaturated acid

$$CH_3-(CH_2)_5-CH=CH-(CH_2)_9-COOH$$

11-Octadecenoic acid ($\Delta^{11}-C_{18:1}$)
(cis-Vaccenic acid)

Δ: Cyclopropane acid

$$\overset{CH_2}{\overset{\diagup\diagdown}{CH_3-(CH_2)_5-CH-CH-(CH_2)_9-COOH}}$$

11, 12-Methyleneoctadecanoic acid
($\Delta C_{19:0}$)
Lactobacillic acid

10-Methyl branched acid

$$\overset{\textstyle CH_3}{\underset{\textstyle |}{CH_3-(CH_2)_7-CH-CH_2-(CH_2)_7-COOH}}$$

10-Methyloctadecanoic acid
(10-Me $C_{19:0}$)
(Tuberculostearic acid)

ω-Cyclohexyl acid

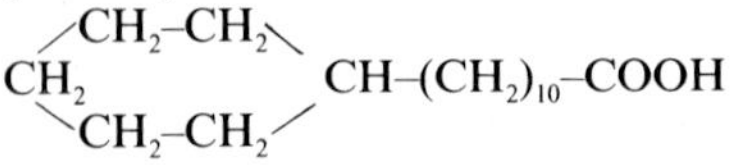

$$\overset{CH_2-CH_2}{\underset{CH_2-CH_2}{CH_2\diagdown\diagup}}CH-(CH_2)_{10}-COOH$$

ω-Cyclohexylundecanoic acid

3-Hydroxy acid

$$CH_3-(CH_2)_{10}-CH(OH)-CH_2-COOH$$

3-Hydroxytetradecanoic acid
(3-OH $C_{14:0}$)

2-Hydroxy acid

$$CH_3-(CH_2)_9-CH(OH)-COOH$$

2-Hydroxydodecanoic acid
(2-OH $C_{12:0}$)

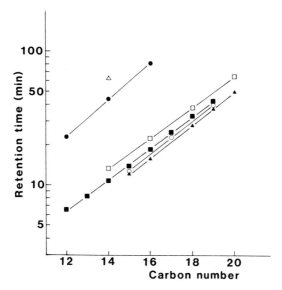

Fig. 3 Relationships between the retention time and the total carbon number of fatty acids: ■, saturated straight-chain acid; □, mono-unsaturated straight-chain acid; ▲, saturated iso-branched acid; ○, saturated anteiso-branched acid; ●, 2-hydroxy-straight-chain acid; △, 3-hydroxy-straight-chain acid (Column: 10% DEGS, 5 m).

1980), strains of the *Cytophaga–Flavobacterium* complex with a low $G + C$ content in their DNA (Oyaizu and Komagata, 1981), *Legionella* (Moss *et al.*, 1977), and *Thermus* (Oshima and Miyagawa, 1974). The fatty acids of these bacteria are predominantly composed of the iso-acids of $C_{15:0}$, with smaller amounts of anteiso-acids.

The pattern of straight-chain saturated and mono-unsaturated fatty acids is found in both Gram-positive and negative bacteria. Gram-positive bacteria of this composition are the lactic acid bacteria (Veerkamp, 1971; Uchida and Mogi, 1972), *Clostridium* (Johnson and Goldfine, 1983), and *Corynebacterium* (Collins *et al.*, 1982a; Suzuki and Komagata, 1983). Most of the Gram-negative bacteria, including Enterobacteriaceae (Kates, 1964; Bergan *et al.*, 1983), *Campylobacter* (Leaper and Owen, 1981), *Pseudomonas* (Moss *et al.*, 1972; Ikemoto *et al.*, 1978) and *Thiobacillus* (Katayama-Fujimura *et al.*, 1982), demonstrate this pattern of composition. Principal components are generally n-$C_{16:0}$, n-$C_{18:1}$, n-$C_{16:1}$ and n-$C_{18:0}$.

The double-bond position of unsaturated acids is characteristic of bacterial taxa (Scheuerbrandt and Bloch, 1962). The $C_{18:1}$ of lactic acid bacteria, *Clostridium*, and Enterobacteriaceae is *cis*-vaccenic acid (Δ^{11}). On the other hand, $C_{18:1}$ of *Corynebacterium* and *Myobacterium* are both oleic acid (Δ^9).

This difference is based on the biosynthetic pathway and is concluded to be biologically significant. Suzuki *et al.* (1982) and Suzuki and Komagata (1983) found a correspondence in groupings based on cellular fatty-acid composition and the double-bond position of unsaturated fatty acids for the genus *Corynebacterium*. The suggested biosynthesis systems based on the double-bond position are confirmed, from the standpoint of the fatty-acid synthase profile (Ariga *et al.*, 1984). A Gram-negative bacterium, *Cytophaga arvensicola*, contains $C_{16:1}$ with a double bond at Δ^{11}, whereas Δ^9 is usually a component of $C_{16:1}$ (Oyaizu *et al.*, 1982).

The position of a double bond affects the secondary products of unsaturated fatty acids, i.e. cyclopropane acids and 10-methyl branched fatty acids derived from the corresponding unsaturated fatty acids. The content of these fatty acids increases in proportion to the cultivation period, i.e. length of incubation time, although the total amount of the derived acids and corresponding unsaturated acids is constant through growth of the culture (Suzuki and Komagata, 1983).

Among the Gram-negative bacteria, the composition of hydroxy fatty acids are useful in classification. Hydroxy fatty acids, usually 3-hydroxy fatty acids, are a component of lipopolysaccharides, which are the distinctive components of cell membranes of Gram-negative bacteria. The hydroxy-fatty-acid profile is useful in the characterization of a *Pseudomonas* and related bacteria (Oyaizu and Komagata, 1983). *Pseudomonas paucimobilis* contains 2-hydroxy fatty acids, taking the place of 3-hydroxy fatty acids (Kawahara *et al.*, 1982).

ω-Cyclohexyl fatty acids are unusual acids found in acidophilic–thermophilic bacilli (De Rosa *et al.*, 1971; Oshima and Ariga, 1975) and *Curtobacterium pusillum* (Suzuki *et al.*, 1981).

Gas–liquid chromatography (GLC) is sensitive enough for analysis of the cellular fatty-acid composition of material extracted from a few milligrams of dried cells. It is not necessary to separate and to determine all the peaks for identification of bacteria. Gas chromatograms can be compared as patterns by a computer (Tanaka *et al.*, 1977). Therefore, this technique will continue to be valuable and widely applied in rapid identification and classification of bacteria.

B. Mycolic acids

Mycolic acids are 2-alkyl-3-hydroxy fatty acids with long alkyl chains, as shown in Fig. 4. The total carbon numbers of mycolic acids range from 24 to 90. Mycolic acids are characteristic lipid components of strains belonging to the genera *Mycobacterium*, *Nocardia*, *Rhodococcus*, and *Corynebacterium*. Bacteria that contain mycolic acids are restricted to those with cell-wall type

$$R-CH-CH-COOH$$
$$\;\;\;\;\;\;\;|\;\;\;\;|$$
$$\;\;\;\;\;\;\;OH\;\;R'$$

Fig. 4.   Structure of mycolic acid.

IV (*meso*-diaminopimelic acid and arabinose and galactose) (Lechevalier and Lechevalier, 1970). The presence of mycolic acids is concluded to be related to acid-fastness. *Gordona* and *Bacterionema* also possess mycolic acids (Alshamaony *et al.*, 1977; Wada *et al.*, 1981). However, the two genera were reclassified among the genera mentioned above (Tsukamura, 1974; Collins, 1982a) and mycolic-acid analysis has proved to be a useful tool for classification of the above taxa at the genus level.

Mycolic acids are located in cell walls of bacteria as free acids, glycolipids and complexes with polysaccharides. Trehalose-6,6'-dimycolate is called a "cord factor" and is used as a marker for mycobacteria. Both extensive and intensive work has been done on the molecular structure, mechanism of biosynthesis, and physiological function of mycolic acids. Provided here is a basic method for mycolic-acid analysis, as an aid in bacterial systematics.

1. Preparation of cellular mycolic-acid methyl esters (MAMEs)

The method is based on that of Tomiyasu and Yano (1984). Approximately 0.5 g of harvested cells are hydrolysed, using 10 ml of 10% KOH–methanol in a tube with a Teflon-lined screw cap for 2 h at 100 °C. The hydrolysate is acidified with 6 N HCl (pH below 2.0). Free fatty acids and mycolic acids are extracted with 10 ml of n-hexane and concentrated to dryness. These acids are methylated with 3 ml of benzene–methanol–H_2SO_4 (10:20:1, v/v) at 100 °C for 3 h in a screw-capped tube. 100 mg of freeze-dried cells can be used for direct transmethylation (Minnikin *et al.*, 1975). However, recovery of mycolic acids is lower than that achieved for the method cited above. Alkaline methanolysis is also recommended (Minnikin *et al.*, 1984a), especially to avoid decomposition of the cyclopropane ring in mycolic acid. However, complete recovery of the cyclopropane ring is not always required for purposes of bacterial systematics.

After 1 ml of water is added, fatty-acid methyl esters (FAMEs) and mycolic-acid methyl esters (MAMEs) are extracted with 4 ml of n-hexane. The mixture of methyl esters is developed with n-hexane–diethyl ether (4:1, v/v) on a silica-gel plate (Merck Kieselgel 60, etc.). Spots are visualized by spraying with 50% H_2SO_4 and charring at 150 °C for 5 min (Fig. 5). MAMEs will appear as spots, with R_f from 0.4 to 0.6, in contrast with non-polar FAMEs (R_f 0.8 or more) and hydroxy FAMEs (R_f 0.3 or less). To fractionate

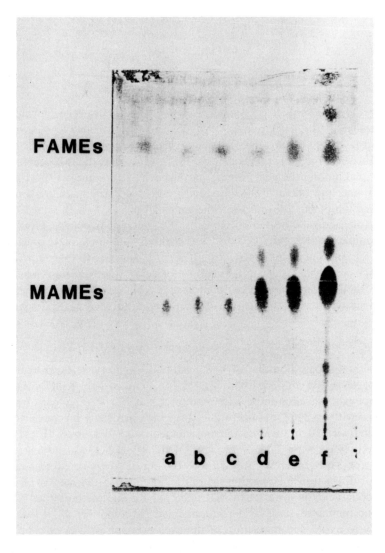

Fig. 5. Thin-layer chromatogram of some mycolic-acid methyl esters. FAME, fatty-acid methyl esters; MAME, mycolic-acid methyl esters. (a) *Rhodococcus equi* CNF 002; (b) *Rhodococcus fascians* CNF 006; (c) *Corynebacterium xerosis* CNF 010; (d) *Rhodococcus erythropolis* CNF 234; (e) *R. erythropolis* JCM 3201; (f) *Rhodococcus rhodochrous* JCM 3202.

mycolic acids, spots of the TLC are visualized by iodine vapour. After the spots disappear, marked areas corresponding to MAMEs are scraped off and the MAMEs eluted with n-hexane.

2. Trimethylsilyl derivatives of mycolic-acid methyl esters

MAMEs are dried and 100 μl BSTFA (N,O-bis(trimethylsilyl)trifluoroacetamide) and 50 μl pyridine added. The mixture is held at 70 °C for 20 min. After the solvent is evaporated, 2 ml of benzene is added and again dried. Samples are dissolved in 100 μl n-hexane and injected into the gas chromatograph.

3. Gas–liquid chromatography (GLC)

There are two methods for analysis of MAMEs by GLC, one of which is pyrolysis–GLC. In this type of analysis, MAMEs are used as the sample for injection. MAMEs will easily decompose at the injection port (which is at temperatures of 300 °C or more) to corresponding FAMEs and meroaldehyde, as shown in Fig. 6 (Etémadi, 1967). However, usually only the FAMEs are analysed and compared, with respect to chain length. The analytical conditions are the same as those for cellular fatty acid, except for the temperature of the injection port.

$$R–CH–CH–COOH_3 \ ----------\ R–CHO \quad + \quad R'–CH_2–COOCH_3$$
$$\underset{OH}{|} \ \underset{R'}{|} \qquad\qquad \text{Pyrolysis}$$

| Mycolic-acid methyl ester | Meroaldehyde | Fatty-acid methyl ester |

Fig. 6. Pyrolysis of mycolic acid.

The other method is the analysis of TMS derivatives of MAMEs. For this analysis, TMS-MAMEs are separated by GLC, according to the total carbon number, as shown in Fig. 7. Short glass columns (approximately 50 cm) packed with OV-101 are employed. The temperatures of the injection port and the detector are set at 350 °C. The column temperature is raised from 180 °C by 2 or 3 °C min.[-1] There is no authentic standard material for the mycolic acids for identification purposes. Therefore, well-known strains should be prepared for reference and compared with results for these strains

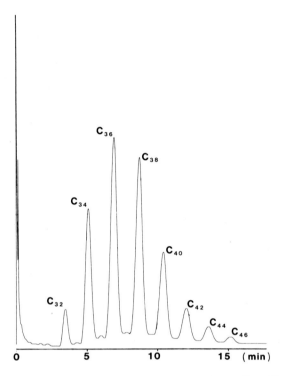

Fig. 7.   Gas–liquid chromatogram of TMS derivatives of mycolic-acid methyl esters from *R. erythropolis* CNF 234. The analytical conditions are as described in the text.

in the literature or mass-spectrometry should be employed. The composition of mycolic acids is determined by GLC of TMS-MAMEs on the basis of the total carbon number.

4. Mass spectrometry

Although each peak corresponds to a mycolic acid with a certain number of total carbons, it will contain several isomers, differing in the combination of two alkyl chains. Determination of the composition of the isomers with the same carbon number requires GLC-MS (Yano and Saito, 1972; Yano *et al.*, 1972). The mass spectra shown in Fig. 8 indicate that the peaks are composed of isomers. TMS-MAMEs are divided into two fragments, as shown in Fig. 8. The two fragments indicate the combinations of two alkyl chains, as shown in Table II. Furthermore, the mass spectra of TMS-MAMEs provide information on the functional bases and number of double bonds of the mycolic acids.

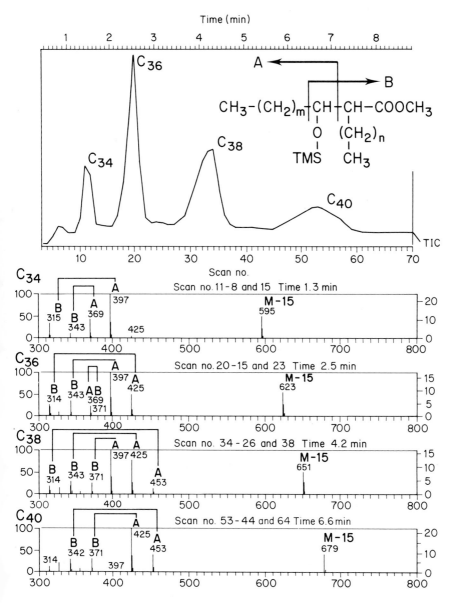

Fig. 8. Fragmentation patterns and mass spectra of trimethylsilyl derivatives of mycolic-acid methyl esters from *R. erythropolis* CNF 234. (See also Table II.)

TABLE II
Combinations of A fragment and B fragment

	Combination of fragments		Branched-chain structure	
	A	B	m	n
$C_{34:0}$	369	343	18	11
	397	315	20	9
$C_{36:0}$	369	371	18	13
	397	343	20	11
	425	315	22	9
$C_{38:0}$	397	371	20	13
	425	343	22	11
	453	315	24	9
$C_{40:0}$	425	371	22	13
	453	343	24	11

5. Application to bacterial systematics

The essential information on mycolic acids for bacterial systematics is the distribution of the total carbon number of mycolic acids of the microorganisms. The total carbon number of mycolic acids decreases as follows: *Mycobacterium* (C_{60-90}), *Norcardia* (C_{46-58}), *Rhodococcus* (C_{38-48}) and *Corynebacterium* (C_{24-36}). In addition, mycobacterial mycolic acids are characterized by a wide distribution in carbon number and possession of various functional bases, for example cyclopropane, dicarboxy and methoxy. Interestingly, a group of strains within the genus *Nocardia* do not contain mycolic acids (Goodfellow and Minnikin, 1981).

Characterization of mycolic acids based on total carbon number can be determined by either TLC, GLC, or GC–MS. Lechevalier *et al.* (1971) used pyrolysis–GLC to distinguish *Mycobacterium* and *Nocardia*, based on the carbon number of fatty acids derived from 2-branch, which were C_{22-26} and C_{14-18} respectively. No difference in the carbon number of 2–branch of mycolic acids was observed between *Nocardia* and *Corynebacterium*. However, the carbon number of the meroaldehyde of *Nocardia* (C_{32-38}) was found to be larger than that of *Corynebacterium* (C_{16-18}) (Lechevalier *et al.*, 1973).

TLC of MAMEs is generally used for classification of the above genera (Minnikin *et al.*, 1975; Goodfellow *et al.*, 1976). The R_f values increase in proportion to the total carbon number of the mycolic acids because of polarity, as shown in Fig. 5. MAMEs of corynebacteria demonstrate the lowest R_f value of the MAMEs. MAMEs of mycobacteria present multispots on TLC plates. The multispots of mycolic acids depend on functional bases and carbon number. Minnikin *et al.* (1984a) reported effective separation of mycobacterial MAMEs by two-dimensional TLC. The pattern of two-dimensional TLC can be used to distinguish species of *Mycobacterium* from other mycobacteria (Minnikin *et al.*, 1982). One or two double bonds are found in mycolic acids from other than *Mycobacterium* (Yano *et al.*, 1972).

Strains of the genus *Bacterionema* also contain mycolic acids. However, the mycolic-acid profile of *Bacterionema* is similar to that of *Corynebacterium* (Alshamaony *et al.*, 1977). In addition, the cell-wall composition and cellular fatty-acid profile support transfer of *Bacterionema matruchotii* (the type species of the genus) to the genus *Corynebacterium* (Collins, 1982a).

The composition of mycolic acids changes in response to growth temperature (Toriyama *et al.*, 1980). It is recommended that culture conditions be standardized through a series of experiments for valid comparison of the species to be identified.

C. Polar lipids

Phospholipids form an essential component of the cell membrane and are related to permeability of the membrane and regulation at the membrane. Phospholipids show a distinctive amphipathic characteristic because they possess not only a hydrophobic region but also a hydrophilic region in the molecule.

The basic structure of representative phospholipids and their abbreviations used below are shown in Table III. PE, PI, PG and DPG are widely distributed, and their presence is useful in bacterial systematics. 3-Phosphatidyl-1'-(3'-*O*-lysyl)glycerol was found in the cells of *Clostridium perfringens* (MacFarlane, 1962). 3-*sn*-Phosphatidyl-1'-(2'-D-glucosaminyl)-*sn*-glycerol is a glycophospholipid found in *Bacillus megaterium* (Op den Kamp *et al.*, 1969). Furthermore, various glycolipids (Shaw, 1970), lipoamino acids (Tahara *et al.*, 1976a, b), and sphingolipids (Miyagawa *et al.*, 1978, 1979; Yamamoto *et al.*, 1978; Yano *et al.*, 1982) have been found in bacterial cells.

TLC is an essential tool for analysis of polar lipids. Radioautography employing ^{32}P was used to detect phospholipids by Shibuya and Maruo (1966) and Komura *et al.* (1975a, b). However, the method has restrictions in handling and specific staining. Here we introduce the method of two-dimensional TLC analysis of the bacterial polar lipid fraction, followed by visualization of spots with various specific reagents for comparison of "fingerprints".

TABLE III
Phospholipids found in bacterial cells

$$H_2COCO-R$$
$$|$$
$$R'-COOCH$$
$$|$$
$$H_2CO-X$$

Compounds	Abbreviation[a]	X
Phosphatidic acid	PA	$-PO_3H_2$
Phosphatidylcholine	PC	
Phosphatidylethanolamine	PE	
Phosphatidylserine	PS	
Phosphatidylinositol	PI	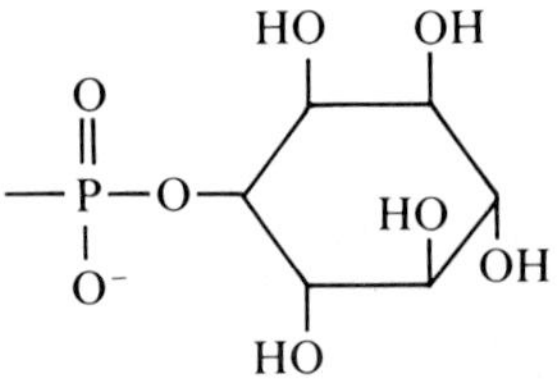
Phosphatidylinositolmannosides	PIMs	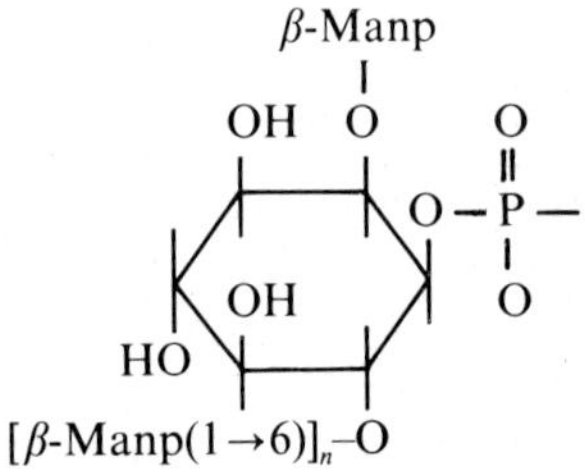
Phosphatidylglycerol	PG	

Diphosphatidylglycerol   DPG

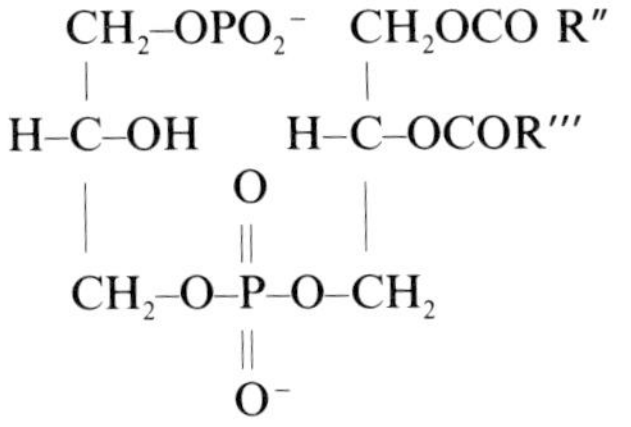

$$\begin{array}{cc} CH_2\text{--}OPO_2^- & CH_2OCO\ R'' \\ | & | \\ H\text{--}C\text{--}OH & H\text{--}C\text{--}OCOR''' \\ | & O \\ & \| \\ CH_2\text{--}O\text{--}P\text{--}O\text{--}CH_2 \\ \| \\ O^- \end{array}$$

Lysylphosphatidylglycerol

$$\begin{array}{c} CH_2\text{--}OPO_2^- \\ | \\ H\text{--}C\text{--}OH \\ | \\ CH_2OCOCH(CH_2)_4NH_2 \\ | \\ NH_2 \end{array}$$

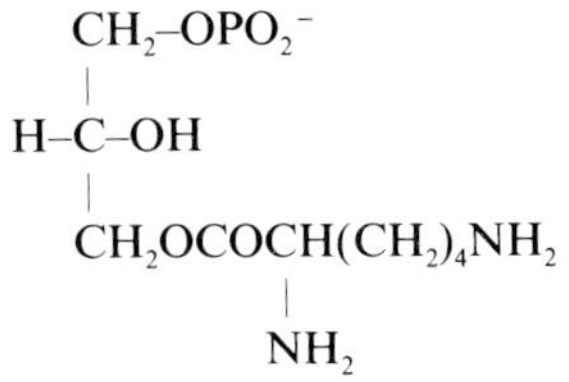

3-sn-Phosphatidyl-1'-
(2'-D-glucosaminyl)-
sn-glycerol

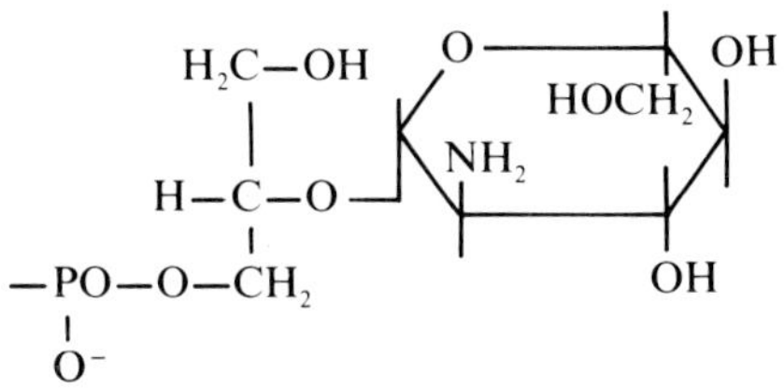

---

^aAbbreviations used throughout this chapter:
R, alkyl; Manp, mannopyranoside.

1. Extraction of polar lipids

The simplest method is to extract polar lipids with chloroform–methanol (2:1, v/v) from dried cells. However, the extract often contains non-lipid materials, which disturb the appearance of the chromatogram of polar lipids (Minnikin *et al.*, 1977b, 1984b). The method of Bligh and Dyer (1959) is generally employed. The following procedure is based on the method of Bligh and Dyer, with the modification of Card (1973).

100 mg of dried cells, or 0.5 g of harvested and washed cells, are suspended in 2 ml of 0.3% saline. 20 ml of methanol are added and the mixture is held at 100 °C for 5 min in a screw-capped tube. After cooling, 10 ml chloroform and 6 ml of the saline are added to the tube. The mixture is shaken for two to three hours and the debris removed by filtration. 10 ml each of chloroform and saline are added to the mixture to partition the two layers. The chloroform layer is collected, concentrated to dryness, and re-dissolved in 100 μl of chloroform–methanol (2:1, v/v).

2. TLC development

10 μl of the samples are applied to a corner of the silica-gel TLC. Minnikin *et al.* (1977a) employed Merck silica gel H TLC (20 cm × 20 cm, 0.5 mm

thickness) impregnated with sodium acetate. Collins and Jones (1980) used HPTLC (Merck Kieselgel 60 F_{254}, 10 cm × 10 cm). HPTLC enables one to develop the plate within a short time (about 15 min), while it takes about an hour to develop the usual TLC plate.

Solvent for the first development should be of low polarity, and the solvent for the second development of rather high polarity. Solvent systems employed for developing are chloroform–methanol–water (65:25:4, v/v) for the first, and chloroform–acetic acid–methanol–water (80:18:12:5, v/v) for the second (Shaw, 1974). Goodfellow et al. (1980) and Collins and Jones (1980) changed the ratio of the second solvent to 80:15:12:4. Yano et al. (1982) employed chloroform–methanol–acetone–acetic acid (90:10:6:1, v/v) and chloroform–methanol–acetic acid–water (100:20:12:5, v/v).

3. Visualization of chromatograms

For comparison of fingerprint patterns of two-dimensional chromatograms, all the lipids are visualized by spraying with 50% H_2SO_4 and charring at 150 °C for 5 min. The spots appear, as shown in Fig. 9. Characteristics of corresponding spots are examined by spraying with the following specific reagents.

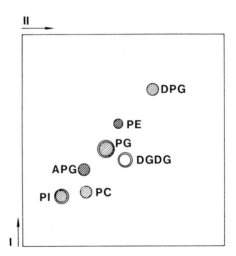

Fig. 9. Polar lipids appearing on a two-dimensional thin-layer chromatogram. See Table III for abbreviations. ◍, phospholipid; ○, phospholipid containing amino group; ◯, periodate–Schiff-reaction-positive lipid. Ascending solvent system: (I) chloroform–methanol–water (65:25:4, v/v); (II) chloroform–acetic acid–methanol–water (80:18:12:5, v/v). (Shaw, 1974.)

(i) *Periodate Schiff reagent* (Shaw, 1968). This is a sensitive reagent for detecting carbohydrates. The plate is first sprayed with 1% solution of sodium periodate for saturation of silicic acid. After 5 or 10 min, the plate is exposed in SO_2 gas to reduce excess periodate to iodine. After the iodine disappears, Schiff reagent (1% pararosaniline–HCl solution decolourized with SO_2 just before use) is sprayed onto the plate.

Glycolipids, including PIMs, present a slowly developing blue colour, while PI presents a yellow colour. Appearance of the yellow colour of the PI takes about 40 min or more. PG shows up as a rapidly developing purple colour. However, 1-substituted monoglyceride also presents the same colour as the non-substituted PG, whereas 2-substituted monoglyceride shows no reaction.

(ii) *Molybdenum blue reagent* (Dittmer and Lester, 1964). A spray of molybdenum blue reagent is used to detect lipids containing phosphate esters. PA, CL, SM, PE, PS, etc. present a rapid appearance as blue spots. Preparation of the reagent is as follows.

Solution I. MoO_3 (40.11 g) is dissolved in 1 litre of 25 N H_2SO_4 (two volumes of concentrated H_2SO_4 is added to one volume of water) with gentle boiling.

Solution II. Molybdenum powder (1.78 g) is added to 500 ml of solution I and boiled gently for 15 min. The residue is removed before use.

Spray reagent. Equal volumes of solutions I and II are mixed, and two volumes of water are added to the mixture. The solution, greenish-yellow in colour, can be stored for several months.

(iii) *α-Naphthol* (Jacin and Mishkin, 1965). α-Naphthol spray is used to visualize the glycolipids, including PIMs. The spraying reagent is a mixture of 10.5 ml of 15% (w/v) α-naphthol ethanol solution, 6.5 ml of conc. H_2SO_4, 40.5 ml ethanol, and 4.0 ml of water. After spraying, the dried plate is held at 100 °C for 5 min or more. Lipids containing carbohydrates appear as blue spots.

(iv) *Ninhydrin.* Polar lipids that contain free amino groups, for example PE and PS, give a positive reaction to ninhydrin spraying. The spray reagent is a 0.1% solution of ninhydrin in water-saturated n-butanol. Spots are visualized by heating the plate at 120 °C for 10 min.

4. Application to bacterial systematics

Fingerprint comparisons of two-dimensional thin-layer chromatograms are more practical for bacterial classification, than identification of each spot, which is difficult to achieve. The fingerprints show good correspondence with other chemotaxonomic criteria (Lechevalier *et al.*, 1977; Minnikin *et al.*, 1977a, b, 1979; Goodfellow *et al.*, 1980; Collins *et al.*, 1980). Gram-negative bacteria do not demonstrate a wide variety of polar-lipid patterns, and contain, in general, PE, PG and DPG. PE is found in strains of *Bacillus*, *Rhodococcus*, *Nocardia* and *Mycobacterium*. PE is not found in *Corynebacterium* (Komura *et al.*, 1975b). The presence of PE is a useful marker for differentiation of the genus *Corynebacterium* from other mycolic-acid-containing taxa. PE is also present in strains of *Planococcus* and *Sporosarcina*, while strains of *Micrococcus* and *Staphylococcus* lack PE (Komura *et al.*, 1975a).

Lechevalier *et al.* (1977) examined the phospholipids of actinomycetes, and were able to identify five groups, based on the pattern shown in Table IV; most of the strains examined contained DPG, PI and PIMs. Although it is difficult to obtain a precise description of the composition of polar lipids, the patterns obtained by polar-lipid analysis are applicable to bacterial systematics.

TABLE IV

Phospholipid types found in actinomycetes (Lechevalier *et al.*, 1977)

Phospholipid type	Marker phospholipids[a]					Actinomycetes
	PG	PC	PE	PME	GLUNU	
PI	−	−	−	−	−	*Actinomadura, Corynebacterium, Microtetraspora, Nocardioides*
PII	−	−	+	−	−	*Actinoplanes, Chainia, Dactilosporangium, Microellobosporia, Micromonospora, Micropolyspora brevicatena, Mycobacterium, Nocardia, Rhodococcus, Streptomyces, Streptoverticillium*
PIII	+	+	−	+	−	*Micropolyspora faeni, Nocardia autotrophica, Nocardiopsis, Pseudonocardia*
PIV	−	−	+	−	+	*Intrasporangium, Microbispora, Streptosporangium*
PV	+	−	−	−	+	*Oerskovia, Promicromonospora*

[a] Abbreviations: PG, phosphatidylglycerol; PC, phosphatidylcholine; PE, phosphatidylethanolamine; PME, Phosphatidylmethylethanolamine; GLUNU, unknown lipid containing glucosamine.

D. Isoprenoid quinones

Isoprenoid quinones are important in the functioning of the electron transport system in respiration. Various kinds of quinones are found in bacterial cells (Table V), with most aerobic bacteria possessing isoprenoid menaquinone and/or isoprenoid ubiquinone. Unusual quinones are also found in some bacteria. The unusual naphthoquinones are chlorobium-quinone from "*Chlorobium thiosulphatophilum*" (Redfearn and Powls, 1968; Powls *et al.*, 1968); demethylmenaquinone from some streptococci (Collins and Jones, 1979), methionaquinone from *Hydrogenobacter thermophilum* (Ishii *et al.*, 1983; Kawasumi *et al.*, 1984). Methylmenaquinone (thermoplas-maquinone) has been isolated from some strains of *Campylobacter* (Carlone and Anet, 1983), *Thermoplasma acidophilum* (Collins and Langworthy, 1983) and *Wolinella succinogenes* (Collins and Fernandez, 1984). Unusual benzoquinones include rhodoquinone from *Rhodospirillum rubrum* and caldariellaquinone from "*Caldariella acidophila*" (De Rosa *et al.*, 1980). Not only the varieties of quinones, but also the number of isoprene units of the chain, and also the degree of hydrogenation of double bonds in the isoprenyl chain are useful in bacterial systematics. Yamada *et al.* (1976a) reported that the isoprenoid quinone composition is typical for genera in bacterial classification. The type of ubiquinone is also useful in yeast taxonomy (Yamada and Kondo, 1973; Yamada *et al.*, 1973, 1976c, d). Yamada *et al.* (1977) studied the position of hydrogen substitution in the isoprenyl chain of menaquinones of some bacteria. However, not enough information for a sufficiently wide group of bacteria has been gathered to employ these data for taxonomic purposes. The following provides an analytical method for isoprenoid quinones, principally menaquinones and ubiquinones.

Mass spectrometry (MS) has been successfully employed for determination of quinones. Recently, high-performance liquid chromatography (HPLC) and reverse-phase thin-layer chromatography have been found to be helpful for rapid and routine analysis of quinones. In addition, HPLC has proven useful for separation and detection of minor components and for quantitative analysis of quinones (Tamaoka *et al.*, 1983).

Menaquinone and ubiquinone are abbreviated as MK-n(H$_m$) and Q-n, respectively, where n is the number of isoprene units and m is the number of hydrogen atoms substituting the isoprenyl chain.

1. Extraction of quinones

Freeze-dried cells (100–300 mg) are suspended in 20 ml of chloroform–methanol (2:1, v/v) and gently stirred overnight. Dried cells should not be stored for too long a time before extraction because exposure of dried cells to air stimulates oxidation of the quinones. After filtration, the extract is evaporated to dryness and dissolved in a small amount of acetone. Acetone solution is applied to silica-gel TLC (Merck Kiesel-gel 60 F$_{254}$, 0.5 mm thickness, etc.) and developed with benzene. Standards for quinones also

TABLE V
Isoprenoid quinones found in bacterial cells

Naphthoquinones	Benzoquinones

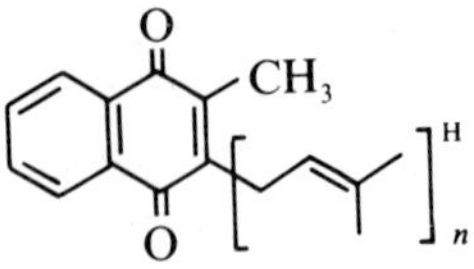

Menaquinone

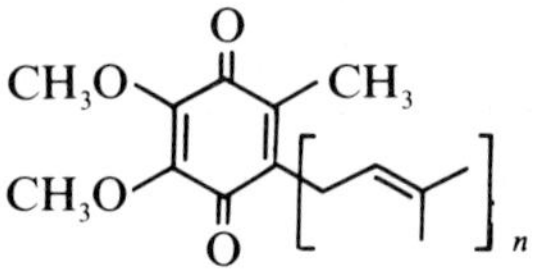

Ubiquinone

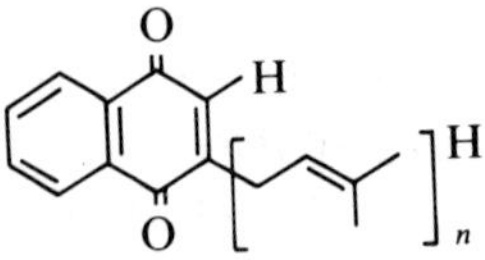

Demethylmenaquinone

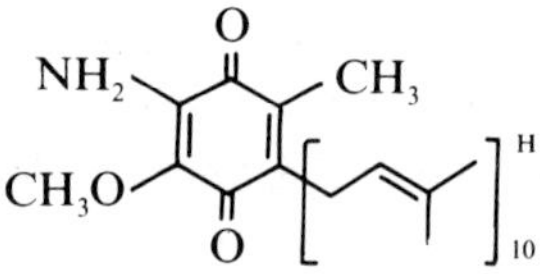

Rhodoquinone

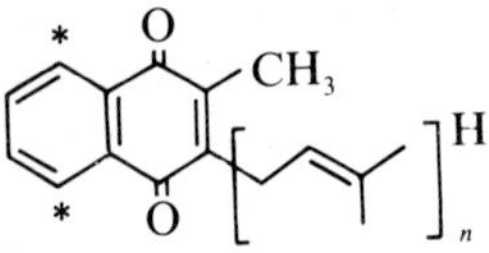

Thermoplasmaquinone
(*, one of these is methylated)

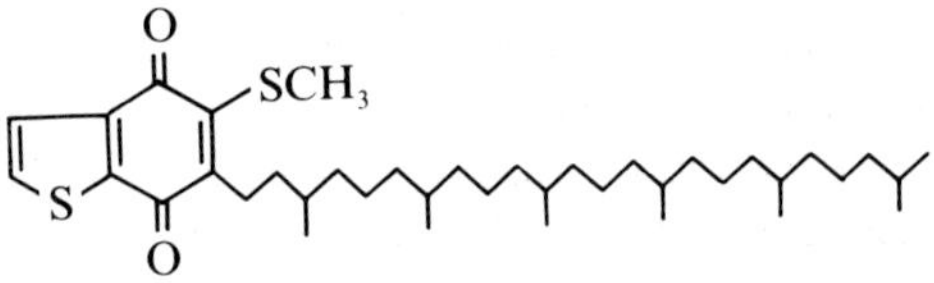

Caldariellaquinone

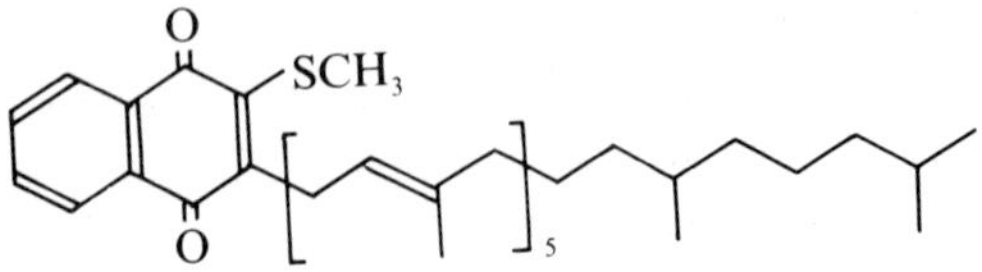

Methionaquinone

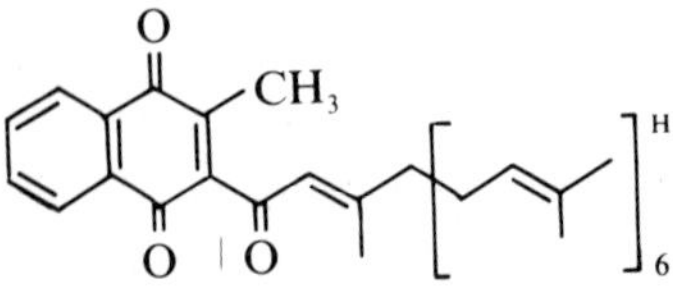

Chlorobiumquinone

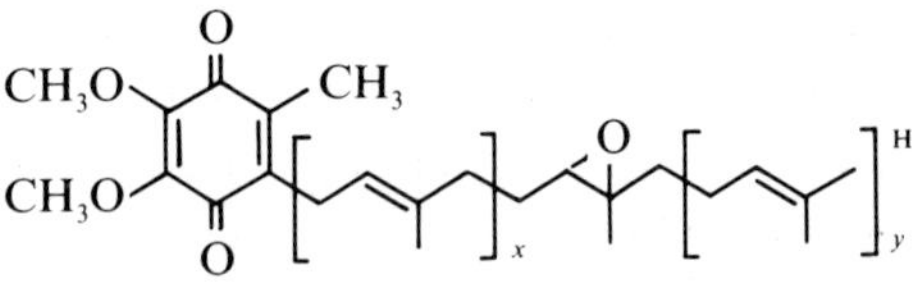

Epoxyubiquinone

should be included. Purified vitamin K is used as the menaquinone standard for TLC. The quinone spots can be visualized by UV light at 254 nm. Menaquinones will appear at R_f ca. 0.7, and ubiquinones at R_f ca. 0.4. The band corresponding to menaquinone appears slightly higher than that of vitamin K. The corresponding spot is scraped off and extracted with acetone. Before concentration, the acetone solution is filtered (e.g. by Columnguard SJFH L04, Millipore Corp., Bedford, Mass., USA). Samples are stored at low temperature in small brown glass tubes.

2. Reverse-phase thin-layer chromatography

The quinone sample is applied on a reverse-phase TLC (e.g. Merck HPTLC RP-18 F_{254}, 10 cm × 10 cm). Developing solvent is acetone–water (99:1, v/v) for menaquinone (Collins et al., 1980) and acetone–acetonitrile (80:20, v/v) for ubiquinone (Collins and Jones, 1981b). Development is complete within 15 min, and the spots are visualized under UV light at 254 nm (Fig. 10).

3. High-performance liquid chromatography

Quinones can be separated by isocratic HPLC (Collins and Jones, 1981b; Collins, 1982b; Tamaska et al., 1983). Quantitative data can be obtained and are based on the area ratio of UV absorbance to molar composition of cellular quinones.

Standard reverse-phase columns, for example Zorbax-ODS (Du Pont) and μ-Bondapak C_{18} (Waters Associates, Milford, Mass., USA) are available. Elution solvent is methanol–isopropanol (4:1, v/v) (Collins and Jones, 1981b) or methanol–isopropyl ether (3:1, v/v) (Tamaoka et al., 1983). The present authors employ methanol–isopropanol (1:1 and 2:1, v/v) with the Radialpak-Novapak C_{18} column (Waters Associates). It should be noted that isopropyl ether often contains aromatic stabilizer, which will absorb UV. Menaquinone and ubiquinone are detected at 270 and 275 nm respectively. An example of a chromatogram is shown in Fig. 11. Clearly, HPLC is useful for separation of quinones containing isoprenyl chains differently hydrogenated.

The logarithmic value of the elution time is linear to the number of isoprene units with an equal hydrogenation number. It is also a linear function of the number of hydrogenations in a given quinone with the same number of isoprene units. Tamaoka et al. (1983) proposed the ENIU (equivalent number of isoprene units) value to describe relative elution times of menaquinone:

$$ENIU_X = A + B \log (ET_X/ET_9) + C [\log (ET_X/ET_9)]^2,$$

where ET_X and ET_9 represent the elution times of X and MK-9 peaks

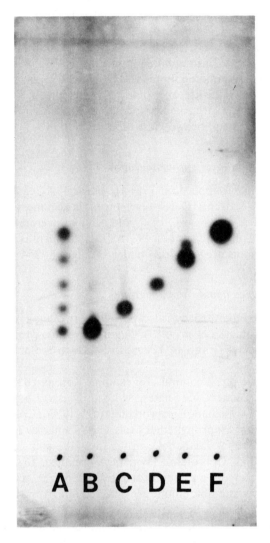

Fig. 10. Reverse-phase thin-layer chromatogram of ubiquinones. A, mixture of B, through F; B, Q-6; C, Q-7, D, Q-8, E, Q-9; F, Q-10. All samples are standard materials from Sigma except Q-8 which was purified from the cells of *Aeromonas sobria* JCM 2139.

respectively. *A*, *B* and *C* are obtained from the elution times of MK-6 to MK-12 by quadratic regression, based on the least-squares method. The ENIU value of MK-n(H$_m$) is, in general, described as $n + 0.4\,m/2$.

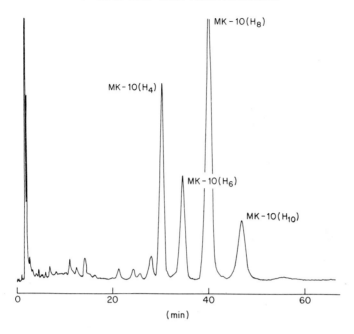

Fig. 11. High-performance liquid chromatogram of menaquinones prepared from the cells of *Micromonospora echinospora* subsp. *echinospora* JCM 3073.

4. Mass spectrometry

Direct-probe mass spectrometry is an essential tool for the determination of isoprenoid quinones. The typical mass spectra of menaquinone and ubiquinone are shown in Fig. 12. Strong fragment ions are m/z 225 and 187 from menaquinones, and m/z 235 and 197 from ubiquinones. In addition, a clear molecular-ion peak (M^+) and some weak fragment peaks that have lost some of the isoprene units ($M - 68n$) are seen. Table VI is helpful in the identification of menaquinones and ubiquinones by MS.

Care should be taken when determining quinones solely by mass spectrometry. In most cases, bacterial isoprenoid quinones are mixtures of homologues. Some bacteria contain quinones with isoprene units partly hydrogenated. One hydrogenation produces a difference of only two mass units. HPLC separates an isoprenoid quinone by the degree of hydrogenation. Menaquinones prepared from the cells of some coryneform bacteria and actinomycetes are often mixtures of homologues of nearly equal amounts. In such cases, quantitative analysis by HPLC is required. The combination of HPLC and MS provides good information for quinone analysis. If necessary, samples fractionated by HPLC can be subjected to MS. On the other

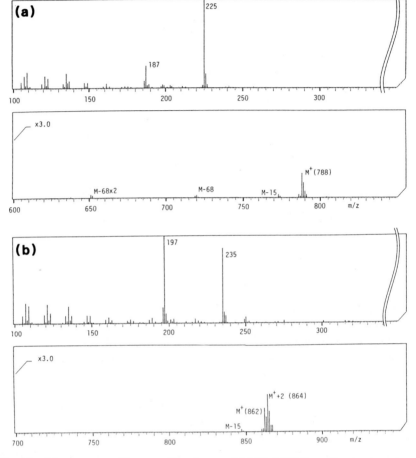

Fig. 12. Mass spectra of isoprenoid quinones: (a) MK-9(H₄) from *Oerskovia turbata* JCM 3160; (b) Q-10 (Sigma).

hand, most bacteria containing ubiquinones are of simple composition. Reverse-phase TLC is useful when many samples must be processed, especially if they contain the usual ubiquinones. Thus in selecting an analytical method, one should consider the purpose for which the determination is being done.

Standards for ubiquinones of six to ten isoprene units can be obtained from Sigma Chemical Co. (St. Louis, Mo., USA). Menaquinone standards are extracted from bacterial cells; see Collins and Jones (1981a). It is convenient to retain representative isoprenoid quinones prepared from authentic microorganisms as reference in the analyses.

TABLE VI

Mass numbers of molecular ions (M^+) of menaquinones and ubiquinones obtained from mass spectrometry

Number of isoprene units	Menaquinones						Ubiquinones		
	—	(H$_2$)	(H$_4$)	(H$_6$)	(H$_8$)	(H$_{10}$)	—	(H$_2$)	(H$_4$)
6	580	582	584	586	588	590	590	592	594
7	648	650	652	654	656	658	658	660	662
8	716	718	720	722	724	726	726	728	730
9	784	786	788	790	792	794	794	796	798
10	852	854	856	858	860	862	862	864	866
11	920	922	924	926	928	930	930	932	934
12	988	990	992	994	996	998			
13	1056	1058	1060	1062	1064	1066			(m/z)

5. Applications to bacterial systematics

The usefulness of quinone analysis for bacterial classification and identification has been reviewed by Collins and Jones (1981a).

Ubiquinone is generally found in Gram-negative bacteria, the major component being restricted to Q-8 to Q-10. Shorter isoprenoid ubiquinones and hydrogenated ubiquinones have been found in some eukaryotic cells, but not in bacterial cells.

Yamada *et al.* (1969) clearly differentiated *Acetobacter* and *Gluconobacter*, on the basis of Q-9 and Q-10 as the major ubiquinone, respectively. However, they also found Q-10 in *Acetobacter xylinum*, suggesting a need to reevaluate the taxonomic status of this species (Yamada *et al.*, 1976b). Further, the "intermediate" strains, characterized by the presence of Q-8 as a major ubiquinone (Yamada *et al.*, 1969), were concluded to constitute a new genus, *Frateuria* (Swings *et al.*, 1980).

The genus *Pseudomonas* comprises five large groups based on nucleic-acid homologies (Palleroni *et al.*, 1973). Ubiquinone type corresponds to the homology groups as follows: homology group I with Q-9, homology groups II, III, and V with Q-8, and homology group IV with Q-10 (Yamada *et al.*, 1982). *P. maltophilia*, a member of group V, contains Q-8 as a major ubiquinone (Ikemoto *et al.*, 1980) and was transferred to the genus *Xanthomonas* (Swings *et al.*, 1983).

Ubiquinone type is a useful characteristic in the taxonomy of methanol-utilizing Gram-negative bacteria. The groups of obligate methylotrophs, facultative methylotrophs and the genus *Hyphomicrobium* have Q-8, Q-10, and Q-9 as a major ubiquinone respectively (Urakami and Komagata, 1979, 1984).

Generally, facultative anaerobic Gram-negative rods contain Q-8 and minor amounts of menaquinone and demethylmenaquinone, with the same number of isoprene units as that of ubiquinone. The quantitative balance of those quinones is dependent upon the amount of oxygen available during growth (Polglase et al., 1966; Whistance and Threlfall, 1968).

The Flavobacterium–Cytophaga complex is a group of pigment-producing Gram-negative bacteria and includes strains of low $G+C$ content of DNA (32–45 mol%), as well as strains of rather high $G+C$ content (63–69 mol%). Oyaizu and Komagata (1981) discovered a correspondence between DNA base composition and presence of isoprenoid quinones in this group of bacteria. The low $G+C$ strains possess MK-6 or MK-7, while high $G+C$ strains contain Q-8.

Gram-positive bacteria contain exclusively menaquinones, with a wide variation among taxa. The major menaquinone of most of the Bacillus strains is uniformly MK-7 (Watanuki and Aida, 1972; Hess et al., 1979). Actinomycetes and aerobic coryneform bacteria contain menaquinones in a wide variety of isoprene chain length, degree of hydrogenation and molar composition. Menaquinone analysis is necessary for classification of coryne-form bacteria to genera, as shown in Table VII. Spore-forming actinomy-cetes contain highly hydrogenated menaquinones with long isoprenoid chains, the composition of which are complicated (Collins et al., 1982b, 1984). On the other hand, actinomycetes of primitive morphology have simple menaquinone composition. For instance, the major menaquinones of Agromyces ramosus and Rothia dentocariosa are unsaturated MK-11 and MK-7 respectively (Collins, 1982c; Collins and Shah, 1984). The genus Oerskovia, proposed as a member of the genus Cellulomonas by Stacke-brandt et al. (1982), based on genetic relatedness, shares a common menaquinone, MK-9(H_4), with Cellulomonas strains (Yamada et al., 1976a), despite the fact that the diamino amino acid of the cell-wall peptidoglycan is different (Schleifer and Kandler, 1972; Seidl et al., 1980).

In conclusion, recently accumulated information on the isoprenoid quin-one content of microorganisms provides a basis for a reproducible method for classification and identification of microorganisms.

III.   Cell-wall analysis for bacterial systematics

Most bacteria have a characteristic wall envelope, composed of peptidogly-can (murein). Only mycoplasma and archaebacteria are known to lack peptidoglycan. Peptidoglycan consists of the glycan moiety, which is an

TABLE VII

Chemotaxonomic characteristics of aerobic coryneform bacteria

Group Yamada and Komagata[a]	Corresponding genus	Cell-wall peptidoglycan — Type	Cell-wall peptidoglycan — Principal amino acid[b]		Glycolate test[c]	DNA G+C content (mol%)[d]	Menaquinone system[e]	Cellular fatty-acid type[f]
6 Pimelobacter			LL–DAP + Glycine			70–73	MK-8(H₄)	IV
1	Corynebacterium	A	meso-DAP	Arabino-galactan	Acetyl	53–55	MK-9(H₂)	I–A
						55–63	MK-8(H₂)	I–B
						52	MK-8(H₂)	I–C
						64–69	MK-8(H₂)/MK-9(H₂)	I–D
	Rhodococcus				Glycolyl	66–70	MK-8(H₂)	I–E
						65–67		I–F
2	Brevibacterium				Acetyl	60–63		II
3	Arthrobacter		L-Lysine	15 variations	Acetyl	58–66	MK-9(H₂)/MK-8, 9	II
4	Cellulomonas	B		A21.5	Acetyl	72–73	MK-9(H₄)	II
5	Curtobacterium		Ornithine	B5	Glycolyl	67–72	MK-9	II
	Aureobacterium			B6		69–71		
	Microbacterium		L-Lysine	B1 or B2	Glycolyl	69–70	MK-11–13	III
7	Clavibacter		DAB	B7	Acetyl	71–72	MK9	II
	Agromyces					69–73	MK10–13	

References: [a]Yamada and Komagata (1972); [b]Schleifer and Kandler (1972) and Claus et al. (1983); [c]Uchida and Aida (1977, 1979); [d]Yamada and Komagata (1970b); [e]Yamada et al. (1976a) and Collins et al. (1977, 1979); [f]Suzuki and Komagata (1983).

alternating polymer of N-acetylglucosamine and N-acetylmuramic acid, and a peptide moiety that links the glycan chain. Variation in the peptide moiety holds significant systematic information especially in Gram-positive bacteria, including the actinomycetes. Since Cummins and Harris (1956) pointed out the amino-acid variation of peptidoglycan, cell wall components of various kinds of bacteria have been studied. Shleifer and Kandler (1972) reviewed the variation and distribution of peptidoglycan structures in bacteria, and indicated its usefulness for bacterial systematics. They determined the structure by their distinctive method (Schleifer and Kandler, 1972; Schleifer and Seidl, 1985). The systematic significance lies mostly in a key amino acid with two amino bases, and determination of a key amino acid is usually sufficient for characterization (Yamada and Komagata, 1972; Bousfield et al., 1985). 2,6-Diaminopimelic acid (DAP) is widely distributed as a key amino acid. It has optical isomers. If DAP is present, bacterial cells generally contain one of the isomers, the LL-form or the meso-(DL-)form, and most of it is located in the peptidoglycan. Determination of the DAP isomer, including a check for its presence, can be carried out by treatment of whole cells. DAP determination is the first step of cell-wall analysis of Gram-positive bacteria. If no DAP isomer is detected then amino-acid analysis should be performed with the purified cell-wall fraction. Peptidoglycan of Gram-negative bacteria is generally present in small amounts and contains meso-DAP; it is not so significant for the systematics.

The glycan moiety of peptidoglycan does not vary as much as the peptide moiety. Some Gram-positive bacteria, including some actinomycetes, have muramic acid whose amino base is substituted by a glycolyl group instead of the acetyl group. This property is referred to as the "glycolyl type" and is useful for characterization.

In addition to peptidoglycan analysis, determination of whole-cell sugars is also discussed in this section. Some bacteria contain characteristic sugars in the cell wall. Usually sugar analysis is done with whole-cell hydrolysate for systematic purposes.

Teichoic acids and teichuronic acid are also components of bacterial cell envelope. Teichoic acids are the phosphodiester polymers of glycerol phosphate or ribitol phosphate. Davison and Baddiley (1963) studied the distribution of teichoic acids in some staphylococci. S. aureus has ribitol-type teichoic acid, while the glycerol type is found in the cells of S. epidermidis (Davison and Baddiley, 1964; Archibald et al., 1968). Teichuronic acid is a polymer of equal proportions of N-acetylgalactosamine and D-glucuronic acid. Teichuronic acid is present in cells of some Bacillus strains (Janczura et al., 1961; Hughes and Thurman, 1970). Further biological properties of teichoic and teichuronic acids are referred to in the review by Ward (1981).

A. Diaminopimelic acid (DAP) isomers

Presence of DAP isomers is one of the most important pieces of information concerning the cell-wall peptidoglycan of Gram-positive bacteria including actinomycetes. If a Gram-positive bacterium has a peptidoglycan containing one of the DAP isomers, the DAP is mostly located in the cell wall. Therefore DAP isomers of peptidoglycan can be determined by whole-cell analysis. DAP isomers are separated by paper chromatography (Becker *et al.*, 1964) or by cellulose thin-layer chromatography (Staneck and Roberts, 1974). Hasegawa *et al.* (1983) reported a further, simplified, method for DAP determination. Tisdall and Anhalt (1979) employed HPLC for separation and determination of DAP isomers. The following is based on the method of Staneck and Roberts (1974).

1. Whole-cell hydrolysis

Approximately 3 mg of dried cells are hydrolysed with 1 ml of 6 N HCl in a screw-capped tube at 100 °C for 18 h. After cooling, the hydrolysate is filtered and 1 ml of water is added to the filter. The combined filtrate is concentrated to dryness by a rotary evaporator. The dried material is dissolved in 1 ml of water and dried again. The residue is redissolved in 0.3 ml of water.

2. Thin-layer chromatography (TLC)

Each sample is applied as 3 μl on the base line of a cellulose TLC plate (20 cm × 20 cm) (e.g. Merck No. 5716, E. Merck, Darmstadt, FRG). As a standard, 1 μl of 0.01 M DL-diaminopimelic acid (Sigma Chemical Co., St. Louis, Mo., USA) is also applied. This authentic material is a mixture of DAP isomers. Two well-known strains that contain *meso*- and LL-DAP respectively should be added for reference purposes. TLC is developed with the solvent system methanol–water–6 N HCl–pyridine (80:26:4:10, v/v). Development will take approximately 3 h or more. The spots are visualized by spraying with 0.2% ninhydrin solution in water-saturated n-butanol followed by heating at 100 °C for 5 min. DAP isomers appear as dark-green spots with R_f 0.29 (LL-isomer) and 0.24 (*meso*- and DD-isomer). 3-Hydroxy-DAP appears lower than the *meso*-isomer (R_f approximately 0.20). Spots of other amino acids run faster than DAP ($R_f = 0.37$–0.80). Spots will gradually disappear in a few hours.

Cellulose high-performance TLC (HPTLC) plates (Merck No. 5787) are effective for shortening development times. It takes approximately 30 min to develop an HPTLC plate with the solvent system mentioned above.

Furthermore, the amount of sample to be applied can be decreased to a half to one third. A normal cellulose TLC analysis presents a better separation than an HPTLC. However, it is quite sufficient to determine the three kinds of DAP isomers.

3. Applications to bacterial systematics

Distribution of diamino acids in the peptidoglycan is well reviewed by Schleifer and Kandler (1972). In the case of actinomycetes, Lechevalier and Lechevalier (1970) defined 9 chemotypes, I–IX, based on the cell-wall amino acids and sugars. Determination of the presence and the kinds of isomers of DAP is helpful for the choice of the next step in the identification of Gram-positive bacteria. *Meso*-DAP is found in the cells of strains of the genera *Bacillus, Brevibacterium, Corynebacterium, Nocardia* and *Mycobacterium* etc. Strains of *Streptomyces* and *Nocardioides* etc. contain LL-DAP. *Kitasatosporia* is the first bacterium recognized as having both *meso*- and LL-DAPs in the cell wall (Omura *et al.*, 1982). In fact, *meso*-DAP is found in the cells of vegetative and filamentous mycelia, while LL-DAP is found in the submerged and aerial spores (Takahashi *et al.*, 1984). In such a case, fractionation is required for cell harvest.

3-Hydroxy-DAP is found in some actinomycetes, for example *Actinoplanes and Ampullariella*. In most cases, 3-hydroxy-DAP is found together with *meso*-DAP.

It is necessary to prepare a cell-wall sample only when none of the DAP isomers are detected by this method and when it is necessary to determine amino acids other than DAP. Further discussion of this is in the next section.

The Gram-negative bacteria generally possess a small amount of peptidoglycan with *meso*-DAP. Therefore an equivalent amount of a whole-cell hydrolysate of a Gram-negative bacterium presents a very weak spot of *meso*-DAP compared with that of a Gram-positive bacterium.

B. Amino-acid composition of peptidoglycan

A simple method of DAP analysis is detailed in the previous section. However, cell-wall preparation is necessary when no DAP is detected by the whole-cell method and when the amino-acid composition of peptidoglycan is required. Peptidoglycan structure is not determined only by its amino-acid composition. For determination of the peptidoglycan structure, partial hydrolysis and two-dimensional TLC or HPLC for analysis of oligopeptides are required. For further information, some useful references are Schleifer and Kandler (1972), Schleifer and Seidl (1985) and König and Kandler (1979).

Peptidoglycan preparation consists of cell disruption and sample purification. Cell disruption is the first step for cell-wall preparation. There are various kinds of methods and instruments for cell disruption, and many of them are suitable for this purpose. In the purification process, proteins, nucleic acids, carbohydrates and lipids should be removed from the sample. The peptidoglycan should be especially freed from amino acids and peptides derived from cellular proteins. Proteinase treatment is usually carried out, even when other enzyme treatments are not performed.

The following method is usually used for amino-acid analysis of peptidoglycan based on the method of Yamada and Komagata (1970a) with some modifications.

1. Preparation of peptidoglycan

Approximately 2 g of wet packed cells are suspended in 6 ml of 0.05 M phosphate buffer (pH 7.2) and sonicated in ice. The degree of disruption is checked by microscopy with Gram staining or by the turbidity of supernatant after slow centrifugation. The sonicated cell suspension is centrifuged at 1800g for 10 min to remove undisrupted cells. The supernatant contains fragments of cell envelope. The recovery is indicated by the turbidity of the supernatant. If the recovery is low then the precipitated cells are sonicated again. The supernatant is centrifuged at more than 12 000g for 1 h and resuspended in 5 ml of the buffer. The suspension is added to 1 ml of 25% sodium dodecyl sulphate (SDS) solution and kept at 100 °C for 40 min. It is then centrifuged at 12 000g for 1 h at 30 °C. The precipitate is washed twice with phosphate buffer. It is suspended in 2 ml of 0.05 M phosphate buffer (pH 7.6) and 100 μl of Pronase E (Kaken Pharmaceutical Co., Ltd., Tokyo, Japan) solution (1 mg ml^{-1}) is added. This enzyme solution is filtered before use. After enzymatic treatment at 37 °C for 2 h, the suspension is centrifuged at 12 000g for 30 min, and washed with the same buffer. The precipitate is suspended in 2 ml of 5% trichloroacetic acid (TCA) and kept at 100 °C for 20 min in a screw-capped tube. After cooling, the suspension is transferred to a glass centrifuge tube with a pipette, freed from chloroform and centrifuged at 12 000g for 30 min. The precipitate is collected and washed three times with phosphate buffer (pH 7.6). It is then washed with 2 ml of ethanol and with 2 ml of diethyl ether with centrifugation. Finally the precipitate is dried in a vacuum oven, scraped from the tube, and offered as a peptidoglycan sample.

Defatted cells used for lipid analysis are also available for peptidoglycan preparation. However, dried cells are generally resistant to cell disruption and yield low recoveries.

2. Hydrolysis and analysis

One millilitre of 6 N HCl is added to 1 or 2 mg of cell wall in a tube with a

Teflon-lined cap. The hydrolysate is filtered and the filter paper is washed with 1 ml of water. The filtrate is combined and dried in a rotary evaporator. The residue is dissolved in 1 ml of water and dried again. This sample is dissolved in dilution buffer for amino-acid analysis. Figure 13 shows examples of chromatograms from an automatic amino-acid analyser. Some peptidoglycan-characteristic amino compounds sometimes overlap with amino acids under normal analytical condition (Fig 13(a)). Under normal conditions, the peak of muramic acid overlaps with that of serine. The conditions in Fig. 13(b) can separate muramic acid and serine, while muramic acid does not separate from homoserine. The sample in Fig. 13 contains serine. The peptidoglycan of group B (see Fig. 14) often contains

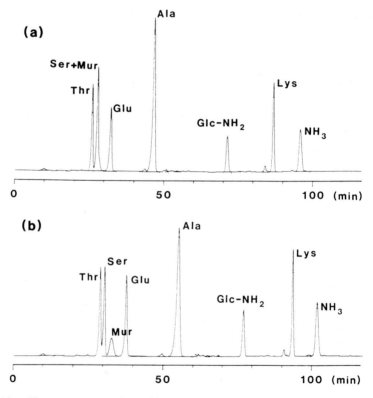

Fig. 13. Chromatograms of peptidoglycan hydrolysate by automatic amino-acid analyser: (a) under normal conditions (the peak of muramic acid overlaps with that of serine); (b) under conditions separating muramic acid from serine. The sample was prepared from cells of *Arthrobacter* sp. JCM 1339. The quantitative data from these analyses are shown in Table VIII. Abbreviations used are: Ala, alanine; Glc-NH$_2$, glucosamine; Glu, glutamic acid; Lys, lysine; Ser, serine; Thr, threonine.

homoserine. Therefore it is useful to compare data produced under different conditions.

The data are obtained as molar ratios of the component amino compounds as shown in Table VIII. However, some constituents decompose during preparation, especially after hydrolysis. The recovery of muramic acid is less than 0.5 (Table VIII). Glucosamine and diaminopimelic acid are

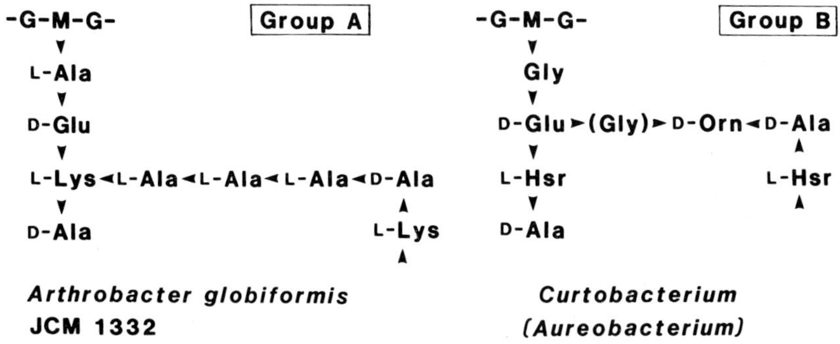

Fig. 14. Examples of peptidoglycan structures of group A and group B (Schleifer and Kandler, 1972). Abbrevations used are: G, N-acetylglucosamine; M, N-acetyl (glycolyl)muramic acid; Ala, alanine; Glu, glutamic acid; Gly, glycerine; Hsr, homoserine; Lys, lysine; Orn, ornithine.

TABLE VIII

Amino-acid analysis of peptidoglycans isolated from some *Arthrobacter* strains

Amino acid and amino sugar	*A. globiformis* JCM 1332[a]			*Arthrobacter* sp. JCM 1339		
	a^b	b	c	a	b	c
Thr[c]				0.99[d]	1.02	1
Mur + Ser	0.46			1.39		
Ser					0.99	1
Mur		0.43	1		0.44	1
Glu	1.04	1.02	1	1.09	1.08	1
Ala	4.15	4.46	5	2.47	2.69	3
Glc-NH₂	0.72	0.67	1	0.73	0.68	1
Lys	1.00	1.00	1	1.00	1.00	1

[a]The peptidoglycan structure of *A. globiformis* JCM 1332 is shown in Fig. 14. [b]*a* and *b* correspond to the analytical condition described in Fig. 13; c is the theoretical value of molar ratio based on the data of Schleifer and Kandler (1972). [c]Abbreviations of amino compounds are the same as those in Fig 13. [d]The values indicate molar ratios to Lys (1.00).

also decomposed to some extent. Homoserine forms lactone and presents two peaks, corresponding to homoserine and its lactone, on the chromatogram. Therefore the recovery should be checked with authentic materials treated with the same hydrolysis conditions in advance for calibration.

Gas chromatography is also useful for quantitative analysis of amino acids (O'Donnell et al., 1982). For the determination of key amino acid (diamino amino acid), TLC is useful for analysis of many strains at once (Bousfield et al., 1985).

3. Applications to bacterial systematics

As shown in Table VII, a key amino acid is one of the essential properties for the classification of coryneform bacteria. In addition to the usual peptidoglycan structure of group A, the structure of group B is found among coryneform bacteria (Fig. 14; Schleifer and Kandler, 1972). The two groups are differentiated by the amino-acid composition other than the key amino acid. Peptidoglycan of some bacteria has an oligopeptide called the interpeptide bridge. For example, *Arthrobacter globiformis* JCM 1332 has trialanine between lysine and alanine in the peptidoglycan (Fig. 14). Table IX shows the variation of interpeptide bridges found in strains of the genus *Arthrobacter*. In most of the bacteria containing *meso*-DAP in the peptidoglycan, for example *Bacillus, Corynebacterium* and Gram-negative bacteria, direct linkage is found between *meso*-DAP and terminal alanine. On the other hand, LL-DAP-containing bacteria, for example *Streptomyces* and *Pimelobacter*, usually have glycine as interpeptide bridge (Schleifer and Kandler, 1972).

C. Cell-wall acyl type

The glycan moiety of cell-wall peptidoglycan is generally an alternating polymer of *N*-acetylglucosamine and *N*-acetylmuramic acid with β-1,4 linkage. It is known that the glycolyl group of the muramic acid is substituted by an acetyl group in some bacteria (Adam et al., 1969; Azuma et al., 1970; Guinard et al., 1970; Vilkas et al., 1970). Uchida and Aida (1977, 1979) extensively studied the distribution of glycolyl type of cell wall in bacteria, and found there is glycolyl-type cell wall in some actinomycetes and coryneform bacteria. They also developed a simplified method for the determination of glycolyl residues in cells and named it the glycolate test (Uchida and Aida, 1979, 1984). This profile of peptidoglycan is called the cell-wall acyl type and is useful for the classification and identification of those groups of bacteria. Colorimetric analysis enables quantitative determination as nanomoles of glycolic acid per milligram of dried cells (Uchida and Aida, 1977, 1979). However, quantitative determination is not usually

TABLE IX

Grouping of *Arthrobacter* species based on peptidoglycan type

Peptidoglycan type[a]	Species	Number of strains	Menaquinones
Lys-Ser-Thr-Ala	*A. oxydans*	1	MK-9(H$_2$)
	A. polychromogenes	1	
Lys-Ala-Thr-Ala	*A. aurescens*	1	
	A. histidinolovorans	1	
	A. ureafaciens	1	MK-9(H$_2$)
	A. ilicis	1	MK-9(H$_2$)
Lys-Ala$_{1-4}$	*A. crystallopoietes*	1	MK-9(H$_2$)
	A. pascens	1	
	A. globiformis	1	MK-9(H$_2$)
	A. ramosus	1	
Lys-Ser-Ala$_{2-3}$	*A. atrocyaneus*	1	
Lys-Thr-Ala$_2$	*A. citreus*	1	MK-9(H$_2$)
Lys-Ala-Glu	*A. nicotianae*	6	MK-8 (MK-9)
	A. protophormiae	6	MK-8 (MK-9)
	A. mysorens	1	
	A. uratoxydans	2	
Lys-Glu	*A. sulfureus*	3	MK-9 (MK-10)

[a] Peptidoglycan type shows the key amino acid (Lys) and the interpeptide bridge. Abbreviations for amino acids are the same as those in Fig. 13. References: Stackebrandt and Fiedler (1979) and Stackebrandt *et al.* (1983).

required for bacterial systematics. The following method is based on that of Uchida and Aida (1984).

1. Chemical reagents

(i) *Acetate-type resin.* Approximately 100 ml of resin (Dowex 1X8, Cl⁻ type, 200–400 mesh) is washed with hot water (60 °C) followed by 0.5 N NaOH (500 ml), water, 1 N HCl (500 ml) and water. The washed resin is suspended in twice its volume of 0.5 N NaOH. After washing with five volumes of water, the resin is resuspended in 1 N acetic acid and stored in it. The resin is washed with water before use. It is confirmed that the eluate is free from Cl⁻ by adding silver nitrate solution to it.

(ii) *DON reagent*.   0.02% of 2,7-dihydroxynaphthalene is dissolved in conc. H_2SO_4. Fresh solution is used after the yellow colour disappears on overnight storage.

2. Sample preparation

10 mg of dried cells are hydrolysed by 100 µl of 6 N HCl at 100 °C for 2 h in a screw-capped tube (13 mm × 100 mm). The hydrolysate is passed through a microcolumn (5 mm inside diameter, acetate type of Dowex 1 × 8 is charged 5 cm high). After the column is washed twice with 1 ml of water and once with 1 ml of 0.5 N HCl, the glycolate fraction is eluted by 2 ml of 0.5 N HCl. 2 ml of DON reagent is added to 100 µl of the glycolate fraction in a screw-capped tube and kept at 100 °C in a bath for 10 min. An obvious red-purple colour will appear when the sample contains a certain amount of glycolic acid.

3. Judgement

The strains that show clear red-purple colour are positive in the glycolate test. Positive and negative controls should be included in a series of experiments. Sometimes the blank gives weak colour production. Standard sodium glycolate solution is prepared as 10 µmol ml^{-1} (98.03 mg/100 ml water). 50 µl of the solution is loaded onto the same microcolumn as the sample. At the same time, 100 µl of the solution is diluted and checked for the colour reaction. Comparing the two, it is possible to check the effect of the column.

Quantitative determination (nmol glycolic acid per mg dried cells) is carried out by colorimetry at 530 nm in comparison with a standard curve drawn with a blank of 100 µl of the sodium glycolate solution (10 µmol ml^{-1}).

4. Applications to bacterial systematics

All the *N*-acetyl groups of muramic acid are not substituted and the ratio of substitution possibly has some physiological relevance. However, usually information on the presence or absence of glycolate residue in the cell is all that is required for systematic purposes. In addition, changes of cellular glycolate content are also observed (Uchida and Aida, 1979). A strain of *Rhodococcus rhodochrous* showed increase of glycolate content in the stationary phase. Cultivating in a medium containing 1% glycerol supresses glycolate content in some rhodococci.

Glycolate-test-positive taxa so far studied are the genera *Mycobacterium, Nocardia, Rhodococcus* (Azuma *et al*., 1970; Guinard *et al*., 1970; Uchida and Aida, 1977, 1979), *Micromonospora* (Vilkas *et al*., 1970; Kawamoto *et al*.,

1981), *Actinoplanes*, *Amorphosphorangium*, *Ampullariella*, *Dactylosporan-gium* (Kawamoto *et al.*, 1981), *Aureobacterium* (Uchida and Aida, 1977, 1979; Collins *et al.*, 1983), and *Microbacterium* (Uchida and Aida, 1977, 1979). Strains of the first eight genera are actinomycetes that have *meso*-DAP in the cell wall. The latter two genera are coryneform taxa without *meso*-DAP. They include some strains that formerly belonged to other genera and demonstrate the heterogeneity of the taxa. At present, reclassification has made the generic relationships clear, and the results of the glycolate test support the newer concept. Some strains of the genus *Nocardia* possess the acetyl type of cell wall and taxonomic problems remain in this taxon.

D. Whole-cell sugars

Bacterial cell walls contain some kinds of sugars, in addition to the glucosamine and muramic acid of peptidoglycan. The sugar composition often presents valuable information on the classification and identification of some bacteria, especially some Gram-positive bacteria and actinomycetes. Whole-cell sugar patterns contribute to the cell-wall chemotypes of actinomycetes proposed by Lechevalier and Lechevalier (1970). However, some bacterial taxa do not have a uniform sugar composition, and this indicates that the evaluation of sugar analysis remains a problem for bacterial systematics.

Usually cell-wall sugar analysis is carried out at whole-cell level for bacterial classification. The following method is based on Staneck and Roberts (1974).

1. Sample preparation

Approximately 50 mg of dried cells are hydrolysed with 1 ml of 1 N H_2SO_4 at 100 °C for 2 h in a screw-capped tube. After cooling, a saturated solution of $Ba(OH)_2$ is added and the pH is adjusted to 5.2–5.5. The precipitate is removed by centrifugation and the supernatant is dried with a rotary evaporator. Addition of a small amount of ethanol prevents foaming during evaporation. The residue dissolved in 0.3 ml of water is used as a sample solution.

2. TLC development

On a cellulose TLC plate (the same as employed for DAP-isomer analysis), 1 µl of the sample is applied and developed with the solvent system n-butanol–water–piridine–toluene (10:6:6:1, v/v). The developing time is approximately 4 h. Sugars are visualized by spraying with acid aniline phthalate (3.25 g of phthalic acid dissolved in 100 ml water-saturated n-butanol and 2 ml aniline). The sprayed plate is heated at 100 °C for 4 min. Hexoses appear as yellowish-brown spots and pentoses appear as maroon-coloured spots.

As standard, 1 μl of 0.1% (w/v) solution of sugar is employed. For routine work, the following two standard solutions are useful, as shown in Fig. 15. One consists of galactose, arabinose and xylose (0.1% w/v for each sugar). The other consists of rhamnose, mannose, glucose and ribose (0.1% w/v for each). Madurose (3-O-methyl-D-galactose), if present, shows almost the same migration as xylose. However, the colour of the spot is yellowish-brown, while that of xylose is maroon.

Paper chromatography (descending) gives good separation, although development takes more than one day. The solvent system used is n-butanol–water–pyridine–toluene (5:3:3:4, v/v) (Lechevalier and Lechevalier, 1970). Madurose and xylose can be separated by paper chromatography.

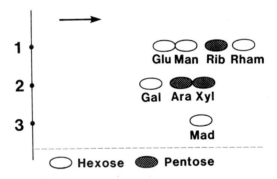

Fig. 15. TLC chromatograms of sugars. 1 and 2 are standard solutions of sugar mixture. 3 shows the migrating position of madurose under the same condition as 1 and 2. Abbreviations used are: Ara, arabinose; Gal, galactose; Glu, glucose; Mad, madurose; Man, mannose; Rham, rhamnose; Rib, ribose.

3. Applications to bacterial systematics

The whole-cell sugar pattern divides the actinomycetes containing *meso*-DAP in the peptidoglycan into four types. Type A is characterized by the presence of arabinose and galactose without xylose. Type B has madurose and not arabinose and xylose. Type C has no characteristic sugars. Xylose and arabinose are found in the strains of type D. The genera *Mycobacterium*, *Nocardia*, *Rhodococcus* and *Corynebacterium* are characterized by the sugars of type A. The presence of madurose is an important marker for some genera of actinomycetes, for example *Actinomadura, Streptosprangium* and *Microbispora*. Keddie and Cure (1977) analysed the cell-wall sugars of some coryneform bacteria. *Brevibacterium linens* and the genus *Corynebacterium* share the same peptidoglycan structure, with *meso*-DAP, although the two are distinguished by the sugar composition. The strains of *Brevibacterium linens* have ribose, galactose and glucose, while *Corynebacterium* strains contain arabinose and galactose. There was some tendency of cell-wall sugars to characterize coryneform taxa, but there were no other consistent profiles useful for classification.

References

Adam, A., Petit, J. F. and Wietzerbin-Falszpan, J. (1969). *FEBS Lett.* **4**, 87–92.
Alshamaony, L., Goodfellow, M., Minnikin, D. E., Bowden, G. H. and Hardie, J. M. (1977). *J. Gen. Microbiol.* **98**, 205–213.
Archbald, A. R., Baddiley, J. and Shaukat, G. A. (1968). *Biochem. J.* **110**, 583–588.
Ariga, N., Maruyama, K. and Kawaguchi, A. (1984). *J. Gen. Appl. Microbiol.* **30**, 87–95.
Azuma, I., Thomas, D. W., Adam, A., Ghuysen, J. M., Bonaly, R., Petit, J. F. and Lederer, E. (1970). *Biochim. Biophys. Acta* **208**, 444–451.
Becker, B., Lechevalier, M. P., Gordon, R. E. and Lechevalier, H. A. (1964). *Appl. Microbiol.* **12**, 421–423.
Bergan, T. B., Grimont, P. A. D. and Grimont, F. (1983). *Curr. Microbiol.* **8**, 7–11.
Bligh, E. G. and Dyer, W. J. (1959). *Can. J. Biochem. Physiol.* **37**, 911–917.
Bousfield, I. D., Keddie, R. M., Dando, T. R. and Shaw, S. (1985). In *Chemical Methods in Bacterial Systematics* (M. Goodfellow and D. E. Minnikin, eds.), pp. 201–219. Academic Press, London.
Bowie, I. S., Grigor, M. R., Dunckley, G. G., Loutit, W. and Loutit, J. S. (1972). *Soil Biol. Biochem.* **4**, 397–412.
Card, G. L. (1973). *J. Bacteriol.* **114**, 1125–1137.
Carlone, G. M. and Anet, F. A. L. (1983). *J. Gen. Microbiol.* **128**, 3385–3393.
Claus, D., Lack, P. and Neu, B. (eds.) (1983). *Deutsche Sammlung von Mikroorganismen, Catalogue of strains*, 3rd edn. Gesellschaft für Biotechnologische Forschung mbH, Braunschweig, West Germany.
Collins, M. D. (1982a). *Zbl. Bakteriol. Hyg., I. Abt. Orig.* **C3**, 364–367.
Collins, M. D. (1982b). *J. Appl. Bacteriol.* **52**, 457–460.
Collins, M. D. (1982c). *FEMS Microbiol. Lett.* **14**, 187–189.
Collins, M. D. and Fernandez, F. (1984). *FEMS Microbiol. Lett.* **22**, 273–276.
Collins, M. D. and Jones, D. (1979). *J. Gen. Microbiol.* **114**, 27–33.
Collins, M. D. and Jones, D. (1980). *J. Appl. Bacteriol.* **48**, 459–470.
Collins, M. D. and Jones, D. (1981a). *Microbiol. Rev.* **45**, 316–354.
Collins, M. D. and Jones, D. (1981b). *J. Appl. Bacteriol.* **51**, 129–134.
Collins, M. D. and Langworthy, T. A. (1983). *Syst. Appl. Microbiol.* **4**, 295–304.
Collins, M. D. and Shah, H. M. (1984). *Arch. Microbiol.* **137**, 247–249.
Collins, M. D., Pirouz, T., Goodfellow, M. and Minnikin, D. E. (1977). *J. Gen. Microbiol.* **100**, 221–230.
Collins, M. D., Goodfellow, M. and Minnikin, D. E. (1979). *J. Appl. Microbiol.* **110**, 127–136.

Collins, M. D., Shah, H. N. and Minnikin, D. E. (1980). *J. Appl. Bacteriol.* **48**, 277–282.

Collins, M. D., Goodfellow, M. and Minnikin, D. E. (1982a). *J. Gen. Microbiol.* **128**, 2503–2509.

Collins, M. D., McCarthy, A. J. and Cross, T. (1982b). *Zbl. Bakteriol. Hyg., I. Abt. Orig.* **C3**, 358–363.

Collins, M. D., Jones, D., Keddie, R. M., Kroppenstedt, R. M. and Schleifer, K. H. (1983). *Syst. Appl. Microbiol.* **4**, 236–252.

Collins, M. D., Faulkner, M. and Keddie, R. M. (1984). *Syst. Appl. Microbiol.* **5**, 20–29.

Cummins, C. S. and Harris, H. (1956). *J. Gen. Microbiol.* **14**, 583–600.

Davison, A. L. and Baddiley, J. (1963). *J. Gen. Microbiol.* **32**, 271–276.

Davison, A. L. and Baddiley, J. (1964). *Nature (London)* **202**, 874.

De Rosa, M., Gambacorta, A., Minale, L. and Bu'Lock, J. D. (1971). *Chem. Commun.*, 1334.

De Rosa, M., De Rosa, S., Gambacorta, A. and Bu'Lock, J. D. (1980). *Phytochemistry* **19**, 249–254.

Dittmer, J. C. and Lester, R. L. (1964). *J. Lipid Res.* **5**, 126–127.

Durham, D. R. and Kloos, W. E. (1978). *Int. J. Syst. Bacteriol.* **28**, 223–228.

Etémadi, A. H. (1967). *J. Gas Chromatogr.* **5**, 447–457.

Girard, A. E. (1971). *Can. J. Microbiol.* **17**, 1503–1508.

Goodfellow, M. and Minnikin, D. E. (1981). *Zbl. Bakteriol. Hyg., I Abt., Suppl.* **11**, 7–16.

Goodfellow, M., Collins, M. D. and Minnikin, D. E. (1976). *J. Gen. Microbiol.* **96**, 351–358.

Goodfellow, M., Collins, M. D. and Minnikin, D. E. (1980). *J. Appl. Bacteriol.* **48**, 269–276.

Guinard, M., Vacheron, M. J. and Michel, G. (1970). *FEBS Lett.* **6**, 37–39.

Hasegawa, T., Takizawa, M. and Tanida, S. (1983). *J. Gen. Appl. Microbiol.* **29**, 319–322.

Hess, A., Hollander, R. and Mannheim, W. (1979). *J. Gen. Microbiol.* **115**, 247–252.

Hughes, R. C. and Thurman, P. F. (1970). *Biochem. J.* **117**, 441–449.

Ikemoto, S., Kuraishi, H., Komagata, K., Azuma, R., Suto, T. and Murooka, H. (1978). *J. Gen. Appl. Microbiol.* **24**, 199–213.

Ikemoto, S., Suzuki, K., Kaneko, T. and Komagata, K. (1980). *Int. J. Syst. Bacteriol.* **30**, 437–447.

Ishii, M., Kawasumi, T., Igarashi, Y., Kodama, T. and Minoda, Y. (1983). *Agric. Biol. Chem.* **47**, 167–169.

Ishizuka, I., Ueta, N. and Yamakawa, T. (1966). *Jpn. J. Exp. Med.* **36**, 73–83.

Jacin, H. and Mishkin, A. R. (1965). *J. Chromtogr.* **18**, 170–173.

Janczura, E., Perkins, H. R., and Rogers, H. J. (1961). *Biochem. J.* **80**, 82–93.

Johnson, N. C. and Goldfine, H. (1983). *J. Gen. Microbiol.* **129**, 1075–1081.

Kaneda, T. (1977). *Bacteriol. Rev.* **41**, 391–418.

Katayama-Fujimura, Y., Tsuzaki, N. and Kuraishi, H. (1982). *J. Gen. Microbiol.* **128**, 1599–1611.

Kates, M. (1964). *Adv. Lipid Res.* **2**, 17–90.

Kawahara, K., Uchida, K. and Aida, K. (1982). *Biochim. Biophys. Acta* **712**, 571–575.

Kawamoto, I., Oka, T. and Nara, T. (1981). *J. Bacteriol.* **146**, 527–534.

Kawasumi, T., Igarashi, Y., Kodama, T. and Y. Minoda (1984). *Int. J. Syst. Bacteriol.* **34**, 5–10.

Keddie, R. M. and Cure, G. L. (1977). *J. Appl. Bacteriol.* **42**, 229–252.

Komura, I., Yamada, K. and Komagata, K. (1975a). *J. Gen. Appl. Microbiol.* **21**, 97–107.

Komura, I., Yamada, K., Otsuka, S. and Komagata, K. (1975b). *J. Gen. Appl. Microbiol.* **21**, 251–261.

König, H. and Kandler, O. (1979). *Arch. Microbiol.* **121**, 271–275.

Langworthy, T. A. (1982). In *Methods in Enzymology*, Vol. 88 (L. Packer, ed.), pp. 396–406. Academic Press, London.

Langworthy, T. A., Tornabene, T. G. and Holzer, G. (1982). *Zbl. Bakteriol. Hyg., I. Abt. Orig.* **C3**, 228–244.

Leaper, S. and Owen, R. J. (1981). *Curr. Microbiol.* **6**, 31–35.

Lechevalier, M. P. and Lechevalier, H. (1970). *Int. J. Syst. Bacteriol.* **20**, 435–443.

Lechevalier, M. P., Horan, A. C. and Lechevalier, H. (1971). *J. Bacteriol.* **105**, 313–318.

Lechevalier, M. P., Lechevalier, H. and Horan, A. C. (1973). *Can. J. Microbiol.* **19**, 965–972.

Lechevalier, M. P., De Bievre, C. and Lechevalier, H. (1977). *Biochem. Syst. Ecol.* **5**, 249–260.

Lennarz, W. J. (1966). *Adv. Lipid Res.* **4**, 175–225.

Macfarlane, M. G. (1962). *Nature* **196**, 136–138.

Minnikin, D. E., Alshamaony, L. and Goodfellow, M. (1975). *J. Gen. Microbiol.* **88**, 200–204.

Minnikin, D. E., Patel, P. V., Alshamaony, L. and Goodfellow, M. (1977a). *Int. J. Syst. Bacteriol.* **27**, 104–117.

Minnikin, D. E., Pirouz, T. and Goodfellow, M. (1977b). *Int. J. Syst. Bacteriol.* **27**, 118–121.

Minnikin, D. E., Collins, M. D. and Goodfellow, M. (1979). *J. Appl. Bacteriol.* **47**, 87–95.

Minnikin, D. E., Minnikin, S. M., Goodfellow, M. and Stanford, J. L. (1982). *J. Gen. Microbiol.* **128**, 817–822.

Minnikin, D. E., Minnikin, S. M., O'Donnell, A. G. and Goodfellow, M. (1984a). *J. Microbiol. Meth.* **2**, 243–249.

Minnikin, D. E., O'Donnell, A. G., Goodfellow, M., Alderson, G., Athalye, M., Shaal, A. and Parlett, J H. (1984b). *J. Microbiol. Meth.* **2**, 233–241.

Miyagawa, E., Azuma, R. and Suto, T. (1978). *J. Gen. Appl. Microbiol.* **24**, 341–348.

Miyagawa, E., Azuma, R., Suto, T. and Yano, I. (1979). *J. Biochem.* **86**, 311–320.

Moss, C. W., Samuels, S. B. and Weaver, R. E. (1972). *Appl. Microbiol.* **24**, 596–598.

Moss, C. W., Samuels, S. B., Liddie, J. and McKinney, R. M. (1973). *J. Bacteriol.* **114**, 1018–1024.

Moss, C. W., Weaver, R. E., Dees, S. B. and Cherry, W. B. (1977). *J. Clin. Microbiol.* **6**, 140–143.

O'Donnell, A. G., Minnikin, D. E., Goodfellow, M. and Parlett, J. H. (1982). *FEMS Microbiol. Lett.* **15**, 75–78.

Omura, S., Takahashi, Y., Iwai, Y., and Tanaka, H. (1982). *J. Antibiot.* **35**, 1013–1019.

Op den Kamp, J. A. F., Bonsen, P. P. M. and van Deenen, L. L. M. (1969). *Biochim. Biophys. Acta* **176**, 298–305.

Oshima, M. and Ariga, T. (1975). *J. Biol. Chem.* **250**, 6963–6968.

Oshima, M. and Miyagawa, A. (1974). *Lipids* **9**, 476–480.

Oyaizu, H. and Komagata, K. (1981). *J. Gen. Appl. Microbiol.* **27**, 57–107.

Oyaizu, H. and Komagata, K. (1983). *J. Gen. App. Microbiol.* **29**, 17–40.

Oyaizu, H., Komagata, K., Amemura, A. and Harada, T. (1982). *J. Gen. Appl. Microbiol.* **28**, 369–388.

Palleroni, N. J., Kunisawa, R., Contopoulou, R. and Doudoroff, M. (1973). *Int. J. Syst. Bacteriol.* **23**, 333–339.

Polglase, W. J., Pun, W. T. and Withar, J. (1966). *Biochim. Biophys. Acta* **118**, 425–426.
Powls, R., Redfearn, E. R. and Trippett, S. (1968). *Biochem. Biophys. Res. Commun.* **33**, 408–411.
Redfearn, F. R. and Powls, R. (1968). *Biochem. J.* **106**, 50P.
Scheuerbrandt, G. and Bloch, K. (1962). *J. Biol. Chem.* **237**, 2064–2068.
Schleifer, K. H. and Kandler, O. (1972). *Bacteriol. Rev.* **34**, 407–477.
Schleifer, K. H. and Seidl, P. H. (1985). In *Chemical Methods in Bacterial Systematics* (M. Goodfellow and D. E. Minnikin, eds.), pp. 201–219. Academic Press, London.
Seidl, P. H., Faller, A. H., Loider, R. and Schleifer, K. H. (1980). *Arch. Microbiol.* **127**, 173–178.
Shaw, N. (1968). *Biochim. Biophys. Acta* **164**, 453–436.
Shaw, N. (1970). *Bacteriol. Rev.* **34**, 365–377.
Shaw, N. (1974). *Adv. Appl. Microbiol.*, **17**, 63–108.
Shibuya, I. and Maruo, B. (1966). *Agric. Biol. Chem.* **30**, 1058–1060.
Stackebrandt, E. and Fiedler, F. (1979). *Arch. Microbiol.* **120**, 289–295.
Stackebrandt, E., Seiler, H. and Schleifer, K. H. (1982). *Zentralbl. Bakteriol. Hyg., I. Abt. Orig.* **C3**, 401–409.
Stackebrandt, E., Fowler, V. J., Fiedler, F. and Seiler, H. (1983). *Syst. Appl. Microbiol.* **4**, 470–486.
Staneck, J. L. and Roberts, G. D. (1974). *Appl. Microbiol.* **28**, 226–231.
Suzuki, K. and Komagata, K. (1983). *Int. J. Syst. Bacteriol.* **33**, 188–200.
Suzuki, K., Saito, K., Kawaguchi, A., Okuda, S. and Komagata, K. (1981). *J. Gen. Appl. Microbiol.* **27**, 262–266.
Suzuki, K., Kawaguchi, A., Saito, K., Okuda, S. and Komagata, K. (1982). *J. Gen. Appl. Microbiol.* **28**, 409–416.
Swings, J., Gillis, M., Kersters, K., De Vos, P., Gosselé, F. and De Ley, J. (1980). *Int. J. Syst. Bacteriol.* **30**, 547–556.
Swings, J., De Vos, P., Van den Mooter, M. and De Ley, J. (1983). *Int. J. Syst. Bacteriol.* **33**, 409–413.
Tahara, Y., Kameda, M., Yamada, Y. and Kondo, K. (1976a). *Agric. Biol. Chem.* **40**, 243–244.
Tahara, Y., Yamada, Y. and Kondo, K. (1976b). *Agric. Biol. Chem.* **40**, 1449–1450.
Takahashi, Y., Iwai, Y. and Omura, S. (1984). *J. Gen. Appl. Microbiol.* **30**, 377–387.
Tamaoka, J., Katayama-Fujimura, Y. and Kuraishi, H. (1983). *J. Appl. Bacteriol.* **54**, 31–36.
Tanaka, S., Suto, T., Isayama, Y., Azuma, R. and Hatakeyama, H. (1977). *Ann. Sclavo* **19**, 67–82.
Tisdall, P. A. and Anhalt, J. P. (1979). *J. Clin. Microbiol.* **10**, 503–505.
Tomiyasu, I. and Yano, I. (1984). *Eur. J. Biochem.* **139**, 173–180.
Toriyama, S., Yano, I., Masui, M., Kusunose, E., Kusonose, M. and Akimora, N. (1980). *J. Biochem.* **88**, 211–221.
Tsukamura, M. (1974). *Jpn. J. Microbiol.* **18**, 37–44.
Uchida, K. and Aida, K. (1977). *J. Gen. Appl. Microbiol.* **23**, 249–260.
Uchida, K. and Aida, K. (1979). *J. Gen. Appl. Microbiol.* **25**, 169–183.
Uchida, K. and Aida, K. (1984). *J. Gen. Appl. Microbiol.* **30**, 131–134.
Uchida, K. and Mogi, K. (1972). *J. Gen. Appl. Microbiol.* **18**, 109–129.
Urakami, T. and Komagata, K. (1979). *J. Gen. Appl. Microbiol.* **25**, 343–360.
Urakami, T. and Komagata, K. (1984). *Int. J. Syst. Bacteriol.* **34**, 188–201.
Veerkamp, J. H. (1971). *J. Bacteriol.* **108**, 861–867.

Vilkas, E., Massot, J. C. and Zissman, E. (1970). *FEBS Lett.* **7**, 77–79.
Wada, H., Okada, H., Suginaka, H., Tomiyasu, I. and Yano, I. (1981). *FEMS Microbiol. Lett.* **11**, 187–192.
Ward, J. B. (1981). *Microbiol. Rev.* **45**, 211–243.
Watanuki, M. and Aida, K. (1972). *J. Gen. Appl. Microbiol.* **18**, 469–472.
Whistance, G. R. and Threlfall, D. R. (1968). *Biochem. J.* **108**, 505–507.
Yamada, K. and Komagata, K. (1970a). *J. Gen. Appl. Microbiol.* **16**, 103–113.
Yamada, K. and Komagata, K. (1970b). *J. Gen. Appl. Microbiol.* **16**, 215–224.
Yamada, K. and Komagata, K. (1972). *J. Gen. Appl. Microbiol.* **18**, 417–431.
Yamada, Y. and Kondo, K. (1973). *J. Gen. Appl. Microbiol.* **19**, 59–77.
Yamada, Y., Aida, K. and Uemura, T. (1969). *J. Gen. Appl. Microbiol.* **15**, 181–196.
Yamada, Y., Okada, T., Ueshima, O. and Kondo, K. (1973). *J. Gen. Appl. Microbiol.* **19**, 189–208.
Yamada, Y., Inouye, G., Tahara, Y. and Kondo, K. (1976a). *J. Gen. Appl. Microbiol.* **22**, 203–214.
Yamada, Y., Nakazawa, E., Nozaki, A. and Kondo, K. (1976b). *J. Gen. Appl. Microbiol.* **22**, 285–292.
Yamada, Y., Arimoto, M. and Kondo, K. (1976c). *J. Gen. Appl. Microbiol.* **22**, 293–299.
Yamada, Y., Nojiri, M., Matsuyama, M. and Kondo, K. (1976d). *J. Gen. Appl. Microbiol.* **22**, 325–337.
Yamada, Y., Inouye, G., Tahara, Y. and Kondo, K. (1977). *Biochim. Biophys. Acta* **486**, 195–203.
Yamada, Y., Takinami-Nakamura, H., Tahara, Y., Oyaizu, H. and Komagata, K. (1982). *J. Gen. Appl. Microbiol.* **28**, 7–12.
Yamamoto, A., Yano, I., Masui, M. and Yabuuchi, E. (1978). *J. Biochem.* **83**, 1213–1216.
Yano, I. and Saito, K. (1972). *FEBS Lett.* **23**, 352–356.
Yano, I., Saito, K., Furukawa, Y. and Kusunose, M. (1972). *FEBS Lett.* **21**, 215–219.
Yano, I., Tomiyasu, I. and Yabuuchi, E. (1982). *FEMS Microbiol. Lett.* **15**, 303–307.

5

Microbial Systematics Based on Electrophoretic Whole-Cell Protein Patterns

PETER J. H. JACKMAN

Division of Microbiology, AFRC Institute of Food Research, Colney Lane, Norwich NR4 7UA, UK

METHODS IN MICROBIOLOGY
VOLUME 19   ISBN 0–12–521519–3

I. Introduction

It can be estimated that some one to two thousand genes in the prokaryote genome are expressed as proteins at one time in the microbial cell. This estimate is partly based on the number of proteins separated by two-dimensional polyacrylamide electrophoresis (2D PAGE) from *Escherichia coli* by O'Farrell (1975). This is currently the highest-resolution technique for the separation of proteins utilizing separation by isoelectric point and then by molecular size to give a pattern of protein spots distributed over a gel.

It is apparent that electrophoretic methods for the description of all the proteins in the cell used comparatively would have wide application in microbial taxonomy, identification and typing.

II. Background

Polyacrylamide gels have the invaluable property of possessing a pore size of the same order as biological macromolecules. Furthermore, the pore size can be varied by using gels of different concentrations (range 3–30%) to allow separation of a whole variety of particles, including whole ribosomes, DNA fragments and proteins down to a molecular weight of perhaps 5000. In a suitable buffer, protein molecules are charged, and when a voltage is applied they migrate through the gel at rates dependent on their charge, size and shape.

Electrophoresis techniques have diversified to include gradient PAGE, isoelectric focusing and 2D PAGE; all under a variety of buffer conditions. For a review of practical techniques see Hames and Rickwood (1981).

Applications of whole-cell protein patterns in microbial systematics have been reviewed by Kersters (1985). Studies include: application of numerical analysis by Kersters and De Ley (1975); numerical analysis of gradient gels (Jackman, 1982); correlation with DNA:DNA hybridization (Owen and Jackman, 1982); epidemiological typing (Hudson *et al.*, 1976); correlation with API tests and GLC of volatile metabolites (van Vuuren *et al.*, 1981); correlation with phage groups (Jarvis and Wolff, 1979); large-scale study (Moore *et al.*, 1980) and 2D PAGE (Roberts *et al.*, 1980; Rodwell and Rodwell, 1978; Mouches *et al.*, 1979; Jackson *et al.*, 1985).

III. Standardization

Although protein pattern comparison has been used taxonomically since the introduction of electrophoresis in 1964 and numerical taxonomic analysis of patterns since 1975, the technique seems still not to have fulfilled its full potential. Some limiting factors have been

(a) lack of an accepted single electrophoretic technique for systematics;
(b) lack of reproducibility of electrophoretic techniques in general;
(c) lack of objective methods of comparison.

Jackman (1985) has proposed that a method based on that of Laemmli (1970) would prove most suitable for adoption as a standard 1D technique for systematics. Briefly the separation parameters are SDS-PAGE in 10 mm long 5% stacking gel and then in a 100 mm long 10% separation gel in the buffer system of Laemmli. Recommended ranges for gel thickness, run current and temperature were given. A detailed description is given later in this chapter.

While 2D PAGE offers the best resolution, it is still considered impracticable for large numbers of strains, and is difficult to standardize. In addition, the fine level of discrimination between strains (a single protein difference can be detected) may not be required for many applications in systematics. One-dimensional SDS-PAGE seems to offer the best combination of resolution and reproducibility; being of higher resolution than non-denaturing systems and higher reproducibility than gradient PAGE or IEF, which can offer somewhat higher resolution. In addition, it is the technique already in most widespread use for separation of proteins by molecular size. Gels of 10% concentration seem to give the best distribution of molecular weights over the gel. Patterns of greater length than 100 mm seem to offer little improvement in resolution of whole-cell extracts and may be precluded by the scan-length restrictions imposed by most densitometers.

IV. Planning a study

It is important to be aware of the limitations of protein pattern systematics before starting an extensive study. One-dimensional protein patterns have a similar level of taxonomic discrimination to DNA:DNA hybridization measurements. They are most useful around the species level in most taxonomic groups. That is to say, there is not usually a genus specific pattern, and so if a very diverse group of organisms is being studied some preselection of strains by other taxonomic criteria is necessary. Conversely, if a very narrow range of organisms is studied (e.g. serotypes) the one-dimensional protein patterns may not discriminate them at all or the differences between patterns may be too small to be sufficiently reproducible between gels. Naturally, it is difficult to predict the range of variation in a new study, and so a pilot study of 10–20 strains estimated to encompass the full range of diversity anticipated should be performed on a single gel.

While it is possible to separate several hundred samples by electrophoresis in a few weeks, often ease of culture and cell breakage will be limiting factors in the speed of the study. For example, if the cells can be broken by lysozyme then less than 0.1 g wet weight of biomass is required, whereas if a French press is needed then some 5–10 g will be required. Research to establish the most efficient cell-breakage method pays dividends if a large number of strains are to be examined.

It is also essential to measure the level of gel-to-gel reproducibility as soon as good patterns are obtained and before a large-scale study is underway. It is important that the reproducibility is objectively measured, as visual estimates tend to be over-optimistic. Reproducibility should be considered in association with the discrimination found in the study. Average similarity between replicate samples from different electrophoretic runs should be at least 80% of the range of discrimination found in a study, where discrimination- $= 100 -$ lowest similarity found.

V. Culture of microorganisms

A medium that supports the growth of all the organisms in the study should be selected. All culture conditions should be kept as constant as possible and studies of pattern variation with time of harvesting, medium composition and other culture variables should be made. Liquid culture for harvest of the organisms at a particular growth phase is preferred but solid culture may prove more convenient. Kersters and De Ley (1975) found a strain of *Agrobacterium* to have fewer bands when grown on a simple defined medium compared with the pattern on a complex medium. Jackman (1981) found small changes with age of culture and presence of serum in the media with a *Corynebacterium* species, but these were within the same range as gel-to-gel variation. More studies of the effects of culture conditions on one-dimensional PAGE patterns need to be made in future.

Reproducibility of culture conditions should be measured by analysis on a single gel of samples prepared from independently grown cultures derived from a single colony isolate.

VI. Sample preparation

It is difficult to standardize sample preparation, as organisms vary greatly in their susceptibility to cell-breakage methods. It is best to employ a method

requiring the minimun biomass. Mechanical breakage is generally inconvenient when working with pathogens.

It is best if the organisms can be broken by boiling in the SDS sample
treatment buffer; if not then pretreatment with lysozyme is the next-best
approach. All steps may be performed in a single 1.5 ml Eppendorf-type
tube. Cells (0.1 g wet weight) are harvested and washed in distilled water and
then suspended in a 1.0 ml of sample treatment buffer (0.625 M Tris-HCl,
pH 6.8; 2% SDS; 5% 2-mercaptoethanol; 10% glycerol). The suspension is
then heated at 100 °C for 10 min. Heating is important for the destruction of
protease activity in samples as well as for protein solubilization and SDS
binding. The extract is then centrifuged at 13 000g for 10 min to remove cell
debris and the supernatent stored at − 20 °C until required. Cell-breakage
methods were reviewed by Coakley et al. (1977). Reproducibility of sample
preparation should be measured by analysis on a single gel of samples
prepared from aliquots of cells from a single culture.

VII.   Electrophoresis

The method described here is that of Laemmli (1970), with a number of
suggestions for standardization. A particular type of apparatus is not
specified, but the multigel apparatus designed by the Hoefer Company can be
recommended (Hoefer Scientific Instruments, 650 Fifth St, Box 77387, San
Francisco, California, USA. Marketed by Bio-Rad and LKB in Europe).

Quantities given here are for six 1.5 mm thick gels in the Hoefer apparatus.

A.   Stock reagents for SDS-PAGE (Laemmli, 1970)

All chemicals are from the Sigma Chemical Company, St Louis, Missouri,
USA, apart from glycine and sodium dodecyl sulphate (specially pure, Prod
44244) from BDH Chemicals Ltd, Poole, Dorset, UK.

Monomer
Acrylamide, 584 g, *N,N'*-bismethylene acrylamide, 16 g; add distilled water
to 2 l; stir and filter.

Stacking-gel buffer
Trizma Base, 30 g; adjust to pH 6.8 with HCl; add distilled water to 500 ml;
stir and filter.

Separation-gel buffer
Trizma base, 363 g; adjust to pH 8.8 with HCl; add distilled water to 2 l; stir
and filter.

Sample-treatment buffer (double working strength)
Stacking gel buffer, 25 ml; SDS, 4 g; glycerol, 20 ml; 2-mercaptoethanol, 10 ml; add distilled water to 100 ml.

The above solutions should be stored at 4 °C in the dark.

10% SDS
SDS, 10 g; add distilled water to 100 ml.

Tank buffer
Trizma base, 48 g; glycine, 230 g; SDS, 16 g; add distilled water to 16 l.

Stain stock
Coomassie Blue R-250, 20 g; add distilled water to 2 l; stir and filter.

Stain
Stain stock, 250 ml; methanol, 1 l; acetic acid, 200 ml; add distilled water to 1 l.

Fast destain
Methanol, 1 l; Acetic acid, 200 ml; add distilled water to 2 l.

Slow destain
Methanol, 1 l; Acetic acid, 700 ml; add distilled water to 10 l.

The above solutions should be stored at room temperature.

B.   Preparation of gels

Day 1: afternoon

Follow the manufacturer's instructions for the construction and sealing of the gel cassettes and then add a small paper label with a unique gel number to the bottom-left corner of each cassette. For six 1.5 mm thick gels the separation gel contains
  monomer (4 °C), 67 ml;
  separation-gel buffer (4 °C), 50 ml;
  distilled water (4 °C) to 193 ml.
Deaerate the above mixture under vacuum (oil vacuum pump) for 10 min in a 500 ml side-arm conical flask with stirring. Then add
  ammonium persulphate (anydrous), 90 mg freshly dissolved in 5 ml distilled water;
  10% SDS (room temp), 2 ml;
  TEMED (4 °C), 60 μl;

swirl to mix, and then fill cassettes using a 50 ml syringe. Insert PVC blank comb to form the top surface of the separation gel 10 mm below the bottom of the well-forming comb for 10 mm of stacking gel. The gels should be set after about 10 min; after 30 min remove the blank combs and flush the newly formed surface with distilled water. Overlay gel surface with fourfold-diluted separation-gel buffer. Leave gels at room temperature overnight to complete polymerization.

Gel-polymerization time is one of the most critical factors in obtaining reproducible separations. It is suggested that the time for polymerization under the conditions described should be maintained at 10 ± 2 min. The most difficult factor to control is the concentration of oxygen in the polymerization mixture; oxygen is a potent inhibitor of polymerization. One method of measuring the polymerization rate is to monitor the temperature rise during polymerization in a portion of the mixture. The time to reach half the overall temperature rise should be maintained at 10 ± 2 min. The polymerization rate is preferably controlled by adjusting deaeration; or otherwise by adjustment of the quantity of persulphate and TEMED.

Day 2: morning

Drain overlay from the surface of the separation gels. The stacking gel contains
  monomer (4 °C), 10 ml;
  stacking-gel buffer (4 °C), 15 ml;
  distilled water (4 °C) to 54 ml.
Deaerate as before and add
  ammonium persulphate (anhydrous), 60 mg freshly dissolved in 5 ml distilled water;
  10% SDS (room temp), 0.6 ml;
  TEMED (4 °C), 40 µl.
Swirl to mix, and briefly rinse and drain the separation-gel surfaces with polymerization mixture. Fill cassettes, insert well-forming combs and allow to polymerize for 30 min. Remove combs and rinse wells thoroughly with distilled water and then fill with tank buffer.

C.   Electrophoretic separation

In general, highest reproducibility is obtained if the study can be completed in the minimum number of electrophoretic runs. This can be achieved by using a multislab apparatus and running as many samples on each gel as possible. Since reproducibility tends to be higher within a gel than between electrophoretic runs, the best strategy is to run the samples in random order to avoid this bias, carry out numerical analysis, and then rerun the samples in their clustered order to check for anomalies. On each gel a replicate whole-cell pattern and a mixture of pure proteins should be run which can be used to measure reproducibility and to correct for gel-to-gel variation. The following mixture is recommended for the standard method: phosphorylase b (94K), albumin (67K), ovalbumin (43K), carbonic anhydrase (30K), trypsin inhibitor (20K) and α-lactalbumin (14K). These are available as a low-molecular calibration kit (Pharmacia Fine Chemicals). Bromophenol Blue is added to the calibration mixture (final concentrations 0.001%) to act as a visible marker during electrophoresis. These two reference samples are best run centrally on each gel.

Reproducibility within gel, within run and from run-to-run should be measured by electrophoresis of aliquots of a single whole-cell sample.

Samples are best applied using a 10–50 μl syringe with repeater. The outer 20 mm of gel should not be used, in order to avoid edge distortion.

Electrophoresis is then performed at a constant current of 30 mA per 1.5 mm gel, which generally takes 3–4 h. Run time and voltage rise during electrophoresis are sensitive measures of separation reproducibility, but no ranges can be specified at present.

After electrophoresis, gels are removed from their cassettes and stained overnight in a stirred solution of Coomassie Blue.

Day 3

Stained gels are destained with stirring Fast Destain for 1 hour and then in Slow Destain until a clear background is obtained. After destaining, patterns are brought back to 100 mm by brief immersion in Fast Destain. Gels are then dried between cellophane under vacuum on a gel drier for long-term preservation.

D.   Accelerated method

The above procedure may be reduced to a single day by omitting the overnight polymerization and running at 500 V if gels are fully immersed in stirred buffer. Staining may be reduced to 1 h, or even less if gels < 1.5 mm thick are used.

E.   Troubleshooting guide

Problem	*Solution*
Polymerization too slow	Check reagents, pH of buffers, deaeration, dry persulphate.

Distorted bands, mixing of samples	Increase polymerization of stacking gel, dialyse sample to remove salts. Reduce loading.
General curvature of bands across gel	Increase cooling, stir lower buffer.
Vertical streaking	Load less sample, centrifuge sample, well damaged by syringe needle.
Large band comigrating with Bromophenol Blue	Proteolysis occurring, heat with SDS longer and/or add inhibitors.
Bromophenol Blue diffuse or double	Sample or buffer solution decomposition.
Run too slow	Buffer too concentrated, current too low.
Run too fast	Buffer dilute, current too high.

VIII. Analysis of patterns

The best currently available method is by numerical taxonomic analysis of densitometric traces as described by Kersters and DeLey (1975), Jackman *et al.* (1983) and Feltham and Sneath (1979).

There are certain situations where analysis by existing computer programs is either unnecessary or fails. First, computer analysis is unnecessary if only a few strains are being studied and can be compared on a single gel, or if in a larger study many strains give identical patterns. Secondly, analysis by current programs fails if it is wished to study fine differences between strains that fall into the same range as gel-to-gel variation as found by Jackman and Pelczynska (1986). The general strategy of analysis is as follows:

(1) recording of absorbance traces from densitometer;
(2) correction of traces for pattern variation (e.g. gel-to-gel);
(3) calculation of similarity between traces;
(4) formation of similarity matrix;
(5) clustering of similarity matrix;
(6) assessment and presentation of microbial relationships.

The first three steps pose many problems unique to protein pattern systematics, while the last three are general to numerical taxonomy.

A.   Recording of patterns

Recording of the protein patterns can be done by using a scanning densitometer with a slit aperture scanning down the centre of each gel track, recording of the whole gel image with a video camera or manual recording of band positions with the aid of a graphics pad; all linked to a computer. Only data acquisition with a scanning densitometer will be considered here.

Current generation densitometers (e.g. Joyce-Loebl Chromoscan 3, LKB Ultrascan) have a built-in computer interface (e.g. RS 232). Earlier models will require an analog-to-digital converter to digitize the output voltage and send the values to the computer. The computer program reads the interface channel and stores the absorbance values as a file in disk memory. Generally a trace of absorbance values measured to one part in 256, taken at 0.1 mm intervals along the pattern will be suitable. Trace-recording programs are very machine-specific, and so advice should be sought from the densitometer manufacturer as to further details.

B.   Pattern correction

A number of factors need to be considered. First, the start and end of each pattern has to be located. Secondly, the variations between gels have to be measured and removed if possible. A possible method is described here, but further research is needed in this area.

If a calibration whole-cell sample is present on every gel as described earlier, variations in the positions of a number of selected calibration peaks from gel to gel can be measured. The assumption is made that variations in the calibration track accurately reflect variations in the test tracks on the same gel. The assumption does not hold if there is curvature of bands across the gel or if local areas of distortion exist. The calibration peaks divide the gel into segments. The segment lengths are calculated on each gel. One calibration pattern is taken as a study reference, and then the corresponding segments in the test patterns on a gel are mathematically expanded or contracted to equal the lengths of the corresponding segments in the study reference pattern.

C.   Calculation of similarity between patterns

Two approaches to pattern comparison are possible: reductive and total. In the reductive approach the information of perceived importance is detected and abstracted from the originally recorded description of the pattern. This information would seem to be peak position and area in protein patterns. However, there is great difficulty in abstracting this information from whole-cell patterns, as in fact the majority of peaks are only partially resolved from one another. This results in unreliable peak detection and measurement of area. Secondly, the character of absolute peak position is the least reproducible in electrophoresis. Thirdly, this approach is known to be inadequate theoretically, as two-dimensional patterns have demonstrated that the majority of peaks in the one-dimensional pattern contain several proteins.

The second approach is to retain all recorded information and use shape or overlap of the absorbance traces to assess similarity. Comparison of shape using the correlation coefficient has been used by most workers so far. The advantages of the shape are that it is fairly insensitive to sample loading and gives some measure of similarity when peaks only partially match. Its main disadvantage is a weighting towards the largest features of the pattern, i.e. large bands or gaps and a consequent insensitivity to resolution. Measurement of overlap has similar properties to shape, but is sensitive to sample loading.

So far no single approach has been completely successful or seems to correspond absolutely with visual assessment, which seems to have an element of feature recognition in it. That is to say, when we compare complex patterns we tend to base the assessment on a few perceived "distinctive" features. Such an approach is unsuitable for taxonomy, which seeks to objectively measure the overall similarity between organisms but may prove useful in identification of species where accepted type strains exist.

Several procedures can be applied to corrected patterns prior to calculation of $\%S$. Firstly the background trend can be removed from the absorbance traces. This emphasizes the peaks and increases the discrimination of the correlation coefficient. Secondly, scaling of trace total areas to be equal helps remove loading variation. Thirdly, $\%S$ can be recalculated at successive displacements of a pair of patterns to detect similar but misaligned patterns.

D. Similarity matrix and clustering

Once similarity between patterns has been calculated, a range of numerical taxonomic procedures can be applied to form a similarity matrix, cluster and present strain relationships as shaded matrices and dendrograms. An example study of 200 strains of oral streptococci using the methods described is shown in Fig. 1.

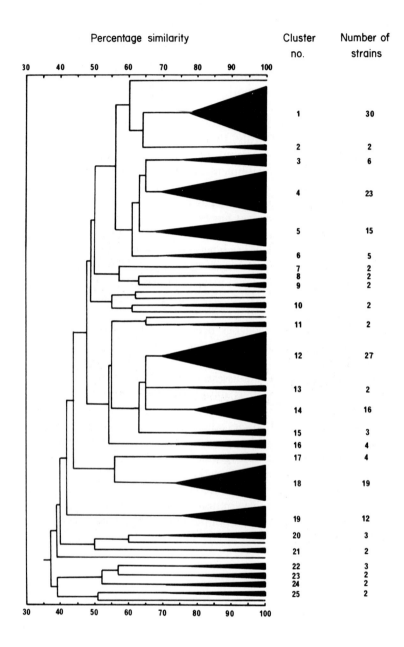

Fig. 1. Numerical taxonomy of 200 strains of oral streptococci based on SDS-PAGE of whole-cell proteins. Similarity was calculated using the correlation coefficient and clustering by UPGMA.

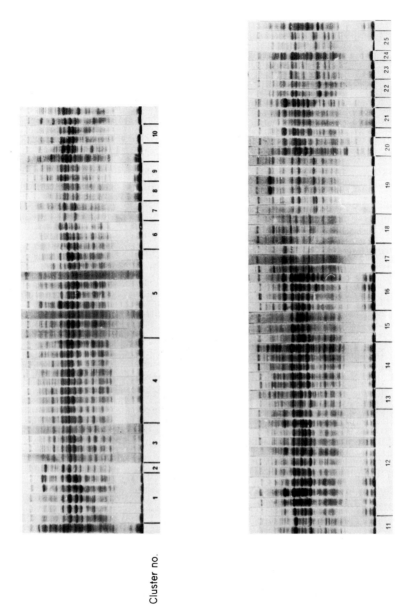

Cluster no.

Fig. 1. (cont). Representative patterns of strains analysed arranged in cluster order.

E. Computer implementation

Generally a single-user computer is necessary to record absorbance traces from the densitometer, as these have to be recorded in real time. It is generally convenient to use a microcomputer for this step. Traces may then be transferred to a bigger computer for the more time consuming processes of trace correction and numerical taxonomy. However, it is quite feasible to perform all procedures with a microcomputer if necessary. Parameters to be considered include mass storage requirements for original and processed traces. For example, standard 100 mm long traces composed of 20 values per mm will require about 4 K bytes storage per pattern. RAM requirements are usually dictated by the size of matrix to be clustered. A study of 200 strains requires a minimum of 21 K for the matrix plus program code. The slowest step is formation of the matrix, and calculation of similarity is the critical routine to optimize for speed. As a very rough guide, formation of a matrix of 100 strains will take several hours on a microcomputer, and this time increases with the square of the number of strains. Programs in BASIC running on the Commodore 3032 are given by Jackman *et al.* (1983). A refined program in UCSD Pascal is available from the author.

F. Identification

Patterns may be used equally for numerical taxonomy, identification of unknowns and typing. The simplest approach to identification is to simply compare the unknown with a data base of all previously recorded patterns. If truly representative type strains are available, these can be used or average patterns created from the clusters formed in numerical taxonomy. Typing of strains can be achieved if there is sufficient discrimination found. Groups found should be described as electropherotypes. There is no reason to presume that electropherotypes should correspond with other schemes such as serotypes.

IX. Potential in the clinical laboratory

There is considerable scope for future use of whole-cell protein patterns in the identification and typing of clinical isolates. However, the following advances will have to be made:

(1) scale down biomass requirement to single colony;
(2) increase speed of processing from cell breakage to dried gel—currently a minimum of about 6 h;
(3) improve reproducibility by commercial supply of ready-made gels;
(4) establish databases of patterns of clinically important species.

Assuming that these advances can be made, the advantages of general application and objectivity of the technique can be fully exploited.

X.   Comparison with other techniques

A.   Comparison with numerical taxonomy based on classical tests

Numerical taxonomy based on whole-cell protein patterns has a number of advantages over that based on classical tests. All the characters are obtained at one time from a single "test", and the results of the "test" can be read by an automated system. Consequently data acquisition is very much faster and objective. The same test can be applied to all groups of organisms; there is no need to select a set of "appropriate" tests for a study of a particular group, and exactly the same methods of analysis may be applied to all groups. Test error in studies published so far has been similar for both methods, but taxonomy based on conventional tests has the advantage of having the possibility of excluding "bad" tests from the study altogether. Taxonomy based on conventional tests also has the advantage that the level of discrimination can be adjusted by test selection to match the level of variation found in a particular group of strains under study. Taxonomy based on whole-cell proteins has a fixed level of discrimination, which may be too high or too low for some studies.

Conventional test taxonomy has the advantage of not requiring any expensive capital equipment to carry out the tests (such as electrophoresis equipment and scanning densitometer), but the cost per strain is less for protein patterns.

B.   Comparison with DNA:DNA hybridization

Whole-cell protein pattern comparison has a similar level of discrimination to DNA:DNA hybridization, but is very much faster since no purification steps are involved and each strain can be compared with each other with no extra effort. The cost of capital equipment is similar (densitometer versus spectrophotometer or scintillation counter), but the cost of consumables per strain is much less with protein patterns.

Both methods have the disadvantage of requiring cell breakage in comparison with classical tests.

C.   Comparison with chemotaxonomy

Chemotaxonomy, meaning chemical analysis of cell constituents such as fatty acids, menaquinones, mycolic acids, polar lipids and peptidoglycan structure is not strictly comparable with the above methods, since the types of analyses applied are very dependent on the microbial group being studied. In addition, it is usually not possible to gain an overall assessment of relationships in terms of a percentage similarity.

XI. Future developments

Adoption of a standardized 1D technique would bring many benefits in the areas of reproducibility and interpretation. Research such as that of Anderson and Anderson (1978a, b) on large-scale application of 2D PAGE may enable more widespread use of that technique in microbial taxonomy. Undoubtedly there is room for further research into standardization and correction in PAGE. Possibly new electrophoretic separation media and or other protein separation methods such as HPLC may be employed in taxonomy. Study of ribosomal or other subsets of whole cell proteins should enable more distant microbial relationships to be measured comparable with rRNA studies. Continuing advances in computation should enhance analysis of patterns.

Acknowledgements

The Medical Research Council are thanked for support of this work. R. A. Whiley, Department of Oral Microbiology, The London Hospital, London EC1 is thanked for Figure 1 and unpublished data.

References

Anderson, N. G. and Anderson, N. L. (1978a). Analytical techniques for cell fractions. XXI. Two-dimensional analysis of serum and tissue proteins: multiple isoelectrical focusing. *Anal. Biochem.* **85**, 331–341.

Anderson, N. G. and Anderson, N. L. (1978b). Analytical techniques for cell fractions. XXII. Two-dimensional analysis of serum and tissue proteins. Multiple gradients slab electrophoresis. *Anal. Biochem.* **85**, 341–354.

Coakley, W. T., Bately, A. J. and Lloyd, D. (1977). Disruption of micro-organisms. *Adv. Microbiol Physiol.* **16**, 279–341.

Feltham, R. K. A. and Sneath, P. H. A. (1979). Quantitative comparison of electrophoretic traces of bacterial proteins. *Comput. Biomed. Res.* **12**, 247–263.

Hames, B. D. and Rickwood, D. (eds.) (1981) *Gel Electrophoresis of Proteins: a Practical Approach.* IRL Press, Oxford.

Hudson, B. W., Quan, T. J. and Bailey, R. E. (1976). Electrophoretic studies of the geographic distribution of *Yersinia pestis* protein variants. *Int. J. Syst. Bacteriol.* **26**, 1–16.

Jackman, P. J. H. (1981). Taxonomy of aerobic axillary coryneforms based on electrophoretic protein patterns. Ph.D. thesis. University of London.

Jackman, P. J. H. (1982). Classification of Corynebacterium species from axillary skin by numerical analysis of electrophoretics protein patterns. *J. Med. Microbiol.* **15**, 485–492.

Jackman, P. J. H. (1985). Bacterial taxonomy based on electrophoretic whole-cell protein patterns. In *Chemical Methods in Bacterial Systematics* (M. Goodfellow and D. Minnikin, eds.), pp. 115–129. Academic Press, London.

Jackman, P. J. H. and Pelczynska, S. (1986). Characterization of Corynebacterium Group JK by whole-cell protein patterns. *J. Gen. Microbiol.* **132**, 1911–1915.

Jackman, P. J. H., Feltham, R. K. A. and Sneath, P. H. A. (1983). A program in BASIC for numerical taxonomy of microorganisms based on electrophoretic protein patterns. *Microbios Lett.* **23**, 87–93.

Jackson, P., Thornley, M. J. and Thompson, R. J. (1985). A study by high resolution two-dimensional polyacrylamide electrophoresis of relationships between *Neisseria gonorrhoeae* and other bacteria. *J. Gen. Microbiol.* **130**, 3189–3201.

Jarvis, A. W. and Wolff, J. M. (1979). Grouping of lactic streptococci by gel electrophoresis of soluble cell extracts. *Appl. Environ. Microbiol.* **37**, 391–398.

Kersters, K. (1985). Numerical methods in the classification of bacteria by protein electrophoresis. In *Computer Assisted Bacterial Systematics* (M. Goodfellow, D. Jones and F. G. Priest, eds.), pp. 337–368. Academic Press, London.

Kersters, K. and De Ley, J. (1975). Identification and grouping of bacteria by numerical analysis of their electrophoretic protein patterns. *J. Gen. Microbiol.* **87**, 333–342.

Laemmli, U. K. (1970). Cleavage of structural proteins during the assembly of the head of bacteriophage T4. *Nature* **227**, 680–685.

Moore, W. E. C., Hash, D. E., Holdeman, L. V. and Cato, E. P. (1980). Polyacrylamide slab gel electrophoresis of soluble proteins for studies of bacterial floras. *Appl. Environ. Microbiol.* **39**, 900–907.

Mouches, C., Vignault, J. G., Tully, T. G., Whitcomb, R. F. and Bove, J. M. (1979). Characterisation of Spiroplasmas by one and two dimensional protein analysis on polyacrylamide slab gels. *Curr. Microbiol.* **2**, 69–74.

O'Farrell, P. H. (1975). High resolution of two-dimensional electrophoresis of proteins. *J. Biol. Chem.* **250**, 4007–4021.

Owen, R. J. and Jackman, P. J. H. (1982). The similarities between *Pseudomonas paucimobilis* and allied bacteria derived from analysis of deoxyribonucleic acids and electrophoretic protein patterns. *J. Gen. Microbiol.* **128**, 2945–2954.

Roberts, G. P., Leps, W. T., Silver, L. E. and Brill, W. J. (1980). Use of two-dimensional electrophoresis to identify and classify Rhizobium strains. *Appl. Environ. Microbiol.* **39**, 414–422.

Rodwell, A. W. and Rodwell, E. S. (1978). Relationships between strains of *Mycoplasma mycoides* sub spp. *mycoides* and *capri* studied by two-dimensional gel electrophoresis of cell proteins. *J. Gen. Microbiol.* **109**, 259–263.

van Vuuren, H. J. J., Kersters, K. and De Ley, J. (1981). The identification of Enterobacteriaceae from breweries: combined use and comparison of API 20E system, gel electrophoresis of proteins and gas chromatography of volatile metabolites. *J. Appl. Bacteriol.* **51**, 51–65.

6

Characterization of Microorganisms by Pyrolysis Mass Spectrometry

COLIN S. GUTTERIDGE

Cadbury Schweppes PLC, Group Research, The Lord Zuckerman Research Centre, The University, Whiteknights, Reading RG6 2LA, UK

METHODS IN MICROBIOLOGY
VOLUME 19 ISBN 0–12–521519–3

I. Introduction

A. The need for automated methods in microbiology

The identification of microorganisms using conventional procedures is a
highly developed routine employing a wide range of morphological, serological, nutritional and biochemical tests. Identification methods have developed
steadily since the beginnings of microbiology, and can be applied to the
characterization of hundreds (thousands?) of different microorganisms.
Unfortunately, relative to modern analytical chemical techniques, conventional diagnostic microbiology is inherently slow because of the need to grow
the organism in the test medium to elicit a response. As demand for faster
identification has increased, conventional methods have been augmented by
rapid diagnostic tests based on immunological or genetic criteria. The
application of, for example, enzyme-linked immunosorbent antibodies and
genetic probes, has thus far been targeted at organisms of public-health
significance because of the high development costs associated with the
commercialization of such systems. Furthermore, these tests are highly
specific, and any one test can only be used to confirm the identity of a single
species or type of organism. In the future it seems possible to hypothesize
machines that will perform a wider range of comparisons against, for
example, isolated DNA, but these are still on the drawing board. Thus,
despite the exciting developments in monoclonal-antibody and DNA-probe
technology, there is still room within the gamut of techniques used by the
microbiologist for systems that can produce rapid comparisons of a wide
range of microorganisms to aid identification and classification.

In the past two decades significant strides have been made in the
application of analytical techniques (e.g. HPLC, gas chromatography,
protein electrophoresis) to problems of microbial taxonomy and identification (Goodfellow and Minnikin, 1985). These approaches have all provided,
in selected areas, important chemotaxonomic information, and some techniques have been developed sufficiently to be exploited as identification
methods. Examples include whole-protein electrophoresis, which is used in
the AMB-ID identification system (V. A. Howe, London) and fatty-acid
methyl-ester profiling, which is carried out by the Hewlett-Packard HP5898A
gas-chromatography identification system. All of these analytical approaches
to identification have some disadvantages, which is why none have really
come to prominence. Two problems that are commonly discussed are (a) the
requirement for a large mass of cells and (b) complex and lengthy extraction
procedures. The demand for rapid identification technology is still being met
by simple miniaturization of conventional tests, coupled, in some systems,
with automated reading.

In discussing the need for more automated approaches to microbial identification, Meuzelaar (1974) considered the essential features of a novel technique for microbial characterization to be as follows.

1. Applicability to a wide range of microorganisms.

2. Specificity; i.e. the technique should be able to characterize organisms at genus, species and subspecies levels, and attribute differences to recognizable chemical characters.

3. Reproducibility.

4. Speed, both for a single sample and with respect to overall throughput of samples.

5. Sensitivity; i.e. the technique should be able to allow the analysis of a single colony from a culture plate.

Most microbiologists would add an additional feature, not considered by Meuzelaar, but of extreme importance. It is the experience of chemotaxonomy that different approaches to the study of the taxonomy of a group of microorganisms produce complementary information, and any novel technique for microbial identification, however rapid, must produce results that are recognizable within accepted schemes.

Meuzelaar considered that his essential features were most likely to be fulfilled by the technique of pyrolysis mass spectrometry (Py-MS), which is not surprising considering that the instrumentation required for Py-MS had been developed in his laboratory with this purpose in mind. A review of the literature since 1974 does not suggest that his optimism for the future role of Py-MS in microbiology was justified. However, the technology used in Py-MS is complex, and it is only recently that user-friendly commercial instrumentation has been available. Also, the data-handling requirements of Py-MS are severe, and sophisticated procedures based on multivariate statistical techniques have had to be developed and tested. For these reasons the role of Py-MS in microbiology is still to be determined, but the technology is now available for this determination to be made over the next five to ten years. This chapter describes the instrumentation and data-handling procedures used in Py-MS, reviews those applications that have been published and discusses the problems of the technique, relative to other chemotaxonomic methods, so that a prediction of its future role can be made.

B.   The origins of pyrolysis mass spectrometry

A mass spectrometer is a device in which electrically neutral molecules are ionized (become positively or negatively charged), are separated on the basis of their mass-to-charge ratios (m/z), and are detected and recorded. Mass spectrometers are used widely in organic chemistry for the structural characterization and identification of compounds, and there is considerable variation between instruments in the method of production, separation, collection and recording of ions (Hill, 1966). With respect to the types of mass spectrometer used for Py-MS the following instrumental variations are worthy of note.

(a) Ion production

1. Electron-impact ionization (high and low voltage): ions are produced by interaction with an electron beam.
2. Chemical ionization: ions are produced by interaction with a reagent gas under pressure.
3. Field ionization: ions are produced by the influence of high-intensity electric fields.

(b) Ion separation

1. Deflection in a magnetic field (magnetic mass analyser).
2. Selection by direct-current voltage and radio-frequency response (quadrupole mass analyser).

(b) Ion detection

1. Amplification of ion currents (analog-to-digital conversion).
   Pulse counting: each pulse corresponds to the arrival of a single ion.

Mass spectrometry of any organic compound is always preceded by vaporization and ionization. Many of the newer developments in mass-spectrometry technology (e.g. fast-atom bombardment) are concerned with achieving the direct vaporization and ionization of intact non-volatile high-molecular-weight compounds. Polymers of intermediate molecular weight (10^3–10^4 repeating units) can now be characterized directly by some mass-spectrometry techniques (Fenselau, 1982). The direct analysis of microorganisms by mass spectrometry is not possible without the addition of a separate vaporizing procedure. This can be achieved by pyrolysis (controlled thermal degradation), which is a chemical process involving the transformation of complex materials into a series of lower-molecular-weight volatile compounds through the agency of heat alone. If pyrolysis is carried out in a chemically inert environment, molecules cleave at specific points to form smaller, more reduced, fragments that are characteristic of the original material.

Pyrolysis was first used in conjunction with gas chromatography (Py-GC), the original idea being credited to Davison *et al.* (1954), who applied the technique to the analysis of technical polymers. The development of Py-GC as a profiling technique, particularly for technical polymers, has been extensively documented (Irwin and Slack, 1978; Irwin, 1979a, b, 1982). In the late 1960s and early 1970s a series of publications from Reiner's group in Atlanta (e.g. Reiner, 1965; Reiner and Ewing, 1968; Reiner *et al.*, 1973) showed the application of Py-GC to microbial characterization. It is often reported that Reiner's interest was stimulated by developments at NASA, where a miniaturized Py-GC device was designed as a means of testing for the presence of extraterrestrial life (Wilson *et al.*, 1962). The original system was intended for the Surveyor series of lunar landers, but was never used. Later NASA developed a miniaturized mass spectrometer, which went to Mars on the Viking landers. Soil samples were heated to generate pyrolysis products, but true organic signals were never confirmed.

Reiner's work stimulated a number of other microbial studies using Py-GC, and those published up to 1978 are reviewed by Gutteridge and Norris (1979). None of this work developed to the stage where organisms could be routinely identified by Py-GC. Three reasons are cited for the poor development of Py-GC over this period.

1. Problems with long-term reproducibility. The chromatography columns used in most Py-GC studies had a finite lifetime, and when they were replaced they did not produce an identical chromatogram. Operating systems were devised to alleviate this problem (French *et al.*, 1980), but were not completely successful.

2. Lack of speed. Typical analysis times per sample for Py-GC range between 15 and 80 min depending on the resolution of the chromatographic column. Although an automated Py-GC system was constructed by Meuzelaar *et al.* (1975), it was difficult to use and it did not stimulate the development of commercially available copies. Hence the volume throughput of samples with Py-GC is inherently low.

3. Inadequate data handling. Many of the early reports of the use of Py-GC for microbial characterization are suspect because of the lack of use of data-handling procedures. Access to suitable statistical packages was restricted, and most workers relied on visual inspection of chromatograms, an approach that is unworkable as the database expands. Also, until recently, there were considerable problems in interfacing gas chromatographs with computers so that data could be captured automatically.

For these reasons Meuzelaar and Kistemaker (1973) argued that the application of pyrolysis for microbial characterization required the use of a different analytical separation and detection methodology. Zemany (1952) had already shown that pyrolysis products of biological materials could be analysed by a mass spectrometer, and Meuzelaar and Kistemaker (1973) undertook the development of the apparatus required to produce fully integrated Py-MS. Their concept was to build an instrument with no degradable parts, equivalent to a chromatography column, capable of analysing samples at a rate of one every five minutes and producing data in a manner suitable for computer processing.

In recent years some improvements have been made to the Py-GC technique, notably in the longevity and reproducibility of chromatography columns (Eudy et al., 1985) and the use of multivariate statistical techniques for data analysis (Magee et al., 1983), but Py-MS holds the advantage of speed. Discussions in this chapter will therefore be confined to Py-MS and, in particular, to the purpose-built instrumentation pioneered by Meuzelaar and Kistemaker (1973). Other methods of interfacing pyrolysis with mass spectrometry will be considered briefly.

II. Techniques and instrumentation

Schulten and Lattimer (1984) have classified the combination of pyrolysis with mass spectrometry into two distinct types of analysis. Pyrolysis gas chromatography can be combined with mass spectrometry (Py-GC-MS) in order to use the mass spectrometer as a detector to identify compounds eluted from the chromatography column. Effective analysis is dependent upon the interfacing of the pyrolysis system and the gas chromatograph and, in most cases, only qualitative data are collected. Microbiological problems have been investigated with Py-GC-MS (Simmonds, 1970; Engman et al., 1984; Eudy et al., 1985), but its true role in relation to Py-MS is as a method of identifying the chemical nature of pyrolysis products so that their origins can be understood.

A. Pyrolysis techniques

Most chemists would regard pyrolysis as a dirty and irreproducible technique to be used only as a last resort. In fact, provided that certain parameters are carefully controlled, the volatilization of samples by pyrolysis can be a highly reproducible degradative system with predictable mechanisms. In the design of any pyrolysis system there are two basic concerns (Schulten and Lattimer, 1984).

1. Time and temperature dependence. The primary decomposition (bond-scission) processes of any organic polymer are time- and temperature-dependent. Degradation reactions are competitive, and many fragmentation processes are completed before an equilibrium pyrolysis temperature T_{eq} is reached. Thus the temperature rise time and total heating time of any pyrolysis system are important factors in determining the composition of the pyrolysis products.

2. Fate of the primary pyrolysis products. If the primary decomposition products are not removed rapidly from the pyrolysis zone then secondary reactions will occur, with inevitable loss of reproducibility and the production of uncharacteristic fragments. The inertness of the transfer line to the mass spectrometer can be an important factor in determining the amount of secondary reactions.

Taking these concerns into account, a well-designed pyrolysis system should fulfil the following criteria.

1. Fast temperature rise times (10–100 ms) to alleviate problems from competitive reactions.

2. An appropriate T_{eq}. If this is too low then incomplete decomposition may result, and if it is too high then uncharacteristic low-molecular-weight fragments, produced by secondary reactions, may dominate the spectrum.

3. Small sample sizes (a few μg) avoid problems of thermal transfer within the pyrolysis unit.

4. Rapid transfer of primary pyrolysis products away from the pyrolysis zone to eliminate or reduce secondary reactions. In Py-GC-MS this is achieved by the use of an inert carrier gas and in Py-MS by the design of low-dead-volume inert inlet systems.

The literature reveals the existence of three different pyrolysis techniques used in Py-MS; direct-probe pyrolysis, laser pyrolysis and filament pyrolysis.

B. Direct-probe pyrolysis

A direct probe is a device, found on the majority of mass spectrometers, that allows a sample to be inserted, via a vacuum lock, into or close to the ion source of the instrument. These probes are fitted with heating units capable of raising the sample temperature up to, typically, 300–400 °C, although specially designed high-temperature probes capable of achieving 700 °C are becoming available for some types of mass spectrometer. Characteristic features of direct-probe techniques are the slow heating rates (maximum $60\,°C\,s^{-1}$), low pyrolysis temperatures (generally less than $300\,°C$) and the relatively long residence time of the pyrolysis products in the pyrolysis zone. Analysis times vary, but are of the order of 15 min per sample, and there are no automated direct probes so volume throughput is low. The design of the probe and the slow heating rate can be advantageous in some circumstances, as they allow pyrolysis to occur directly in the ion source, thereby preventing loss of products on transfer lines. Furthermore, the slow heating rate permits the use of slow-scanning magnetic-sector mass spectrometers while affording time-resolved registration of the pyrolysis patterns (Meuzelaar et al., 1982). However, direct probe techniques are notorious for contaminating the ion source, which affects long-term reproducibility, and for producing secondary pyrolysis reactions owing to the long residence time of products in the pyrolysis zone. For these reasons, direct-probe techniques are not suitable for longer-term work such as the establishment of databases for challenging with unknowns.

The application of direct-probe Py-MS to the differentiation of microorganisms was first shown by Anhalt and Fenselau (1975), who produced spectra from freeze-dried bacteria by thermal degradation within the ion source of a magnetic mass spectrometer operated with a high ionization voltage (70 eV), a technique that was repeated by Puckey et al. (1980) who showed the discrimination of five Pseudomonas species. Risby and Yergey (1976, 1978) used chemical ionization and a solids probe ramped at $20\,°C\,min^{-1}$ to $400\,°C$. Their technique was called linear-programming thermal-degradation mass spectrometry, and was distinctive because the slow heating rates allowed data on the evolution of individual ions to be collected and examined to achieve the discrimination of selected genera, species and strains. Adkins et al. (1984a, b) followed up these early reports with some detailed studies on cell-wall components of Bacillus strains and lipopolysaccharide preparations from Salmonella serotypes. Gutteridge and Puckey (1982) and Shaw et al. (1985) applied direct-probe Py-MS to the discrimination of some food-spoilage bacteria. A Finnigan 4000 mass spectrometer was used; the layout of the direct probe system is shown in Fig. 1. Samples of bacteria were transferred directly from the surface of agar culture plates to small quartz-glass tubes. Each sample was heated by the probe at $60\,°C\,m^{-1}$ from ambient to $300\,°C$ adjacent to the ion source of the instrument, which was operated at a reduced electron voltage (25 eV). The evolution of ions was monitored (examples of ion-current profiles are shown in Fig. 2) and an averaged spectrum obtained over a standardized region of the trace. Unfortunately the probe used for this work had an upper limit of $300\,°C$, and complete pyrolysis of the bacteria was not achieved.

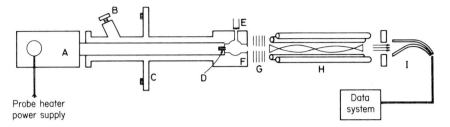

Fig. 1. Layout of a direct-probe Py-MS system: A, probe; B, valve; C, mass-spectrometer housing; D, probe tube; E, ion source; F, ionization region; G, lenses; H, quadrupole rods; I, electron multiplier. From Gutteridge and Puckey (1982).

Nevertheless, by the use of multivariate analysis techniques applied to averaged spectra, Gutteridge and Puckey (1982) were able to discriminate seven groups of Gram-negative bacteria belonging to the genera *Citrobacter*, *Serratia*, *Pseudomonas*, *Hafnia*, *Klebsiella*, *Acinetobacter* and *Proteus*. A library was created and challenged with unknowns belonging to the database with a 97% success rate, depending on the matching procedure used. Typical spectra of a *Citrobacter* and *Proteus* strain produced by averaging the ion-current profiles are shown in Fig. 3. In common with all Py-MS spectra of microorganisms, they are characterized by the absence of qualitative differences, and differentiation of the bacteria depends on the recognition of reproducible quantitative differences in particular ions, which requires the use of computing techniques. Direct-probe spectra contain signals up to m/z 400, with the ion clusters around m/z 236 and m/z 313 being attributed to membrane lipids. In contrast with filament Py-MS techniques, direct-probe systems detect strong lipid signals because of the proximity of the probe to the ion source. In filament Py-MS techniques lipids are condensed onto the transfer lines, which, for practical reasons, cannot be maintained at high temperatures (above 150 °C).

Shaw *et al.* (1985) carried out an extensive direct-probe Py-MS study of a group of lactic acid bacteria from vacuum-packaged meats. Again, by the application of multivariate statistical techniques to the quantitative (ion-intensity) data, the strains could be characterized into five groups, producing a classification with a close similarity to that obtained by conventional techniques. Tas *et al.* (1985) compared a different probe technique—direct chemical ionization (DCI)—with direct-probe electron-impact-ionization and chemical-ionization Py-MS. The DCI technique is a soft-ionization method in which bacteria are introduced into a hot source (240 °C) containing a reagent gas. Using *Serratia* and *Pseudomonas* strains, Tas *et al.*

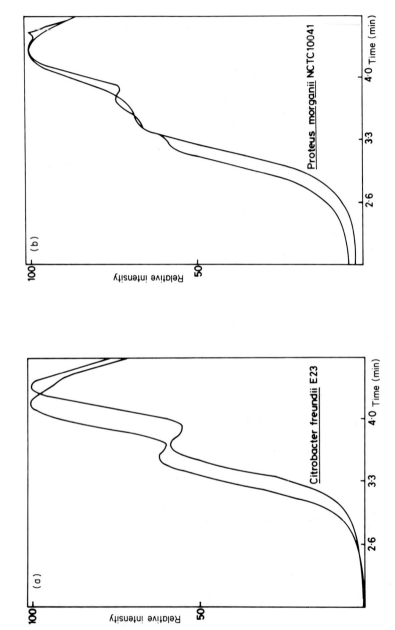

Fig. 2. Typical ion-current profiles for duplicate analyses of (a) *Citrobacter freundii* E23 and (b) *Proteus morganii* NCTC 10041. From Gutteridge and Puckey (1982).

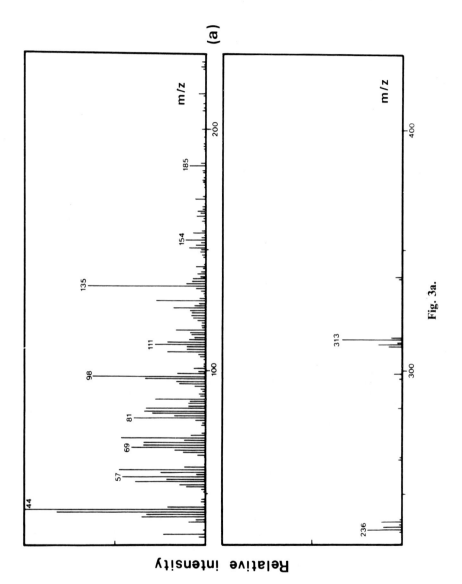

(a)

Relative intensity

m/z

m/z

Fig. 3a.

238

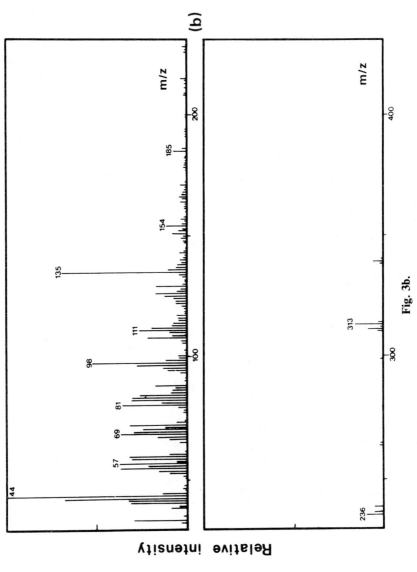

Fig. 3. Direct-probe Py-MS spectra of (a) *Citrobacter freundii* E23 and (b) *Proteus morgani* NCTC 10041. From Gutteridge and Puckey (1982).

reported the DCI technique to be faster and more sensitive than other probe techniques, and also gave spectra that could be interpreted chemically with greater ease.

C. Laser pyrolysis

Laser pyrolysis enables rapid and direct heating of a sample while avoiding the heating of large reactive substrate areas. This high spatial resolution allows the analysis of minute amounts of material. Potential designs of a laser-MS interface have been reported (Meuzelaar *et al.*, 1974; Kistemaker *et al.*, 1975), but there are problems in controlling the amount of energy deposited by unit sample volume, in defining the optimum parameters and in constructing mass spectrometers suitable for laser Py-MS (Meuzelaar *et al.*, 1982).

One instrument that employs laser pyrolysis is the laser microprobe mass analyser (LAMMA) (Kaufmann *et al.*, 1972; Wechsung *et al.*, 1978), which is in essence a combination of a microscope and a fast-scanning mass spectrometer. Samples are located by microscopy on a grid and are then vaporized and ionized by a high-power laser, which follows the same optical path. At high power density the technique produces spectra that are typical of pyrolysis, although they also contain fragments derived from desorption and ionization of intact molecular species (Hercules, 1983). LAMMA was originally designed for the surface analysis of materials for trace metals. When applied to biological systems, it is unique in that it can be used to analyse samples as small as a single bacterial cell and can produce information on inorganic and organic species. For example, Lindner and Seydel (1983) used LAMMA to examine the time-dependent changes in the intracellular Na^+/K^+ ratio of *Escherichia coli* under stress from a nitrofuran-based antibacterial agent.

There have so far been few applications of LAMMA to microbial systematics. Lindner and Seydel (1984) showed the differentiation of several species of *Mycobacterium* by the application of multivariate-analysis techniques to the positive ion spectra obtained from single cells. Bohm *et al.* (1985) have shown the discrimination of several closely related species of *Bacillus* by LAMMA.

D. Filament pyrolysis

Two types of filament pyrolyser have been used in Py-MS systems. Pyroprobes (Chemical Data Systems, Pennsylvania, USA) are galvanically heated platinum foils or coils that can be interfaced to a mass spectrometer via a chromatography column. Samples are placed directly onto the filament and excess water or solvent dried off before analysis. Pyroprobes have been used by Hudson *et al.* (1982) in a study of bacterial cell walls by Py-GC-MS, but are in general difficult to interface efficiently to mass spectrometers, and most Py-MS systems employ the alternative filament-pyrolysis technique—Curie-point pyrolysis.

First described by Giacobbo and Simon (1964), Curie-point pyrolysis differs from the conventional filament approach in that heating is generated inductively by a high-frequency coil. The pyrolysis temperature is determined by the composition of the metal alloy employed. At the Curie-point of a metal it ceases to be ferromagnetic, and a radio-frequency will no longer induce eddy currents and heating. Thus the Curie-point acts as a thermostatic switch, and different pyrolysis temperatures can be obtained through the use of different alloys, for example pure nickel 358 °C, pure iron 770 °C, 40% nickel/60% iron 610 °C.

The attractions of the Curie-point technique are its simplicity and ease of automation. A Curie-point filament can be a wire or a foil, onto which the sample is placed, and the wire plus sample can be contained within a glass sample tube, which is permeable to radio-frequency waves. Thus the glass tube can be used as a carrier to take the filament into the mass spectrometer, and this approach has been taken with all the automated Py-GC and Py-MS systems that have been constructed.

E.   Dedicated pyrolysis mass spectrometers

The stringent requirements of interfacing pyrolysis with mass spectrometry argue strongly for the construction of dedicated instrumentation. Some useful work has been carried out in fields other than microbiology on conventional mass spectrometers by employing an empty chromatography column as a surrogate expansion chamber (Hickman and Jane, 1979; Bracewell *et al.*, 1980). The use of an expansion chamber is crucial to the design of a dedicated system, as will become evident later.

The first dedicated Py-MS system was designed and built by Meuzelaar and Kistemaker (1973) at the FOM Institute in Amsterdam. The system used a glass-tube/wire Curie-point pyrolysis system with a reactor enclosed in the vacuum system and connected to the open electron-impact ionizer of a quadrupole mass spectrometer through a heated gold-coated expansion chamber. The expansion chamber serves two purposes: (a) it acts as a buffer volume to slow down the passage of the pyrolysis products and allow a sufficient number of scans to collect representative spectra; and (b) it minimizes contamination of the ion source, although most of the pyrolysis products with low volatility (e.g. lipids) condense on the cold walls of the glass tube (reaction tube). Expansion chambers are gold-coated to ensure that the walls are chemically inert and avoid degradation of the pyrolysis products, and heated to minimize condensation of low-molecular-weight species. Further technical development led to the construction of a fully automated system utilizing high-speed ion counting and computerized data-processing techniques (Muezelaar *et al.*, 1976). A schematic of this instrument is shown in Fig. 4. Two commercial copies of this system were manufactured: the Extranuclear 5000 (Extranuclear Laboratories, Pittsburgh, Pennsylvania, USA), which is an exact copy of the FOM design; and the Pyromass 8–80 (VG Gas Analysis, Middlewich, Cheshire, UK), which uses the same design concepts but employs a small magnetic mass analyser. The Pyromass 8–80 has been described in detail by Gutteridge *et al.*(1984) and Shute *et al.* (1984).

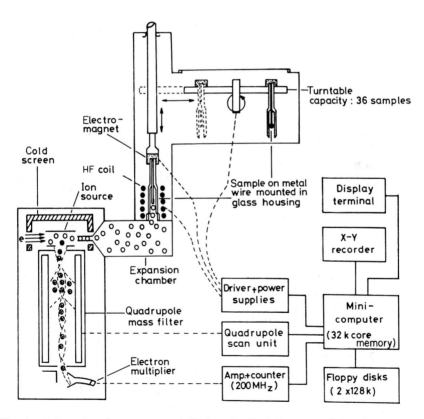

Fig. 4.   Schematic of an automated Curie-point Py-MS system (Meuzelaar *et al.*, 1976).

All of the Py-MS systems described so far, including Py-GC-MS techniques and LAMMA, are highly sophisticated instruments based on existing mass-spectrometry technology that is used for a number of applications. Consequently all these Py-MS systems are prohibitively expensive, costing upwards of £100 000. Recently a pyrolysis mass spectrometer has been developed for Prutec (London, UK) by P. A. Technology (Cambridge, UK). This instrument (Fig. 5) is marketed currently by Horizon Instruments (Heathfield, Sussex, UK) and promises to be the first low-cost (< £50 000) dedicated Py-MS instrument, and should increase the number of laboratories with access to the technique. The novel aspects of the Prutec system (PYMS 200X) concern the sample carrier, sample inlet and automation systems. The design concept hinges on the use of a thin V-shaped foil as the sample carrier rather than the Curie-point wire used on the FOM design. Foils have been used in Py-GC (Coulter and Thompson, 1977), but never in Py-MS. Samples for analysis are dried onto foils, which are inserted into small rimless glass tubes. The use of glass tubes permits two key design features. First, the tube can form the wall of the vacuum system during analysis, obviating the need for a valve to close off the inlet systems as in the Pyromass 8–80. Secondly, the radio-frequency generating coil can be held at atmospheric pressure, eliminating the need for costly feedthroughs into the vacuum system. A three-position valve (Fig. 6) enables a sample to be

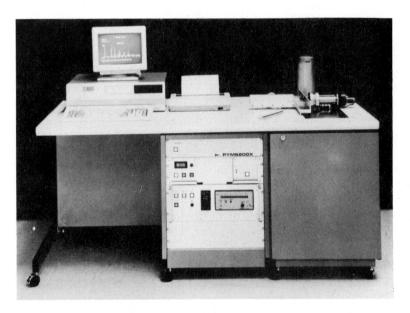

Fig. 5.   PYMS 200X automated Curie-point pyrolysis mass spectrometer.

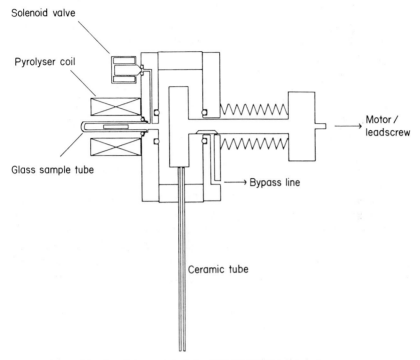

Fig. 6.   Schematic of the PYMS 200X inlet system.

loaded, evacuated and pyrolysed. A detailed account of the operation sequence is reported by Aries *et al.* (1986). Individual sample tubes are pushed through the pyrolyser coil by the arm of the automatic tube-handling system, and seal on the front face of the pyrolysis chamber by pressure on a Viton O-ring. After evacuation, the sample is subjected to Curie-point pyrolysis and the resulting pyrolysate passes into a gold-coated and heated (140 °C) expansion chamber. The pyrolysate enters the ion source as a molecular beam from a ceramic tube, and low-voltage electron-impact ionization (20 eV) spectra are collected following separation using a small quadrupole mass analyser and detection by high-speed ion counting. The instrument makes 160 scans of the pyrolysate, and produces an averaged spectrum over the range m/z 11–200. Raw mass-intensity data are normalized to the total ion count and are stored on floppy diskettes. The instrument is controlled by an IBM-PC-compatible microcomputer, which has the potential to carry out all necessary data processing. However, at the current stage of development, data are transferred to a mainframe computer for analysis.

The automation system (Fig. 7) uses a single motor to drive a mechanism

Fig. 7. Automation system of the PYMS 200X mass spectrometer.

that captures and lifts a tube from the magazine, pushes it through the pyrolyser coil, and then provides a constant axial force to seal the O-ring during analysis. When all the data have been collected the motor is reversed and the tube drops back into the rack, which is indexed along to the next position. The entire analysis cycle takes less than three minutes per sample, comparing favourably with other designs such as the Pyromass 8–80 (five minutes per sample). The development of a reliable automated inlet system is the major achievement of the PYMS 200X, as it brings the prospects of high-volume-throughput applications within reach.

One final and extraordinary type of Py-MS system was described by Sinha *et al.* (1985), who called it particle-beam mass spectrometry. The method involves the generation of a beam of single whole bacterial cells, which are forced to impact on the hot filament of a conventional electron-impact ion source, where they undergo immediate vaporization and ionization. The spectra obtained have a superficial similarity to LAMMA spectra, but are totally unlike Curie-point Py-MS spectra. The spectra contain enough information to discriminate species, but the instrument is so complex, large and expensive that it is doubtful if it will compete with systems such as the PYMS 200X as a routine fingerprinting method. Sinha *et al.* propose the use of particle-beam mass spectrometry for monitoring clean-air environments such as hospital operating theatres, but this seems rather far-fetched given the prohibitive cost of the equipment.

F.   Preparation of samples for Curie-point Py-MS

Curie-point filaments are cleaned by immersion in 10% hydrochloric acid for 30 min, followed by rinses in tapwater, distilled water and acetone or tetrachloroethylene and overnight vacuum drying at 200 °C. Glass tubes are cleaned by a similar procedure, following an overnight soaking in chromic acid.

One of the great advantages of Py-MS for the analysis of microorganisms is that colonies can be sampled from culture plates by direct transfer of biomass to the filament using a disposable loop. Since sample sizes are of the order of a few µg, a single colony can provide enough material for three replicate analyses. Samples from solution or suspension can be pipetted onto the filaments. Good operating practice is to vacuum-dry samples for 30 min prior to analysis. This is not strictly necessary, but limits the amount of water entering the mass spectrometer and improves the background over a long period of time.

III.   Data handling

A.   Why is data handling needed?

The need to use sophisticated data-handling procedures in tandem with Py-MS has already been stressed. In fact, it is true to say that without good data handling the application of Py-MS to microbiological problems is virtually impossible. To understand why data handling for Py-MS is such a complex problem, it is necessary to consider the structure of the data and the factors that influence its reproducibility.

Figure 8 shows pyrolysis mass spectra of peptidoglycan and teichoic acid, both purified from *Bacillus subtilis* (Meuzlaar *et al.*, 1982). These spectra are typical of those obtained using Curie-point Py-MS with most of the signals confined to the range m/z 16–250. Comparison of the spectra shows that the overall fragmentation pattern of both polymers is different, but they have many masses in common. The quantitative (mass-intensity) data are highly correlated chemically because each mass has a multiple origin during the thermal-degradation process. Consequently if two microorganisms are to be differentiated on the basis of the relative amounts of the pyrolysis products of peptidoglycan and teichoic acid, this is unlikely to be achievable using a

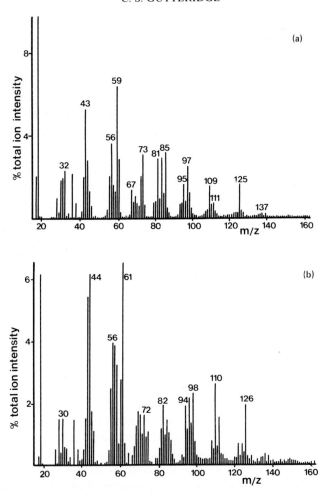

Fig. 8. Pyrolysis mass spectra of *Bacillus subtilis* peptidoglycan (a) and teichoic acid (b) (Meuzelaar *et al.*, 1982).

single mass, and usually a complex combination of several masses is required. A further complication arises from the use of normalization procedures to remove the effect of differing sample sizes. This necessary data-handling step also adds considerably to the correlations within the data.

The final influence on data structure is reproducibility. Pyrolysis mass spectrometry is a complex analytical technique, and although instruments are set up to a standard specification, a certain amount of "noise" in the data is inevitable. The spectra in Fig. 9 are duplicate analyses of whole cells of

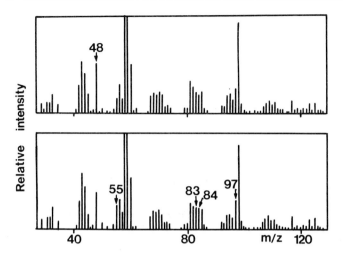

Fig. 9. Duplicate pyrolysis mass spectra of a *Listeria* (serotype IVb) strain (Eshuis *et al.*, 1977). Mass intensities differing by > 10% are allowed.

a *Listeria* serotype described as IVb (Eshuis *et al.*, 1977). Five masses have intensities that differ by more than 10%, a degree of difference between duplicates that is typical of Py-MS "noise". The overall aim of the data analysis is therefore to amplify differences between spectra that are reproducible and can provide information useful for the discrimination of microorganisms.

B. Systems and packages

A typical batch of Py-MS data may contain more than 30 000 mass-intensity measurements. Hence most data handling, to date, has been carried out off-line on mainframe computers using general-purpose statistical packages with multivariate analysis options. Examples include GENSTAT (Nelder, 1979), SPSS (Nie *et al.*, 1975), BMDP (Dixon, 1975) and ARTHUR (Kowalski, 1975). The ARTHUR package was designed specifically for minicomputers and features a version of the specialized program SIMCA (Wold, 1976, 1978). In addition to these general-purpose packages, the complexity of the Py-MS data-handling problem has stimulated the development of some purpose-written software, including FOMPYR (Eshuis *et al.*, 1977)—a package based on nonlinear mapping—NORMA (Huff *et al.*, 1981)—a program for interactive preprocessing—and HILDA (Gutteridge *et al.*, 1984)—an interactive stepwise discriminant analysis program. Recently an entire package of programs has been assembled for a microcomputer. Called SIGMA, this system promises to be the first user-friendly multivariate statistics package for small computers, but it is still to be reported properly, and is probably the forerunner of a number of similar packages.

C. Experimental design

Monitoring of reproducibility is an important part of any Py-MS study given the level of "noise" associated with any mass-spectrometric technique. Fortunately, Py-MS is such a rapid method that the simple expedient of analysing each sample in triplicate can usually be employed within the time constraints of routine analysis. This contrasts with conventional numerical taxonomy, where only a small percentage of samples are repeated to assess reproducibility. When Py-MS is applied to pure cultures the usual approach is to grow each strain as two separate cultures and to analyse two samples from each culture. This procedure ensures that variability due to culturing and sample preparation methods is reflected fairly within the data set. Generally, replicates are analysed sequentially to avoid complex formatting problems during computation.

As a check on longer-term reproducibility, it is advisable to analyse a few samples more than once. In all other respects the design of a Py-MS classification study should adhere to the accepted practices of numerical taxonomy with regard to such factors as the number of strains compared and choice of type cultures. The use of discriminant analysis techniques, however, may impose some constraints on the numbers of groups, the number of samples in a group and the analysis of unrelated groups.

D. Data-handling methodology

The various approaches to handling the complex data produced by Py-MS have been discussed in detail in a number of publications (MacFie and Gutteridge, 1982; Meuzelaar et al., 1982; Gutteridge et al., 1985). A summary of the major stages in a typical analysis is given in Fig. 10. In the author's laboratory, Py-MS data are analysed using a combination of two packages, HILDA and GENSTAT. HILDA (Highly Interactive Linear Discriminant Analysis) is a specially written Fortran 77 program containing procedures for normalization, error detection, calculation of characteristicity values (Eshuis et al., 1977), exploratory univariate displays and stepwise discriminant analysis. The GENSTAT program has been developed over a number of years of practical use of Py-MS, and contains routines for normalization, principal components analysis (PCA), canonical variates

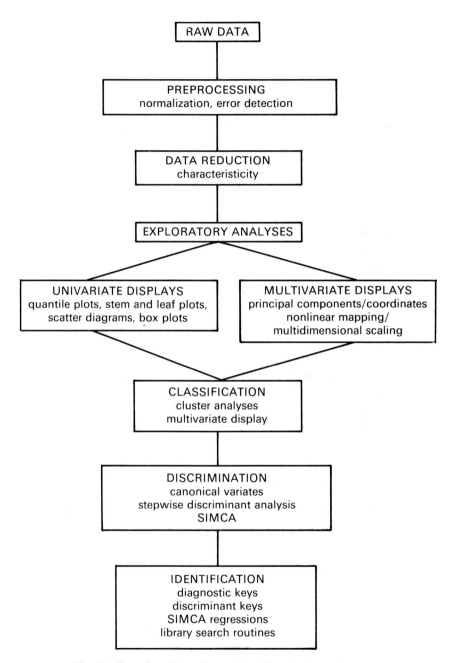

Fig. 10 Data-handling scheme (MacFie and Gutteridge, 1982).

analysis (CVA), cluster analysis and a type of "factor analysis" to allow chemical interpretation of the differences between the spectra.

E. Data pretreatment

The first stage in the data analysis is normalization, also known as pattern scaling. Each mass intensity is expressed as a percentage of the total ion intensity to compensate for variations caused by factors unrelated to the analytical problem such as sample size or instrument sensitivity. The procedure works better as the number of masses increases and as the variation in the individual mass intensities decreases (Gutteridge *et al.*, 1985). Problems arise with masses of very large intensity, since they affect the relative intensity of all other masses and can influence further data analysis. To overcome this problem, Johansson *et al.* (1984) proposed that variables of large magnitude should be eliminated from multivariate data sets and that only masses of similar mean and standard deviation should be employed in the normalization procedure.

F. Data reduction

Elimination of some data is usually necessary to reduce the amount of computer processing time required when dealing with large batches of Py-MS data. The feature-scaling method for achieving data reduction designed by Eshuis *et al.* (1977) is most elegant and illustrates vividly the underlying aim of the data analysis. In all data sets some features (i.e. mass intensities) may be constant across all the features observed (i.e. features that represent some aspect of the technique or a chemical compound occurring in all the samples). Other features may show large variations between replicates of the same sample. This high inner variance may be due to variability in the sample or experimental procedure and will contribute "noise" that may obscure the detection of differences between samples, i.e. the outer variance. Eshuis *et al.* (1977) proposed mathematical expressions for inner variance (reproducibility) and outer variance (specificity) of each feature. The variability of each feature was scaled to unity and then weighted by these expressions. The most effective choice of weight was found to be the ratio of outer to inner variance (characteristicity). This characteristicity factor is closely related to the well-known Fisher ratio, and large data sets can be reduced by selecting only those mass intensities with high characteristicity values.

   A classic illustration of the power of this data-reduction technique is provided by the analysis of the spectra representing the two *Listeria* serotypes (Fig. 9) using a multivariate display technique known as nonlinear mapping (Eshuis *et al.*, 1977). A nonlinear map of the raw data is shown in

Fig. 11(a). The two serotypes are not discriminated, and a good deal of replicate variation is apparent. In Fig. 11(b) the same data set is presented, but with the mass intensities scaled for reproducibility. A small improvement is obvious, but the two serotypes are still mixed. In Fig. 11(c) the data are weighted according to specificity, and the two serotype groups are revealed. In Fig. 11(d) the data are weighted by characteristicity, and the two serotypes are completely differentiated. Averaged spectra for these two serotypes are shown in Fig. 12, and the small differences in mass intensities responsible for the discrimination of the serotypes are marked. Figure 12 can be compared directly with Fig. 9, illustrating that, in a complex data set, reproducible and discriminatory mass intensities can be found by an appropriate data-handling technique. It should be emphasized that the differentiation of serotypes in this case was achieved without using prior information, and the success of the technique is due to the use of replicates to provide calculations of inner variance.

G. Principal components and canonical variates

Since the work of Eshuis *et al.* (1977), data-handling practice for Py-MS studies has changed in that PCA is used as a data-reduction technique and discriminant analysis, or its close analogue CVA (MacFie *et al.*, 1978), is applied to some or all of the principal components with non-zero variances (Windig *et al.*, 1983) in an attempt to discriminate between the groups of sample replicates. The original motivation for this change was to avoid the necessity of throwing away data by making a selection through characteristicity calculations.

Principal-components analysis is a well-known multivariate technique, which has been used extensively in numerical taxonomy and ecological studies. Apart from data reduction, its role is to display relationships within the data set and to detect outliers (Gutteridge *et al.*, 1979; MacFie and Gutteridge, 1982; Shute *et al.*, 1984). PCA treats each pyrolysis mass spectrum as a single sample, and does not take account of the replicate variation within the database. Thus its ability to discriminate is reduced by the complexity of the correlations within the data. In contrast, CVA uses prior knowledge of a group structure (*a priori* groups). In early studies the *a priori* groups were the genera, species or physiological types to which strains had been assigned by other techniques (see e.g. Gutteridge *et al.*, 1980). This was obviously unsatisfactory, but has been replaced by the declaration of groups of replicates, which requires no assumed microbiological information. The calculated principal components provide the input to the CVA. The raw mass intensities cannot be used because the number of variables would exceed the number of groups and render the analysis statistically invalid.

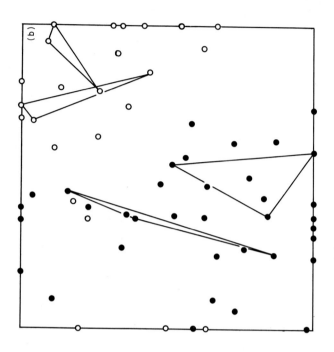

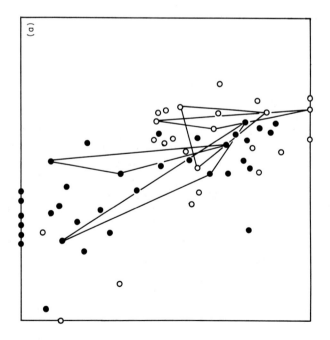

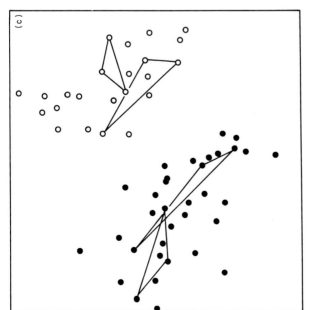

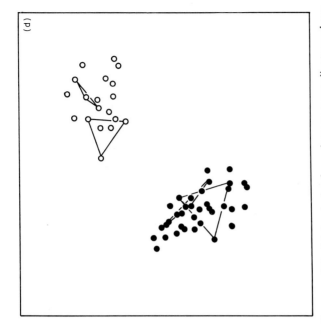

Fig. 11 Nonlinear maps of two *Listeria* serotypes: ○, Serotype I; ●, Serotype IVb. (a) Analysis of raw data; some replicate analyses are linked. (b) Analysis of data scaled by reproducibility. (c) Analysis of data weighted by specificity. (d) Analysis of data weighted by characteristicity. Taken from Eshuis *et al.* (1977).

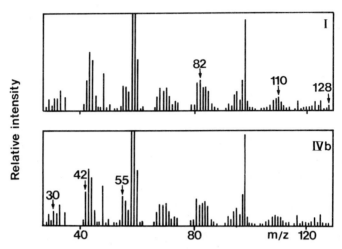

Fig. 12. Averaged pyrolysis mass spectra of two *Listeria* serotypes (I and IVb) (Eshuis *et al.*, 1977). Masses responsible for the discrimination seen in Fig. 11(d) are arrowed.

This approach to data handling has so far been restricted to Py-MS studies, but provides a powerful discriminating tool, which could be applied to data in other branches of microbiology (Gutteridge *et al.*, 1985).

H.   Cluster analysis

Determining the hierarchical relationships between strains analysed by Py-MS is of course an important task for the microbiologist. Unfortunately conventional cluster analysis, as used in numerical taxonomy, seems to produce confusing and unreliable results when applied directly to Py-MS data. This has been attributed to the lack of a suitable similarity coefficient that can cope with the complex correlations and inherent "noise" associated with Py-MS data (Gutteridge *et al.*, 1985). For example, when cluster analysis was applied to data from a direct-probe Py-MS study of Gram-negative bacteria (MacFie and Gutteridge, 1982), *Acinetobacter calcoaceticus* and *Serratia liquefaciens* were not discriminated and certain replicates did not cluster satisfactorily. These problems were not apparent with CVA.

Gutteridge *et al.* (1985) developed a cluster-analysis technique suitable for Py-MS data by mathematically transforming the Mahalanobis distance matrix produced by CVA to a similarity matrix, which could be addressed by average linkage clustering to produce a dendrogram. Dendrograms produced by this method have particular properties, and have to be interpreted with care and with reference to other methods such as CVA and minimum spanning trees (nearest-neighbours analysis).

I. Chemical interpretation

A great deal is now known about the chemistry of pyrolysis products and the mechanisms by which they are formed. Such details are beyond the scope of this chapter, but are covered by Irwin (1982) and Schulten and Lattimer (1984), and an excellent atlas of reference spectra and their interpretation has been published by Meuzelaar et al. (1982).

The pyrolysis of whole microorganisms yields a complex mixture of products from the thermal breakdown of the polymers that constitute the cell. Thus the interpretation of differences between spectra of microorganisms in chemical terms is exceedingly difficult. Schulten et al. (1973) and Schulten (1977), using specialized mass-spectrometric techniques, have assigned the pyrolysis products of whole bacteria cells to specific chemical classes. Hudson et al. (1982) and Eudy et al. (1985) have elucidated some of the pyrolysis products of bacterial cell walls using Py-GC-MS. The difficulty of getting a precise identification of an ion in a Py-MS spectrum is illustrated by a study conducted by Louter et al. (1980) to identify the origins of m/z 59, a critical mass for the discrimination of pathogenic and non-pathogenic mycobacteria. A highly specialized mass spectrometer had to be designed for the experiment. A collision cell was used to produce "daughter spectra" of the ions produced by Curie-point Py-MS. The identity of m/z 59 was eventually attributed to acetamide derived from N-acetylaminosugars in the cell wall, but this was the major and not the only source.

Fortunately it is not always necessary to revert to such complex mass spectrometry to extract chemical information from Py-MS spectra. The fragmentation of polymers to a series of ions provides an opportunity to extract some chemical information by recognizing the pattern of masses within a more complex spectrum of a whole sample. Data-handling techniques for achieving this have been developed and are loosely termed "factor analysis". The application of these techniques to Py-MS was pioneered during some chemotaxonomic studies on yeasts (Windig and Haverkamp, 1982; Windig and de Hoog, 1982; Windig et al., 1982a, b). The factors are often synonymous with principal components or canonical variates. In PCA and CVA the components or variates are linear combinations of the original mass intensities and are related to them by a set of coefficients known as loadings. Large loadings reflect masses that contribute significantly to the variation between samples shown by a particular principal component or canonical variate. Loadings can be rotated so that the masses relate to a single factor or axis projecting through a group of samples or a direction of interest, i.e. the factors can be realigned to emphasize pure properties in the underlying pyrolysis mass spectra. These can be plotted as simplified "factor spectra", which can be interpreted more easily in terms of known pyrolysis chemistry than the spectra of, for example, whole cells.

An example of factor analysis is provided in Figs. 13 and 14. The CVA plot in Fig. 13 shows the discrimination of sporulated and non-sporulated cells of a *Bacillus licheniformis* strain. In this case the main "factor" lies across the central axis (i.e. is the first canonical variate) and rotation is not required. The extracted factor spectrum (Fig. 14) has a positive and negative component. The positive part of the spectrum shows the masses that contribute most to the discrimination of sporulated cultures. Using the accumulated knowledge of studies on pure polymers (Meuzelaar *et al.*, 1982), we can attribute most of the masses in the positive (sporulated) part of the spectrum to pyrolysis products of proteins, i.e. m/z 34 (H_2S from cysteine and methionine), m/z 64 (SO_2, S_2 from all sulphur-containing amino acids), m/z 95 (C_5H_5NO from amino-sugars), m/z 107 (C_7H_9N, dimethylpyridine, m/z 108 (C_7H_8O, cresol from tyrosine), m/z 117 (C_8H_7N, indole and phenylacetonitrile from tryptophan and phenylalanine) and m/z 120 (C_9H_{12}, alkylbenzenes from tyrosine-containing proteins). In addition m/z 79 (C_5H_5N, pyridine) is suspected to be the major pyrolysis fragment from dipicolinic acid.

The negative part of the spectrum shows the masses that contribute most to the discrimination of the non-sporulated cultures. Many can be interpreted as pyrolysis products of hexose-containing polymers, including m/z 28

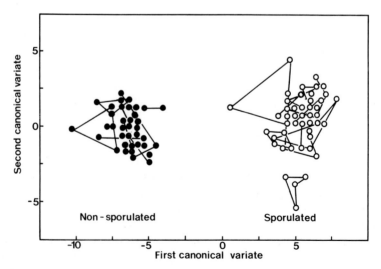

Fig. 13. Canonical variates analysis, showing differentiation of sporulated and non-sporulated forms of *Bacillus licheniformis*.

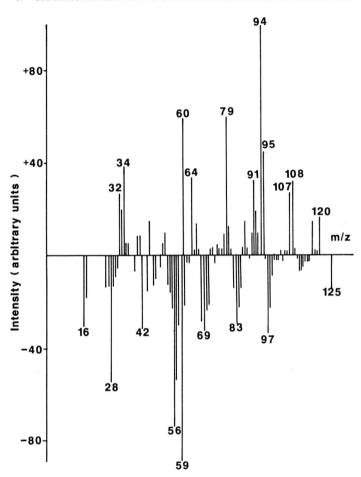

Fig. 14. Factor spectrum showing masses that contribute most to the discrimination of sporulated (positive masses) and non-sporulated (negative masses) forms of *Bacillus licheniformis* (see Fig. 13).

(C_2H_4, ethene), m/z 42 (C_3H_6, propene), m/z 56 (C_4H_8, butene) and m/z 68 (C_4H_4O, furan). Others are characteristic of aminosugars, including m/z 59 (C_2H_5NO, acetamide), m/z 69 (C_4H_7N, 2–methylpropanenitrile), m/z 97 (C_5H_7NO) and m/z 125 (uncharacterized).

The interpretation of the factor spectrum in Fig. 14 makes sense in terms of what is known about the difference in structure between a spore and a vegetative cell. Spores are protein-rich and contain dipicolinic acid. The spectrum corresponding to the vegetative cell is dominated by the kinds of fragments derived from the bacterial cell wall. In fact, in a detailed study of the Curie-point Py-MS spectra of whole cells, cell walls and isolated cell wall polymers of *Bacillus subtilis* var *niger* WM, Boon *et al.* (1981a) were able to interpret the differences between magnesium and phosphate-limited cells in terms of masses characteristic for teichuronic and teichoic acid. It should be emphasized, however, that there is no absolute proof for such assignments— they are based on the interpretation of spectra against reference standards. Also, as is the case in Fig. 14, not all of the masses can be assigned or their role as a discriminating feature explained. In the future, Py-GC-MS studies can be expected to advance knowledge of the pyrolysis products of microorganisms and improved methods for clarifying the essential factors that discriminate samples will become more widely available. The VARDIA technique used by Windig *et al.* (1984, 1986) holds promise as a means of eliminating the subjectivity of chemical interpretation, but at this stage it requires further work.

IV.   Microbiological applications of Py-MS

Before discussing the role of Py-MS as a characterization technique for microorganisms, it is worth considering a few other areas of microbiology where the techniques might have an impact.

A.   Detection of microorganisms

Pyrolysis mass spectrometry cannot be used to estimate numbers of microorganisms in a sample, because the spectra obtained reflect the mass of cells pyrolysed, whereas a count is an indication of the ability of individual cells to reproduce and form a colony. Estimates of biomass by weight are possible by Py-MS, but are of little practical use to microbiologists.

A further possibility is that Py-MS could be used to detect products of microbial activity as a means of early detection of growth. The use of analytical chemical techniques for the detection of microbial activity has never proved successful, because there is no improvement in sensitivity over traditional methods. For example, in a study of the spoilage of vacuum-packed beef, Edwards *et al.* (1985) found that the concentration, as measured by gas chromatography, of the two main constituents of off-odours, cadaverine and putrescine, only increased significantly when bacterial numbers exceeded 10^7 cells ml^{-1}. At this level the growth of spoilage organisms can be observed visually. There are no published accounts of the application of Py-MS to the detection of microbial products, but a pilot study in the author's laboratory could not detect the growth of lactic acid bacteria in orange juice until numbers exceeded 10^6 ml^{-1}.

The possibilities for more sensitive detection of microbial metabolites have been shown by the study of Boon *et al.* (1984), who looked at the complete culture environment of the anaerobic bacterium *Bacteroides gingivalis*. Gaseous metabolites were sampled by coating a Curie-point wire (358 °C) with an absorbent layer of activated charcoal and leaving it above the culture. Trapped volatile metabolites were evaporated from the wire directly into the mass spectrometer, while bacterial cells and growth medium were analysed using the standard Curie-point method. Different spectra were obtained in each case, and sensitive alterations to the growth medium could be monitored.

A recent study by Huff *et al.* (1986) considered the application of Py-MS to antibiotic-sensitivity testing. Exposure of *Escherichia coli* cells to toxic levels of penicillin and gentamycin produced clear changes in the Py-MS spectra in as little as two hours. Healthy growing bacteria gave spectra with prominent DNA, RNA, amino-acid and peptide signals, while unhealthy non-growing bacteria gave spectra dominated by organic acids and ketones.

B. Ecology and biotechnology

The potential of Py-MS as a tool within microbial ecology was first demonstrated by Boon and Haverkamp (1979), who investigated, on a laboratory scale, a marine benthic ecosystem designed to study the effects of bioturbation of the lugworm *Arenicola marinarum* on the marine biota. The upper layers of the surface sediment were found to produce Py-MS spectra dominated by the pyrolysis products of proteins, polysaccharides and *N*-acetylaminosugars derived from algae. Signals obtained from lower layers were attributed to end products of metabolism of sulphate-reducing bacteria. Boon *et al.* (1981b) used Py-MS as one of a battery of analytical techniques to study the make-up of solar-lake laminated cyanobacterial mats.

Attention has been drawn to the potential of Py-MS as a tool for biotechnology (Gutteridge and Norris, 1983). Possible uses include checking the purity of biological preparations, the monitoring of growth or the production of metabolites in a fermenter, and the characterization of structural polymers. Windig *et al.* (1981) were able to detect the presence of DEAE-dextran in suspensions of poliovirus produced in microcarrier culture of primary monkey-kidney cells. The DEAE-dextran gave a characteristic mass at m/z 86, which was used to produce a standard curve allowing the detection of as little as 20 ppm by Py-MS analysis of the whole virus preparation. A similar application was reported by Wieten *et al.* (1982), and involved the detection of trichloroacetic acid (TCA) in purified protein derivative (PPD), which is a refined version of tuberculin and is used as a diagnostic for previous mycobacterial infections (Mantoux test). A distinctive series of masses (m/z 83, 85, 87) was used to detect TCA in PPD with a lower limit of sensitivity of 10 ppm. Haverkamp *et al.* (1980) showed the application of Py-MS to the structural characterization of biopolymers by the analysis of *Neisseria meningitidis* capsular polysaccharides containing sialic acid. The group B, C, W-135 and Y capsular polysaccharides were differentiated, and a large number of partially purified group B preparations were shown to have the same basic structure.

C. Characterization of microorganisms

From the small number of Py-MS characterization studies that have been carried out over the past decade, it is possible to make the following general points.

1. The successful use of Py-MS for the discrimination of microorganisms requires cultures to be presented for analysis in a similar form. In practice, this means standardization of the growth medium and culture conditions so that organisms are in a similar physiological state. This is not always easy to achieve, especially when comparing unrelated organisms from differing ecological niches. Shute *et al.* (1984) have shown that pyrolysis mass spectra of strains of the aerobic sporeforming bacterium *Bacillus* vary according to the age (physiological state) of the culture, and this affects the observed relationships between different species. When young actively growing cultures were analysed, four species (*B. subtilis, B. amyloliquefaciens, B. pumilus* and *B. licheniformis*) could all be differentiated. In contrast, when sporulated cultures were analysed, three species (*B. subtilis, B. amyloliquefaciens* and *B. pumilus*) could not be distinguished.

2. The discrimination of closely related microorganisms at the strain level is a common feature of Py-MS studies. A classical illustration of this has been provided by some work on *E. coli* strains documented by Wieten *et al.* (1984). These authors showed that 18 strains could be sorted by Py-MS into two groups corresponding to the presence or absence of the K1 polysaccharide antigen (Fig. 15). Factor analysis of the data produced a factor spectrum (Fig. 16) showing that the main factor differentiating the two serotype groups was almost identical with the pyrolysis mass spectrum of the isolated K1 polysaccharide antigen—colominic acid (Fig. 17). This example illustrates the remarkable specificity of Py-MS in that it represents the examination of a single antigenic difference using a small sample of biomass taken directly from a culture plate. However, strain differentiation is not always as easily interpreted as this example, and it is unrealistic to expect Py-MS to differentiate a vast range of serotypes as the antigenic differences will be too subtle to produce unique patterns of pyrolysis products. More commonly,

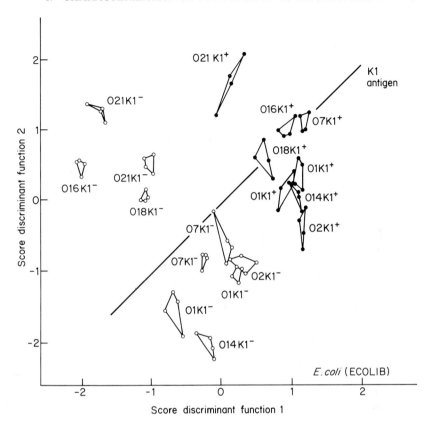

Fig. 15. Discriminant analysis of a series of *Escherichia coli* spectra showing differentiation of K1$^+$ and K1$^-$ strains (Wieten *et al.*, 1984).

Py-MS produces groupings of strains that cannot be correlated with existing typing schemes and can only be referred to as "pyrotypes". Borst *et al.* (1978) found two pyrotypes of *Neisseria gonorrhoeae* by Py-MS, which correlated loosely with the rate of glucose metabolism.

3. Pyrolysis mass spectrometry can be used to differentiate species of microorganisms. In terms of numerical taxonomy, there has been little work on the differentiation of higher orders, such as genera, the direct-probe study reported by Gutteridge and Puckey (1982) being an exception. Most Py-MS studies have concentrated on defined and narrow groups where there are special problems with conventional identification methods. For this reason,

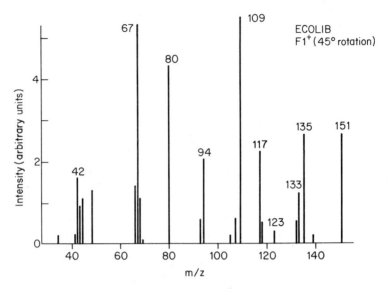

Fig. 16. Factor spectrum showing the series of masses associated with *Escherichia coli* K1⁺ strains (Fig. 15) (Wieten *et al.*, 1984).

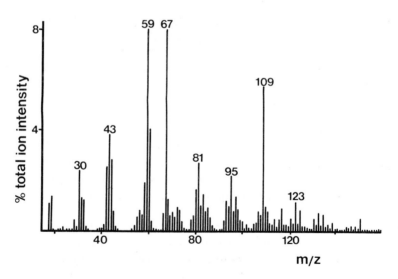

Fig. 17. Pyrolysis mass spectrum of the K1 capsular polysaccharide of *Escherichia coli* (Wieten *et al.*, 1984).

the group of microorganisms most studied by Py-MS is the slow-growing mycobacteria. Meuzelaar *et al.* (1976) analysed 97 strains of mycobacteria representing 14 species. Lowenstein medium was observed to provide more characteristic Py-MS spectra than either Sauton or Middlebrook medium. Most species could be differentiated, but *Mycobacterium bovis* was heterogeneous, overlapping with *M. avium* and *M. xenopi*. Wieten *et al.* (1981a, b) developed a Py-MS database, based on a small set of key masses, for discriminating the important pathogens of the "tuberculosis complex"—*M. tuberculosis*, *M. bovis* and *M. bovis BCG*. This database was challenged with 125 strains and 118 were correctly identified using conventional techniques as the reference. The database was shown to be stable over one year. Other Py-MS studies on mycobacteria have included a series of *M. kansasii* strains (Wieten *et al.*, 1979) and batches of *M. leprae* isolated from Armadillo liver (Wieten *et al.*, 1982).

It is doubtful whether Py-MS will ever become a general-purpose identification technique for microbiology. There are a number of reasons for this. First, despite the reproducibility reported for mycobacteria by Wieten *et al.* (1981b), there are immense technical difficulties in keeping a pyrolysis mass spectrometer stable for long periods of time so that unknowns can be matched against libraries of reference spectra. Unlike conventional mass-spectrometric library matching procedures, identification by Py-MS would require absolute quantitative precision throughout the spectrum. Unpublished work in the author's laboratory suggests that, over a year, "source-ageing effects" gradually alter ion transmission and affect the intensities detected. Consequently, data sets on the same group of bacteria, grown and sampled in an exactly identical manner, but obtained a year apart, could not be added together. When they were analysed separately the same biological differentiation was achieved, but by using a different combination of masses. Further research is required to determine whether this "ageing effect" is predictable. If it is then it might be possible to design an algorithm that can be used to correct for drift on a daily basis. This might create the conditions where a library matching approach would succeed.

An alternative approach to identification has been termed "operational fingerprinting" (Meuzelaar *et al.*, 1982). This involves running reference strains with every batch of unknown strains and identifying by use of the distance to the nearest reference by using a discriminant analysis procedure such as CVA. In "operational fingerprinting" the mass spectrometer works in a batch mode so long-term reproducibility is not a concern.

Another obstacle to widespread use of Py-MS as a microbiological identification tool is the nature of the information produced when a microorganism is pyrolysed. Pyrolysis mass spectrometry examines aspects of the cellular composition, and the spectrum can be dominated by particular features, for example the production of an extracellular polysaccharide or an intracellular protein crystal. Such features represent only a single taxonomic criterion, but their dominance of the spectrum will cause strains to be clearly differentiated. Hence Py-MS can sometimes produce results that cannot be interpreted in terms of existing taxonomies.

Figure 18 is a dendrogram produced by the analysis of Curie-point Py-MS data of some closely related Gram-negative bacteria. The strains do not cluster according to genus or species, and in particular two of the salmonellae are clear outliers of the database. Examination of the factor spectrum accounting for this differentiation (not shown) suggests that the spectra of the two salmonellae are dominated by a complex polysaccharide of unknown origin.

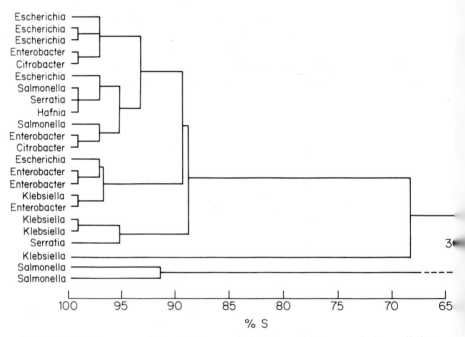

Fig. 18. Dendrogram obtained using average-linkage cluster analysis applied to similarities calculated from Mahalanobis distances and showing clustering of some Gram-negative bacteria.

In a Py-MS study of *Thermus* bacteria, isolated in New Zealand from hot springs, Donnison *et al.* (1986) produced a grouping that does not exactly match the taxonomy produced by conventional techniques. In the absence of further information about the chemical nature of the differences between the spectra, the Py-MS classification cannot be interpreted or explained. In contrast, there have been many Py-MS studies where the results can be interpreted in terms of existing taxonomies and have often added to the specification of a group of microorganisms. Studies on lactic acid bacteria (Shaw *et al.*, 1985), *Bacillus* (Shute *et al.*, 1984), mycobacteria (Meuzelaar *et al.*, 1976), *Legionella* (Kajioka and Tang, 1984) and various fungi (Weijman, 1977; Weijman and Meuzelaar, 1979) have all supported the role of Py-MS as a chemotaxonomic method. Perhaps the key is that Py-MS data should always be used in conjunction with other types of taxonomic data, and not in isolation. Pyrolysis mass spectrometry is at its most useful when used as a confirmatory tool as the first stage in the development of an identification system.

In the author's laboratory Py-MS has proved valuable for the rapid screening of batches of new isolates to gain an appreciation of the number of different types of organism present, so that an informed selection of key strains can be made for further study. These screening operations are usually applied to a single habitat, so the organisms isolated can be expected to be of broadly similar type. An example of this particular application is shown in Fig. 19, which shows the dendrogram obtained after cluster analysis of

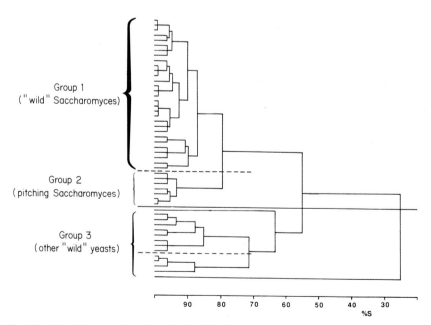

Fig. 19. Dendrogram showing relationships between 51 yeast strains isolated from a home-brew product.

spectra of 51 yeast strains isolated from a home-brew product. Data were collected and analysed in 48 h, producing a functional classification that divided the yeasts into four groups. Subsequently, conventional tests were applied to the strains, and it was found that Py-MS had successfully discriminated wild *Saccharomyces* strains (Group 1) from the pitching (brewing) yeasts (Group 2) and other wild yeasts (Group 3). The strains in Group 3 could be further subdivided by Py-MS, but the taxonomic basis of this was not determined. In this case a selection of strains for physiological studies was made within two days of the isolation of the yeasts. Although strain selection was made ahead of classification, this approach was vindicated by the subsequent taxonomic studies, which took a few weeks to complete. This study points the way to the use of Py-MS as an epidemiological tool. The application of Py-MS to the analysis of 20 different *Klebsiella* isolates from a number of hospital patients has been reported (Meuzelaar *et al.*, 1982), and appears to be a viable method for tracing the route of infections. Whether this kind of use for Py-MS can be developed to compete with conventional typing schemes remains to be seen.

V. Conclusions

The application of Py-MS to microbiology remains underdeveloped and ill-defined. The advent of low-cost instrumentation should increase the access of microbiologists to the method. It should be borne in mind, however, that low-cost in this context is compared with other forms of mass spectrometry, and the cost of a Py-MS system for the microbiology laboratory is unlikely to be < £50 000, a substantial investment for any laboratory. Using the criteria suggested by Meuzelaar (1974), the advantages of Py-MS as a characterization technique are its applicability to a wide range of organisms, the ability to differentiate at genus, species and subspecies levels, and its speed and sensitivity, i.e. the ability to produce a fingerprint from a single colony, taken directly from a culture plate, in less than five minutes. With respect to reproducibility, there are some significant problems to address, and the technology required to run a pyrolysis mass spectrometer for long periods of time (years), with continuous challenging of the same databases, does not yet exist. The development of software, both to control the instrument, and to handle the data on-line is an important priority for future research.

Perhaps the most significant obstacles to the more widespread use of Py-MS is the lack of understanding about what pyrolysis mass spectra represent and why they can be used to differentiate organisms. Detailed studies of microbial pyrolysis products by Py-GC-MS techniques are required to identify the cell constituents that contribute to the spectra and hence the differentiation of microorganisms. In the future, Py-MS should be used in tandem with other chemotaxonomic techniques, so that an improved understanding of the chemical basis of differences between spectra can be acquired.

References

Adkins, J. A., Risby, T. H., Scocca, J. J., Yasbin, R. E. and Ezzell, J. W. (1984a). Linear-programmed thermal degradation methane chemical-ionisation mass spectrometry. I. Peptidoglycan, cell walls and related compounds from *Bacillus. J. Anal. Appl. Pyrolysis* **7**, 15–33.

Adkins, J. A., Risby, T. H., Scocca, J. J., Yasbin, R. E. and Ezzell, J. W. (1984b). Linear-programmed thermal degradation methane chemical-ionisation mass spectrometry. II. Defined compounds and lipid-containing envelope constituents from *Salmonella. J. Anal. Appl. Pyrolysis* **7**, 35–51.

Anhalt, J. P. and Fenselau, C. (1975). Identification of bacteria using mass spectrometry. *Anal. Chem.* **47**, 219–224.

Aries, R. E., Gutteridge, C. S. and Ottley, T. W. (1986). Evaluation of a low cost, automated pyrolysis mass spectrometer. *J. Anal. Appl. Pyrolysis* **9**, 81–98.

Bohm, R., Kapr, T., Schmitt, H. U., Albrecht, J. and Wieser, P. (1985). Application of the laser microscope mass analyser (LAMMA) to the differentiation of single bacterial cells. *J. Anal. Appl. Pyrolysis* **8**, 449–461.

Boon, J. J. and Haverkamp, J. (1979). Pyrolysis mass spectrometry of a benthic marine ecosystem—the influence of *Arenicola marina* on the organic matter cycle. *Neth. J. Sea Res.* **13**, 457–458.

Boon, J. J., de Boer, W. R., Kruyssen, F. J. and Wouters, J. T. M. (1981a). Pyrolysis mass spectrometry of whole cells, cell walls and isolated cell wall polymers of *Bacillus subtilis* var *niger* WM. *J. Gen. Microbiol.* **122**, 119–127.

Boon, J. J., Hines, H., Burlingame, A. L., Klok, J., Rijpstra, W. I. C., de Leeuw, J. W., Edmunds, K. E. and Eglinton, G. (1981b). Organic geochemical studies of solar lake laminated cyanobacterial mats. *Adv. Org. Geochem.*, 207–227.

Boon, J. J., Tom, A., Brandt, B., Eijkel, E. B., Kistemaker, P. G., Notten, F. J. W. and Mikx, F. H. W. (1984). Mass spectrometric and factor discriminant analysis of complex organic matter from the bacterial culture environment of *Bacteroides gingivalis. Anal. Chim. Acta* **163**, 193–205.

Borst, J., van der Snee-Enkelaar, A. C. and Meuzelaar, H. L. C. (1978). Typing of *Neisseria gonorrhoeae* by pyrolysis mass spectrometry. *Antonie van Leeuwenhoek* **44**, 253.

Bracewell, J. M., Robertson, G. W. and Williams, B. L. (1980). Pyrolysis mass spectrometry studies of humification in a peat and a peaty podzol. *J. Anal. Appl. Pyrolysis* **2**, 53–62.

Coulter, G. L. and Thompson, W. C. (1977). Automatic analysis of tyre rubber blends by computer-linked pyrolysis gas chromatography. In *Analytical Pyrolysis* (C. E. R. Jones and C. A. Cramers, eds.), pp. 1–5. Elsevier, Amsterdam.

Davison, W. H. T., Slaney, S. and Wragg, A. L. (1954). A novel method of identification of polymers. *Chem. Ind.*, p. 1356.

Dixon, W. J. (1975). *Biomedical Computer Programs*. University of California Press, Los Angeles.

Donnison, A. M., Gutteridge, C. S., Norris, J. R., Morgan, H. W. and Daniel, R. M.

(1986). A preliminary grouping of New Zealand *Thermus* strains by pyrolysis mass spectrometry. *J. Anal. Appl. Pyrolysis* **9**, 281–285.

Edwards, R. A., Dainty, R. H. and Hibbard, C. M. (1985). Putrescine and cadaverine formation in vacuum packed beef. *J. Appl. Bacteriol.* **58**, 13–19.

Engman, H., Mayfield, H. T., Mar, T. and Bertsch, W. (1984). Classification of bacteria by pyrolysis–capillary column gas chromatography–mass spectrometry and pattern recognition. *J. Anal. Appl. Pyrolysis* **6**, 137–156.

Eshuis, W., Kistemaker, P. G. and Meuzelaar, H. L. C. (1977). Some numerical aspects of reproducibility and specificity. In *Analytical Pyrolysis* (C. E. R. Jones and C. A. Cramers, eds.), pp. 151–166. Elsevier, Amsterdam.

Eudy, L. W., Walla, M. D., Hudson, J. R., Morgan, S. L. and Fox, A. (1985). Gas chromatography–mass spectrometry studies on the occurrence of acetamide, propionamide, and furfuryl alcohol in pyrolysates of bacteria, bacterial fractions and model compounds. *J. Anal. Appl. Pyrolysis* **7**, 231–247.

Fenselau, C. C. (1982). Mass spectrometry of middle molecules. *Anal. Chem.* **54**, 105A–116A.

French, G. L., Gutteridge, C. S. and Phillips, I. (1980). Pyrolysis gas chromatography of *Pseudomonas* and *Acinetobacter* species. *J. Appl. Bacteriol.* **49**, 505–516.

Giacobbo, H. and Simon, W. (1964). Methodik zur prolyseund anschliebenden gaschromatographischen analyse von probemengun unter einem mikrogramm. *Pharm. Acta Helv.* **39**, 162–167.

Goodfellow, M. and Minnikin, D. E. (1985). *Chemical Methods in Bacterial Systematics*. Academic Press, London.

Gutteridge, C. S. and Norris, J. R. (1979). A review: the application of pyrolysis techniques to the identification of micro-organisms. *J. Appl. Bacteriol.* **47**, 5–43.

Gutteridge, C. S. and Norris, J. R. (1983). Possible applications of pyrolysis mass spectrometry to biotechnology. In *Biotech '83*, pp. 919–929. Online Publications, Northwood.

Gutteridge, C. S. and Puckey, D. J. (1982). Discrimination of some Gram-negative bacteria by direct probe mass spectrometry. *J. Gen. Microbiol.* **128**, 721–730.

Gutteridge, C. S., MacFie, H. J. H. and Norris, J. R. (1979). Use of principal components analysis for displaying variation variation between pyrograms of micro-organisms. *J. Anal. Appl. Pyrolysis* **1**, 67–76.

Gutteridge, C. S., Mackey, B. M. and Norris, J. R. (1980). A pyrolysis gas–liquid chromatography study of *Clostridium botulinum* and related organisms. *J. Appl. Bacteriol.* **49**, 165–174.

Gutteridge, C. S., Sweatman, A. J. and Norris, J. R. (1984). Potential applications of Curie-point pyrolysis mass spectrometry with emphasis on food science. In *Analytical Pyrolysis Techniques and Applications* (K. J. Voorhees, ed.), pp. 324–328. Butterworths, London.

Gutteridge, C. S., Vallis, L. and MacFie, H. J. H. (1985). Numerical methods in the classification of micro-organisms by pyrolysis mass spectrometry. In *Computer Assisted Bacterial Systematics* (M. Goodfellow, D. Jones and F. G. Priest, eds.), pp. 369–401. Academic Press.

Haverkamp, J., Meuzelaar, H. L. C., Beuvery, E. C., Boonekamp, P M. and Teisjema, R. H. (1980). Characterisation of *Neissera meningitidis* capsular polysaccharides containing sialic acid by pyrolysis mass spectrometry. *Anal. Biochem.* **104G**, 407–418.

Hercules, D. M. (1983). Organic mass spectrometry using the laser microprobe. *Pure Appl. Chem.* **55**, 1869–1885.

Hickman, D. A. and Jane, I. (1979). Reproducibility of pyrolysis mass spectrometry using three different pyrolysis systems. *The Analyst* **104**, 334–347.

Hill, H. C. (1966). *Introduction to Mass Spectrometry*. Heyden, London.

Hudson, J. R., Morgan, S. L. and Fox, A. (1982). Quantitative pyrolysis gas chromatography-mass spectrometry of bacterial cell walls. *Anal. Biochem.* **120**, 59–65.

Huff, S. M., Meuzelaar, H. L. C., Pope, D. L. and Kjeldsberg, C. R. (1981). Characterisation of leukemic and normal white blood cells by Curie-point pyrolysis mass spectrometry. 1. Numerical evaluations of the results of a pilot study. *J. Anal. Appl. Pyrolysis* **3**, 95–110.

Huff, S. M., Matsen, J. M., Windig, W. and Meuzelaar, H. L. C. (1986). Pyrolysis mass spectrometry of bacteria from infected human urine. I. Influence of culturing and antibiotics. *Biomed. Environ. Mass Spectrom.* **13**, 277–286.

Irwin, W. J. (1979a). Analytical pyrolysis—an overview. *J. Anal. Appl. Pyrolysis* **1**, 1–25.

Irwin, W. J. (1979b). Analytical pyrolysis—an overview. *J. Anal. Appl. Pyrolysis* **1**, 89–122.

Irwin, W. J. (1982). *Analytical Pyrolysis. A Comprehensive Guide*. Marcel Dekker, New York.

Irwin, W. J. and Slack, J. A. (1978). Analytical pyrolysis in biomedical studies, a review. *The Analyst* **103**, 673–704.

Johansson, E., Wold, S. and Sjodin, K. (1984). Minimising effects of closure on analytical data. *Anal. Chem.* **56**, 1685–1688.

Kajioka, R. and Tang, P. W. (1984). Curie-point pyrolysis-mass spectrometry of *Legionella* species. *J. Anal. Appl. Pyrolysis* **6**, 59–68.

Kaufmann, R., Hillenkamp, F. and Remy, E. (1972). Die lasermikrosonde. *Microscopia Acta* **73**, 1–18.

Kistemaker, P. G., Boerboom, A. J. H. and Meuzelaar, H. L. C. (1975). Laser Py-MS: some aspects and applications to technical polymers. *Dyn. Mass Specrom.* **4**, 139–152.

Kowalski, B. R. (1975). Measurement analysis by pattern recognition. *Anal. Chem.* **47**, 1152A–1162A.

Lindner, B. and Seydel, U. (1983). Mass spectrometric analysis of drug-induced changes in Na^+ and K^+ contents of single bacterial cells. *J. Gen. Microbiol.* **129**, 50–55.

Lindner, B. and Seydel, U. (1984). Mass spectrometric analysis of single bacterial cells with LAMMA 500. In *Proc 2nd LAMMA Workshop, Borstel, W. Germany, 1–2 Sept. 1983*, pp. 111–118. Leybold Heraeus, Koln.

Louter, G. J. Stalmeier, P. F. M., Boerboom, A. J. H., Haverkamp, J. and Kistemaker, J. (1980). High sensitivity in CID mass spectrometry, structure analysis of pyrolysis fragments. *Z. Naturforsch.* **35**, 6–11.

MacFie, H. J. H. and Gutteridge, C. S. (1982). Comparative studies on some methods for handling quantitative data generated by analytical pyrolysis. *J. Anal. Appl. Pyrolysis* **4**, 175–204.

MacFie, H. J. H., Gutteridge, C. S. and Norris, J. R. (1978). Use of canonical variates analysis in differentiation of bacteria by pyrolysis gas-liquid chromatography. *J. Gen. Microbiol.* **104**, 67–74.

Magee, J. T., Hindmarch, J. M. and Meechan, D. F. (1983). Identification of staphylococci by pyrolysis gas–liquid chromatography. *J. Med. Microbiol.* **16**, 483–495.

Muezelaar, H. L. C. (1974) Identification of bacteria by pyrolysis gas chromatography and pyrolysis mass spectrometry. Ph.D. thesis. University of Amsterdam.

Muezelaar, H. L. C. and Kistemaker, P. G. (1973). A technique for fast and reproducible fingerprinting of bacteria by pyrolysis mass spectrometry. *Anal. Chem.* **45**, 587–590.

Muezelaar, H. L. C., Kistemaker, P. G. and Posthumus, M. A. (1974). Recent advances in Py-MS of complex biological materials. *Biomed. Mass Spectrom.* **1**, 312–319.

Muezelaar, H. L. C., Ficke, H. G. and den Harink, H. C. (1975). Fully automated pyrolysis gas-liquid chromatography. *J. Chromatogr. Sci.* **134**, 12–17.

Muezelaar, H. L. C., Kistemaker, P. G., Eshuis, W. and Engel, H. W. B. (1976). Progress in automated and computerised characterisation of micro-organisms by pyrolysis mass spectrometry. In *Rapid methods and Automation in Microbiology* (S. W. B. Newsom and H. H. Johnston, eds.), pp. 225–230. Learned Information, Oxford.

Muezelaar, H. L. C., Haverkamp, J. and Hileman, F. D. (1982). *Pyrolysis Mass Spectrometry of Recent and Fossil Biomaterials.* Elsevier, Amsterdam.

Nelder, J. A. (1979). GENSTAT Reference Manual. Scientific and Social Service Program Library, University of Edinburgh.

Nie, N. H., Hull, C. H., Jenkins, J. G., Steinbrenner, K. and Bent, D. H. (1975). *Statistical Package for the Social Sciences (SPSS)*, 2nd edn. McGraw-Hill, New York.

Puckey, D. J., Norris, J. R. and Gutteridge, C. S. (1980). Discrimination of micro-organisms by direct mass spectrometry. *J. Gen. Microbiol.* **118**, 535–538.

Reiner, E. (1965). Identification of bacterial strains by pyrolysis gas-liquid chromatography. *Nature (London)* **206**, 1272–1274.

Reiner, E. and Ewing, W. J. (1968). Chemotaxonomic studies of some Gram-negative bacteria by means of pyrolysis gas-liquid chromatography. *Nature (London)* **217**, 191–194.

Reiner, E., Hicks, J. J. and Sulzer, C. R. (1973). Leptospiral taxonomy by pyrolysis gas-liquid chromatography. *Can. J. Microbiol.* **19**, 1203–1206.

Risby, T. H. and Yergey, A. L. (1976). Identification of bacteria using linear programmed thermal degradation mass spectrometry. The preliminary investigation. *J. Phys. Chem.* **80**, 2839–2845.

Risby, T. H. and Yergey, A. L. (1978). Linear programmed thermal degradation mass spectrometry. *Anal. Chem.* **50**, 326A–334A.

Schulten, H. R. (1977). Pyrolysis field ionisation and field desorption mass spectrometry of biomacromolecules, micro-organisms and tissue material. In *Analytical Pyrolysis* (C. E. R. Jones and C. A. Cramers, eds.), pp. 17–28. Elsevier, Amsterdam.

Schulten, H. R. and Lattimer, R. P. (1984). Applications of mass spectrometry to polymer analysis. *Mass. Spectrom. Rev.* **3**, 2310–315.

Schulten, H. R., Beckey, H. D., Meuzelaar, H. L. C. and Boerboom, A. J. H. (1973). High resolution field ionisation mass spectrometry of bacterial pyrolysis products. *Anal. Chem.* **45**, 191–195.

Shaw, B. G., Puckey, D. J., MacFie, H. J. H and Bolt, S. J. (1985). Classification of some lactic acid bacteria from vacuum-packed meats by direct probe mass spectrometry. *J. Appl. Bacteriol.* **59**, 157–165.

Shute, L. A., Gutteridge, C. S., Norris, J. R. and Berkeley, R. C. W. (1984) Curie-point pyrolysis mass spectrometry applied to the characterisation of selected *Bacillus* species. *J. Gen. Microbiol.* **130**, 343–355.

Simmonds, P. G. (1970). Whole micro-organisms studied by pyrolysis gas chromatography mass spectrometry: significance of extraterrestrial life detection experiments. *Appl. Microbiol.* **20**, 567–572.

Sinha, M. P., Platz, R. M., Friedlander, S. K. and Vilker, V. L (1985). Characterisation of bacteria by particle beam mass spectrometry. *Appl. Environ. Microbiol.* **49**, 1366–1373.

Tas, A. C., van der Greef, J., de Waart, J., Bouwman, J. and ten Noever de Brauw, M. C. (1985). Comparison of direct chemical ionisation and direct-probe electron impact/chemical ionisation pyrolysis for the characterisation of *Pseudomonas* and *Serratia* bacteria *J. Anal. Appl. Pyrolysis* **7**, 249–255.

Wechsung, R., Hillenkamp, F., Kaufmann, R., Nitsche, R. and Vogt, M. (1978). Laser-mikrosonden-massen-analysator (LAMMA): Ein neues analysenverfahren für forschung und technologie. *Microsokopie* **34**, 47–54.

Weijman, A. C. M. (1977). The application of Curie-point pyrolysis mass spectrometry in fungal taxonomy. In *Analytical Pyrolysis* (C. E. R. Jones and C. A. Cramers, eds.) pp. 225–233. Elsevier, Amsterdam.

Weijman, A. C. M. and Meuzelaar, H. L. C. (1979). Biochemical contributions to the taxonomic status of the Endogonaceae. *Can. J. Bot.* **57**, 284–291.

Wieten, G., Haverkamp, J., Engel, H. W. B. and Tarnok, I. (1979). Pyrolysis mass spectrometry in mycobacterial taxonomy and identification. In *Twenty-five Years of Mycobacterial Taxonomy* (G. P. Kubika, L. G. Wayne and L. S. Good, eds.), pp. 171–189. CDC Press, Atlanta.

Wieten, G., Haverkamp, J., Engel, H. W. B. and Berwald, L. G. (1981a). Application of pyrolysis mass spectrometry to the classification and identification of mycobacteria. *Rev. Infect. Diseases* **3**, 871–877.

Wieten, G., Haverkamp, J., Meuzelaar, H. L. C., Engel, W. W. B. and Berwald, L G. (1981b). Pyrolysis mass spectrometry: a new method to differentiate between the mycobacteria of the "Tuberculosis complex" and other mycobacteria. *J. Gen. Microbiol.* **122**, 109–118.

Wieten, G., Haverkamp, J., Berwald, L. G., Groothuis, D. G. and Draper, P. (1982). Py-MS: its application to mycobacteriology including *Mycobacterium leprae. Ann. Microbiol. (Paris)* **133b**, 109–118.

Wieten, G., Meuzelaar, H. L. C. and Haverkamp. J. (1984). Analytical pyrolysis in clinical and pharmaceutical microbiology. In *Gas Chromatography Mass Spectrometry Applications in Microbiology* (G. Odham, L. Larsson and P. A. Mardh, eds.), pp. 335–380. Plenum Press, London.

Wilson, M. E., Oyama, V. and Vango, S. P. (1962). Design features of a lunar gas chromatograph. In *Proc. 3rd Int. Symp. on Gas Chromatography* (N. Brenner, ed.), pp. 329–338. New York, Academic Press.

Windig, W. and de Hoog, G. S. (1982). Pyrolysis mass spectrometry of selected yeast species. II. *Sporidiobolus* and relationships. *Stud. Mycol.* **22**, 60–64.

Windig, W. and Haverkamp, J. (1982). Pyrolysis mass spectrometry of selected yeast species. I. *Rhodosporidium. Stud. Mycol.* **22**, 56–59.

Windig, W., Haverkamp, J. and van Wezel, A. L. (1981). Control on the absence of DEAE-polysaccharides in DEAE-Sephadex-purified poliovirus suspensions by pyrolysis mass spectrometry. *Dev. Biol. Standard.* **47**, 160–177.

Windig, W., Kistemaker, P. G. and Haverkamp, J. (1982a). Chemical interpretation of differences in pyrolysis-mass spectra of simulated mixtures of polymers by factor analysis with graphical rotation. *J. Anal. Appl. Pyrolysis* **3**, 199–212.

Windig, W., de Hoog, G. S. and Haverkamp, J. (1982b). Chemical characterisation of yeasts and yeast-like fungi by factor analysis of their pyrolysis mass spectra. *J. Anal. Appl. Pyrolysis* **3**, 213–220.

Windig, W., Haverkamp, J. and Kistemaker, P. G. (1983). Interpretation of a set of pyrolysis mass spectra by discriminant analysis and graphical rotation. *Anal. Chem.* **55**, 387–391.

Windig, W., Meuzelaar, H. L. C., Shafizadeh, F. and Kelsey, R. G. (1984). Biochemical analysis of wood and wood products by pyrolysis mass spectrometry and multivariate analysis. *J. Anal. Appl. Pyrolysis* **6**, 233–250.

Windig, W., McClennen, W. H., Stolk, H. and Meuzelaar, H. L. C. (1986). Unsupervised chemical pattern recognition in complex mass spectra. *Opt. Engng.* **25**, 117–122.

Wold, S. (1976). Pattern recognition by means of disjoint principal components models. *Patt. Recogn.* **8**, 127–139.

Wold, S. (1978). Cross validatory estimation of the number of components in factor and principal components analysis. *Technometrics* **20**, 397–406.

Zemany, P. D. (1952). Identification of complex organic materials by mass spectrometric analysis of their pyrolysis products. *Anal. Chem.* **24**, 1709–1713.

7

Labelled-Antibody Methods for Detection and Identification of Microorganisms

SHIREEN M. CHANTLER and M. B. McILLMURRAY

Wellcome Research Laboratories, Langley Court, Beckenham, Kent, UK

I. Introduction

For many decades identification of an infective agent was reliant upon satisfying Koch's postulates. While many investigators were aware of the need to simplify methods for the detection of microorganisms, little progress

METHODS IN MICROBIOLOGY
VOLUME 19 ISBN 0–12–521519–3

was made until Landsteiner's work on the specificity of immunobiological reactions, which paved the way for the development of practical methods for identifying microorganisms. Considerable information became available on the antigenic characteristics of microorganisms, but identification still involved isolation and culture of pure organisms, followed by biochemical and serological analyses. Rapid detection and identification of the infective agent in clinical specimens became a practical possibility with the advent of labelled-antibody techniques using antibody of defined specificity. For the first time microorganisms could be detected despite the presence of extraneous material, on the basis of immunological specificity and morphology.

Interaction between a microbial antigen and its corresponding antibody, unlike conventional methods, is not dependent upon the purity of the organism. Furthermore, the target antigen does not need to be a component of the intact organism, and secreted components are effective provided that antigenicity is retained. The primary reaction of antibody with antigen is not usually visible, but it can be made so by linking the antibody to labels that can be detected with great sensitivity themselves, give rise to readily demonstrable reaction products or, alternatively, promote secondary lattice formation resulting in macroscopic aggregation. In this way, the specificity of an immunological reaction is combined with the inherent sensitivity of the label for the detection and identification of microorganisms. The exploitation of this approach stems from observations made more than 40 years ago that coloured substances or fluorochromes could be linked to an antibody without deleterious effects upon its specific ability to combine with the homologous antigen (Marrack, 1934; Coons et al., 1941).

Labelled-antibody procedures, largely as a consequence of improved methods of preparing antibodies of defined specificity, now offer a number of potential opportunities in large and small laboratories as an alternative or adjunct to conventional methods for detection of microorganisms. The technical approach adopted in a particular laboratory will clearly depend upon the type of information required. The choice of methodology is arguably easier in research laboratories, where labelled antibodies are used to provide information on microbial structure and on antigenic relationships between different organisms as an aid to classification, and in routine diagnostic laboratories, in which the spectrum of likely microorganisms is clearly defined. In quality-control laboratories, however, where the mass screening of products constitutes the major function, other factors such as the need to detect all contaminants, irrespective of whether they are viable or non-viable, and to exclude toxic substances may complicate the selection of a comprehensive series of tests.

Labelled-antibody methods are commonly considered to be synonymous with microscope-associated techniques such as immunofluorescence and immunoperoxidase staining or with enzyme-linked immunosorbent assays (ELISA). In recent years considerable research effort has been devoted towards the development of these and other labelled-antibody techniques, and many are already taking their place in the repertoire of tests available for the detection and identification of microorganisms. In this chapter we have extended the definition of antibody label to include particles, as we believe these have an important application in microbiological laboratories. Our intention is to provide detailed procedures for selected purposes, which can serve as a basis for adaptation to alternative specific needs. Caution should be exercised, however, in the premature widespread adoption of new procedures before adequate agreement with conventional cultural methods has been confirmed.

II.   Principles of labelled-antibody techniques

Labelled-antibody techniques may be considered in two main categories: first those in which the interaction between antigen and antibody is detected by virtue of the property of the label itself, and secondly those in which detection is reliant upon the secondary phenomenon of lattice formation resulting in demonstrable aggregation.

Techniques within the first group utilize antibodies labelled with fluorochromes, enzymes, electron-dense particulate suspensions and radioisotopes. Other tracers have been described, such as chemiluminescent compounds (Cheng *et al.*, 1982). In some variations the label is incorporated into the system by secondary immunological interaction rather than chemical coupling, while in others it is incorporated by means of non-immunological interactions with high binding affinity. Irrespective of the label used, the principles of the staining methods are similar, and the differences lie in the methods used to visualize or measure the label. Hence a variety of basic procedures are available that, with minor modifications, are applicable to all types of labelled antibodies.

A.   Direct staining procedures

In the direct staining method a suitable preparation of the test sample is incubated with labelled antibody of known specificity. If the homologous antigen is present then labelled antibody is bound, and on examination by the appropriate detection system shows reactivity (Fig. 1a). Although this simple single-stage procedure is used most frequently with fixed specimens on microscope slides, a similar principle is employed for the detection of infective agents in specimens that are unsuitable for this purpose. In these

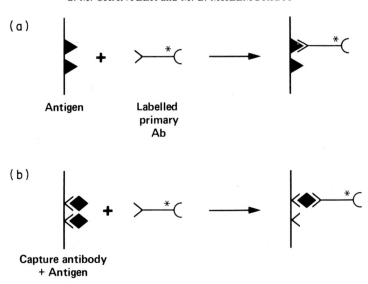

Fig. 1.   Principle of direct staining methods.

instances the microorganisms are selectively immobilized or captured on an inert solid phase, such as a microtitre plate, plastic tube or bead, coated with antibody of the desired specificity (Engvall *et al.*, 1971; Wolters *et al.*, 1976; Brandt *et al.*, 1981). Contaminants are removed by washing before the application of labelled specific antibody (Fig. 1b). The direct staining method may be used to detect two antigenically unrelated microorganisms in a single preparation by coupling the specific antibodies with different labels which provide adequate contrast for separate resolution. These may include two fluorochromes (Batty and Walker, 1963), enzymes (Nakane, 1968; Mason and Sammons, 1978) or homogeneous colloidal gold preparations containing particles of differing size (Bendayan, 1982). While double-labelling staining methods are invaluable for certain purposes, it is imperative to confirm the absence of cross-reactivity in the test components.

B.   Indirect staining procedures

Several methods of varying complexity may be included within this category, and the choice will be influenced by the need for increased sensitivity, obtained by amplification, and the effect of chemical labelling on the biological activity of the antibody used. In the simplest indirect staining method (Figs. 2a, b) the test specimen is incubated first with unlabelled antiserum of known immunological reactivity. After washing, a labelled

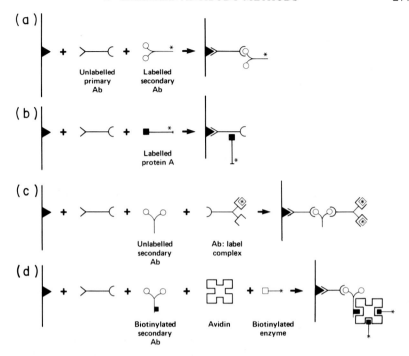

Fig. 2. Principle of indirect staining methods.

reagent directed against the immunoglobulins of the species donating the first serum is applied. Following a further incubation and wash, the presence of bound labelled antibody is determined by the appropriate detection system. If the homologous organisms are present, antigen:antibody interaction occurs during the first incubation. Uncombined antibody is removed by washing, and the labelled secondary antibody reacts with the complex during the second incubation.

The conjugate used in this procedure is commonly a labelled anti-species immunoglobulin or labelled protein A, derived from certain strains of *Staphylococcus aureus*, which has a strong binding affinity for receptors on the Fc part of immunoglobulin molecules of several animal species (Kronvall *et al.*, 1970). Although protein A is frequently described as a "universal" reagent, caution should be exercised in its indiscriminate use: substantial variations in affinity are present with immunoglobulins of different species, with different classes of immunoglobulins and, in our experience, with immunoglobulins of a single murine isotype (unpublished observations). Furthermore, other microorganisms carry immunoglobulin binding factors analogous to protein A (Myhre and Kronvall, 1977, 1980) and certain viruses generate Fc receptors on the surface of infected cells (Schmidt *et al.*, 1983). The contribution of these non-immunological interactions should always be considered if erroneous conclusions are to be avoided.

Several modifications of the basic indirect staining method do exist, but they are infrequently used for the detection and identification of microorganisms. In the Sternberger bridge procedure (Fig. 2c), unlabelled second antibody serves as an immunological link to bind a complex of label and anti-label antibody, thus eliminating the need for chemical coupling (Sternberger *et al.*, 1970; Mason *et al.*, 1982; Clark *et al.*, 1982; Cordell *et al.*, 1984). A variation of this approach utilizes the non-immunological but highly efficient binding between molecules of avidin and biotin (Guesdon *et al.*, 1979; Wilchek and Bayer, 1984) to label the immunologically specific reactant indirectly (Fig. 2d).

Irrespective of label and method of staining adopted, the specificity and sensitivity of the result will depend upon the quality and optimal use of the reagents. Preliminary testing must be undertaken to determine the spectrum of reactivity and specificity of each component employed in order to exclude the possibility of unwanted immunological interaction resulting from natural antibodies and confusing non-immunological specific or non-specific interactions. In these evaluations, attention must be paid to the differing sensitivities of multistep staining procedures and caution should be exercised in assuming that specificity defined in one system is equivalent to that of another inherently more sensitive procedure (Chantler and Haire, 1972). The working dilutions of each reagent must be established by appropriate titration to ensure the selection of reagents giving maximum specificity, sensitivity and freedom from non-specific interactions.

The choice of labelled-antibody procedure will depend on a number of factors, which include the type of samples handled, the expertise and equipment available and individual preferences. The direct method is dependent upon the availability of a comprehensive range of labelled antibodies of defined specificity and high potency. While, in our experience, most polyclonal and monoclonal sera of suitable potency can be labelled without a major loss of antibody activity, difficulties do occasionally arise. In these situations and those of proven inadequate sensitivity, indirect methods are used. Practical advantages of the indirect methods include increased sensitivity due to amplification and the ability to use a single labelled reagent in a variety of tests designed to detect and identify a number of antigenically distinct organisms, provided the specific intermediary sera used are raised in a single species of animal.

Labelled-antibody methods allow considerable flexibility in use. A single specimen may be examined for the presence of multiple organisms by treating replicate samples either with intermediary sera or with conjugates of known but different specificity. Similarly, several samples may be examined for the presence of a single defined microorganism. The use of multispot Teflon-coated slides for microscope-linked procedures and microtitre plates for ELISA methods facilitates the handling of large numbers of specimens and greatly reduces the workload (Goldman, 1968; O'Neill and Johnson, 1970; Voller *et al.*, 1976).

C. Agglutination procedures

The nature of the label is a central feature of agglutination techniques, and positive or negative results are determined by gross appearance following interaction with homologous antigen. The procedure requires a suspension of small particles such as polystyrene latex, bacteria or erythrocytes to which antibodies can be attached. In this state the particles remain in uniform suspension, but on addition of homologous antigen they aggregate to form visible clumps (Fig. 3). The antigen may be soluble or particulate: in the latter case the reaction may be referred to as coagglutination, although this term is usually restricted to reactions involving *Staphylococcus aureus* as the antibody carrier.

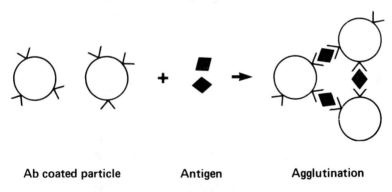

Ab coated particle　　　　**Antigen**　　　　**Agglutination**

Fig. 3.　Principle of agglutination reaction.

III.　Preparation of antisera

The specificity and sensitivity of labelled-antibody techniques are dependent upon the quality of the primary and secondary antibodies employed, which may be of monoclonal or polyclonal origin. As labelled anti-species immunoglobulin conjugates are widely available commercially, details of these preparations are excluded. However, if monoclonal anti-species immunoglobulin antibodies of restricted epitope specificity are used, it is essential to establish that the antibody is reactive with the immunoglobulin class and isotype of all the primary antibodies used. Similarly, when using polyclonal or monoclonal antibody in direct tests or as the primary layer in indirect tests the user should maintain an awareness of the possibility of antigenic similarity or shared epitopes in certain groups of organisms, not all of which have been identified.

A. Polyclonal antisera

Conventional methods of raising potent polyclonal antisera by inoculation of whole organisms give rise to antibodies of many different specificities. Antibodies of unwanted specificity either resulting from immunization or naturally occurring in animal sera are removed by absorption, but it can be difficult to prepare highly specific antisera in this way and retain good potency. Abortive attempts are seldom described in the literature, yet anyone with practical experience of making useful antibodies will be aware that methods published as being successful in certain circumstances at other times fail to give the desired results. Good polyclonal sera that perform well in labelled antibody techniques can nevertheless be prepared, and selected procedures for immunogen preparation, immunization schedules, antiserum purification and methods of antibody evaluation are considered here.

(i) *Choice of animal*

In theory, any available animal species can be used, but frequently the choice is determined by the volume of antiserum required and the type of test used, for example the need for uniformity to facilitate the use of a single anti-species conjugate or the need to select species that have a strong affinity for protein A (Kronvall *et al.*, 1970; Notermans *et al.*, 1982). Rarely, selection is determined by the proven ability to mount a satisfactory immune response to a particular immunogen. Wallace *et al.* (1978) have shown that the chicken alone produces a satisfactory response to lipopolysaccharide from *Neisseria gonorrhoeae*. Prior to immunization, it may be prudent to test the animals for the absence of high levels of natural antibodies, which may interfere in the intended test system, or consider the use of pathogen-free animals. Despite these precautions, it must be remembered that antibodies of unwanted specificity may arise during the course of immunization as a result of natural exposure or the presence of altered or common antigens in the inoculum.

(ii) *Immunogen*

Conventional immunization stimulates a heterogeneous population of antibodies, which differ with respect to affinity and specificity. The extent of this heterogeneity of response will vary in individual animals of the same species, even if identical immunogen and immunization schedules are used. Although the immunization procedure may be manipulated to favour the production of antibodies of predominantly high or low affinity, the specificity of response is less amenable to control. In principle it is wise to use highly purified antigens for immunization and the elegant work of Lindberg and coworkers (Svenson and Lindberg, 1981; Ekwall *et al.*, 1982), who synthesized immunodeterminant antigenic structures of Salmonella O serotypes, has proved the value of this approach in raising highly specific, potent antisera of a quality rarely obtained by conventional procedures using whole microbial cells. Immunogen synthesis is complex and requires appropriate expertise, whereas the purification of protein or polysaccharide immunogens is relatively simple and can give good results. However, purified antigens frequently stimulate a lower response than whole microbial cells, and the potential advantage of a more specific antibody response must be weighed against the possibility of decreased potency. Pure lipopolysaccharide is poorly immunogenic, and the use of whole microbial cells is usually necessary to achieve a satisfactory response although protein conjugates of lipopolysaccharide provide good immunogens (Svenson and Lindberg, 1979). The use of recombinant DNA technology to generate specific antigens that are difficult to obtain by cultural procedures, such as with *Treponema pallidum* (Stamm *et al.*, 1983) offers great promise. In our experience, highly purified virus, preferably prepared by density-gradient centrifugation (Talbot and Almeida, 1977), should be used as immunogen for the preparation of polyclonal anti-viral sera (Gardner and McQuillan, 1980).

For some applications a broad spectrum of antibody activity is desirable and polyspecific antibodies can be prepared with relative ease by using pooled microbial cells.

(a) Preparation of somatic antigens

Whole microbial cells (modified from Edwards and Ewing, 1972)

1. Inoculate a nutrient-agar slope and incubate overnight at 37 °C.
2. Cover the culture with physiological saline, resuspend the organisms and transfer the suspension to a clean bottle.
3. Heat the suspension in a boiling water bath or in unpressurized steam for two hours. Allow to cool. (Boiling is usually sufficient to destroy flagellar antigens, but with *Vibrio cholerae* autoclaving may be necessary; Burrows and Pollitzer, 1958).
4. Centrifuge at 4000*g* for 15 min and retain the pellet.

5. Resuspend the pellet in saline containing 0.25% formalin to an opacity of approximately 2×10^9 organisms per ml. Store at 4 °C until required.

Lipopolysaccharide (based on Westphal and Jann, 1965; Lambden and Heckels, 1982)

1. Grow bacteria as described above and suspend them in distilled water at approximately 20 mg (dry weight) per ml.
2. Add an equal volume of 90% phenol and equilibrate to 68 °C. Shake thoroughly and incubate at 68 °C for 15 min.
3. Centrifuge at 1000g for 30 min.
4. Recover the upper aqueous phase. Dialyse extensively against distilled water or running tap water at room temperature.
5. Centrifuge at 5000g for 15 min.
6. Centrifuge the supernatant from step 5 at 100 000g for 2 h. Discard the supernatant.
7. Resuspend the lipopolysaccharide pellet in distilled water and wash twice in distilled water with centrifugation at 100 000g for 2 h.
8. Resuspend in a few millilitres of distilled water. The yield of lipopolysaccharide is usually determined by dry weight following freeze-drying. The product may be stored frozen at -20 °C for many months.

(b) Preparation of flagellar antigens

Highly motile cultures, grown in a Craigie tube containing semisolid agar medium, should be used for the preparation of flagellar antigens.

Whole microbial cells (modified from Edwards and Ewing, 1972)

1. Inoculate a bottle of nutrient broth with highly motile organisms.
2. Incubate at 37 °C for 8–18 h.
3. Add an equal volume of physiological saline containing 0.6% formalin, mix gently and allow to stand overnight at room temperature.
4. Centrifuge at 4000g for 15 min and retain the pellet.
5. Gently resuspend the pellet in physiological saline containing 0.25% formalin and adjust the opacity of the suspension to approximately 2×10^9 organisms per ml. Store at 4 °C until required.

Purified flagella (Ada *et al.*, 1964)

1. Culture motile bacteria on heart-infusion broth containing 0.9% agar, incubated overnight at 37 °C.

2. Flood the surface of the agar with saline containing 0.01% merthiolate and suspend the organisms in the saline using a scraper.
3. Harvest the suspension into a bottle and shake vigorously for a few minutes to shear the flagella from the cells. Alternatively, treat in a blender for a few minutes using appropriate safety precautions.
4. Centrifuge at 4000g for 20 min to sediment the bacteria, and retain the supernatant.
5. Subject the supernatant containing the flagellar suspension to four cycles of differential centrifugation. In each cycle clarify the suspension at 5000g for 25 min, then recover the flagella from the supernatant by centrifugation at 40 000g for 45 min, followed by resuspension of the pellet in saline.
6. With some flagella, further purification may be accomplished by adding 1/20 volume of 1 N hydrochloric acid to depolymerize the flagella to flagellin monomers. Stand at room temperature for 30 min and then centrifuge at 80 000g for 1 h at 4 °C. Following neutralization of the supernatant using 1 N sodium hydroxide, the repolymerized flagella may be recovered simply by storage of the solution, or by ammonium sulphate precipitation.
7. Protein concentration should be determined using conventional procedures. The suspension should be stored frozen at about 1 mg ml^{-1} or freeze-dried until required for use.

(c) Preparation of polysaccharide capsular antigens

The preparative procedures and the stability of the derived product may vary for different organisms.

Whole microbial cells

For *Neisseria meningitidis* fresh overnight cultures should be grown on nutrient agar containing 5% defibrinated sheep blood in CO_2-enriched air. Harvest the growth in cold physiological saline containing 0.5% formalin and inoculate suspensions immediately.

For best results with *Haemophilus influenzae* a very fresh (4–6 h) culture grown on Levinthal's agar in a CO_2 atmosphere is recommended (Turk and May, 1967). Strong iridescence indicates good capsule production. Harvest the growth in ice-cold saline containing 0.5% formalin, and keep at 4 °C until injected. This suspension may be kept at 4 °C for up to a week.

For *Streptococcus pneumoniae* a culture in 5% serum broth is recommended (Lund, 1960). After 4–7 h active growth of strains shown to have good capsule production by the Quellung reaction, kill the organisms by adding formalin to 2%. The following day, recover the cells by centrifugation at 5000g for 15 min and resuspend in phosphate buffered saline containing 0.5% formalin. A suspension prepared thus, at approximately 2×10^{10} organisms per ml, may be stored for a period of years at 4 °C.

Purified polysaccharide (Gotschlich et al., 1969)

Negatively charged capsular polysaccharides may be purified by the following procedure.

1. Inoculate a suitable broth culture medium and incubate overnight at 37 °C.
2. Add 10% hexadecyl trimethylammonium bromide (Cetavlon) solution to give a final concentration of 0.1% (w/v).
3. Recover the precipitate by centrifugation at 20 000g for 5 min.
4. Wash the precipitate with distilled water and recover by centrifugation at 13 000g for 15 min.
5. Extract the precipitate two or three times with 0.9 M calcium chloride, centrifuging at 13 000g for 15 min, and pool the extracts.
6. Add absolute ethanol to a concentration of 25% (v/v) and spool off any fibrous precipitate (nucleic acid). Retain at 4 °C for 3 h, and centrifuge at 13 000g for 15 min at 2 °C.
7. Collect the supernatant and increase the ethanol concentration to 80%. Centrifuge at 1300g for 10 min.
8. Redissolve the precipitate in a small volume of distilled water and store frozen at −20 °C or freeze-dried. Concentration may be determined by dry weight or using a biochemical assay appropriate for the constituent sugars in the preparation: the two methods may not give identical results, but either may be used.

(iii) Specimen immunization schedules

The choice of immunization schedule is related to the type of immunogen used. Whole bacterial cells produce a strong response following an intravenous course of injections over a three to four week period, whereas some of the subcellular fractions require an intramuscular course of immunogen in Freund's complete adjuvant over a period of at least six to eight weeks. Specimen schedules for immunization of rabbits are given below.

Intravenous immunization. Amendments to this schedule may be necessary depending upon the toxicity or immunogenicity of the immunogen. Inject a suspension of microbial cells (10^9 organism per ml) into the marginal ear vein slowly according to the following schedule:

Day 1	0.25 ml
Day 3	0.5 ml
Day 5	1 ml
Day 7	2 ml
Day 9	3 ml
Day 11	3 ml
Day 16–21	Bleed into a suitable glass vessel (clot formation may not occur in plastic containers). If the antibody level, when assayed, is not sufficiently high, further injections may be given.

Intramuscular immunization. This schedule may be used for intramuscular injection of purified antigens, and may be extended if necessary, or followed by intravenous injections of soluble antigens.

Emulsify the antigen in a ratio of 1:3 in Freund's complete adjuvant until a stable emulsion is formed that does not separate on standing. Inject into the hind-leg muscles using a short, sharp, broad-gauge needle. For a rabbit, a dose in the range 0.1–0.5 mg antigen should be satisfactory.

Day 1	2 ml
Day 21	2 ml
Day 28	Bleed.

Collection and storage of serum. To recover the serum, allow the blood to stand for several hours or overnight until a clot has formed and retracted. If necessary, release the clot from the glass wall of the vessel. Recover the serum and centrifuge at 4000g for 10 min to remove residual blood cells. The serum may be stored pending further processing at 4 °C for a few days or frozen at −20 °C. If longer storage at 4 °C is necessary then preservative such as 0.1% sodium azide should be added. (Note: azide is toxic and can form explosive salts in copper or lead plumbing systems. When disposing of azide-containing materials flush with large quantities of water).

B. Monoclonal antibodies

Recent developments in the production of monoclonal antibodies of defined specificity by somatic cell hybridization techniques (Kohler and Milstein, 1975) have had considerable impact on the use of labelled-antibody procedures for the detection and identification of microorganisms. In this procedure (Fig. 4) splenic lymphocytes from an immunized donor mouse are fused with a non-secreting myeloma cell line that has a defective enzyme system and is unable to survive in certain selective media. Hybrid cells derived from this fusion survive and grow in the selective media, and those

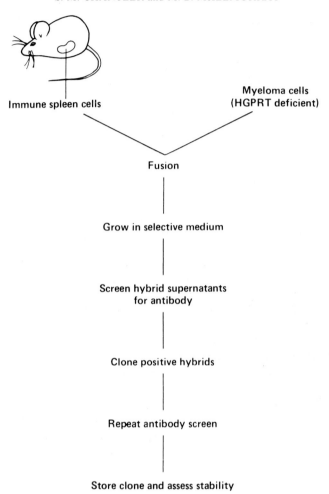

Immune spleen cells

Myeloma cells
(HGPRT deficient)

Fusion

Grow in selective medium

Screen hybrid supernatants
for antibody

Clone positive hybrids

Repeat antibody screen

Store clone and assess stability

Fig. 4.   Monoclonal-antibody production.

clones secreting antibody of the required specificity are identified by screening the culture supernatants. At this stage, culture wells containing antibody of the appropriate specificity may contain a heterogeneous population of hybrid cells secreting a variety of clone products. Additional recloning procedures are undertaken to ensure that the cells growing within a particular well are derived from a single parent hybrid cell. Following tests to ensure retention of antibody secretion, the cellular contents of positive wells are recloned to establish functional stability. *In vitro* production of antibody is achieved by growing the hybridomas in tissue culture, or alternatively antibody production can be obtained *in vivo* by inoculation of hybridoma cells into syngeneic recipient animals. Readers interested in detailed methodology should refer to recent reviews on the subject (Goding, 1980; Hurn and Chantler, 1980; Langone and van Vunakis, 1983).

(i) *Choice of animal*

The choice of animal for monoclonal antibody production will be determined by the phylogenetic relationship between the cells utilized in hybridization studies, the immune responsiveness to a particular immunogen and the availability of histocompatible recipient animals for the *in vivo* growth of derived hybrid clones.

(ii) *Immunogen*

As monoclonal antibodies are obtained by selective cloning procedures, the need for highly purified antigen for immunization is, theoretically, unnecessary. In our experience, immunogens of differing purity as used for polyclonal antibody production are effective, but the use of purified immunogens may increase the incidence of suitable hybrids. The choice of immunogen and its purity will need to be determined by experiment in many cases and may be influenced by the need for defined antigen preparations for precise analysis of the derived antibody at a later stage. Synthetic antigens such as peptides (Shinnick *et al.*, 1983) and saccharides (Svenson and Lindberg, 1981) have been used.

(iii) *Immunization schedule*

The type of schedule used to prime the potential spleen-cell donor will depend upon the physical properties and immunogenicity of the antigen. While variables such as the dose, use of adjuvant, route and timing of injections may vary in different studies and may need to be determined by experiment, the following schedule is effective, in our experience, for immunization of mice with several microbial antigens:

Day 1   Emulsion of 1 volume antigen:2 volumes Freund's complete adjuvant, 0.2 ml intramuscular route.

Day 28   Emulsion of 1 volume antigen: 1 volume Freund's incom-
                plete adjuvant, 0.2 ml intramuscular.
Day 38–42   Test response.
Day 56   If response inadequate then repeat injection 2.

If an adequate response is obtained then inject spleen donor with 0.1 ml of
antigen in saline by the intraperitoneal route 2–3 days before fusion.

C.   Evaluation of antibodies

Assay systems for assessing the reactivity of both polyclonal and monoclonal
antibodies should be simple but provide information on both potency and
specificity. For polyclonal antibodies, in which the number of individual
serum samples to be tested is relatively small, preliminary evaluation can be
performed conveniently by titration in a suitable indirect system, adapted
from those described later, using a range of dilutions of sera as the
intermediary layer followed by the appropriate labelled anti-species immunoglobulin conjugate. The test preparations should represent both positive
(antigen-containing) and negative (non-antigen-containing or unrelated-
antigen-containing) materials. Antisera exhibiting the highest level of activity
and specificity should be selected for further processing.

The range of antigens used for testing potency and specificity should be
selected for relevance in the system of intended use, and it is difficult to
provide specific recommendations. If the antibody is intended for a screening
test then it may be more important to test for a broad spectrum of
homologous reactivity than for cross reactions. In contrast, for a specific test
necessitating the use of a monospecific reagent, the range of heterologous
activity examined should include a series of closely related strains and
unrelated organisms commonly encountered in the types of test specimens to
be examined. Specificity tests performed at this stage may show non-
immunological reactions with some microorganisms, particularly *Staphylococcus aureus* and some strains of streptococcus, due to surface Fc receptors
(Kronvall, 1973a). The immunological specificity of labelled antibody techniques is dependent upon specific interaction between the antibody-combin-
ing site in the variable region of the immunoglobulin and its corresponding
antigenic determinant on the microorganism. However, immunoglobulin
molecules may bind to the surface of a variety of microorganisms and cells
by another mechanism involving a site in the constant (Fc) portion of the
molecule. This second mechanism operates if a surface receptor, specific for a
site on the Fc portion of immunoglobulin, is present on the target microor-

ganism. Antisera exhibiting good specific potency and minimal unwanted reactivity are absorbed, preferably before labelling.

The initial selection of monoclonal antibodies requires rapid, sensitive and reproducible assays for screening the hybrid cell products at an early stage in order to identify those with the desired reactivity. Unlike tests performed on polyclonal antisera, the number of tests on hybrid-cell supernatants is large, the volume available for testing is small, the concentration of antibody present may be very low and the time available for determining reactivity is limited by the need to initiate selective cloning. The major consideration in the design of these assays is that they should detect all antibodies reactive against the selected antigen. We have found the enzyme-linked immunosorbent assay (ELISA) to be extremely useful for this type of initial antibody screen using antigen bound to wells of a microtitre plate. In our hands it is sensitive, reproducible, extremely time-efficient in screening large numbers of cell products and gives a good estimation of potency. In this procedure the presence of antibody is determined by incubating the culture supernatant with antigen immobilized on polystyrene microtitre plates. Known positive and negative antisera, preferably of mouse origin, are included in each run. After a period of incubation, the supernatants are removed and the wells are washed. The working dilution of enzyme-labelled anti-mouse immunoglobulin is then added. After a further incubation the conjugate is removed and the wells are washed. The presence of bound enzyme is then detected by the addition of enzyme substrate and chromogen. If antibody is present in the initial supernatant then the enzyme-labelled anti-species conjugate is bound, which in turn results in the development of colour in positive wells on substrate addition. A difference in the rate of colour development gives a useful indication of potency.

Many protein antigens may be immobilized on a solid phase by passive absorption without affecting antigenicity. Other antigens may require special treatment to ensure that relevant antigenic determinants are attached. Whole organisms, purified antigens or synthetic antigens can be used, and several combinations of immunogen and solid phase have been used successfully to select monoclonal antibodies. If the target antigen is resistant to conventional immobilization on plastic then an alternative antibody-capture method can be employed. If this method is used then it is imperative to include suitable controls to ensure that the anti-mouse immunoglobulin does not react with the coating complex. The optimum concentrations of antigens or capture antibodies used do vary, but in our experience levels of 5–25 μg ml^{-1} are suitable for most purposes. While these tests provide a rapid screening assay, the results do not provide absolute definition of antibody specificity. It is mandatory to characterize the final monoclonal antibody reactivity by a wide range of different procedures before allocating a particular specificity. The feasibility of the assay system must be determined well in advance of the screening need, and can be achieved by the use of appropriate polyclonal sera. The specificity of the assay system should be determined by utilizing the specific antigen and control antigens of irrelevant specificity, and its applicability for mouse antibodies can be confirmed prior to fusion by introducing sera taken from immunized mice before the intended fusion. In this way the optimum dilutions of conjugate, the sensitivity of the system and the shortest incubation times necessary can be established.

(i) *Preparation of antigen-coated solid phase*

(a) Lipopolysaccharide (LPS) (Gustafsson *et al.*, 1982)

1. Prepare a solution of LPS at $25 \, \mu g \, ml^{-1}$ in 0.01 M phosphate-buffered saline pH 7.2 (PBS).
2. Dispense $100 \, \mu l$ into each well of a microtitre plate.
3. Incubate overnight at 37 °C. Discard fluid.
4. Dispense $100 \, \mu l$ of a 5% solution of bovine serum albumin in PBS containing 0.05% Tween 20 into each well. Leave for 15 min at 22 °C. This blocks unreacted sites and has been found to reduce non-specific reactions in some systems.
5. Rinse three times with $100 \, \mu l$ of PBS containing 0.05% Tween 20.

With some lipopolysaccharides, adsorption to polystyrene may be improved by the addition of 0.02 M magnesium chloride to all buffers used (Ito *et al.*, 1980).

(b) Polysaccharide (Moreno *et al.*, 1983)

1. Dispense $200 \, \mu l$ of a solution of poly-L-lysine ($100 \, \mu g \, ml^{-1}$ mol. wt 50 000 in PBS) into each well of a flexible microtitre plate.
2. Incubate for 1 h at room temperature.
3. Wash 5 times with PBS.
4. Prepare a solution of polysaccharide at $10 \, \mu g \, ml^{-1}$ in PBS and dispense $100 \, \mu l$ into each well.
5. Incubate for 1 h at room temperature.
6. Wash 5 times with PBS.
7. Dispense $250 \, \mu l$ of a 3% solution of bovine serum albumin in PBS into each well.
8. Incubate for 30 min at room temperature.
9. Wash 5 times with PBS.

(c) Whole cells (Polin and Kennett, 1980)

1. Prepare a suspension containing approximately 4×10^7 bacteria per ml in PBS. Dispense 100 μl into each well of a polyvinyl chloride plate.
2. Centrifuge the plate at 4000*g* for 5 min.
3. Add 100 μl of 0.5% of glutaraldehyde solution in ice-cold PBS to each well.
4. Incubate for 15 min at room temperature.
5. Remove liquid and wash twice in PBS.
6. Dispense 200 μl 1% bovine serum albumin solution containing 0.1 M glycine (pH 7.6) into each well.
7. Incubate at room temperature for 30 min.
8. Wash in PBS. Plates, when dried, may be stored at room temperature for up to six months.

As with polysaccharide, binding of antigen to the plastic may be improved by precoating the wells with poly-L-lysine (50 μg ml^{-1}) in PBS for 30 min at room temperature immediately before sensitization (Ison *et al.*, 1981).

(d) Protein (Strandberg Pedersen *et al.*, 1982)

1. Prepare a solution of the protein at 25 μg ml^{-1} in 0.01 M phosphate-buffered saline, pH 7.4 (PBS).
2. Dispense 100 μl into each well of a microtitre plate.
3. Incubate overnight at 4 °C. Discard fluid.
4. Wash three times with PBS containing 0.05% Tween 20.
5. Dispense 125 μl of a 1% solution of bovine serum albumin in PBS into each well.
6. Incubate overnight at 4 °C.
7. Wash three times in PBS and use immediately, or store in PBS containing albumin for up to one week.

(ii) *ELISA method* (modification of Gustafsson *et al.*, 1982)

1. Dispense 100 μl of each tissue-culture supernatant, positive and negative control using different pipette tips into separate wells in the microtitre plate. (It may be useful to ensure that the ELISA plate replicates the format of the tissue culture plate.)
2. Incubate for 1 h at 37 °C.
3. Rinse three times with PBS containing 0.05% Tween 20.
4. Dispense 100 μl of the working dilution of horseradish-peroxidase-labelled rabbit anti-mouse immunoglobulin in PBS containing 0.05% Tween 20 into each well. The working dilution of the conjugate must be

established by titrations and shown to react with all immunoglobulin isotypes.

5. Incubate for 30 min at 37 °C.
6. Rinse three times with PBS containing 0.05% Tween 20.
7. Dissolve 20 mg 1,2-phenylenediamine dihydrochloride in 50 ml 0.05 M citrate buffer pH 5.0. Just before use add 50 µl of 30% hydrogen peroxide. Dispense 100 µl to each well of the microtitre plate.
8. Incubate for 5 min at 37 °C.
9. Terminate the reaction with 50 µl of 1 M sulphuric acid.
10. Read visually or measure optical density at 492 nm using a suitable plate reader. An acceptable cut-off for positivity relative to background should be determined for each assay.

(iii) *Radioimmunoassay method* (Moreno *et al.*, 1983)

1. Dispense 100 µl of tissue-culture supernatant to each well in the microtitre plate.
2. Incubate at room temperature for 1 h.
3. Wash five times with 0.01 M phosphate-buffered saline, pH 7.2 (PBS).
4. Dispense 100 µl ^{125}I-labelled rabbit anti-mouse immunoglobulin (1–3×10^4 cpm per well, 7–8×10^6 cpm per µg).
5. Incubate at 4 °C overnight.
6. Wash five times with PBS.
7. Count in a suitable gamma counter.

These procedures can be adapted as required, and initial specificity testing can be incorporated into the primary screen as follows (modification of Tam *et al.*, 1982).

1. Prepare several replicate microtitre plates sensitized with different antigens.
2. Dispense 100 µl of culture fluid into corresponding wells of the different plates.
3. Incubate for 45 min at 37 °C.
4. Wash twice with PBS containing 1% bovine serum albumin.
5. Dispense ^{125}I-labelled rabbit anti-mouse immunoglobulin (as above but ten times concentrated) in PBS containing 1% bovine serum albumin, into each well.
6. Incubate for 45 min at 37 °C.
7. Wash three times with PBS.
8. Perform autoradiography by standing the plates overnight at -70 °C on Kodak XR-5 film. Compare the autoradiographs. These may be enhanced using a Du Pont Cronex X-ray intensifying screen.

Once antibody-producing clones have been isolated and shown to be stable, the products should be re-evaluated for sensitivity and specificity in the test of intended use as described for polyclonal antisera.

D. Absorption of polyclonal antisera

Preliminary assessment of polyclonal antiserum is essential to confirm adequate potency and to identify the degree of unwanted reactivity in order to select appropriate absorption procedures. Antisera can be rendered specific by removal of the unwanted antibody or by selective absorption and elution of antibodies of the required specificity. The former procedure eliminates the possibility of deleterious effects of the eluting agent on the specific antibody, but fails to remove all non-antibody globulins.

(i) *Procedure for removal of antibody of unwanted specificity (batch absorption method)* (modification of Edwards and Ewing, 1982)

1. Prepare agar-plate cultures of organisms that represent the unwanted cross-reactions. The quantities required will depend upon the strength of the cross-reactivity and the volume of serum used.
2. Harvest the organisms in physiological saline containing 0.5% formalin. Mix well with a pipette to suspend the organisms, and centrifuge at 4000*g* for 20 min.
3. Discard the supernatant and resuspend the pellet in the serum.
4. Incubate on a magnetic stirrer at 37 °C for 2 h.
5. Centrifuge at 4000*g* for 20 min.
6. Recover the serum and retest for specificity and potency in comparison with an unabsorbed serum sample. Reabsorb as necessary.
7. Filter absorbed serum through a 0.22 μm membrane.

(ii) *Procedure for immunopurification of selected antibodies*

Most antibodies may be purified by this method if a suitable antigen immunoadsorbent can be prepared. Antibodies to *Pseudomonas aeruginosa* lipopolysaccharide have been purified as follows (Fick *et al.*, 1980):

1. Dialyse the antigen (40 mg of *Pseudomonas* lipopolysaccharide) against coupling solution, 0.1 M sodium bicarbonate in 0.5 M sodium chloride at pH 8.0.
2. Wash 6 g (dry weight) of cyanogen-bromide-activated Sepharose 4B (Pharmacia) thoroughly with 1200 ml 1 mM hydrochloric acid.
3. Add the activated Sepharose and antigen to 30 ml coupling solution in a 50 ml conical plastic tube.

4. Mix on a rotator for 2 h at room temperature.
5. Stand for 16 h at 4 °C.
6. Wash the gel on a sintered-glass filter with 250 ml coupling solution.
7. Block any remaining active groups with 1 M ethanolamine, pH 9.0, for 2 h.
8. Wash as in step 6 with alternating 50 ml volumes of coupling solution and sodium acetate buffer, pH 4.0 (0.1 M acetate in 0.5 M sodium chloride).
9. The gel may be stored in borate buffer pH 8.0 (0.2 M boric acid in 0.5 M sodium chloride) for several months at 4 °C. Before use, wash thoroughly with 0.05 M glycine–hydrochloric-acid buffer, pH 2.4, then re-equilibrate in borate buffer.
10. The gel may be used in a batch or column procedure. For a typical batch procedure, dialyse 5–10 ml of serum against borate buffer, pH 8.0, at 4 °C.
11. Add the dialysed serum to 20–40 ml of gel at room temperature and stir occasionally over 30 min.
12. Recover the gel on a sintered-glass filter and wash while still on the filter with borate buffer until the effluent has a baseline absorbance when read in a spectrophotometer at 278 nm.
13. Elute the antibodies by passing 0.05 M glycine–hydrochloric-acid buffer, pH 2.4, through the filter and collect the effluent in a flask containing a small volume of 5% ammonium bicarbonate.
14. Dialyse against 0.9% saline and concentrate as necessary by pressure dialysis.
15. Wash the gel in borate buffer and store as described in step 9 above.

E.   Advantages and limitations of monoclonal and polyclonal antibodies

Hybridization techniques provide an excellent opportunity for generating monoclonal antibodies of defined epitope specificity, thereby eliminating the need for the multiple absorptions that are usually required to render polyclonal antisera suitably specific. Furthermore, monoclonal antibodies rarely show the variation in reactivity between batches of ascitic fluid prepared on different occasions from the same cell clone as so often is experienced with polyclonal antisera prepared at different times with the same immunogen and immunization schedule. Products of a particular clone are homogeneous with regard to specificity, antibody affinity and avidity, in contrast with the heterogeneous nature of antibodies in a polyclonal antiserum. Despite these advantages, potential users should be aware of limitations that may influence the applicability of some monoclonal antibodies in labelled-antibody techniques. Although the specificity of monoclonal and polyclonal antibodies may be apparently similar, other properties may make them unsuitable for a particular application (Peterfy et al., 1983).

The immunoglobulin class and isotype of monoclonal antibodies differ, and if indirect methods are employed it is essential to establish that the second labelled reagent reacts effectively with the primary monoclonal antibody. IgM class antibodies are unsuitable for most protein A-associated methods, and monoclonal secondary antibodies of restricted epitope specificity may be incapable of reacting with primary antibodies of differing immunoglobulin class or isotype. All monoclonals are not suitable for direct labelling procedures, as their susceptibility to inactivation during labelling varies (Nowinski et al., 1983). Individual clones vary, and the functional stability of each cell line and its products should be assessed.

Narrow specificity is advantageous in some procedures, but in others that are dependent on secondary lattice formation, reactivity against several epitopes or repeating epitopes is necessary. This may be achieved by pooling selected monoclonal antibodies that recognize different epitopes to manufacture a "pseudopolyclonal" serum. In the same way, if a particular epitope is not uniformly represented on all microbial strains to be detected, a carefully defined pool must be prepared (Tam et al., 1982). Occasionally, monoclonal antibodies exhibit cross-reactivity due to interspecies possession of common epitopes, as experienced between Escherichia coli K antigens and Neisseria meningitidis group antigens (Chalker et al., 1983).

Irrespective of whether monoclonal or polyclonal antibodies are employed as primary or secondary antibodies, readers should maintain an awareness of the possibility of antigenic similarity or shared epitopes in certain groups of organisms and occurrence of natural antibodies against microorganisms, which can give rise to unwanted immunological interaction.

IV. Immunoglobulin preparation for conjugation

Satisfactory conjugates can be prepared only by labelling purified antibodies derived by affinity chromatography, or the immunoglobulin fraction separated from antiserum, ascitic fluid or culture supernatant. If the latter procedure is used, it is essential to select potent antisera to ensure that the proportion of specific antibody to total immunoglobulin is high in order to avoid non-specific reactivity due to labelled non-antibody immunoglobulins in the final reagent. Although not generally recognized by those inexperienced in the day-to-day preparation of immunoglobulins and the derived labelled reagents, some denaturation of antibody activity may occur during immunoglobulin preparation, irrespective of the method used. Although this loss is insignificant for practical purposes in the majority of cases, it is important to realize that the percentage loss of antibody does vary with different antibodies prepared in different ways. In our experience this is particularly so for IgM monoclonal antibodies, but in some instances major losses due to denaturation have been observed with monoclonal antibodies of other immunoglobulin class or isotype.

A. Preparation of immunoglobulin fraction

Several methods are available for the preparation of the immunoglobulin fraction from whole serum or ascites (Hurn and Chantler, 1980). The choice of method employed will, to a large extent, depend on the preference of the individual and the facilities available in a particular laboratory. Practical details of procedures for the preparation of immunoglobulin fraction by precipitation methods and affinity chromatography are given below. In our experience, protein A chromatography is a simple single-step procedure for isolation of immunoglobulin, provided, of course, that the particular immunoglobulin has a high affinity for protein A. It cannot be assumed that this is so with all mouse monoclonal antibodies, even if an immunoglobulin isotype has previously been shown to have a high affinity for protein A (R. J. S. Duncan, personal communication).

(i) *Protein A chromatography* (modification of Ey *et al.*, 1978)

Materials.   Protein A Sepharose CL-4B (Pharmacia); 0.1 M potassium phosphate/0.05 M Tris/NaOH, pH 8.0; 1 M acetic acid.

Method

1. Prepare a column (1 cm × 10 cm) of Protein A Sepharose previously swollen in phosphate/Tris buffer. Use approximately 5 ml gel per 20 ml serum.
2. Dialyse sample against phosphate/Tris buffer overnight at 4 °C.
3. Load filtered sample onto column at 5 ml h^{-1}.
4. Wash the column with phosphate/Tris buffer at 5 ml h^{-1} until the eluate is free of protein.
5. Reverse the flow and elute IgG with 1 M acetic acid at a flow rate of 20 ml h^{-1} into tubes containing triethanolamine base (50:50 in water) to neutralize the product.
6. Pool eluate fractions, dialyse against saline and concentrate if necessary by an appropriate method.
7. Wash the column immediately with phosphate/Tris buffer or with saline containing 0.01% sodium azide if the column is to be stored.

(ii) *Precipitation with caprylic acid (Steinbuch and Audran, 1969) and ammonium sulphate*

Materials. 0.06 M acetate buffer, pH 4.0; caprylic acid; saline; saturated ammonium sulphate (756 g l^{-1} at 20 °C).

Method

1. Add two volumes of acetate buffer to the antiserum in a beaker. Check and adjust the pH of the mixture to 4.8.
2. Add 0.74 ml of caprylic acid dropwise to each 10 ml of antiserum or ascitic fluid. Stir the mixture continuously on a magnetic stirrer at room temperature.
3. Continue stirring for 30 min.
4. Centrifuge at 4000g to remove the precipitate (or filter on a Buchner funnel).
5. Retain the supernatant containing the immunoglobulin. Place in Visking tubing and dialyse extensively against saline at 4 °C.

Since the final volume of immunoglobulin solution is approximately three times the volume of the starting material, concentration is usually necessary. This can be readily achieved by precipitation with ammonium sulphate as described below.

6. Place the immunoglobulin solution in a beaker, measuring the volume by weight.
7. Add an equal volume of saturated ammonium sulphate solution dropwise from a separating funnel, stirring gently on a magnetic stirrer throughout.
8. Place at 4 °C for at least 6 h to allow the immunoglobulin precipitate to flocculate.
9. Centrifuge at about 4000g for 20 min, preferably in a refrigerated centrifuge, and discard the supernatant.
10. Dissolve the precipitate in the smallest volume of saline.
11. Place the immunoglobulin solution in Visking tubing and dialyse extensively against several changes of saline, or remove ammonium sulphate by chromatography on a Sephadex G25 column.
12. Check for residual sulphate ions by adding a few drops of the immunoglobulin solution to a tube containing a small volume of barium chloride solution. Any cloudiness indicates the presence of sulphate ions and the need for further dialysis.
13. Measure the volume of immunoglobulin solution and calculate the protein concentration by measuring the absorbance of a 1:25 dilution at a wavelength of 280 nm using a cuvette of 1 cm path length:

$$\text{concentration} = \frac{A_{280} \times 25}{1.34} \text{ mg ml}^{-1}$$

(The factor 1.34 can be used for immunoglobulins of most animal species.)

The homogeneity of the derived preparation and its freedom from contaminating non-immunoglobulin protein must be determined prior to labelling. The purity of the immunoglobulin preparation can be conveniently tested by immunoelectrophoresis using the globulin preparation, preferably at 5 mg ml^{-1}, in the wells and anti-whole serum directed against the appropriate species in the trough during the diffusion phase.

B. Preparation of F(ab')$_2$ fragments (Madsen and Rodkey, 1976)

Materials.   0.1 M sodium acetate buffer, pH 4.3; 0.1 M sodium acetate buffer, pH 7.0; Borate–saline buffer, pH 8.0; immunoglobulin preparation; pepsin.

Method

1.   Dialyse the immunoglobulin solution against 0.1 M acetate buffer pH 7.0.
2.   Dissolve pepsin in 0.1 M acetate buffer pH 4.3 using 1 mg pepsin : 25 mg protein.
3.   Adjust pH of immunoglobulin to 4.3 and add an appropriate volume of pepsin solution.
4.   Incubate at 37 °C with agitation for 8 hours.
5.   Transfer to Visking tubing and dialyse the digest against several changes of borate–saline buffer pH 8.0. Redialyse against saline and concentrate by an appropriate method.

V.   Labelling procedures and methods of use

A.   Fluorescent labels

The observation that an antibody of known specificity could be coupled to a fluorescent dye and used to localize the complementary antigen in histological preparations (Coons et al., 1941) stimulated the application of fluorochrome-labelled antibody techniques for the demonstration of a variety of microbial antigens (Nairn, 1976). This technique combines the unique specificity of an immunological reaction with the high sensitivity obtained by fluorescence emission such that the site of interaction between the antigen and labelled antibody can be observed by fluorescence microscopy (Ploem, 1967; Herzog *et al.*, 1973; Taylor and Heimer, 1973). This enables detection and presumptive identification of the microorganism on the basis of both antigenicity and morphological appearance.

The choice of fluorochrome used in immunofluorescent studies is dependent upon its availability in a purified and stable form, the ease with which it can be coupled to an antibody without deleterious effects upon its biological activity and upon the availability of optical systems that enable detection of the emitted fluorescent light. The derivatives of two fluorochromes, fluorescein and rhodamine, fulfil these criteria, and, as they provide a good colour contrast, are eminently suitable for the simultaneous detection of two antigens.

Visualization of a fluorescent marker is achieved by exposure of the specimen to excitation light of a wavelength maximally absorbed by the fluorochrome. This results in the emission of high-intensity visible light detected by fluorescence microscopy. Considerable advances in filter technology have occurred in the last decade, and highly efficient filters for narrow-band excitation suitable for single- and double-labelling immunofluorescence studies are now available. For investigations employing antibodies labelled with two different fluorochromes, whose absorption and emission peaks are in close proximity, it is essential to use filter combinations with clearly defined characteristics to ensure that the fluorescence observed is contributed by one or other fluorochrome alone. Users, particularly those involved in double-labelling studies, should ensure that the recommended filters are satisfactory in use, and this can be readily confirmed by examining preparations stained with the two fluorochrome-labelled antibodies separately before proceeding to double-labelling experiments.

The methods given below refer to the use of fluorescent-labelled antibodies in microscope techniques, but they can also be used with fluorimeters in specialized automated techniques of flow cytometry (Sahar *et al.*, 1983) and fluorescence-activated cell sorting.

(i) *Labelling of antibody globulins with fluorescein isothiocyanate*

Materials. Fluorescein isothiocyanate, isomer I (FITC); 0.1 M carbonate/bicarbonate buffer, pH 9.0; immunoglobulin preparation in saline (10 mg ml^{-1}); phosphate-buffered saline, pH 7.5 (PBS); Sephadex G50 (Medium).

Method

1. Prepare a standard solution of FITC in carbonate/bicarbonate buffer (1.5 mg FITC ml^{-1}).

2. Place a measured volume of the immunoglobulin solution in a small beaker and add one-tenth of the volume of carbonate/bicarbonate buffer.
3. Add one-tenth volume of FITC solution dropwise while stirring the immunoglobulin solution gently on a magnetic stirrer. Check pH and adjust to pH 9.0 with 0.1 N NaOH if necessary.
4. Cover the reaction vessel and stir *gently* at 4 °C overnight.
5. Dialyse conjugate against several changes of phosphate-buffered saline (PBS) to remove unbound FITC. For large volumes of conjugates (> 5 ml) further separation by gel-filtration chromatography on Sephadex G50 (Medium) is recommended.
6. Prepare Sephadex G50 column equilibrated with PBS such that the packed volume is at least six times the volume of conjugate to be applied. Allow a disc of filter paper, cut to fit the dimensions of the column, to float onto the top of the column (this facilitates the even application of conjugate).
7. Apply the conjugate onto the column. When all the conjugate has passed into the column, elute with PBS and collect the first coloured peak to emerge (this contains the labelled immunoglobulins).
8. Most conjugates can be stored at 4 °C or in aliquots at −20 °C after the addition of a preservative such as 0.1% sodium azide without significant deterioration of antibody activity. Repeated freezing and thawing is to be avoided. The stability of conjugates derived from monoclonal antibodies should be determined by experimentation.

(ii) *Evaluation of conjugate*

A variety of tests can be used to determine the efficiency of conjugation and the suitability of the conjugate in use. The efficiency of labelling can be determined very simply by measuring the absorbance of the conjugate at the 280 nm protein peak and at the maximum absorbance wavelength of the label used. In our experience a ratio of A_{495}/A_{280} between 0.7 and 0.9 is most appropriate for the general detection of microorganisms in microscope preparations (Wells *et al.*, 1966; Hebert *et al.*, 1981). These values give a rough guide of the success of conjugation, and are by no means optimal for every test system. The test fails to show whether biological activity is present in the conjugate; this can only be determined by using the conjugate in the immunofluorescence system of intended use. Performance testing by titration (direct method) or chessboard titration (indirect method) is essential in order to select the optimal working dilution of the reagent and to test its specificity under working laboratory conditions.

(iii) *Staining procedures*

Fluorochrome-labelled antibody methods have been extensively used to detect and identify a variety of microorganisms in clinical specimens and culture isolates (Cherry and Moody, 1965). These include enteropathogenic *Escherichia coli* (Thomason and Cherry, 1971), *Salmonella typhi* (Thomason and McWhorter, 1965; Bisset *et al.*, 1969) and *Shigella* (Taylor and Heimer, 1964) in faeces, *Salmonella* in smears prepared from selective pre-culture of faeces, food and environmental samples (Thomason and Wells, 1971; Insalata *et al.*, 1973; Mohr *et al.*, 1974), *Neisseria gonorrhoeae* in clinical specimens (Danielsson and Forsum, 1975), *Chlamydia* (Richmond and Caul, 1975; Thornley *et al.*, 1983) and many viruses (Gardner and McQuillan, 1980; Goldstein *et al.*, 1983; Schmidt *et al.*, 1983). Selected examples to illustrate the practical aspects of the methods used are given below.

(a) Detection of Toxoplasma gondii *(direct method)*

Method

1. Mark slides with water-insoluble-ink pen and place in humidified chamber.
2. Prepare working dilution of FITC anti-*Toxoplasma gondii* and control conjugate of unrelated specificity in PBS containing 1% Evans blue.
3. Cover antigen area with conjugate, place lid on the chamber and incubate at 37 °C or room temperature for 30 min.
4. Remove excess conjugate from each antigen spot by gentle aspiration but do not allow slides to dry out.
5. Wash in PBS using three 5 min wash cycles.
6. Mount in buffered glycerol (Johnson and Araujo, 1981), apply coverslip and view by fluorescence microscopy.

Reading and interpretation of results

In positive specimens intense yellow/green fluorescence of the entire membrane is observed, which contrasts well with the red internal cytoplasmic staining due to counterstain. Preparations stained with the control conjugate do not show membrane fluorescence, but the organisms are readily identified by their reaction with counterstain.

(b) Detection and identification of Clostridium septicum *and* Clostridium chauvoei *(double-labelling direct method)* (Batty and Walker, 1963)

Method

1. Smear the culture or a portion of the suspected lesion onto microscope slides and leave for a few moments until dry.
2. Fix by immersing in reagent grade anhydrous acetone for 10 min. Fan dry to evaporate fixative and mark slides.
3. Place slides in humid chamber and cover the antigen area with the appropriate conjugate (or mixture of fluorescein and rhodamine conjugates).
4. Leave in a humid chamber for 30 min at room temperature.
5. Gently aspirate the conjugate, taking care not to disturb the antigen area. Finally wash for at least 10 min in several changes of PBS.
6. Blot but do *not* rub with clean absorbent paper.
7. Mount preparations by covering with mounting fluid and cover slip.
8. View by fluorescence microscopy and record results.

Reading and interpretation of results

The slides should be screened initially using 40 × magnification objective to locate the organisms. Subsequent examination with the appropriate filter combinations is best performed with 50 × water immersion objective. Known positive antigen slides should be included in each run to ensure that the light source and optical alignment are satisfactory.

(c) Detection of Respiratory Syncytial Virus (indirect method)

Test specimens.   Suitably fixed, prepared slides of exudates, for example nasopharyngeal secretions, cough/nasal swabs or slide/coverslip preparations of infected tissue cultures.

Method

1. Mark slide preparations with a felt-tip pen and place in humid chamber.
2. Prepare the working dilution of unlabelled bovine anti-RSV serum and control non-immune or immune bovine serum of proven unrelated specificity in PBS.
3. Cover antigen on marked slides with appropriate sera ensuring that the entire area is covered and that no contamination occurs between adjacent antigen spots.
4. Cover chamber and place at 37 °C or room temperature for 30 min.
5. Remove excess antiserum by gentle aspiration, and carefully rinse with PBS, taking care that the antigen areas are undisturbed.

6. Wash in at least 3 changes of PBS for a total of 30 min.
7. Prepare working dilution of FITC-labelled anti-bovine immunoglobulin in PBS containing 1% Evans blue.
8. Remove slides from wash, drain and blot but do *not* rub on a pad of absorbent paper. Do not allow slides to dry out.
9. Replace in humid chamber and cover antigen areas with diluted conjugate as in step 3.
10. Incubate as in step 4.
11. Remove excess conjugate as in step 5 and wash as in step 6.
12. Remove slides from wash, drain and mount in buffered glycerol.
13. Examine by fluorescence microscopy and record results.

Reading and interpretation of results

In positive specimens intense granular fluorescence is observed in the cytoplasm of cells. In clinical specimens the inclusions are present in ciliated respiratory epithelial cells and macrophages. The intensity of staining may be reduced in samples taken several days after the onset of illness. If RSV is absent, fluorescent cytoplasmic granular staining is not observed. Samples treated with negative control serum and uninfected cell controls treated with positive anti-RSV serum should be negative. Thick clumps of cells may exhibit non-specific staining, and these should be avoided when reading the results. In tissue-culture preparations damaged or old, small, rounded cells may show non-specific staining. These are readily distinguished from the positive granular intracytoplasmic fluorescence described above and by comparison with the appearance of infected cultures treated with negative control serum.

(iv) *General technical parameters*

The success of immunofluorescence procedures is determined by the suitability of the test specimen (antigen substrate) and the quality of the antibodies and conjugates used, but several factors, some all too obvious but frequently overlooked, can influence the quality of the result achieved. An awareness of common technical pitfalls and a little attention to detail will serve to avoid this type of unnecessary problem. Several of these parameters apply to other labelled-antibody procedures and should be considered as general recommendations.

(a) Sample preparation

Multispot Teflon-coated slides, widely available commercially, are very satisfactory for testing a large number of samples with great saving of time.

They can be used for a variety of antigens, including bacteria, protozoa, virus-infected cultures and cryostat sections of tissues, and the coating is resistant to most fixatives. Good bacterial and protozoal preparations may be made from suspensions of cultured organisms by placing a drop on each uncoated area, allowing this to remain for approximately one minute and then removing excess liquid with a Pasteur pipette, thus leaving a thin film of antigen which dries rapidly. If crude preparations containing extensive extraneous material are to be used, it is preferable to smear the specimen over a larger surface area to obtain a thin film. After fan drying, the slides are dipped rapidly in distilled water to remove residual salts, redried and fixed. Mucus-containing secretions (e.g. nasopharyngeal exudates) must be processed as follows to prepare a cell suspension free of mucus.

1. Add excess **PBS** to tube containing clinical specimen.
2. Centrifuge at 1500 rpm for ten minutes at 4 °C. Discard supernatant and resuspend the cells in **PBS** by aspiration with a Pasteur pipette. Repeat this washing process.
3. Suspend the deposit in a small volume of **PBS** to dilute the specimen beyond the point where the suspension is sticky.
4. Outline two areas on a microscope slide with a diamond pen, or alternatively use a Teflon-coated slide with uncoated areas of large diameter.
5. Spread two drops of the test-cell suspension over the marked area and allow to dry. (Alternatively a cytocentrifuge may be used for antigen preparation. Although the cellular morphology obtained is excellent, the use of this procedure may be limited by the infectious nature of material handled and the need for speed.)
6. Fix immediately in acetone at 4 °C for 10 min.

Antigen substrate slides may be stored for prolonged periods at −20 °C provided they are thoroughly dry. The following procedure is suitable for a variety of antigens.

1. Place required number of slides on top of each other, separated at each end by small pieces of paper to prevent contact.
2. Wrap each group in cellophane (transparent material made from viscose) and seal.
3. Label and place in a Minigrip (self-sealing) polythene bag containing silica gel and moisture indicator.
4. Label top of the bag with a water-insoluble felt pen for easy identification and store at −20 °C.

Packed slides, removed from $-20\,°C$ for use, should be kept at room temperature for a short while before being opened. This prevents surface condensation, which can have deleterious effects on antigen retention.

Unsatisfactory antigen substrates are frequently responsible for poor results. Uneven distribution with subsequent clumping of bacteria and cells, damaged cells and extraneous materials (e.g. mucus) can give rise to non-specific staining and diminished contrast. Dilution of broth constituents or salts in bacterial suspensions using distilled water immediately prior to slide preparation greatly enhances the ease of detection, but overexposure may result in lysis. Overdilution of suspensions and subsequent loss of antigen during the procedure decreases the ease of interpretation. A negative test result must be confirmed to be due to absence of staining rather than loss of organisms by the use of phase-contrast or other appropriate microscopy. Inappropriate fixation or repeated freezing and thawing may denature antigen, fail to retain antigen or cause undesirable distortion of morphological appearance. Timing of specimen collection is important, particularly following virus infection. The specimen should be collected during the period of maximal virus shedding after onset of symptoms.

(b) Conjugate optimization

The sensitivity and ease of interpretation of an immunofluorescence test is determined by the contrast between high specific activity and low background staining. Satisfactory results can only be achieved by utilizing reagents (of previously proven specificity) at the optimal dilution of use in a particular test system. The optimal or working dilution of each reagent must be tested by titration, and each batch of new reagent must be reassessed. Reconstituted undiluted conjugates may be stored in the dark in a refrigerator for at least six months. If longer storage is required, the undiluted reagent may be divided into aliquots and stored at $-20\,°C$. Repeated freezing and thawing can give rise to denaturation. Diluted conjugate should be discarded after use.

Unsatisfactory reagent application can give erroneous results. Evaporation of antibody or conjugate during staining may decrease contrast and produce artifacts; a humidified chamber must always be used. Care should be taken to ensure that contamination between antigen areas on slides treated with reagents of differing specificity does not occur. Rinse excess reagents from individual antigen areas prior to placing in washing vessel.

(c) Fluorescence intensity

The selection of appropriate filters, adequacy of light source and optical alignment of the microscope are essential for satisfactory observations to be made. It is useful to include a known positive freshly prepared reference slide in each test run to confirm the proper functioning of the microscope. Prolonged exposure of specimens to excitation light gives rise to fading of fluorescence. Unnecessary exposure should be avoided. The use of mountants containing phenylenediamine is extremely effective in minimizing fading (Johnson and Araujo, 1981). The intensity of fluorescence emission observed is influenced by the pH of the mounting fluid, and is optimal at a pH of 8–9. Glycerol mixed with buffers of neutral pH is often slightly acidic on preparation, or may become so upon storage. In extreme cases this can give rise to negative results.

B. Enzyme labels

The introduction of enzymes as antibody labels for the detection of antigens in microscope preparations (Nakane and Pierce, 1966; Avrameas and Uriel, 1966) and in non-microscope-associated procedures (Engvall and Perlmann, 1971) has resulted in an explosive application of enzyme-labelled antibody techniques in microbiology. The principles of the techniques are analogous to those already described for fluorescent labels, but the detection of bound enzyme-labelled antibody requires an additional incubation with the appropriate enzyme substrate and chromogen to give a coloured reaction product. By appropriate selection of chromogen, the reaction product may be insoluble and detected by conventional light or electron microscopy, or soluble and observed by the naked eye or measured in a spectrophotometer or ELISA reader. In addition, highly sensitive fluorimetric (Soini and Hemmilä, 1979; Labrousse et al., 1982) and luminometric (Halmann et al., 1977; Whitehead et al., 1983) analyses are being explored.

Enzymes are available commercially in a purified form, and several including horseradish peroxidase, alkaline phosphatase, glucose oxidase, β-galactosidase and urease can be coupled to antibody with minimal effect on immunological activity (Takashi and Kayoko, 1977; Ford et al., 1978; Chandler et al., 1982, Tanimori et al., 1983). Conjugates of Fab' fragments may also be made (Yoshitake et al., 1979). Similarly, a variety of chromogens are available for use in microscope-associated and solid-phase assays. This allows considerable versatility in the type of procedure and specimen that can be used, and provides the opportunity for an objective measurement of the reaction.

(i) Labelling of antibody globulins with horseradish peroxidase

A variety of methods can be used for coupling enzymes to antibodies, but the conjugation procedures most commonly used with horseradish peroxidase (HRP) include two-stage glutaraldehyde (Avrameas and Ternynck, 1971), periodate oxidation (Wilson and Nakane, 1978) and sulphydryl–maleimide (Duncan *et al.*, 1983) methods. Conjugates prepared by any of these procedures are suitable for immunoenzyme-labelled antibody methods, and details for the first two are given below.

(a) Glutaraldehyde conjugation method (Avrameas and Ternynck, 1971)

Materials.   Horseradish peroxidase RZ 3.0 (HRP); 25% solution of glutaraldehyde; 0.1 M phosphate buffer, pH 6.8; Sephadex G25; saline; immunoglobulin preparation; 0.5 M carbonate/bicarbonate buffer, pH 9.5; 1.0 M lysine solution, pH 7; 0.01 M phosphate-buffered saline, pH 7.5 (PBS); saturated ammonium sulphate; glycerol.

Method

1. Prepare 1% glutaraldehyde in phosphate buffer.
2. Dissolve 10 mg HRP in 0.2 ml of the freshly prepared glutaraldehyde solution and stand at room temperature for 18 h.
3. Pass through Sephadex G25 column equilibrated with saline to remove excess glutaraldehyde. Collect the coloured fractions containing activated peroxidase, pool and concentrate to 1 ml.
4. Add 1 ml of immunoglobulin solution (5 mg ml^{-1} in saline) to the peroxidase solution.
5. Add 0.2 ml of carbonate/bicarbonate buffer and leave for 24 h at 4 °C.
6. Add 0.1 ml of lysine solution and leave the mixture at 4 °C for 2 h. Dialyse against several changes of PBS at 4 °C.

Free enzyme may be removed by precipitation with saturated ammonium sulphate. Add an equal volume of saturated ammonium sulphate dropwise to the conjugate and allow to stand at 4 °C for 4 h. Centrifuge for 20 min at 4000g and discard the supernatant. Dissolve the precipitate in approximately 1 ml of saline and remove sulphate ions by extensive dialysis against PBS or by Sephadex G50 chromatography.

(b) Periodate oxidation conjugation method (Wilson and Nakane, 1978)

In this method, periodate oxidation of the carbohydrate moiety of peroxidase results in the generation of active aldehyde groups. These combine with the amino groups of added immunoglobulin to form Schiff bases, which are subsequently stabilized by borohydride reduction.

Materials.   Horseradish peroxidase RZ 3.0 (HRP); 0.1 M sodium metaperiodate (freshly prepared); 0.001 M acetate buffer, pH 4.4; 0.01 M carbonate/bicarbonate buffer, pH 9.5; immunoglobulin preparation; 0.2 M carbonate/bicarbonate buffer, pH 9.5; sodium borohydride; Sephacryl$^{(R)}$ S200; 0.01 M phosphate-buffered saline, pH 7.5 (PBS).

Method

1. Activate HRP by dissolving 4 mg in 1 ml distilled water, then add 0.2 ml of freshly prepared sodium metaperiodate to the enzyme solution and stir for 20 min at room temperature.
2. Dialyse against acetate buffer overnight at 4 °C.
3. Prepare the immunoglobulin solution containing 8 mg protein in 1 ml 0.01 M carbonate/bicarbonate buffer.
4. Adjust activated HRP solution to approximately pH 9 by addition of 20 µl of 0.2 M carbonate/bicarbonate buffer and immediately add the globulin preparation. Stir for 2 h at room temperature.
5. Add 0.1 ml of freshly prepared sodium borohydride solution containing 4 mg ml^{-1} and leave at 4 °C for 2 h.
6. Unreacted enzyme may be separated from the mixture by chromatography on a column of Sephacryl S200 equilibrated with PBS or by salt precipitation with an equal volume of saturated ammonium sulphate.

If purification of conjugates is performed by gel chromatography, the appropriate fractions should be pooled and concentrated prior to storage at − 20 °C. Addition of albumin (10 mg per ml of conjugate) and an equal volume of glycerol prior to freezing in small aliquots is recommended. Repeated freezing and thawing should be avoided.

(ii) *Evaluation of conjugate*

The activity of the resultant conjugate and efficacy in use must be determined by appropriate tests. Performance testing by titration is essential, as with fluorescein conjugates, to determine the optimal working dilution that provides a good contrast between specific and non-specific reactivity in the procedure of its intended use. Experience has shown that the optimal working dilution of a single enzyme-labelled antibody may differ by more than 100 fold in methods employing microscope preparations and solid-phase immunoassays. For these reasons, the specificity evaluation must be performed in the test system of ultimate use.

(iii) *Staining procedures*

The basic procedures used for the detection and identification of microorganisms in microscope preparations are analogous to those described for fluorescent, gold or ferritin labels, with the addition of an incubation step with chromogen and enzyme substrate, which results in deposition of an insoluble reaction product at the site of antigen:antibody interaction detectable by conventional microscopy. Non-microscopy procedures utilize antibodies physically adsorbed or chemically linked to the solid phase as the primary reactant, and are most commonly, but not exclusively, used with chromogens giving soluble coloured reaction products, which are readily detected by the naked eye or appropriate instrumentation. The principle of this enzyme-linked immunosorbent assay (ELISA) described by Engvall *et al.* (1971) for the detection of antigen is illustrated in Fig. 5. In this procedure the test specimen is placed in contact with the antibody-coated solid phase, which may be a microtitre well, plastic tube or sphere. Following incubation, unbound constituents are removed and the solid phase is washed prior to addition of enzyme-labelled antibody directed against the test antigen. After a further incubation, excess conjugate is removed by washing and bound enzyme is detected by the addition of enzyme substrate and chromogen, which gives a coloured reaction product with positive samples. Both types of enzyme-labelled-antibody procedure have been used for the detection and identification of microorganisms in a variety of specimens, but the practical

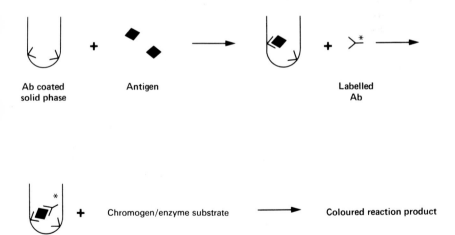

Fig. 5.   Principle of ELISA for detection of microbial antigens.

advantages of ELISA procedures have resulted in their more extensive application (Engvall, 1977; Schuurs and van Weeman, 1977; Vestergaard and Jensen, 1981; Ziegler *et al.*, 1983). The following examples illustrate the technical steps involved in the two types of procedures. It will be appreciated that these may be adapted for a particular need.

(a) Detection of Herpes Simplex Virus (HSV) by microscopy (indirect immunoperoxidase method)

Method

1. Place appropriately marked fixed slide preparations in humidified chambers.
2. Prepare working dilution of rabbit anti-HSV serum in PBS.
3. Cover antigen area with the diluted anti-HSV and a control spot with PBS or diluted non-immune rabbit serum.
4. Cover chamber and incubate at 37 °C or room temperature for 30 min.
5. Remove excess antibody by gentle aspiration and carefully rinse each antigen area with PBS, taking care that the antigen areas are undisturbed and that contamination between adjacent areas is avoided.
6. Wash in at least 3 changes of PBS for a total of 30 min.
7. Prepare working dilution of HRP-labelled anti-rabbit IG conjugate in PBS.
8. Remove slides from wash, drain and blot, but do *not* rub on a pad of absorbent paper. Do not allow slides to dry out.
9. Replace in humid chamber and cover antigen areas with diluted conjugate as in step 3.
10. Incubate as in step 4.
11. Remove excess conjugate as in step 5 and wash as in step 6.
12. Prepare chromogen/enzyme substrate by dissolving 5 mg 3,3-diaminobenzidine tetrahydrochloride (DAB) in 10 ml 0.05 M Tris/HCl, pH 7.5. Immediately before use add 50 µl of 30% hydrogen peroxide.
13. Remove slides from wash, drain and replace in humid chamber.
14. Flood slides with enzyme substrate/chromogen mixture and leave for 4 min.
15. Wash in 3 rapid changes of PBS, drain and mount in aqueous mountant. (Alternatively the preparations may be dehydrated through alcohol and xylene and mounted in DPX.)
16. Examine by conventional light microscopy.

Reading and interpretation of results

Brown intracytoplasmic or nuclear staining may be seen in HSV-infected cells treated with known positive serum. Samples treated with negative control serum or PBS should not stain; the presence of staining indicates interaction due to Fc receptors. Clumps of cells or damaged small rounded cells may exhibit non-specific staining, and should be avoided when reading results.

(b) Enzyme-linked immunosorbent assay (ELISA) for the detection of Herpes Simplex Virus (HSV) (modification of Vestergaard and Jensen, 1981)

Method

1. Prepare solution containing 10 µg ml^{-1} of unlabelled anti-HSV in 0.1 M carbonate/bicarbonate buffer.
2. Coat flat- or round-bottomed polystyrene microtitre wells by dispensing 100 µl of anti-HSV solution per well.
3. Cover and place at 37 °C for 1–3 h, followed by overnight at 4 °C.
4. Aspirate contents and wash twice in Tween/Saline.
5. Dispense 100 µl of test sample, known strong and weak antigen positive and negative controls each into two wells. Cover plate and stand at room temperature (RT) for 2 h.
6. Aspirate contents and wash wells three times in Tween/Saline.
7. Prepare working dilution of HRP-labelled anti-HSV in Tween/PBS containing 1% BSA.
8. Dispense 100 µl of conjugate into all wells, cover and stand at RT for 2 h.
9. Aspirate contents and wash as in step 6, leaving last wash fluid in wells.
10. Prepare chromogen/enzyme substrate just before use. Dissolve 20 mg *o*-phenylenediamine (OPD) in 50 ml 0.05 M citrate buffer, pH 5.0, and add 50 µl 30% hydrogen peroxide immediately before use.
11. Aspirate contents of wells and dispense 100 µl of chromogen into all wells, including blank wells to serve as reader blanks.
12. Note development of colour and terminate reaction by adding 50 µl 2 N H$_2$SO$_4$ when visual discrimination between weak positive and negative is just detectable (approximately 15 min).
13. Blank ELISA reader on chromogen blank wells treated with acid and read results at 495 nm.

Reading and interpretation of results

Control wells treated with chromogen or with known negative preparations should be colourless or very pale yellow. The test is unsatisfactory if a strong coloured reaction is observed in control wells. Wells containing the weak and strong positive controls will be yellow/orange, the intensity of the colour reaction being related to the strength of the sample. All samples giving a reaction equivalent to or more than the low positive control are clearly positive.

(iv) *General technical parameters*

The success of microscope-associated immunoperoxidase procedures is determined by the same general considerations outlined for immunofluorescence methods. In addition, users should be aware of the possibility of endogenous enzyme in certain cells, for example peroxidase in polymorphonuclear lymphocytes, which lead to erroneous interpretation of a positive result. The occurrence of this type of reactivity will be seen in control preparations, and may be inhibited by a variety of procedures (Zehr, 1978; Fink *et al.*, 1979; Bulman and Heyderman, 1981; Schmidt *et al.*, 1983). However, care should be taken to ensure that the methods used to destroy endogenous enzyme do not impair antigenicity of the microorganism.

Enzyme-linked immunosorbent assays (ELISA) offer considerable advantages for the detection of microbial antigens, as large numbers of samples can be processed rapidly, and interference by extraneous materials is minimized by their removal by washing. Soluble antigens are readily detected, and both subjective and objective methods may be used to measure reactivity. The volume of publications describing applications is legion, but relatively little attention has been given to the technical parameters that determine the success of a particular procedure (McLaren *et al.*, 1981). Several variables exist, and the success of a particular application will be reliant upon the quality of the reagents employed and optimization of the test procedure (Voller and Bidwell, 1983).

(a) *Antibody-coated solid phase*

Both the choice of solid phase and coating antibody determine the sensitivity, specificity and precision of the assay. Immunoglobulin is readily attached to polystyrene and polyvinyl chloride (PVC) by passive physical adsorption, but variations in adsorptive capacity occur between different sources and between batches from a single source (Cantarero *et al.*, 1980; Shekarchi *et al.*, 1984). Many manufacturers now provide polystyrene microtitre plates for ELISA studies, and these should be selected whenever possible. Immunoglobulin preparations derived from potent antisera should be used for coating at concentrations between 5–50 μg ml^{-1}. Higher levels, in our experience, often decrease the sensitivity of the assay, but in any event the optimum level of protein and duration of coating must be determined by experiment. The choice of suitable coating antibody must be determined by experiment, and it is valuable to select potent polyspecific antibody for initial optimization studies. Monoclonal antibodies may often be used to great advantage, but, in our experience, the efficacy of monoclonal antibodies of similar specificity but derived from different clones varies considerably.

(b) Enzyme-labelled antibody

The potency and specificity of the conjugate, the dilution used and incubation conditions affect test performance. The optimal dilution of conjugate must be determined by titration using known positive and negative samples; the dilutions giving the best contrast between positive and negative controls should be used for further studies. The incubation temperature and time can then be adapted to determine the optimal conditions. In general, shorter incubation periods can be used with higher temperature, but very short incubation periods (<30 min) may result in decreased precision.

(c) Sample preparation

Occasionally an unacceptably high level of non-specific reactivity is present, despite the optimization of reagent dilutions, incubation times and temperature. Every effort should be made to determine the causative factors by the use of appropriate controls. The addition of selected proteins in diluent buffers or the use of reagents of different specificity may be helpful.

(d) Quantitation

The measurement of bound enzyme is reliant upon a kinetic reaction in which the enzyme acts as a catalyst. The rate of reaction is dependent upon a number of factors, which include the concentration of enzyme and other reactants, temperature and pH. Variations of these parameters can produce significant problems of reproducibility and quantitation in ELISA systems and difficulties in determining absolute quantitative values for expression of results. If the test endpoint is based on time alone, control of variables that influence the reaction rate is of paramount importance. Alternatively, the reaction of test samples may be related to the response obtained with a reference, minimally reactive, control sample or by terminating the assay when the control reaches a predetermined absorbance. All approaches present difficulties in interpreting the reactivity of samples giving values greater than that of the known negative but less than the low positive or cut-off level. In order to interpret these with confidence, information on the assay precision is mandatory, and should include data on both inter- and intra-assay reproducibility on samples of known but varying activity. The acceptable levels of precision will depend upon the need for qualitative or precise quantitative information, but readers should be cautious in assigning cut-off absorbance values in new applications in the absence of data on assay precision. Alternative approaches to the quantitation of ELISA tests are included in several reviews (de Savigny and Voller 1980; Heck et al., 1980; Ritchie et al., 1981).

C. Radioisotope labels

Radioactive isotopes can be incorporated into antibodies without deleterious effects on immunological activity. The bound label can be detected by using either a counter appropriate to the isotope or a photographic film or emulsion.

(i) Labelling procedure

A variety of radioisotopes are available, but iodine-125 is most commonly used. Several conjugation procedures are available; the chloramine T method leads to some denaturation of antibody activity and other, gentler, procedures employing Iodo-gen™, 1, 3, 4, 6-tetrachloro-3,6-diphenylglycouril (Pierce Chemicals) are preferable. This iodinating agent is insoluble in aqueous solvents, but stable and active when coated on a solid phase. For use, Iodo-gen™ is dissolved in an organic solvent, placed in a plastic tube, and during solvent evaporation the reagent becomes coated onto the wall of the tube. Tubes prepared in this way may be stored for long periods ready for use. Following conjugation, termination of the reaction is achieved by simple removal of the reaction mixture from the tube. It is important that appropriate safety precautions are taken while performing this procedure because of the toxicity of radioactive substances.

1. Dissolve Iodo-gen™ at $100 \, \mu l \, ml^{-1}$ in dichloromethane.
2. Dispense 5 μl of the solution into a suitable small plastic tube. Rotate the tube at an angle to coat the inside of the base of the tube with the oxidizing agent as the solvent evaporates.
3. Place a small volume, around 50 μl, of PBS, pH 7.4, containing between 50 and 500 μg immunoglobulin in the tube and add an aliquot of sodium ^{125}iodide, 5 or 10 μl containing 1 mCi.
4. Cap the tube and mix every minute for 10 min.
5. Make up the volume in the tube to 500 μl with PBS. Load onto a small column of Sephadex G25 (5–10 ml). Wash through the column with PBS containing 0.1% bovine serum albumin. This separates the immunoglobulin from unbound iodine.

(ii) *Method of sample preparation and test procedure*

Radiolabelled antibodies may be used in two different types of procedure. One of these, radioautography using transmission electron microscopy, is used more frequently to localize particular antigens in mammalian tissues, and will not be described here. The other type of procedure is radioimmunoassay, and several modifications exist. The direct sandwich solid-phase radioimmunoassay has been used to detect cell-free antigen in urine from patients with Legionnaire's disease (Kohler *et al.*, 1981); the method is summarized as follows.

1. Prepare a solution of anti-Legionella immunoglobulin in 0.01 M tris-(hydroxymethyl)aminomethane hydrochloride, pH 7.0, to contain $20 \, \mu g \, ml^{-1}$ IgG.
2. Coat tubes by dispensing $100 \, \mu l$ IgG solution to each of a series of $10 \, mm \times 70 \, mm$ polystyrene tubes and incubate at 37 °C for 1 h.
3. Wash the tubes with Tris buffer.
4. Block by dispensing $100 \, \mu l$ Tris buffer containing 5% bovine serum albumin into each tube and incubate at 37 °C for 1 h.
5. Wash with Tris buffer.
6. Dispense $100 \, \mu l$ test urine to each tube; each sample should be tested in triplicate.
7. Incubate at 37 °C for 1 h.
8. Wash with Tris buffer.
9. Dispense $100 \, \mu l$ radioiodinated anti-Legionella IgG ($2-5 \, \mu g$ antibody ml^{-1}) to each tube.
10. Incubate at 37 °C for 1 h.
11. Wash with Tris buffer.
12. Count the tubes in a suitable gamma counter.

Reading and interpretation of results

Calculate the mean of the triplicate samples. In each run include a series of ten known negative urines and calculate the mean counts obtained with these samples to determine background. Calculate the ratio of counts in each test sample to background. Ratios of 2 or greater may be considered positive.

(iii) *General technical parameters*

Radioimmunoassays are affected by similar factors to those described for ELISA tests. In theory, the number of potential applications of radiolabelled antibodies is almost as great as for enzyme labels, but in practice there has been little exploitation of the technology. Sensitivity is usually good, large volume batch processing is possible, but expensive, sophisticated equipment is required, shelf life of the labelled antibodies is relatively short, and concern has been expressed about the hazardous aspect of radioisotopes. Therefore enzyme labels have frequently been selected in preference.

D. Particulate labels

Antibodies can be coupled to solid particles to make them readily visible. Microscopic particles of colloidal gold are directly visible in electron microscopy, and alternatives such as viruses, bacteriophages or small latex spheres have also been used (Perkins and Koehler, 1978). Ferritin is a protein that because of its iron content possesses high electron-scattering power, giving a particulate appearance in electron microscopy. Electron-dense products of selected substrates for horseradish peroxidase activity have already been mentioned, and these too give a particulate appearance (Raybould et al., 1981). Larger particles such as bacterial cells, latex or red blood cells, sensitized with multiples of antibody molecules, are used in visible agglutination reactions.

(i) *Ferritin*

(a) Labelling procedure (Hsu et al., 1963; Walker et al., 1971)

The successful application of ferritin-labelled antibody techniques depends upon the activity and specificity of the antibody employed. It is useful to screen antibodies for suitability by a simple procedure before undertaking the relatively arduous immunoelectron-microscopy method. Antibodies can be labelled successfully with both ferritin and fluorescein, hence the performance of the conjugate can be assessed by fluorescence microscopy before embarking on the more complex technique. Conjugation with fluorescein may be performed before or after the ferritin label is attached by the following procedure (Rifkind et al., 1964).

1. Obtain horse-spleen ferritin and recrystallize 4 or 5 times using 5% cadmium sulphate.
2. Redissolve the ferritin in 2% ammonium sulphate and precipitate it again in 50% saturated ammonium sulphate. Repeat the process twice to remove residual cadmium ions.
3. Dissolve the ferritin in a small volume of water and dialyse extensively against cold running tap water.
4. Continue dialysis against 0.05 M phosphate buffer, pH 7.5, overnight at 4 °C.

5. Centrifuge at 100 000g for 2 h.
6. Discard the upper layer, approximately 3/4 of the fluid, in the centrifuge tubes. Mix the remainder with 0.85% saline and 0.3 M borate buffer, pH 9.5, to give a final concentration of 2.5% ferritin in 0.1 M borate buffer.
7. Add 0.1 ml fresh xylylene m-diisocyanate for each 100 mg ferritin on a stirrer, and mix for 45 min at 0 °C.
8. Centrifuge in the cold for 30 min.
9. Recover the supernatant and place in an ice bath for 1 h.
10. On a magnetic stirrer add one part antibody to four parts of activated ferritin by weight, and stir at 4 °C for 48 h
11. Dialyse against 0.1 M ammonium carbonate overnight.
12. Dialyse against 0.05 M phosphate buffer, pH 7.5, for 4–6 h.
13. Centrifuge at slow speed and discard the pellet.
14. Centrifuge three times at 100 000g for 4 h, resuspending each time with 0.05 M phosphate buffer, pH 7.5. The final protein concentration should be approximately 2%.
15. The resulting conjugate may be sterilized by filtration, and should be stored at 4 °C.

(b) Method of sample preparation and test procedure (Swanson *et al.*, 1969; Hsiung, 1982)

1. Fix bacterial cells by suspending them in 2% glutaraldehyde in 0.01 M phosphate buffered saline, pH 7.2 (PBS).
2. Incubate at room temperature for 30 min.
3. Rinse several times with PBS.
4. Centrifuge at 4000g for 15 min to pellet the cells.
5. Mix 0.25 ml packed cells with 0.25 ml of a solution of the ferritin-labelled antibodies (38 mg ml^{-1}). Incubate for 30 min at 4 °C.
6. Wash five times with PBS.
7. Resuspend the cells in 0.1 M sodium cacodylate buffer, pH 6.8, containing 2% glutaraldehyde. Incubate for 30 min at room temperature.
8. Wash several times with 0.1 M sodium cacodylate buffer.
9. Proceed with osmium tetroxide fixation, dehydration, embedding, sectioning and counterstaining as in conventional electron-microscopy techniques. Examine the sections in a suitable electron microscope.

Reading and interpretation of results

Ferritin molecules can easily be seen as electron-opaque spots, 120 Å in diameter, located at the site of homologous antigens in the cell sections.

(c) General technical parameters

The use of ferritin labelling is limited to transmission electron microscopy, which takes advantage of the electron-dense nature of the molecules. They do not provide sufficient definition for scanning electron microscopy. This means that the technique is of considerable value for the localization of antigens, but provides limited information about their surface distribution.

The labelled antibodies can be used to stain cells prior to or after embedding and sectioning. In the former, the antibodies do not penetrate the cells significantly, but the technique is of value for localization of surface antigens, for example, the protein-type antigens of group B streptococci (Kasper and Baker, 1979). To localize intracellular components, sections must be stained, but some embedding media have been reported to stain non-specifically with ferritin (Walker *et al.*, 1971).

(ii) *Gold*

Colloidal gold suspensions of uniform and defined particle size (range 3–20 nm) can be prepared (Frens, 1973; Geoghegan *et al.*, 1980; Roth, 1982). The particles are unstable, but can be stabilized by coating with protein such as immunoglobulin or protein A, which confers binding specificity. Particles in the larger size range may be used in agglutination tests (Geoghegan *et al.*, 1980), although these have rarely been exploited in microbiology. Their major application has been in electron microscopy. Not only are the particles visible in the transmission microscope, but particles of different sizes can be discriminated with ease, thus enabling two antigens to be detected simultaneously (Bendayan, 1982).

(a) Labelling procedure

Optimal absorption of protein onto the gold particles takes place at a pH just to the alkaline side of the isoelectric point (p*I*) of the protein (Geoghegan *et al.*, 1980). The technique is particularly applicable to monoclonal antibodies which have a defined and reproducible p*I*, but conditions need to be established for each antibody. The procedure given below is suitable for sensitization of protein A, which is extensively used in indirect labelling techniques.

1. Measure the pH of the colloidal gold suspension. A gel-filled combination electrode should be used, since other electrodes can become clogged by the gold. Adjust the pH to 6.9 using 0.2 M potassium carbonate.

2. Dissolve 1 mg of protein A in 0.1–0.2 ml distilled water and transfer to a siliconized flask.
3. While shaking, add 10 ml of the gold suspension.
4. After 2 min add 0.2 ml of a 1% aqueous solution of polyethylene glycol, molecular weight 20 000 and mix.
5. Centrifuge at 100 000g for 1 h at 4 °C. Smaller particles may require slightly longer, for example 105 000g for 90 min at 4 °C.
6. Discard the clear supernatant, which contains free protein A. Resuspend the sediment in 6 ml PBS, pH 7.4, containing 0.02% polyethylene glycol. Store at 4 °C.

(b) Sample preparation and test procedure

Although the majority of published references concerning immunogold labelling relate to its use in mammalian histology, it does have potential in microbiology. Detailed electron-microscopy techniques cannot be given here, and standard works of reference should be consulted for these. In brief, cells should be fixed, embedded and sectioned prior to staining.

1. Mount a suitable section on an electron-microscope grid. Dispense a drop of antiserum onto one surface and incubate for 2 h at room temperature.
2. Wash several times with PBS.
3. Dispense a drop of protein A–gold complex onto the same surface of the grid. Incubate for 1 h at room temperature.
4. Wash several times with PBS.
5. Stain with 5% aqueous uranyl acetate for 15 min. Rinse with distilled water and examine in a suitable electron microscope.

Reading and interpretation of results

Gold particles, easily visible in electron microscopy, are localized at the site in the cell where homologous antigenic structures are situated.

(c) General technical parameters

Antibodies labelled with gold particles may be used in the direct and indirect methods described earlier, but are particularly valuable for the simultaneous demonstration of two antigenic determinants. This method involves labelling two sides of the grid, each with a separate antibody. Care must be taken to ensure that there is no contamination between reagents—the application of carbon and celloidin between staining each side greatly reduces the possibility of contamination (J. Beesley, personal communication). The gold labels of different diameter are easily discriminated in the electron microscope, allowing simultaneous localization of two antigens in a single section.

(iii) *Bacteria*

Bacterial cells are useful particles as antibody carriers for visualization of an immunological reaction by agglutination. The cells themselves are too small to be seen individually with the naked eye, but fairly small complexes of the cells can easily be seen. It is possible to coat a variety of bacterial species with antibody, but certain species possess properties that make them ideal for antibody coating. In the cell walls of some bacteria there exist proteins that bind immunoglobulins by a specific, but non-immunological, mechanism. The best-studied of all these factors is protein A from *Staphylococcus aureus* (Goding, 1978). Protein A interacts with the Fc part of certain immunoglobulins, which means that the absorbed antibodies are orientated with their antigen-combining sites directed outwards from the cell, in contrast with the situation with other sensitized particles, which coat in random orientation. This property contributes to the value of stabilized *S. aureus* cells as antibody labels.

(a) Labelling procedure

Preparation of reagent cells (Kronvall, 1973b; Edwards and Hilderbrand, 1976)

1. The recommended strain of *S. aureus* is Cowan I (NCTC 8530; ATCC 12598). If a negative control is required, Wood 46 will be suitable. Grow a broth culture overnight in CCY broth (Arvidson *et al.*, 1971) or in Trypticase soy broth.
2. Harvest the bacteria by centrifugation and wash them at least twice with phosphate buffered saline (PBS; 0.12 M sodium chloride, 0.03 M phosphate, pH 7.4, 0.1% sodium azide).
3. Resuspend the bacteria in PBS containing 0.5% formaldehyde (0.5 ml 37% formaldehyde added to 36.5 ml PBS). Hold at room temperature for at least 3 h.
4. Wash three times in PBS.
5. Resuspend in PBS to approximately 10% by volume. Heat the suspension with continuous stirring at 80 °C for 1 h.
6. Wash the bacteria three times with PBS, resuspend in PBS to 10% by volume, and store at 4 °C.

The bacteria may be stained, if desired, for easier visualization.

Sensitization

1. To 1 ml reagent staphylococci add 0.1 ml antiserum and mix thoroughly.
2. Wash the sensitized cells in PBS and resuspend to a final concentration of 1% in PBS. Stored at 4 °C, the reagent will retain activity for several months.

It is recommended that a negative control reagent should be prepared by duplicating this procedure using a non-immune serum.

(b) Test procedures

Direct

1. Place one drop of saline or PBS on a glass slide or alternative suitable test surface. Emulsify a few colonies of the culture to be tested in the saline. Alternatively, place one drop of broth culture, bacterial extract, or fluid suspected to contain bacteria or antigen on the glass slide.
2. Add one drop of test reagent and mix.
3. Rotate the test slide for up to 2 min.

Reading and interpretation of results

Observe for the appearance of coagglutination, clearly visible to the naked eye. The test has been performed by emulsifying bacteria directly into the test reagent, but if the culture is rough, non-specific agglutination may result— this can be detected in the procedure given above if the emulsion is checked prior to addition of the test reagent.

The technique is rather susceptible to non-specific coagglutination reactions, particularly with body-fluid specimens. These can usually be detected by performing a parallel test using control cells (or a test reagent with unrelated specificity). When the control reagent agglutinates to a similar extent to the test reagent, the result should be regarded with suspicion. It has been suggested that false reactions with body fluids can sometimes be eliminated by adding a drop of soluble protein A to the fluid prior to the test reagents or by heating the specimen at 80 °C for 5 min before testing.

Colony test

A different procedure has been described for identification of bacterial colonies growing on solid media (Edwards and Hilderbrand, 1976). This has rather limited value, but has been used to identify *Streptococcus, Shigella* and *Salmonella* and illustrates the potential of sensitized staphylococci.

1. Surround a colony or portion of growth with a ring of paraffin grease.
2. Put a drop of test reagent in the ring and rock the plate to and fro for up to 3 min. As controls, put a drop of test reagent in a ring on an uninoculated portion of the plate as well as a drop of control reagent on a similar area of growth.

Reading and interpretation of results

Inspect the reagents for the appearance of agglutination. This can be seen with the naked eye, but is more satisfactorily visible using a dissecting microscope. Agglutination in the test module only indicates the identity of the colony.

(c) General technical parameters

The technique was first described by Kronvall (1973b) for the identification of *Pneumococcus* cultures. Since then it has been used for detection and identification of a wide variety of organisms and antigens, including salmonella, streptococci, *Neisseria gonorrhoeae* and *N. meningitidis, Haemophilus influenzae* and *Escherichia coli* enterotoxin. There has been relatively little success in using the technique directly on mixed clinical specimens owing to lack of specificity.

The coagglutination procedure is quick and easy to perform, and can be used to identify bacterial surface antigens as well as to detect antigens in fluid samples. It is a sensitive technique, yet is economical in terms of antibody consumption. It is not necessary to isolate and purify the antibody prior to labelling, because the immunoglobulin specifically reacts with the protein A independent of other proteins that may be present. However, the technique is not applicable to all immunoglobulins, some of which do not react with protein A. This is a particular limitation for monoclonal antibodies, although if these are of reactive isotypes then particularly good reagents may be made. Rabbit and mouse antibodies sensitize well, but human antibodies do not, because they tend to clump the staphylococci during sensitization. The major limitation to the use of staphylococcal particles is due to the fact that they themselves are not completely inert and are susceptible to non-specific aggregation due to a number of causes. Results must be interpreted with caution.

(iv) *Latex*

For some of the techniques previously described it was necessary to adsorb antibodies onto the surface of a solid phase such as polystyrene microtitre plates. Latex particles are small uniform polystyrene spheres with sizes in the range 0.1–1 μm, to which antibodies can be adsorbed in an analogous fashion. These sensitized particles agglutinate in the presence of homologous antigen, either cell-bound or cell-free. It is worth pointing out that a large variety of different particles are available that might make suitable alternatives. These include carboxyl- and amino-derivatized polystyrene as well as polyglutaraldehyde, from which magnetic particles may be made (Margel *et al.*, 1979), polyacrylic plastic beads (Pachmann *et al.*, 1980), polyurea and polyurethane (Kobayashi *et al.*, 1983).

Although the range of particles available for research use is large, the particles described most frequently are unmodified polystyrene of 0.8 μm diameter. The exact conditions for sensitization may need to be determined for particular antibodies. The clarity of reaction and sensitivity of commercial reagents may not easily be achieved without considerable effort. Nevertheless, perfectly serviceable reagents may be prepared using the following procedure (Ruch and Smith, 1982).

(a) Labelling procedure

1. Prepare a solution of antibody at approximately 0.5 μg ml^{-1} in glycine (0.1 M) saline (0.9%) buffer, pH 8.2 (GBS).
2. Prepare a 2.5% suspension of 0.8 μm latex particles in the same buffer.
3. Mix equal volumes of antibody and latex.
4. Incubate at 37 °C for 2 h, with occasional shaking.
5. Dilute with an equal quantity of GBS containing 0.1% bovine serum albumin and 0.15% sodium azide. Store at 4 °C until required. A control latex reagent may be prepared by a parallel procedure using non-immune globulins. To be suitable for use, the latex suspension must be quite smooth.

(b) Test procedure

1. Place one drop of cell suspension, bacterial extract, broth culture supernatant or body-fluid specimen on a glass slide or suitable alternative test surface.
2. Add one drop of latex reagent and mix.
3. Rotate the test slide for up to 3 min.

Reading and interpretation of results

Observe for agglutination, clearly visible to the naked eye. The speed of appearance and quality of the agglutination pattern depends upon the strength of the antigen and the sensitivity of the latex. Fine granularity of the suspension should be easy to distinguish from a positive reaction. Some samples, particularly of body fluid, can cause non-specific agglutination, and, although latex reagents tend to be less susceptible to these than sensitized staphylococci, a control latex test, using latex sensitized with heterologous or non-immune antibody, should be included in each test. If the specific antigen is heat-stable, non-specific reactions may often be eliminated by boiling the specimen for 2–5 min prior to testing. Absorption of the globulins with polymerized human plasma prior to sensitization has also been reported to remove non-specific reactions (Kaldor *et al.*, 1977).

(c) General technical parameters

Latex reagents have a similar range of applications to those described for staphylococcal coagglutination. Both methods have been used to develop a number of commercially available products. Monoclonal antibodies have been used to sensitize latex, but do not appear to confer a significant advantage over the corresponding polyclonal material (Ruch and Smith, 1982). As latex reagents seem to be less susceptible to non-specific interference than staphylococcal reagents, they may be useful for direct examination of clinical specimens (Edwards *et al.*, 1982; Petts, 1984). Latex reagents exhibit considerable sensitivity for the detection of infections in neonates and *Haemophilus influenzae* type b infections. Some other infections have not been detected quite as sensitively. It is possible to increase sensitivity using nephelometric procedures, but this possibility has not been explored for microbiological applications (Grange *et al.*, 1977).

In common with coagglutination, the latex-agglutination procedure is rapid and easy to perform and clear to read. It can be used to detect and identify bacterial surface antigens, either cell-bound or cell-free. Viable or non-viable cells react, and antigens may be detected in the absence of living cells. It is possible to obtain non-specific reactions due to *S. aureus* and other similar organisms that carry immunoglobulin binding proteins, although these can usually be ruled out by Gram-staining.

(v) *Red cells*

Red blood cells, somewhat larger than most other particles used for antibody labelling, provide a suitable carrier for use in serological tests. Most of the test systems in microbiology that have been reported have involved coating the erythrocyte surface with antigen, and using the sensitized particles to detect the presence of antibody. However, antibody-coated cells have been prepared and used successfully in a limited number of antigen-detection systems, and there is no reason why this principle should not be more fully exploited. In theory, any source of erythrocytes may be used, but because of availability, citrated sheep blood is frequently chosen. If rapid settling of the cells is advantageous in the test system, nucleated turkey erythrocytes should be selected.

(a) Labelling procedure

Two different sensitization procedures are described that illustrate the flexibility of the test system.

Sensitization method 1 (Sequeira and Eldridge, 1973). This method involves fixation and tanning of the cells prior to sensitization.

1. Wash the cells (citrated turkey blood) using saline until a colourless supernatant is obtained.
2. Resuspend to 7% in PBS, pH 7.2.
3. Prepare an equal volume of 7% (w/v) formaldehyde in PBS, pH 7.2. Add one quarter of this to the red cells, mix and incubate for 1 h at 37 °C with frequent shaking.
4. Add the rest of the formaldehyde solution and incubate for 24 h at 37 °C with frequent shaking during the first few hours.
5. Wash 10 times in saline.
6. Resuspend at 10% in saline containing 0.1% sodium azide. Store until required at 4 °C.
7. Make a 1% solution of tannic acid (BP grade) in distilled water. Dilute a suitable volume in saline to 0.005%.
8. Dilute a suitable volume of 10% cells to 3.75% in saline. Add an equal volume of the tannic acid. Incubate for 15 min at 37 °C, shaking once during incubation.
9. Wash twice in PBS, pH 6.4.
10. Resuspend in PBS, pH 6.4, to a 3.75% suspension.
11. To one volume of tanned cells add 4 volumes of PBS, pH 6.4, and 1 volume of antibody, diluted to a previously determined level.
12. Incubate for 30 min at 37 °C, shaking twice.
13. Wash once in saline.
14. Resuspend in 4 volumes of saline containing 1.5% normal rabbit serum.
15. Store at 4 °C until required.

Sensitization method 2 (Bradburne *et al.*, 1979; Cranage *et al.*, 1983). This method uses trypsin pretreatment of the cells, which is reported to increase the sensitivity of the test system, followed by coupling to antibody using chromic chloride.

1. Wash the cells (citrated sheep blood) five times in PBS.
2. Resuspend to 10% in Earle's Balanced Salt Solution containing 0.025% crystalline trypsin. Incubate for 30 min at 37 °C.
3. Wash 3 times in PBS.
4. Cover the cell pellet with 0.02% trypsin inhibitor in PBS and leave for 10 min.
5. Wash twice in 0.85% saline. Cells may be stored at this stage for up to 1 week at 4 °C.
6. As a stock solution of chromic chloride, stable for up to 2 months at room temperature, dissolve 1% chromic chloride in distilled water and adjust the pH periodically to 5.2 with 0.2 M sodium hydroxide. One hour before use, dilute a sample 1:50 in saline.
7. Centrifuge the required volume of trypsin-treated red cells to give 0.5 ml or less packed cells. Estimate the volume of the pellet and mix with an equal volume of immunoglobulin at 3 mg ml^{-1}.
8. Mix the suspension vigorously while adding chromic chloride using a suitable diluter set to dispense 10 or 20 µl at 1 s intervals, to a total volume equivalent to that of the cells plus antibody.
9. Slowly mix the suspension on a rotator for 1 h at room temperature.
10. Dilute tenfold in PBS, and wash gently 3 times in PBS.
11. Resuspend to 1% in PBS containing 0.1% sodium azide.
12. To 2 ml of this suspension add 20 µl 0.1% glutaraldehyde (25% electron-microscope grade, diluted in saline), with continuous agitation. Incubate at room temperature for 1 h.
13. Wash 4 times in PBS.
14. Resuspend to 1% in PBS containing 0.1% sodium azide.

(b) Method of test (Cayzer *et al.*, 1974; Cranage *et al.*, 1983)

Viral antigen in tissue culture is released from the cells prior to the test by sonication or by detergent lysis, using a solution containing 0.001 M Sodium chloride, 0.001 M Tris, pH 7.4, 1% Triton X-100 and 1% sodium desoxycholate. Serum samples may require preabsorption with unsensitized cells, but this need will become apparent if the appropriate unsensitized cell controls are included in the test.

1. Using PBS as diluent, dispense 25 µl samples or dilutions into wells of a

U-bottomed microtitre plate. Settling patterns may be improved by adding small quantities of normal human, horse or turkey serum to the buffer.

2. Add 1 drop of sensitized cells to the wells.
3. Shake gently.
4. Incubate on a stable surface at room temperature for 90 min (sheep cells) or 30 min (turkey cells).

Reading and interpretation of results

Read the agglutination patterns without disturbing the plate. Positive reactions appear as a carpet of cells over the base of the well, whereas unagglutinated cells settle into a button or tight ring in the centre of the well. Prozones can occur, in which the agglutinated pattern collapses into the centre of the well. For purposes of quantitation, the titre may be recorded as the last dilution in the series that still shows detectable agglutination.

(c) General technical parameters

Haemagglutination provides a simple sensitive test system, although it is less rapid than latex-based tests. It is particularly important that the cells be left to settle undisturbed, and plates should not be placed near to centrifuges, shakers or other motorized apparatus, or all reactions will appear to be negative. The sensitized cells may be used equally for qualitative screening tests or quantitative titrations. A particular advantage of the technique is that confirmation of the presence of a particular antigen may be obtained by a neutralization procedure. Addition of liquid antibody specific for the antigen under test will neutralize the antigen and inhibit haemagglutination.

VI.   Summary

Labelled-antibody techniques have been in existence for many years, but have been relatively little used for routine microbial antigen detection and identification. Several factors, including lack of expertise in biochemical and immunological aspects of preparing and assessing reagents, limited availability of potent specific antisera and the need to undertake extensive and laborious comparative studies with established cultural procedures, have limited their potential exploitation. However, the extended range of commercially prepared labelled antibodies, recent availability of monoclonal antibodies of good specificity and a greater awareness of the practical advantages of selected techniques have done much to restimulate interest in

328 S. M. CHANTLER and M. B. McILLMURRAY

assessment of these methods in recent years. Procedures offering a range of sensitivity, flexibility, speed and sophistication are now well documented, and it is hoped that an awareness of the principles involved, the advantages and limitations will serve as an impetus for evolving further methods to facilitate the detection and identification of antigens in microbiology.

References

Ada, G. L., Nossal, G. J. V., Pye, J. and Abbot, A. (1964). *Aust. J. Exp. Biol. Med. Sci.* **42**, 267–282.
Arvidson, S., Holme, T. and Wadström, T. (1971). *Acta Pathol. Microbiol. Scand.* B **79**, 399–405.
Avrameas, S. and Ternynck, T. (1971). *Immunochemistry* **8**, 1175–1179.
Avrameas, S. and Uriel, J. (1966). *C. R. Acad. Sci. Paris* **262**, 2543–2545.
Batty, I. and Walker, P. D. (1963). *J. Pathol. Bacteriol.* **85**, 517–521.
Bendayan, M. (1982). *J. Histochem. Cytochem.* **30**, 81–85.
Bisset, M. L., Powers, C. and Wood, R. M. (1969). *Appl. Microbiol.* **17**, 507–511.
Bradburne, A. F., Almeida, J. D., Gardner, P. S., Moosai, R. B., Nash, A. A. and Coombs, R. R. A. (1979). *J. Gen. Virol.* **44**, 615–623.
Brandt, C. D., Kim, H. M., Rodriguez, W. J., Thomas, L., Yolken, R. H., Arrobio, J. O., Kapikian, A. Z., Parrott, R. H. and Chanock, R. M. (1981). *J. Clin. Microbiol.* **13**, 976–981.
Bulman, A. S. and Heyderman, E. (1981). *J. Clin. Pathol.* **34**, 1349–1351.
Burrows, W. and Pollitzer, R. (1958). *Bull. WHO* **18**, 275–290.
Cantarero, L. A., Butler, J. E. and Osborne, J. W. (1980). *Anal. Biochem.* **105**, 375–382.
Cayzer, I., Dane, D. S., Cameron, C. H. and Denning, J. V. (1974). *The Lancet* i, 947–949.
Chalker, S. J., Cook, G. D., Jones, D. M., Eldridge, J., Moreno, C., Shand, F. L. and McIllmurray, M. B. (1983). *Med. Trop.* **43**, 81–84.
Chandler, H. M., Cox, J. C., Healey, K., MacGregor, A., Premier, R. R. and Hurrell, J. G. R. (1982). *J. Immunol. Meth.* **53**, 187–194.
Chantler, S. M. and Haire, M. (1972). *Immunology* **23**, 7–12.
Cheng, P. J., Hemmilä, I. and Lövgren, T. (1982). *J. Immunol. Meth.* **48**, 159–168.
Cherry, W. B. and Moody, M. D. (1965). *Bacteriol. Rev.* **29**, 222–250.
Clark, C. A., Downs, E. C. and Primus, F. J. (1982). *J. Histochem. Cytochem.* **30**, 27–34.
Coons, A. H., Creech, H. J. and Jones, R. N. (1941). *Proc. Soc. Exp. Biol. Med (NY)* **47**, 200–202.
Cordell, J. L., Falini, B, Erber, W. N., Ghosh, A. K., Abdulaziz, Z., Macdonald, S., Pulford, K., Stein, H. and Mason, D. Y. (1984). *J. Histochem. Cytochem.* **32**, 219–229.
Cranage, M. P., McLean, C. S., Buckmaster, E. A., Minson, A. C., Wildy, P. and Coombs, R. R. A. (1983). *J. Med. Virol.* **11**, 295–306.
Danielsson, D. and Forsum, U. (1975). *Ann. NY Acad. Sci.* **254**, 334–349.
de Savigny, D. and Voller, A. (1980). *J. Immunoassay* **1**, 105–128.
Duncan, R. J. S., Weston, P. D. and Wrigglesworth, R. (1983). *Anal. Biochem.* **132**, 68–73.

Edwards, E. A. and Hilderbrand, R. L. (1976). *J. Clin. Microbiol* **3**, 339–343.

Edwards, E. A., Phillips, I. A. and Suiter, W. C. (1982). *J. Clin. Microbiol* **15**, 481–483.

Edwards, P. R. and Ewing, W. H. (1972). *Identification of Enterobacteriaceae*, 3rd edn. Burgess Publishing Co., Minneapolis.

Ekwall, E., Svenson, S. B. and Lindberg, A. A. (1982). *J. Med. Microbiol.* **15**, 173–180.

Engvall, E. (1977). *Med. Biol.* **55**, 193–200.

Engvall, E. and Perlmann, P. (1971). *Immunochemistry* **8**, 871–874.

Engvall, E., Jonsson, K. and Perlmann, P. (1971). *Biochim. Biophys. Acta* **251**, 427–434.

Ey, P. L. Prowse, S. J. and Jenkin, C. R. (1978). *Immunochemistry* **15**, 429–436.

Fick, R. B., Naegel, G. P. and Reynolds, H. Y. (1980). *J. Immunol. Meth.* **38**, 103–116.

Fink, B., Loepfe, E. and Wyler, R. (1979). *J. Histochem. Cytochem.* **27**, 1299–1301.

Ford, D. J., Radin, R. and Pesce, A. J. (1978). *Immunochemistry* **15**, 237–243.

Frens, G. (1973). *Nature Phys. Sci.* **241**, 20–22.

Gardner, P. S. and McQuillan, J. (1980). *Rapid Virus Diagnosis*, 2nd edn. Butterworth, London.

Geoghegan, W. D., Ambegaonkar, S. and Calvanico, N. J. (1980). *J. Immunol. Meth.* **34**, 11–21.

Goding, J. W. (1978). *J. Immunol. Meth.* **20**, 241–253.

Goding, J. W. (1980). *J. Immunol. Meth.* **39**, 285–308.

Goldman, M. (1968). *Fluorescent Antibody Methods*. Academic Press, New York and London.

Goldstein, L. C., Corey, L., McDougall, J. K., Tolentino, E. and Nowinski, R. C. (1983). *J. Infect. Dis.*, **147**, 829–837.

Gotschlich, E. C., Liu, T. Y. and Artenstein, M. S. (1969). *J. Exp. Med.* **129**, 1349–1366.

Grange, J., Roch, A. M. and Quash, G. A. (1977). *J. Immunol. Meth.* **18**, 365–375.

Guesdon, J.-L., Ternynck, T. and Avrameas, S. (1979). *J. Histochem. Cytochem.* **27**, 1131–1139.

Gustafsson, B., Rosen, A. and Holme, T. (1982). *Infect. Immunol.* **38**, 449–454.

Halmann, M., Velan, B. and Sery, T. (1977). *Appl. Environ. Microbiol.* **34**, 473–477.

Hebert, G. A., Pittman, B. and McKinney, R. M. (1981). *J. Clin. Microbiol.* **13**, 498–502.

Heck, F. C., Williams, J. D. and Pruett, J. (1980). *J. Clin. Microbiol.* **11**, 398–401.

Herzog, F., Albini, B. and Wick, G. (1973). *J. Immunol. Meth.* **3**, 211–219.

Hsiung, G. D. (1982). *Diagnostic Virology Illustrated by Light and Electron Microscopy*, 3rd edn. pp. 68–76. Yale University Press, New Haven and London.

Hsu, K. C., Rifkind, R. A. and Zabriskie, J. B. (1963). *Science* **142**, 1471–1473.

Hurn, B. A. L. and Chantler, S. M. (1980). *Meth. Enzymol.* **70**, 104–142.

Insalata, N. F., Mahnke, C. W. and Dunlop, W. G. (1973). *Appl. Microbiol.* **26**, 268–270.

Ison, C. A., Hadfield, S. G. and Glynn, A. A. (1981). *J. Clin. Pathol.* **34**, 1040–1043.

Ito, J. I., Wunderlich, A. C., Lyons, J., Davis, C. E., Guiney, D. G. and Braude, A. I. (1980). *J. Infect. Dis.* **142**, 523–537.

Johnson, G. D. and Araujo, G. M. (1981). *J. Immunol. Meth.* **43**, 349–350.

Kaldor, J., Asznowicz, R. and Buist, D. G. P. (1977). *Am. J. Clin. Pathol.* **68**, 284–289.

Kasper, D. L. and Baker, C. J. (1979). *J. Infect. Dis.* **139**, 147–151.

Kobayashi, S., Yamaya, S.-I., Sugahara, T. and Matuhasi, T. (1983). *Brit. J. Vener. Dis.* **59**, 1–7.

Kohler, G. and Milstein, C. (1975). *Nature (Lond)* **256**, 495–497.

Kohler, R. B., Zimmerman, S. E., Wilson, E., Allen, S. D., Edelstein, P. H., Wheat, J. and White, A. (1981). *Ann Int. Med.* **94**, 601–605.

Kronvall, G. (1973a). *J. Immunol.* **111**, 1401–1406.

Kronvall, G. (1973b). *J. Med. Microbiol.* **6**, 187–190.

Kronvall, G., Seal, U. S., Finstad, J. and Williams, R. C. (1970). *J. Immunol.* **104**, 140–147.

Labrousse, H., Guesdon, J.-L., Ragimbeau, J. and Avrameas, S. (1982). *J. Immunol. Meth.* **48**, 133–147.

Lambden, P. R. and Heckels, J. E. (1982). *J. Immunol. Meth.* **48**, 233–240.

Langone, J. L. and Van Vunakis, H. (eds.) (1983). *Meth Enzymol.* **92**, Part E.

Lund, E. (1960). *Bull. WHO* **23**, 5–13.

McLaren, M. L., Lillywhite, J. E. and Au, A. C. S. (1981). *Med. Lab. Sci.* **38**, 245–251.

Madsen, L. H. and Rodkey, L. S. (1976). *J. Immunol. Meth.* **9**, 335–361.

Margel, S., Zisblatt, S. and Rembaum, A. (1979). *J. Immunol. Meth.* **28**, 341–353.

Marrack, J. (1934). *Nature (London)* **133**, 292–293.

Mason, D. Y. and Sammons, R. (1978). *J. Clin. Pathol.* **31**, 454–460.

Mason, D. Y., Cordell, J. L., Abdulaziz, Z., Naiem, M. and Bordenave, G. (1982). *J. Histochem. Cytochem.* **30**, 1114–1122.

Mohr, H. K., Trenk, H. L. and Yeterian, M. (1974). *Appl. Microbiol.* **27**, 324–328.

Moreno, C., Hewitt, J., Hastings, K. and Brown, D. (1983). *J. Gen. Microbiol.* **129**, 2451–2456.

Myhre, E. B. and Kronvall, G. (1977). *Infect. Immunol.* **17**, 475–482.

Myhre, E. B. and Kronvall, G. (1980). *Infect. Immunol.* **27**, 808–816.

Nairn, R. C. (1976). *Fluorescent Protein Tracing*, 4th edn. Livingstone, Edinburgh.

Nakane, P. K. (1968). *J. Histochem. Cytochem.* **16**, 557–560.

Nakane, P. K. and Pierce, G. B. (1966). *J. Histochem. Cytochem.* **14**, 929–931.

Notermans, S., Timmermans, P. and Nagel, J. (1982). *J. Immunol. Meth.* **55**, 35–41.

Nowinski, R. C., Tam, M. R., Goldstein, L. C., Strong, L., Kuo, C.-C., Corey, L., Stamm, W. E., Handsfield, H. H., Knapp, J. S. and Holmes, K. K. (1983). *Science* **219**, 637–644.

O'Neill, P. and Johnson, G. D. (1970). *J. Clin. Pathol.* **23**, 185–187.

Pachmann, K., Thierfelder, S. and Rodt, H. (1980). *Biomedicine* **33**, 210–211.

Perkins, W. D. and Koehler, J. K. (1978). In *Advanced Techniques in Biological Electron Microscopy*. II. *Specific Ultrastructural Probes* (J. K. Koehler, ed.). Springer-Verlag, Berlin.

Peterfy, F., Kuusela, P. and Mäkelä, O. (1983). *J. Immunol.* **130**, 1809–1813.

Petts, D. N. (1984). *J. Clin. Microbiol.* **19**, 432–433.

Ploem, J. S. (1967). *Z. Wiss. Mikr.* **68**, 129–142.

Polin, R. A. and Kennett, R. (1980). *J. Pediatrics* **97**, 540–544.

Raybould, T. J. G., Beasley, J. E. and Chantler, S. M. (1981). *Infect. Immunol.* **32**, 318–322.

Richmond, S. J. and Caul, E. O. (1975). *J. Clin. Microbiol.* **1**, 345–352.

Rifkind, R. A., Hsu, K. C. and Morgan, C. (1964). *J. Histochem. Cytochem.* **12**, 131–136.

Ritchie, D. G., Nickerson, J. M. and Fuller, G. M. (1981). *Anal. Biochem.* **110**, 281–290.

Roth, J. (1982). *Histochem. J.* **14**, 791–801.

Ruch, F. E. and Smith, L. (1982). *J. Clin. Microbiol.* **16**, 145–152.

Sahar, E., Lamed, R. and Ofek, I. (1983). *Eur. J. Clin. Microbiol.* **2**, 192–195.

Schmidt, N. J., Dennis, J., Devlin, V., Gallo, D. and Mills, J. (1983). *J. Clin. Microbiol.* **18**, 445–448.

Schuurs, A. H. W. M. and van Weeman, B. K. (1977). *Clin. Chim. Acta* **81**, 1–40.

Sequeira, P. J. L. and Eldridge, A. E. (1973). *Brit. J. Vener. Dis.* **49**, 242–248.

Shekarchi, I. C., Sever, J. L., Lee, Y. J., Castellano, G. and Madden, D. L. (1984). *J. Clin. Microbiol.* **19**, 89–96.

Shinnick, T. M., Sutcliffe, J. G., Green, N. and Lerner, R. A. (1983). *Ann. Rev. Microbiol.* **37**, 425–446.

Soini, E. and Hemmilä, I. (1979). *Clin. Chem.* **25**, 353–361.

Stamm, L. V., Kerner, T. C., Bankaitis, V. A. and Bassford, P. J. (1983). *Infect. Immunol.* **41**, 709–721.

Steinbuch, M. and Audran, R. (1969). *Arch. Biochem. Biophys.* **134**, 279–284.

Sternberger, L. A., Hardy, P. H., Cuculis, J. J. and Meyer, H. G. (1970). *J. Histochem. Cytochem.* **18**, 315–338.

Strandberg Pedersen, N., Sand Petersen, C., Vejtorp, M. and Axelsen, N. H. (1982). *Scand. J. Immunol.* **15**, 341–348.

Svenson, S. B. and Lindberg, A. A. (1979). *J. Immunol. Meth.* **25**, 323–335.

Svenson, S. B. and Lindberg, A. A. (1981). *Infect. Immunol.* **32**, 490–496.

Swanson, J., Hsu, K. C. and Gotschlich, E. C. (1969). *J. Exp. Med.* **130**, 1063–1075.

Takashi, K. and Kayoko, S. (1977). *Clin. Chim. Acta* **76**, 67–77.

Talbot, P. and Almeida, J. D. (1977). *J. Gen. Virol.* **36**, 345–349.

Tam, M. R., Buchanan, T. M., Sandström, E. G., Holmes, K. K., Knapp, J. S., Siadak, A. W. and Nowinski, R. C. (1982). *Infect. Immunol.* **36**, 1042–1053.

Tanimori, H., Ishikawa, F., and Kitagawa, T. (1983). *J. Immunol. Meth.* **62**, 123–131.

Taylor, C. E. D. and Heimer, G. V. (1964). *Brit. Med. J.* **2**, 165–166.

Taylor, C. E. D. and Heimer, G. V. (1973). *Assoc. Clin. Pathologists Broadsheets* **76**.

Thomason, B. M. and Cherry, W. B. (1971). *Am. J. Med. Technol.* **37**, 258–259.

Thomason, B. M. and McWhorter, A. C. (1965). *Bull. WHO* **33**, 681–685.

Thomason, B. M. and Wells, J. G. (1971). *Appl. Microbiol.* **22**, 876–884.

Thornley, M. J., Lusher, M., Scott, M. L., Coombs, R. R. A., Evans, R. T., Thomas, B. J. and Taylor-Robinson, D. (1983). *FEMS Microbiol. Lett.* **17**, 45–49.

Turk, D. C. and May, J. R. (1967). *Haemophilus influenzae: Its clinical importance.* English Universities Press, London.

Vestergaard, B. F. and Jensen, O. (1981). In *The Human Herpes Viruses* (A. J. Nahmias, W. R. Dowdle and R. F. Schinazi, eds.), p. 391. Elsevier, New York.

Voller, A. and Bidwell, D. E. (1983). *Biologie Prospective—5e Coll. Int. de Pont-a-Mousson*, pp. 217–222.

Voller, A., Bidwell, D. and Bartlett, A. (1976). In *Manual of Clinical Immunology* (N. R. Rose and H. Friedman, eds.), p. 506. *Am. Soc. Microbiology*, Washington, D.C.

Walker, P. D., Batty, I. and Thomson, R. O. (1971). *Meth. Microbiol.* **5A**, 219–254.

Wallace, R., Ashton, F. E., Ryan, A., Diena, B. B., Malaysheff, C. and Perry, M. B. (1978). *Can. J. Microbiol.* **24**, 124–128.

Wells, A. F., Miller, C. E. and Nadel, M. K. (1966). *Appl. Microbiol.* **14**, 271–275.

Westphal, O. and Jann, K. (1965). In *Meth. Carbohydrate Chem.* **5**, 83–91.

Whitehead, T. P., Thorpe, G. H. G., Carter, T. J. N., Groucutt, C. and Kricka, L. J. (1983). *Nature (London)* **305**, 158–159.

Wilchek, M. and Bayer, E. A. (1984). *Immunology Today*, **5**, 39–43.

Wilson, M. B. and Nakane, P. B. (1978). In *Immunofluorescence and Related Staining Techniques* (W. Knapp, K. Holubar and G. Wick, eds.), p. 215. Elsevier/North Holland Biomedical Press, Amsterdam.

Wolters, G., Kuijpers, L., Kacaki, J. and Schuurs, A. (1976). *J. Clin. Pathol.* **29**, 873–879.

Yoshitake, S., Hamaguchi, Y. and Ishikawa, E. (1979). *Scand. J. Immunol.* **10**, 81–86.

Zehr, D. R. (1978). *J. Histochem. Cytochem.* **26**, 415–416.

Ziegler, T., Meurman, O. H., Arstila, P. P. and Halonen, P. E. (1983). *J. Virol. Meth.* **7**, 1–9.

8
Identification of Microorganisms by Rapid DNA–DNA Hybridization

T. P. TOUROVA and A. S. ANTONOV

A. N. Belozersky Laboratory of Molecular Biology and Bioorganic Chemistry, Moscow State University, Moscow 119899, USSR

I. Introduction

Identification of a microorganism is an essential aspect of the work of many microbiologists: any such investigation begins with examination of the test organism and its assignment to a particular taxon. Identification of pathogens is the main problem in medical and sanitary microbiology. It is therefore not surprising, that the latest data on morphological, physiological, biochemical and other properties of microorganisms find ever broader application in microbial identification and systematics. There exists, how-

METHODS IN MICROBIOLOGY
VOLUME 19   ISBN 0–12–521519–3

ever, another approach based on the technique of DNA–DNA (or DNA–RNA) molecular hybridization. There are several reasons for the use of this method in modern microbial taxonomy. To begin with, the genotypes, and not the phenotypes, of microorganisms are compared, and so the method offers new possibilities for quantitative evaluation of the phylogenetic relatedness of the microorganisms studied. In some cases it proves indispensable for taxonomic identifications. The method has enabled some new taxa of microorganisms to be defined, for example the family Legionellaceae (Brenner *et al.*, 1978, 1981), the genus *Alterovibrio* (Tourova and Levanova, 1980b), the genus *Allomonas* (Tourova *et al.*, 1983), the species *Vibrio fluvialis* (Lee *et al.*, 1981; James *et al.*, 1983) and the species *Propionibacterium coccoides* (Vorobyeva *et al.*, 1983).

The molecular-hybridization technique also makes it possible to differentiate among groups of bacteria that are difficult to distinguish phenotypically (sibling taxa), for example *Alcaligenes* and *Comamonas* (Levanova and Tourova, 1977), *Aeromonas* and *Vibrio* (Nacesku and Ciufecu, 1977), *Altermonas* and *Pseudomonas* (Baumann *et al.*, 1971), *Aeromonas* and *Pseudoaeromonas* (Levanova *et al.*, 1980).

So-called atypical strains pose a particular difficulty for practical research; they may reveal properties inherent in different groups of bacteria. Their rapid and precise identification in medical research is of great importance. For example, we have studied a strain phenotypically similar to members of the Enterobacteriaceae but possessing the O-antigen of cholera vibrios. With the help of DNA–DNA molecular hybridization, data were obtained indicating that the strain is, in fact, *Escherichia coli* (Tourova and Levanova, 1980a).

Thus it is obvious that DNA–DNA hybridization is valuable for the purposes of identification, yet it is a method that is not used routinely in microbiology because it is time-consuming and complicated for the non-biochemist.

Many authors (Wotska and Kinicki-Goldfinger, 1977; Valiejo-Roman, 1980; Grimont *et al.*, 1980) have compared various techniques of molecular hybridization, and we shall not review that issue here. At present, the method of molecular hybridization employing nitrocellulose filters has been widely used in microbial taxonomy for more than a decade (Gillespie and Spiegelman, 1965; Denhardt, 1966).

Furthermore, the technique is convenient because it allows for large-scale experimentation where many DNA samples can be handled simultaneously. Application of the same method in many laboratories yields data that can be processed by statistical methods permitting intertaxa comparisons.

Overall, the nitrocellulose filter technique for DNA–DNA hybridization consists of several basic steps:

(1) harvesting the bacteria;
(2) cell-wall rupture, with subsequent lysis of the cells;
(3) DNA isolation and purification (removal of RNA, protein and polysaccharides);
(4) labelling of reference DNA;
(5) immobilization of DNA on filters;
(6) incubation of immobilized DNA with reference DNA, removal of unbound labelled DNA, thermoelution (if necessary), and radioactivity counting.

In its classical form, DNA molecular hybridization is certainly difficult to perform; in practical investigations, it takes a few days to obtain final results. To make it more convenient, several suggestions have been offered to shorten and simplify the individual steps.

II.   Membrane-filter methods for DNA–DNA molecular hybridization

The above scheme applies to most investigations involving bacterial DNA–DNA molecular hybridization. Variations in the steps of an experiment depend on the aim of the research being done, on the group of bacteria studied, and other factors. Yet there are certain conventional approaches, which are considered below.

A   DNA isolation

The methods presently employed to isolate DNA from microorganisms yield highly purified preparations, free from admixture with other compounds, and with minimal damage to the DNA during isolation.

The most common procedures used are those of Kirby (1957) and Marmur (1961); for fixed cells, the method of Arrighi et al. (1968) can be employed, or a combination of these methods. The combined technique is advantageous in our experience, and it is performed as follows.

(1) Bacteria (1–2 g of fresh cells) in logarithmic growth phase are collected by centrifugation and washed in 50 ml of standard saline–citrate (SSC) solution containing 0.15 M NaCl + 0.015 M sodium citrate, pH 7.0. The cells are then suspended in 25 ml of 0.15 M NaCl + 0.1 M EDTA, pH 8.0, supplemented with a 25% solution of sodium dodecyl sulphate (SDS) to a final concentration of 0.5% and pronase to a final concentration of 100 μg ml^{-1}. The mixture is incubated for 10 min at 60 °C for cell lysis. A considerable increase in viscosity takes place at this stage.

(2) On cooling, an equal volume of freshly distilled neutralized phenol,

saturated with SSC solution, is added to the lysate; the mixture is shaken cold for 30–40 min and then centrifuged for 5 min at 5–10 000 rev min^{-1}. The DNA-containing aqueous phase is separated; DNA is precipitated with 2 volumes of ethanol.

(3) The DNA fibres are suspended in 10–15 ml SSC, diluted 10-fold (0.1 × SSC), dissolved, supplemented with 1/10 volume of 10 × SSC and shaken for 15 min with an equal volume of a chloroform–isoaminol mixture (24:1). The mixture is centrifuged, and the aqueous DNA-containing layer removed for further purification. Deproteinization is repeated 3 or 4 times until the intermediate layer of denatured proteins disappears, after which the DNA is precipitated with ethanol.

(4) The partially purified DNA is redissolved in SSC; RNase (50 μg ml^{-1}), preheated for 10 min at 80 °C in 0.15 M NaCl so as to inactivate possible DNase impurities, is added. The mixture is incubated for 30 min at 37 °C.

(5) To digest the RNase and residual proteins, pronase is added to a final concentration of 100 μg ml^{-1} and incubated for 2 h at 37 °C.

(6) Deproteinization with chloroform–isoaminol (24:1) is performed 2 or 3 times, until the disappearance of the intermediate layer of denatured proteins. Ethanol is used to precipitate the DNA from the aqueous phase.

(7) The DNA precipitate is dissolved in 9 ml of 0.1 × SSC and then 1 ml of 3 M sodium acetate + 0.001 M EDTA (pH 7.0) and 0.5–0.6 volume of isopropanol is added dropwise with vigorous mixing. DNA alone is precipitated, while RNA debris and polysaccharides remain in solution. The DNA is redissolved in SSC, precipitated with ethanol and stored as a precipitate under 70% ethanol, or in SSC with a drop of chloroform at 0–4 °C.

B. Membrane-filter DNA–DNA hybridization

Techniques used for molecular hybridization on membrane filters are widely known and well described (e.g. Gillespie and Spiegelman, 1965; Denhardt, 1966; De Ley and Tijtgat, 1970). They are based on the same principle: denatured "cold" DNA from one of the microorganisms to be compared is filter-fixed and then hybridized with the fragmented isotopically labelled DNA of the reference microorganism. The number of hybrid molecules is determined by the radioactivity level retained on the filter. The procedure of this experiment may be represented as follows.

(1) High-molecular-weight DNA is denatured by heating or with alkali. Heating is useful for denaturing preparations with low salt and DNA concentration. In this case DNA solution in 0.1 × SSC and at a concentra-

tion of 100–140 µg ml^{-1} are incubated for 10–15 min at 100 °C and then quickly cooled, with the salt concentration being brought to 6 × SSC. Alkaline denaturation is more convenient, since neither salt nor DNA concentration has any effect on it. A DNA solution in 6 × SSC is supplemented with NaOH to a final concentration of 0.1 M and incubated for 20 min at 37 °C. The solution is then quickly chilled on ice and neutralized with HCl.

(2) Nitrocellular membrane filters (diameter 24 mm, with a pore-diameter of 0.2–0.4 µm) are soaked in a 2 × SSC solution beforehand and then mounted into the vacuum filtration device. Each filter is washed with 10 ml of this solution. The solution of denatured DNA (6–10 µg ml^{-1}) in 6 × SSC is then passed slowly through the prepared filters, and the filters are washed through with 50 ml of the 2 × SSC solution to remove unbound DNA. The filters with fixed DNA are demounted, air-dried at room temperature overnight and then *in vacuo* for 2 h at 80 °C and stored at 4 °C. Smaller filters may be used if the specific radioactivity of labelled DNA is high.

(3) It is necessary to know exactly the quantity of the filter-fixed "cold" DNA. The most frequently employed method for assay is to measure the optical density of denatured DNA solution at 260 nm before and after passage through membrane filters. It is also possible to determine the amount of DNA on the filters by using hydrolysis in perchloric acid (Spirin, 1958). In this case, a filter with fixed DNA is held in 3 ml of 0.5 M HCO$_4$ for 20 min at 100 °C; on cooling, the absorption value of the solution is measured at 270 and 290 nm. A clean filter treated in the same way is used as a control. The concentration of fixed DNA (in µg ml^{-1}) is given by the formula

$$C = 10.1 \times \frac{A_{270} - A_{290}}{0.19}$$

where A_{270} and A_{290} are the absorbance values at 270 and 290 nm respectively, 10.1 is the quantitation factor for nucleic phosphorus per nucleic acid, and 0.19 is the difference in specific absorbance at 270 and 290 nm, determined experimentally.

Using this technique, the DNA initially fixed on the filter can be measured; the amount of the DNA involved in hybridization and remaining on the filter after washing can be determined by immobilizing the labelled high-polymer DNA.

(4) Filters with fixed DNA are incubated in a 2 × SSC solution containing the labelled denatured fragments of DNA of the reference microorganism. The finite volume of the solution is usually 0.5–1.5 ml per 24 mm filter. On incubation, the labelled DNA fragments may be non-specifically attached to

the filters, which can affect the hybridization results. To avoid this source of error, the filters with fixed DNA are pre-incubated in a Denhardt medium (Denhardt, 1966) containing 0.02% w/v. Ficoll, polyvinylpyrrolidone and bovine albumin in $3 \times$ SSC for 2 h at the incubation temperature.

It has been shown (McCarthy and Bolton, 1963; Hoyer et al., 1964) that the ratio of hybrid duplexes increases with a decrease in the relative amount of labelled DNA, and becomes constant if the proportion of labelled and high-molecular-weight DNAs is 1:100 or less. Furthermore, the proportion of hybrid duplexes increases with a longer incubation time, and becomes constant after 18 h incubation. These conclusions are taken into consideration in selecting reaction conditions.

The optimal incubation temperature should be lower than the T_m of native DNA by approximately 25 °C (Johnson and Ordal, 1968; Anderson and Ordal, 1972). Addition of formamide to the incubation medium (McConaughy et al., 1969) makes it possible to lower the temperature (1% of formamide decreases the incubation temperature by 0.6 °C), which reduces uncontrollable DNA losses from filters during incubation.

(5) After incubation, each filter is washed free from unbound labelled fragments of DNA in 50–100 ml of $2 \times$ SSC or in 0.003 M Tris–HCl buffer, pH 9.4. The filters are then dried and a radioactive count is taken. The percentage DNA homology is determined by assuming the binding in a homologous reaction to be 100%.

The methods described above are widely and successfully used in DNA sequence comparisons for the classification and identification of bacteria. These techniques are distinguished for high accuracy of results, but are rather time-consuming. Many investigations involving bacterial identification by DNA–DNA molecular hybridization require special rapid procedures. These will be considered in subsequent sections.

III.   Acceleration of DNA–DNA molecular hybridization at different stages of the experiment

A.   Bacterial harvesting

It is generally accepted that highly purified DNA must be used in hybridization experiments; usually about 10 g of bacterial biomass is needed to obtain 8–10 mg of such DNA. The DNA yield varies depending on the species, on the age of the culture and on the methods for cell lysis, DNA purification etc. To obtain the maximum yield, the cells should be collected in mid-logarithmic growth phase when the DNA per cell content is highest.

The duration and complexity of the biomass-accumulation stage may vary significantly, depending on the group of microorganisms. Thus for slow-growing cultures requiring special cultivation conditions (for instance, rickettsiae) this stage may prove to be a very long and complex one (Myers and Wisseman, 1980).

It follows from the description of some rapid methods of DNA hybridization (see below) that the stage of bacterial harvesting may be simplified and shortened, as less DNA is needed. For example, bacterial cells may be directly collected on the surface of nitrocellulose filters by suction, thus omitting the centrifugation step. If the bacterial mass is to be analysed from a solid growth medium, it may be suspended in an appropriate buffer solution and applied to the filter.

If highly labelled reference DNA samples are used, the amount of DNA immobilized on the filters may be rather low (several micrograms). For *Escherichia coli* the DNA content in bacterial cells at the optimal stage of their development is up to 5%; this means that 0.1–1.0 mg of bacteria (dry weight) must be collected on the filter surface, corresponding to 10^8–10^9 bacterial cells. Starting from the known density of a bacterial culture, it is easy to determine the volume of a sample to be passed through each filter (Antonov et al., 1978).

B. Cell-wall rupture and subsequent cell lysis

Bacterial cells differ greatly in their resistance to lysis by various methods, either mechanical or carried out by means of a lytic agent.

Among the former, manual disintegration, disintegration with the help of mechanical devices, ultrasound disintegration, the freeze–thaw technique and other methods may be employed. Their application to different groups of microorganisms, and the mechanism of their action on cell walls and membranes, as well as side-effects on the cellular products obtained, are reviewed in detail by Coakley et al. (1977).

In brief, mechanical disintegration may be the only possibility for some groups of microorganisms. The efficacy of the procedure is usually controlled microscopically. To avoid DNA depolymerization from action of nucleases or hydrodynamic shear forces, the intensity and duration of mechanical disintegration should be determined experimentally in each case. Nuclease inhibitors must be added to the disintegration medium.

The methods of cell disintegration with lytic agents are simpler and more rapid than mechanical ones. Therefore replacing mechanical methods with such procedures permits accelerating this stage of the experiment.

For many bacterial species, both Gram-positive and Gram-negative, lysozyme treatment has been shown to be efficient (Marmur, 1961). In our view, lysozyme treatment, in combination with detergents and proteolytic enzymes, is optimal for bacterial cell lysis. This procedure is widely used and requires 1–3 h in its various modifications.

Special procedures have been developed to treat lysozyme-resistant cells. Thus antibiotics (penicillin, sencephalin), followed by treatment with proteolytic enzymes and SDS have been used to lyse the growing cells of some corynebacteria (Komatsu, 1979). For some other lysozyme-resistant bacteria, a combined procedure, involving detergents and osmotic shock in 20% sucrose solution, appeared to be effective (Schwinghamer, 1980). To speed up the lysis of Gram-positive asporogenic bacteria, they were treated with lysozyme solution in Tris-buffer with polyethylene glycol (Chassy and Giuffrida, 1980). *Klebsiella pneumoniae* cells were pretreated with a 50% solution of dimethyl sulphoxide to dissolve the capsules and then lysed by standard methods (Lambert, 1982). In our opinion, these examples illustrate the successful search for special procedures, making it possible to avoid time- and labour-consuming mechanical disintegration of cells.

C.   DNA isolation and purification

To isolate DNA from bacterial cells, the Kirby (1957) and Marmur (1961) methods are widely used, sometimes with minor modifications. If fixed material is to be used (which is often the case with pathogenic cultures), the Arrighi procedure (Arrighi *et al.*, 1968) seems to be the most effective.

To evolve a rapid technique, it is essential to utilize modifications of those basic methods that curtail and simplify DNA extraction and purification procedures or to find some new options. We shall examine methods for obtaining semipurified DNA samples suitable for molecular hybridization of nucleic acids.

Option I (Antonov *et al.*, 1978)

It follows from the results of DNA–DNA and DNA–RNA hybridization *in situ* that the specificity of this process is very high, even in the presence of cellular components. This was the starting point of our experiments to investigate the necessity for meticulous purification of DNA samples for hybridization tests.

One of the techniques developed is a modification of the Marmur procedure (Marmur, 1961); acceleration is achieved by changing the deproteinization stage and by simplifying some other procedures. The semipurified preparations of DNA were obtained as follows. The bacterial cells were suspended in a buffer solution (0.15 M NaCl, 0.1 M EDTA, 0.015 M sodium citrate and 0.1 M Tris, pH 8.0) and then lysed with sodium dodecylsulphate (SDS), 1%, in the presence of pronase (100 μg ml^{-1}) for 30 min at 37 °C. On lysis, after the suspension became clear, NaCl was added to the lysate up to a final concentration of 2 M, and the partially deproteinized DNA was precipitated with ethanol. The gelled DNA clot was then dissolved in 0.3 M sodium acetate and the DNA precipitated by adding 0.5–0.6 volumes of isopropanol dropwise, with vigorous mixing. By this process, some DNA purification from polysaccharides and RNA was achieved. For further extraction DNA was redissolved in 0.1 × SSC.

Before immobilization on filters DNA was denatured by 1 M NaOH up to a final concentration of 0.3–0.5 M and incubated for 30 min at 60 °C. Such treatment, apart from DNA denaturation, leads to a partial hydrolysis of residual RNA. Immobilization on filters was performed by conventional methods.

The degree of DNA purification was about 75% for proteins and 80% for polysaccharides. It was found to be sufficient for DNA molecular-hybridization experiments.

Only an insignificant amount of DNA is lost in the process. With *E. coli* cultures of different age, the DNA yield varied from 2.7 to 3.9% of the dry weight of the cells, while the overall content of DNA in bacterial cells ranged from 3 to 5%, depending on the growth stage. In other words, this method gave a high DNA yield: an advantage when the quantity of bacterial mass is a limiting factor.

The specificity of DNA–DNA hybridization performed with preparations obtained by this method was verified for several groups of microorganisms and proved to be very high (Table I).

As can be seen from the table, semipurified DNA preparations obtained by this rapid technique are sufficiently reactive in hybridization with homologous and heterologous DNAs, and the differences between the results obtained by the new and classical methods are within the experimental error. A certain decrease in the absolute binding of reference DNA—probably due to lesser DNA accessibility on the filters—has no effect on the specificity of the reaction.

Option II (Davis *et al.*, 1980)

This variant of rapid isolation of partially purified bacterial DNA is similarly based on the principles of enzymatic hydrolysis, with subsequent removal of part of other cellular components and selective precipitation of DNA with organic solvents.

The following procedures were employed: the bacterial cells were suspended in 50 mM Tris (pH 8.5), 50 mM EDTA, 15% sucrose and 1 mg ml^{-1} lysozyme, and incubated for 10 min at room temperature. Then diethyl

TABLE I

Comparison of molecular DNA–DNA hybridization results obtained by conventional and option I methods in some bacterial groups

Experiment no.	Strains	Percentage of homology with labelled DNAs of reference strains[b]	
		Conventional method	Option 1
1	E.coli B[a]	100 ± 3 (62)	100 ± 7 (32)
	E.coli 761	78 ± 4	80 ± 6
	E.alcalescens 1601	65 ± 3	61 ± 1
	E.crim 91	53 ± 3	55 ± 5
	Atypical strain 1067	28 ± 2	33 ± 4
2	Alcaligenes faecalis 45[a]	100 ± 12 (20)	100 ± 7 (14)
	Alcaligenes faecalis 5788	93 ± 8	94 ± 8
3	Listeria murrayi L-44[a]	100 ± 5 (60)	100 ± 9 (26)
	L.monocytogenes 9-127	16 ± 1	21 ± 1
	L.denitrificans C-212	5 ± 1	5 ± 1

[a]Reference strain. [b]Values in parentheses are of the absolute binding of labelled DNA in a homologous reaction.

oxydiformate was added to a final concentration of 0.2% for the inactivation of cellular nucleases. Thereafter, the cells were lysed with 0.2% SDS solution for 5 min at 70 °C. A 5 M solution of potassium acetate was added to a final concentration of 0.5 M, and the mixture was held for 30 min in the cold to precipitate cellular debris, proteins and SDS. The pellet was removed by centrifugation in the cold for 15 min. DNA was precipitated from the supernatant with ethanol, and then dissolved in 10 mM Tris (pH 7.5), 1 mM EDTA and incubated in the presence of 1 μg ml^{-1} of RNase to remove residual RNA.

It is obvious that the result is a semipurified DNA preparation. Nevertheless, we have successfully utilized such preparations in hybridization experiments to detect bacterial clones. Since there is no essential difference between these experiments and those involving routine procedures of DNA–DNA molecular hybridization for bacteria identification, we believe this rapid method can also be used, along with others, in bacterial taxonomy.

Option III (Antonov et al., 1978)

This procedure is based on the well-known principle of alkaline hydrolysis of bacterial cells (Schmidt and Tannhauser, 1945) when DNA is quantitatively separated from RNA and proteins and is denatured. DNA was isolated in the following manner. The bacterial cells were suspended in saline solution containing 0.15 M NaCl and 0.1 M EDTA, pH 7.0–8.0, supplemented with 1 M NaOH to a final concentration of 0.5 M; the mixture was incubated for 1 h at 37 °C (or for 30 min at 60 °C). The suspension cleared as a result of cellular lysis. A drop of pH-indicator solution was added and the alkali was neutralized roughly by 1 M HCl in the cold and finally by 1 M Tris–HCl buffer, pH 7.4–7.8.

On neutralization, RNase (50 µg ml^{-1}) was added to the lysate and incubated for 30 min at 37 °C to complete RNA hydrolysis; and then 100–200 µg ml^{-1} of pronase was added. After 1 h incubation at room temperature, the lysate was passed through nitrocellulose membrane filters and then the filters with adsorbed DNA were washed with 2 × SSC, 70% ethanol and chloroform. The filters were dried and kept in the cold.

The DNA yield was about 50% of DNA in the lysate, which is comparable to the yield according to the Marmur procedure (Marmur, 1961).

This rapid method is particularly useful for groups of microorganisms whose cells are resistant to sodium dodecyl sulphate and enzymes.

Data on the specificity of the DNA–DNA hybridization reaction performed with DNA samples obtained by this procedure, compared with highly purified DNA preparations, are presented in Table II. Semipurified

TABLE II

Comparison of molecular DNA–DNA hybridization results obtained by conventional and option III methods in some bacterial groups.

Experiment Strains no.		Percentages of homology with reference strains[b]	
		Conventional method	Option III
1	*E.coli* B[a]	100 ± 3 (62)	100 ± 7 (48)
	E.coli 761	78 ± 4	87 ± 5
	E.crim 91	53 ± 4	54 ± 1
	Atypical strain 1067	28 ± 2	15 ± 1
2	*Listeria denitrificans* C-212[a]	100 ± 4 (59)	100 ± 5 (20)
	L.murrayi L-44	7 ± 1	9 ± 1
	L.monocytogenes 9-127	8 ± 1	6 ± 1
3	*Azospirillum sp.* B-5[a]	100 ± 3 (32)	100 ± 6 (14)
	A.brasilense Sp-7	7 ± 1	6 ± 1
	A.sp. 137	10 ± 1	15 ± 3

[a]Reference strain. [b]Values in parentheses are percentages of the absolute binding of labelled DNA in a homologous reaction.

DNA preparations obtained by this rapid procedure, can be utilized for hybridization experiments. A certain reduction in the degree of absolute binding of labelled DNA fragments does not affect the accuracy of the results.

D. Labelling of reference DNA

Proper choice of reference strain and of the method of isotopic labelling of DNA is of crucial importance for microorganism identification by DNA hybridization. Only type strains, should be selected, otherwise erroneous conclusions are possible. In our opinion, the sometimes contradictory data published on the taxonomy of bacteria obtained by DNA–DNA molecular hybridization may most often be explained by a wrong choice of reference strains. Furthermore, if type strains are used, the results may be easily verified in other laboratories.

Frequently, labelled preparations of bacterial DNAs are obtained by cultivation in media with the labelled DNA precursors (e.g. thymidine). This method of obtaining labelled DNA preparations *in vivo* has its advantages, notably in that no special biochemical procedures are needed and the labelled DNA is extracted in the same way as the unlabelled DNA. Yet this method also has certain drawbacks. ^{3}H- or ^{14}C-DNA samples obtained *in vivo* have a relatively low specific activity ($10–15 \times 10^3$ cpm per μg DNA). Although ^{32}P-labelled DNA preparations possess a higher specific radioactivity ($> 10^5$ cpm μg^{-1}), the fact that this is a short-lived isotope makes it impossible to use such labelled preparations in long-term experiments.

The same restrictions also apply to ^{32}P- and ^{125}I-DNAs labelled *in vitro*. The most commonly used method of obtaining ^{3}H-labelled preparations *in vitro* involves various modifications of tritiation reactions (Searcy, 1968; Drutsa *et al.*, 1974; Drutsa, 1978). This is a time-consuming technique, making it possible to obtain samples with a relatively low specific radioactivity (up to 10^5 cpm per μg DNA).

A procedure coming into use of late allows highly ^{3}H-labelled preparations of bacterial DNAs to be obtained *in vitro*. This procedure has obvious advantages. It is based on enzymatic methylation of DNA fragments with a mixture of bacterial DNA-methylases (Bogdarina *et al.*, 1977; Buryanov *et al.*, 1982).

To obtain labelled preparations, fragmented DNA is first dialysed in buffer used for methylation (see below) and denatured by heating for 10 min in a boiling water bath. The methylation reaction is performed in an incubation medium composed of 40 mM Tris-HCl (pH 7.6–7.8), 5 mM EDTA, 10 mM 2–mercaptoethanol, 1.5×10^{-6} M S-adenosyl-L-methionine (methyl-^{3}H) (specific activity 15 Ci mmol^{-1}; Amersham, England); 200 units of DNA methylase *Eco* RII and 200 units of DNA methylase *Eco* dam; 20 μg of DNA, final volume 100 μl. The reaction is performed for 2 h at 37 °C. The labelled DNA fragments are separated from the residual *S*-adenosylmethionine on Sephadex G100 or hydroxyapatite columns. The specific activity of the labelled DNA samples is 10^5–10^6 cpm μg^{-1}.

The ^{3}H-labelled DNA samples, obtained by enzymatic methylation, are stable and do not lose their specific radioactivity for a long time when frozen at −20 °C. This is particularly important for experiments intended to identify bacteria by molecular DNA–DNA hybridization, since it provides the opportunity to set up a bank of reference labelled DNA samples.

It has been shown that ^{3}H-methylation of DNA sequences with bacterial methylases does not affect the physicochemical properties of DNA (Greenberg and Krasna, 1976), the quantity of the hybrid duplexes formed in hybridization experiments, or the thermostability of the duplexes (Chernishev, 1981). In our experience, reference DNA preparations thus obtained are suitable for DNA–DNA molecular-hybridization experiments. We have used such labelled DNA to study the taxonomy of different groups of bacteria: Rhodospirillaceae (Tourova *et al.*, 1982b), *Kurthia* (Cherevach *et al.*, 1983), *Propionibacterium* (Vorobyeva *et al.*, 1983) and others.

If very high specific activity of reference DNA samples is desirable, the method of labelling by the "nick-translation" mechanism may be recommended (Rigby *et al.*, 1977; Murray *et al.*, 1977; Balmain and Birnie, 1979). This method has been used successfully in hybridization experiments requiring more sensitivity than can be achieved with nucleic acids labelled *in vivo* or *in vitro* by enzymatic methylation (Maniatis *et al.*, 1975; Angerer *et al.*, 1976; Holland and Skinner, 1977; Braun *et al.*, 1978; Kunkel *et al.*, 1979). It is based on the ability of *E. coli* DNA polymerase I to catalyse a "nick-translation" reaction (Kelly *et al.*, 1970). With labelled deoxynucleoside triphosphates as substrates, the pre-existing unlabelled nucleotides in the DNA template are replaced by radioactive ones; the specific activity of the products depends upon the specific activity of the substrates and the amount of the labelled nucleotide incorporated. It may be up to 10^8 dpm per μg DNA.

For labelling, the incubation mixture (final volume 100 μl) includes 5 mM potassium phosphate buffer solution, pH 7.5; 30 μM dATP, dGTP, dCTP, dCTP, (^{3}H)TTP; 5 mM MgCl$_2$; 1.5 units of DNA polymerase I (Boehringer, FRG) and 10 μg of DNase I. The mixture is incubated for 4 h at 13.5 °C and then the reaction is stopped by adding 0.1 volume of 0.5 M Na-EDTA and incubating for 10 min (70 °C). Labelled DNA is isolated by gel filtration (Kunkel *et al.*, 1979).

When choosing a labelling method, the price of isotopically labelled compounds used should be taken into consideration, especially if numerous experiments are to be performed.

E. Immobilization of DNA on filters

A conventional method for immobilization of high-polymer DNA on nitrocellulose membrane filters (Gillespie and Spiegelman, 1965; Denhardt, 1966; De Ley, and Tijtgat, 1970) is as follows. DNA solutions in $0.1 \times$ SSC are denatured by heating or NaOH treatment, with subsequent neutralization. The concentration of salts is brought up to $1-2$ M NaCl, and then the solution is passed through nitrocellulose filters. The filters are washed several times with $2 \times$ SSC to eliminate the unfixed DNA. Usually as much as 60–80% of DNA is bound to the filters. The duration of the procedure depends mainly on the filtration rate, and takes about an hour for each DNA preparation. With mass sample analyses, frequently required for bacterial identification by DNA–DNA molecular hybridization, the time for this stage of the experiment is considerably increased because of the need for a battery of vacuum filtration devices, which can be difficult to operate.

The immobilization of a large amount of DNA samples can be achieved by employing the following procedure: concentrated DNA solutions (about $500\,\mu g\,ml^{-1}$) in $0.1 \times$ SSC are denatured by heating up to $100\,°C$, quickly frozen and then incubated with an equal volume of 1 M NaOH for 20 min at room temperature. The DNA sample is neutralized by adding 0.5 volume of 1 M NaCl, 0.3 M sodium citrate, 0.5 M Tris–HCl and 1 M HCl (pH 8.0); the solution is mixed and quickly cooled. The DNA solution is pipetted on to filters, $5\,\mu l$ each time, the total amount for a 9 mm filter being $10\,\mu g$. The filters are air-dried for 1 h and then washed twice in $6 \times$ SSC solution. With this procedure it is possible to handle a large number of filters simultaneously and achieve a substantial acceleration of mass analyses. Using this method, 90–100% of DNA is adsorbed.

The DNA-filters are air-dried at room temperature and then for 2 h *in vacuo* at $78\,°C$. This procedure is necessary for efficient DNA fixation.

Nitrocellulose membrane filters are generally used at present to immobilize DNA. However, with these filters non-specific losses of DNA occur during incubation with labelled fragments, washing and especially thermoelution of labelled DNA fragments (De Ley and Tijtgat, 1970). To overcome this limitation, the use of diazobenzyloxymethyl instead of nitrocellulose filters has been suggested (Stark and Williams, 1979). Non-specific DNA binding and the efficacy of hybridization in experiments with such filters and with nitrocellulose filters are similar, but DNA is associated covalently on the diazobenzyloxymethyl filters, so it is possible to avoid losses. Apart from that, the use of such filters saves time, since, after thermoelution of the bound labelled DNA for a subsequent radioactivity count, the same filters can be reused for hybridization with the DNA of another reference strain.

F. DNA hybridization

Here we consider mainly the DNA-filter technique of hybridization, now a routine method in microbial taxonomy. Although the method is worth practising, it should always be remembered that there does exist the far more accurate method of DNA hybridization in solution. The reason for this being less popular among microbiologists is that the belief is widespread that it is laborious and needs more experienced personnel. This opinion is certainly erroneous. Modern modifications of methods of DNA hybridization in solution allow numerous DNA samples to be handled simultaneously. Because the physico-chemical background of this method is better understood than that of the DNA filter, it gives more accurate results, especially in DNA thermostability measurements. Numerous papers have been published concerning the details of this method (e.g. Britten and Kohne, 1968; Britten et al., 1978).

Since by its very nature, this is a rapid method, it is recommended for broader application in microbial taxonomy. Although highly purified DNA preparations are necessary for hybridization in solution, the work may be expedited by simultaneous use of batteries of thermostatted HAP columns, fraction collectors and liquid-phase radioactivity-measurement methods. Even compared with the speediest variants of the DNA-filter technique, hybridization in solution has certain advantages, mainly because of the accuracy of its various steps. For example, no DNA leakage from HAP columns is observed, a stumbling block for the DNA-filter method.

Bearing in mind that the DNA-filter technique has become a traditional method of microbial taxonomy and is consistent with its requirements, we shall now turn to new modifications of this method, which prove to be useful for its practical application.

In DNA-filter hybridization experiments, time-saving is possible at this stage as well. According to the conventional hybridization method (Gillespie and Spiegelman, 1965; Denhardt, 1966) at the optimal temperature for DNA reassociation and in 2–$6 \times$ SSC, it is recommended that experiments are continued until the saturation levels of bound labelled DNA are obtained (i.e. for 14–18 h). As time-course changes in the specificity of DNA binding in hybridization reactions have not been studied in detail, we performed such experiments to find out if the incubation period may be shortened (Antonov et al., 1978). As follows from our data presented in Table III, the incubation time may be shortened to 8 h; a progressive decrease in the amount of bound

TABLE III

Comparison of molecular DNA–DNA hybridization results obtained at optimal and reduced time intervals.

Strains	Percentage of homology at different incubation times[b]		
	16 h	8 h	4 h
E.coli B[a]	100 ± 7 (32)	100 ± 14 (11)	100 ± 8 (4)
E.coli 761	80 ± 6	89 ± 6	119 ± 30
E.alcalescens 1601	61 ± 1	67 ± 5	63 ± 3
E. crim 91	55 ± 5	62 ± 5	72 ± 24
Atypical strain 1067	33 ± 4	30 ± 4	39 ± 2

[a]Reference strain. [b]Values in parentheses are percentages of the absolute binding of labelled DNA in a homologous reaction.

DNA is observed when the incubation time is shortened. This, however, is not very important, in view of the high radioactivity level of the labelled fragments used. Incubations shorter than 8 h under standard conditions often give erroneous results.

The incubation time may also be decreased by altering the conditions of the reaction. De Ley and De Smedt (1975) showed that if $2 \times$ SSC supplemented with 20% formamide is used as an incubation medium then the saturation time becomes 8–10 h.

Even greater shortening of the time taken by the DNA–DNA hybridization step is possible. It has been established (Wetmur, 1975) that adding dextran sulphate to the hybridization medium up to a final concentration of 10% increases the DNA reassociation rate in a homogeneous solution by 10-fold. In our experience, this occurs mainly owing to the concentration of the DNA in solution. In a two-phase system, i.e. during hybridization of labelled fragments with filter-bound DNA, the rate of increase is even higher—by 100-fold (Wahl *et al.*, 1979). Consequently, the time of the reaction is reduced to 1 h and even less. This procedure has also been successfully used in *in situ* hybridization reactions (Szabo and Ward, 1982).

Thus there exists a spectrum of time-saving modifications of DNA hybridization reactions, and the choice of the appropriate one depends mainly on the aim of an experiment.

IV. Hybridization *in situ*

As shown in hybridization experiments of eukaryotic nucleic acids in cytological preparations, the specificity of the reaction remained high even in the presence of ordinary cellular components (Pardue *et al.*, 1970).

This is also true of prokaryotes; it appears possible to use not only DNA preparations in hybridization experiments, but also to perform hybridization in microbial colonies directly, treated in a special way (hybridization *in situ*). Such experiments are particularly common in genetic-engineering research for detecting clones carrying recombinant plasmids.

There are many techniques for treating bacterial colonies for hybridization *in situ* (e.g. Jones and Murray, 1965; Grunstein and Hogness, 1975; Cami and Kourilsky, 1978; Le Blanc *et al.*, 1978; Thayer, 1979). All these procedures include lysis of the colonies directly on filters, partial purification, denaturation, immobilization of DNA on filters and subsequent incubation with radioactively labelled DNA probes, followed by autoradiography. Since no mechanical methods of cell disintegration are possible here, various procedures involving lytic agents are used. ^{32}P-labelling is most frequently used, but ^{3}H can similarly be incorporated (Wotska *et al.*, 1977; Bartnik *et al.*, 1981).

We have examined the possibility of applying the hybridization method *in situ* for bacterial identification (Tourova *et al.*, 1982a).

Filters with colonies of the bacteria to be identified were placed for 1 min on the surface of a stack of filter paper and moistened with one of the reagents (see below) and finally with 6 × SSC. The filters were treated at room temperature, each operation being repeated 4 times. The following reagents were used: (1) lysozyme solution (1.5 µg ml^{-1} in 50 mM Tris–HCl in a buffer, containing 25% sucrose, pH 8.0); (2) 0.25% solution of SDS; (3) 0.5 M NaOH; (4) 1 M Tris–HCl buffer, pH 7.8; (5) pronase solution (100 µg ml^{-1}) in 6 × SSC; (6) 6 × SSC. Finally, filters were dried at room temperature and then *in vacuo* for 2 h at 80 °C.

DNA–DNA molecular hybridization was conducted according to the procedure of Denhardt (Denhardt, 1966); enzymatically methylated DNA fragments were added (Buryanov *et al.*, 1982). The unbound labelled fragments of DNA were washed off by 6 × SSC (10 ml per filter, 4 times for 5 min). Then the filters were dried at 80 °C and the amount of the bound label was determined in a liquid scintillation counter. This method (rather than autoradiography) was chosen because autoradiography is a time-consuming process and because it yields qualitative, but not quantitative, results. Two main factors influence the binding of the labelled DNA of the reference strain with the DNA on the filters: an inadequate level of cellular lysis in different colonies (which reduces DNA accessibility for hybridization) and a partial elution of DNA from the filters during the incubations and washings.

According to Thayer (1979), considerable DNA losses occur at ionic strengths below 0.5 M. After 20 h incubation in 6 × SSC, 20–50% of the DNA was lost from each filter in our experiments. The size and age of the colonies were also critical. Losses were considerably less for small, 10–12 h old colonies than for large ones. Therefore it is advisable to employ small freshly cultivated colonies of the same age for such experiments. The results of some *in situ* colony DNA hybridization experiments are listed in Table IV.

For comparison, we used filters with purified DNA from each bacterial species. The binding of the label with the DNA isolated from the colonies on the filters was considerably reduced, compared with the pure DNA. However, given a sufficiently high specific radioactivity of labelled DNAs of the reference strains, this level of binding makes it possible to determine homologies in the DNAs compared. It follows from the data given in Table IV that the *E. coli*, showing no DNA homologies with bacteria of the genus *Bacillus*, is clearly separated. On the other hand, *B. thuringiensis* and *B. cereus*, members of the same genus, were not differentiated. The latter are closely related and not easily distinguished in experiments employing highly purified DNA obtained by conventional procedures (Seki *et al.*, 1978).

As is well known, binding of reference DNA with DNA immobilized on filters, under conditions of incomplete saturation, depends on the ratio of these DNAs. Therefore it is important to avoid significant fluctuation in the amounts of DNA present on the filters by utilizing colonies of the same age

TABLE IV

Comparison of molecular DNA–DNA hybridization results obtained by conventional and colony methods.

Reference DNA	Strains	Percentage of bound labelled fragments
E.coli g-53	*E.coli* g-53 (pure DNA)	40.0
	E.coli g-53 (colony)	10.0
	B.thuringiensis (69-6)	0
	B. cereus 372	0
	Ps. putida Pp g6	0
B. cereus 372	*B. cereus* 372 (pure DNA)	40.0
	B. cereus 372 (colony)	3.0
	B. thuringiensis 69-6	2.8
	E.coli g-53	0
	Ps. putida Pp g6	0
B. thuringiensis 69-6	*B.thuringiensis* 69-6 (pure DNA)	23.0
	B.thuringiensis 69-6 (colony)	3.4
	B. cereus 372	3.0
	E.coli g-53	0
	Ps. putida Pp g6	0

and size and treating them in exactly the same way. The amount of labelled reference DNA should be minimal and is determined by its specific activity. Thus it is particularly important to employ highly labelled DNA. Provided that these conditions are met, it is possible not only to achieve qualitative information, indicating the presence of a given species among those tested, but also quantitative details thus giving results more or less similar to those obtained by classical DNA–DNA molecular hybridization techniques. The procedure described can be employed for bacterial identification to a genus and, in some cases, to the species level.

The suggested method is useful for bacteria whose cell walls are readily destroyed by different lytic agents. It has certain advantages over the previously described rapid methods based on semipurified DNA prepara- tions, although it is not as accurate. First, this method is suitable for bacterial identification in mixed cultures and allows separate investigation of the colony of each species; secondly, it does not require a significant amount (biomass) of the test bacteria; and thirdly, it is fast and simple—treatment of the colonies on a series of filters takes no more than 30 min.

These methods can find application in microbiological studies especially for large-scale ecological analyses of microbial associations, including sani- tary or public-health microbiology. For each association, it is possible to select reference DNAs of the most typical or frequently occurring microorganisms, and follow changes in such associations.

V.   Bacterial identification in animal tissues

A method has been suggested for specific and semiquantitative determi- nation of trace amounts of bacterial DNA in the tissues of infected animals with the help of hybridization of nucleic acids (Steinman, 1975). Pathogenic bacteria of the species *Listeria monocytogenes* and *Erysipelothrix* sp. were taken as the standard. Mouse liver cells and spleen cells of mice infected with one of these microorganisms were used; for control, those of healthy mice were taken. The amount of tissue used in the experiments ranged from 1 to 10 g. After mincing, the tissue was disrupted with a Teflon–glass tissue grinder (10 strokes at 2 000 rev min^{-1} in an electric hand drill). The mixture was then frozen and thawed 3 times and treated for 1 min with a Polytron homogenizer, Type PT-2000. DNA was isolated according to Marmur's procedure, with an additional phenol treatment (Kirby, 1957). For hybridi- zation, RNA samples of the standard microorganisms treated *in vivo* were used, and the process was performed in a solution with subsequent immobili- zation of the hybrids on nitrocellulose membrane filters, followed by RNase treatment.

It was established that the minimal amount of the bacterial DNA that could be assayed by this method was 10^{-4} µg per 20 µg of animal DNA, i.e. 1 bacterial cell per 50 cells of the infected animal.

As far as the specificity of the method is concerned, RNA–DNA hybridization allows detection of bacterial DNA with a high degree of accuracy, both in a mixture with a considerable amount of animal DNA and in infected tissues directly. Consequently, the method makes it possible to differentiate tissues of animals infected with various microorganisms.

We believe that this method may be helpful in medical microbiological investigations. It can be used to discover pathogenic bacteria in the tissues of diseased organisms, especially during chronic infections, when conventional cultural and serological methods fail. In addition, this method can be applied for identifying the pathogenic agent and for its differentiation from other bacteria present in the isolates obtained from diseased tissues.

This method differs from those previously described in that the acceleration is achieved not at the DNA isolation and hybridization stage, but as early as the preliminary stage, essential for the other variants of the method, of isolating the pure culture of the microorganism tested. The cells of some pathogenic bacteria may be lysis-resistant, and so special procedures are needed for their lysis. It may be difficult to distinguish such bacteria in animal tissues. The use of RNA instead of DNA narrows the range of application of the method, since differences at the level of DNA–RNA hybridization with taxonomically related pathogens may be insignificant.

Taking these limitations into account, as well as possible modifications, this method of detecting trace quantities of bacterial DNAs in the tissues of diseased animals may find valuable application in the identification of pathogenic microorganisms.

VI. Conclusions

The methods and procedures described above do not introduce essential changes into DNA–DNA molecular-hybridization techniques. Yet they show how the procedures can be simplified and accelerated bringing these methods closer to routine microbiological laboratory application and satisfying such requirements for microbial identification as speed, accuracy and reliability. The choice of a rapid method involving hybridization experiments depends, in each case, on the group of microorganisms under investigation and the aim of the experiments. As a rule, these procedures do not require investments in special equipment and complex reagents. On the contrary, they allow work to be carried out with a small amount of the stock material and treatment of a large number of samples. They make possible highly specific identification, characteristic of DNA–DNA molecular hybridization, within a brief time. Some of these procedures are so simple that they can be performed even under field conditions, or filters with bound DNA may be sent to a base laboratory. These considerations enable us to recommend the described rapid methods for broad application in microbiological laboratories.

Acknowledgement

The authors are grateful to Professor J. R. Norris for his valuable remarks and suggestions concerning the text of this paper.

References

Anderson, R. S. and Ordal, E. J. (1972). *J. Bacteriol.* **109**, 696–706.
Angerer, R. C., Davidson, E. H. and Britten, R. J. (1976). *Chromosoma* **56**, 213–226.
Antonov, A. S., Belousova, A. A., Lysenko, A. M. and Tourova, T. P. (1978). *Mikrobiologiya* **47**, 1049–1054 (English transl.).
Arrighi, F., Bergendahl, J. and Mandel, M. (1968). *Exp. Cell Res.* **50**, 47–54.
Balmain, A. and Birnie, G. D. (1979). *Biochim. Biophys. Acta* **561**, 155–166.
Bartnik, E., Borsuk, P. and Pieniazek, S. J. (1981). *Anal. Biochem.* **116**, 237–240.
Baumann, P., Baumann, L. and Mandel, M. (1971). *J. Bacteriol.* **107**, 268–294.
Bogdarina, I. G., Buryanov, Ya. I. and Baev, A. A. (1977). *Dokl. Akad. Nauk. SSSR* **233**, 498–501 (English transl.).
Braun, B. A., Schanke, K. E. and Graham, D. E. (1978). *Nucl. Acids Res.* **5**, 4283–4303.
Brenner, D. J., Steigerwalt, A. G., Weaver, R. E., McDade, J. E., Feeley, J. C. and Mandel, M. (1978). *Curr. Microbiol.* **1**, 71–75.
Brenner, D. J., Steigerwalt, A. G., Pohl, S., Behrens, H., Maunheim, W. and Weaver, R. E. (1981). *Int. J. Syst. Bacteriol.* **31**, 89–90.
Britten, R. J. and Kohne, D. E. (1968). *Science* **161**, 529–540.
Britten, R. J., Cetta, A. and Davidson, E. H. (1978). *Cell* **15**, 1175–1186.
Buryanov, Ya. I., Bogdarina, I. G., Nesterenko, V. F. and Baev, A. A. (1982). *Biokhimiya* **47**, 587–588 (English transl).
Cami, B. and Kourilsky, P. (1978). *Nucl. Acids Res.* **5**, 2381–2390.
Chassy, B. M. and Giuffrida, A. (1980). *Appl. Environ. Microbiol.* **39**, 153–158.
Cherevach, N. V., Tourova, T. P. and Belikova, V. L. (1983). *FEMS Microbiol. Lett.* **19**, 243–245.
Chernishev, V. A. (1981). *Biologicheskie Nauki* **9**, 105–109.
Coakley, W. T., Bater, A. J. and Lloyd, D. (1977). *Adv. Microbiol. Physiol.* **16**, 279–341.
Davis, R. W., Thomas, M., Cameron, J., John, T. P. A., Sherer, S. and Padgett, R. A. (1980). *Meth. Enzymol.* **65**, 404–411.
De Ley, J. and De Smedt, J. (1975). *Antonie van Leeuwenhoek* **41**, 287–307.
De Ley, J. and Tijtgat, R. (1970). *Antonie van Leeuwenhoek* **36**, 461–474.
Denhardt, D. T. (1966). *Biochem. Biophys. Res. Commun.* **23**, 641–646.

Drutsa, V. L. (1978). In *Physico-Chemical Methods in Molecular Biology*, pp. 33–40. Moskow University Publishing House, Moscow.

Drutsa, V. L., Sokolova, N. I. and Shabarova, Z. A. (1974). *Molek. Biologiya* **8**, 921–926 (English translation).

Gillespie, D. and Spiegelman, S. (1965). *J. Mol. Biol.* **12**, 829–842.

Greenberg, J. and Krasna, A. I. (1976). *Arch. Biochem. Biophys.* **177**, 468–479.

Grimont, P. A. D., Popoff, M. J., Grimont, F., Coynault, C. and Lemelin, M. (1980). *Curr. Microbiol.* **4**, 325–330.

Grunstein, M. and Hogness, D. S. (1975). *Proc. Natl Acad. Sci. USA* **72**, 3961–3965.

Holland, C. A. and Skinner, D. M. (1977). *Chromosoma* **63**, 223–240.

Hoyer, B. H., McCarthy, B. J. and Bolton, E. T. (1964). *Science* **144**, 959–967.

James, D., Oliver, J. D., Warner, R. A. and Cleland, D. R. (1983). *Appl. Environ. Microbiol.* **45**, 985–998.

Johnson, J. L. and Ordal, E. J. (1968). *J. Bacteriol.* **95**, 893–900.

Jones, K. W. and Murray, K. (1965). *J. Mol. Biol.* **96**, 455–460.

Kelly, R. B., Cozzarelli, N. R., Deutcher, H. P., Lehman, I. R. and Kornberg, A. (1970). *J. Biol. Chem.* **245**, 39–45.

Kirby, K. S. (1957). *Biochem. J.* **66**, 495–504.

Komatsu, Y. (1979). *J. Gen. Microbiol.* **113**, 407–408.

Kunkel, L. M., Smith, K. D. and Boyer, S. H. (1979). *Biochemistry* **18**, 3343–3353.

Lambert, K. J. (1982). *Agric. Biol. Chem.* **46**, 3079–3080.

Le Blanc, H., Dujon, B., Guerineau, M. and Slonimski, P. P. (1978). *Mol. Gen. Genetics* **161**, 311–315.

Lee, J. V., Shread, P., Furniss, A. L. and Bryan, T. N. (1981). *J. Appl. Bacteriol.* **50**, 73–94.

Levanova, G. F. and Tourova, T. P. (1977). *Microbiologiya* **46**, 92–95 (English translation).

Levanova, G. F., Lavrovskaya, V. M. and Shvetsov, U. P. (1980). *Zh. Mikrobiol.* **8**, 14–16.

McCarthy, B. J. and Bolton, E. T. (1963). *Proc. Natl Acad. Sci. USA* **50**, 156–164.

McConaughy, B. L., Laird, C. D. and McCarthy, B. J. (1969). *Biochemistry* **8**, 3289–3295.

Maniatis, T., Jeffrey, A. and Kleid, D. G. (1975). *Proc. Natl Acad. Sci. USA* **72**, 1184–1188.

Marmur, J. (1961). *J. Mol. Biol.* **3**, 208–218.

Murray, M. G., Belford, H. S. and Thompson, W. F. (1977). *Carnegie Inst. Wash. Year Book* **76**, 262–267.

Myers, W. F. and Wisseman, C. L. (1980). *Int. J. Syst. Bacteriol.* **30**, 143–150.

Nacesku, N. and Ciufecu, C. (1977). *Bacteriol. Virusol. Parasitol. Epidemiol.* **22**, 109–113.

Pardue, M. L., Gerbi, S. A., Eckhardt, R. A. and Gall, J. G. (1970). *Chromosoma* **29**, 268–273.

Rigby, P. W. J., Dieckmann, M., Rhodes, C. and Berg, P. (1977). *J. Mol. Biol.* **113**, 237–251.

Schmidt, G., Tannhauser, S. (1945). *J. Biol. Chem.* **161**, 83–87.

Schwinghamer, E. A. (1980). *FEMS Microbiol. Lett.* **7**, 157–162.

Searcy, D. (1968). *Biochim. Biophys. Acta* **166**, 360–370.

Seki, T., Chi-Kwan, C., Mikami, H. and Oshima, Y. (1978). *Int. J. Syst. Bacteriol.* **28**, 182–189.

Spirin, A. S. (1958). *Biochimiya* **23**, 656–659.

Stark, G. R. and Williams, J. G. (1979). *Nucl. Acids Res.* **6**, 195–203.

Steinman, C. R. (1975). *J. Lab. Clin. Med.* **86**, 164–174.

Szabo, P. and Ward, D. C. (1982). *Trends Biochem. Sci.* **7**, 425–427.

Thayer, R. E. (1979). *Anal. Biochem.* **98**, 60–63.

Tourova, T. P. and Levanova, G. F. (1980a). In *Biochemistry and Biophysics of Microorganisms*, pp. 28–30 Gorky, (In Russian).

Tourova, T. P. and Levanova, G. F. (1980b). *Zh. Microbiol.* **3**, 27–29.

Tourova, T. P., Troitsky, A. V., Ignashev, V. G. and Svetlichkin, V. V. (1982a). *Laboratornoe Delo* **4**, 239–243.

Tourova, T. P., Ivanova, T. L. and Antonov, A. S. (1982b). *Izv Akad. Nauk SSSR Ser. Biol.* **5**, 763–767.

Tourova, T. P., Grafova, T. I. and Badalova, I. M. (1983). *Zh. Microbiol.* **1**, 22–24.

Valiejo-Roman, K. M. (1980). In *Molecular Bases of Genosystematics*, pp. 86–105. Moscow University Publishing House, Moscow (In Russian).

Vorobyeva, L. I., Tourova, T. P., Kraeva, N. I. and Alekseeva, M. A. (1983). *Mickrobiologiya* **53**, 465–471 (English transl.).

Wahl, G. M., Stern, M. and Stark, G. R. (1979). *Proc. Natl Acad. Sci. USA* **76**, 3683–3687.

Wetmur, J. G. (1975). *Biopolymers* **14**, 2517–2524.

Wotska, K. I. and Kinicki-Goldfinger, W. J. H. (1977). *Acta Microbiol. Pol.* **26**, 447–449.

9
Isolation, Purification and Enzymatic Sequencing of RNA

M. T. MACDONELL*

Centre of Marine Biotechnology, University of Maryland, Baltimore, Maryland 21202, USA

J. N. HANSEN

Department of Chemistry, Division of Biochemistry, University of Maryland, College Park, Maryland 20742, USA

B. A. ORTIZ-CONDE

Department of Microbiology, University of Maryland, College Park, Maryland 20742, USA

*Present address: Biotechnology Group, Idaho National Engineering Laboratory, P.O. Box 1625, Idaho Falls, ID 83415 USA

METHODS IN MICROBIOLOGY
VOLUME 19 ISBN 0–12–521519–3
Copyright © 1987 by Academic Press Limited
All rights of reproduction in any form reserved

I. Introduction

The dramatic advances in molecular biology that have been made in recent years owe much to the development of nucleic-acid sequencing techniques. Once arduous, it is now possible for a small laboratory to produce thousands of nucleotides of RNA sequence within a span of a few days. Although the powerful enzymatic and chemical methods for generating sequence ladders from a nested set of end-labelled fragments were first perfected for DNA, suitable modifications have enabled similar procedures to be used for RNA. Irrespective of the type of nucleic acid being sequenced, a primary requirement is the availability of a sufficient quantity of the species in highly-purified form, free of contaminating nucleic-acid fragments and/or degradation products. If the fragment to be sequenced is not sufficiently pure, the sequence ladder becomes uninterpretable as a consequence of extraneous ladders superimposed on it.

Because of the requirements of excellent fragment purity for sequencing experiments, novel techniques for the isolation and purification of nucleic-acid species have developed in parallel with sequencing and other recombinant DNA methodologies. A suitable separation method must meet the minimal requirements of adequate resolution and be useful for both analytical and preparative scale experiments. Methods such as ultracentrifugation and column chromatography can be undertaken preparatively, but do not afford adequate resolution. Conversely, techniques like thin-layer chromatography may resolve well, but are not readily scaled up. An HPLC method for the purification of small RNAs has been described (MacDonell et al., 1986), but is dependent upon rather expensive hardware.

Fortunately, gel electrophoresis is one technique that can be adapted successfully for superb resolution on an analytical scale, and can be used for large preparative samples as well. Widely employed for protein work, gels made from acrylamide are capable of exquisite resolution of nucleic acids, mainly on the basis of molecular size, although base composition can influence the separations of shorter oligonucleotide fragments (see Section XI.D). Another gel material, which complements the use of acrylamide, is agarose. Unlike acrylamide, which is a simple polymer made from small organic molecules, agarose is a complex natural polysaccharide. The acrylamide gel matrix is maintained by covalent bonds, whereas agarose gels are maintained by hydrogen bonds. Considerations governing the choice of agarose or acrylamide include the sizes and quantities of the nucleic-acid fragments being separated, and the purpose of the separation. If only size analysis is desired then acrylamide is the gel of choice for fragments of about 1000 nucleotides or less, whereas agarose is preferable for fragments with lengths greater than 1000 nucleotides. Since we are concerned here mainly with small RNA molecules, acrylamide will generally be the material of choice, although some RNA species are large enough to require agarose.

Both types of gels can be used preparatively, but certain limitations should be taken into account. For example, the inherent complexity of the natural agarose polymer gives the experimenter less knowledge and control over the composition of the gel than can be achieved with the simpler polyacrylamide. Consequently, some agarose lots, particularly from different suppliers, may contain various substances that interfere erratically with enzymes used to modify nucleic acids after isolation from the gels. For example, difficulty may be encountered with certain restriction enzymes or in carrying out ligation reactions. Another common observation is that many agarose lots contain inhibitors of polynucleotide kinase. For this reason, many workers prefer to use acrylamide for preparative-scale separations, even when the molecules being separated are too large (i.e. greater than 1 kilobase) for the optimal fractionation range of acrylamide. Unfortunately, standard methylene-bis-acrylamide cross-linked polyacrylamide affords mediocre resolution for fragments larger than 1 kilobase. Moreover, the usual methods of fragment recovery from these gels are not very satisfactory. This is because the methods usually employed for recovering fragments from polyacrylamide depend on passive diffusion or electroelution. Neither works well for large molecules. As is discussed below, bis-acrylylcystamine (BAC), i.e. disulphide cross-linked gels, do much to alleviate these problems.

Although not all of the methods and innovations discussed below will be necessary, or even useful, for a particular application, they are presented here in the hope of increasing the repertoire of techniques available to the individual investigator.

A. Approaches to recovery of nucleic acids from polyacrylamide gels

A frustration experienced by many workers is that of being confronted by a polyacrylamide gel that contains a highly purified molecular species of interest, resolved as a sharp band, and not knowing how to proceed with its extraction. For reasons that are often obscure, experimenters often encounter great difficulty in attempts at recovery of the species from the gel with adequate yield and in undegraded form.

There are two main approaches to the recovery of macromolecules from polyacrylamide gels. One is to cause the macromolecules to migrate or diffuse out of the gel matrix. Both electroelution and "crush-and-soak" methods fall into this category. Each of these will be discussed in turn below. The other approach is to liquify the gel by disrupting the gel matrix, and then recover the macromolecules. An ion-exchange material is useful for recovery from liquified gels, although other methods can be employed.

Methods in which the gel matrix is not disrupted are in much more common use. For example, numerous papers describe methods for recovery using electroelution or diffusion approaches (Hansen, 1976). One of the simplest electroelution techniques involves putting a gel slice into a dialysis bag in an electrophoretic field, and electrophoresing the sample out of the gel and into the surrounding buffer. As individual molecules exit from the gel they then move rapidly through free solution until they collide with the wall of the dialysis bag. This method is straightforward in principle (see Section V.C), but difficulties are frequently encountered in practice. Yields are often poor for obscure reasons, and since one is often working with numerous samples in any given experiment, the causes are inconvenient to trace. Poor yields are almost always encountered when attempting to recover large nucleic acids from acrylamide gels, or small nucleic acids if the gels are fairly concentrated. It seems likely that such problems could be obviated if there were some way to disrupt the gel matrix before attempting to recover the macromolecules.

B. Solubilizable disulphide cross-linked gels

The conventionally employed polyacrylamide gel is prepared by polymerizing a mixture of acrylamide and methylene-bis-acrylamide by a free-radical reaction. The free radicals are generated by catalysing the breakdown of ammonium persulphate using tetramethylethylenediamine (TEMED). The persulphate radicals initiate chain formation by reacting with the double bond of acrylamide, and the chain is propagated from the end of the chain as a free-radical intermediate derived from acrylamide. The resulting three-dimensional gel matrix is maintained by carbon–carbon bonds within the polyacrylamide chains, and by carbon–nitrogen bonds in the cross-links. Such a matrix is quite stable, and provides a strong and inert hydrophilic material that is quite ideal for electrophoresis. In instances where the procedure is being carried out preparatively, the problem then arises of sample recovery from the gel. The strong inert matrix of the gel, which was so suitable as an electrophoretic medium, cannot readily be broken down as an aid to sample recovery. This is because any treatment that would disrupt the covalent bonds of the gel matrix would simultaneously disrupt covalent bonds within the molecules being isolated. This problem is exacerbated by the fact that biological macromolecules are very easily denatured, even without covalent-bond cleavage. As a consequence, conventional bis-cross-linked polyacrylamide gels are never disrupted prior to sample recovery. Instead, methods that cause the molecules to migrate out of the matrix have been devised, as mentioned above.

An obvious solution to this problem would be to devise some alternative to bis-cross-linked polyacrylamide that contains linkages that can be disrupted under suitably mild conditions, while still possessing the strength and rigidity required by the electrophoresis step. To date, very few alternatives have been devised. One reason is that the limitations are so constraining that very few suitable alternatives can be proposed, let alone developed. First of all, one does not wish to depart from acrylamide as the backbone of the matrix, because its properties and simplicity of use are so nearly ideal. Consequently, modifications must be directed toward the cross-link that holds the polyacrylamide chains together. If some chemical group that contains a cleavable bond were to be substituted for the methylene in methylene-bis-acrylamide then it would be possible to convert the gel to a liquid by cleaving the sensitive bond. Few such alternative cross-links have been made and tested. One type is a periodate-sensitive 1,2-diol, such as dihydroxyethylene-bis-acrylamide (DHEBA) (O'Connell and Brady, 1977), or diallyltartardiamide (DATD) (Anker, 1970). Another type is a cross-link that contains a disulphide group that can be cleaved with mercaptoethanol or dithiothreitol. The only example of this type is bis-acrylylcystamine (BAC) (Hansen, 1981).

II.   Isolation and purification of RNA

A.   RNA extraction from bacterial cells

For the purpose of sequence analyses, washed and pelleted bacterial cells from approximately 100 ml of an exponentially growing broth culture, or one Petri plate of confluent growth, will be more than adequate for the recovery of sufficient quantities of RNA from most heterotrophic bacterial species. This includes the RNAs in the size range of tRNA and the ribosomal RNAs, etc. Gram-negative bacterial cells can generally be lysed efficiently using a freeze–thaw technique (Zablen *et al.*, 1975). In the case of Gram-positive cells, however, it may be necessary to resort to the use of a French pressure cell or sonication in order to rupture the cell envelope. Of the two, sonication is the less desirable. RNA oligomers of less than 700 bases, which include tRNAs and 5S rRNA, will not be susceptible to mechanical shear from the use of a French pressure cell. In the case of most Gram-negative bacterial cells, resuspension of the washed cell pellet in 50 mM Tris–borate–EDTA (TBE) buffer (Table I), rather than the buffered lyso-zyme solution employed by Zablen *et al.* (1975) results in immediate cell lysis. This (i) eliminates the need for continuing with subsequent freeze–thaw steps, and (ii) significantly reduces the amount of exposure of RNAs both to endogenous RNases and to lysozome preparations, which are likely to be sources of additional RNases. Cell lysis is evidenced by a rapid and marked increase in the viscosity (as well as a noticeable clearing) of the cell suspension. Since RNA degradation through the activity of exogenous RNases is a prime concern, TBE buffer employed in RNA extractions should be autoclaved prior to use. *Shortcuts must be avoided!* The use of non-sterile buffers, reagents and glassware in RNA extraction and purification is an invitation to disaster.

TABLE I
Preparation of stock (20X) Tris-borate-EDTA (TBE) buffer

121.2 g Tris base	1.0 M Tris
7.3 g EDTA free acid	2.0 mM EDTA
55.6 g boric acid	1.0 M borate
750 ml distilled water	

Adjust to pH 8.3 with boric acid or Tris base, then adjust to 1 litre with distilled water. The pH of tris buffers is notoriously dependent upon temperature; take care to adjust the pH while the stock buffer is approximately 25°C. After preparation, filter the stock buffer through a Whatman No. 1 (or equivalent) filter and autoclave. 50mM TBE is prepared as a 20-fold dilution of the stock.

The crude cell lysate should be brought to 0.5 M NaCl and mixed with an equal volume of chloroform for several minutes. The aqueous and organic phases are then separated by centrifugation at 12 000g for 10 min at 4 °C. We find that extraction with cloroform, rather than phenol, results in greater overall yields of nucleic acid. A possible explanation is that some proteins in close association with DNA (basic proteins, for example) may not be as readily precipitated in chloroform as in phenol. Whatever the explanation, a single extraction using chloroform appears to allow a large proportion of the total protein fraction to be cleared from solution without entangling nucleic-acid molecules in the interface material. Chloroform and phenol remove proteins from aqueous solutions by different mechanisms. Since virtually all chloroform-precipitable proteinaceous material is removed with the first chloroform extraction, subsequent chloroform extractions are of little value and need not be attempted. However, the converse is true for phenol, in which case subsequent extractions result in increased purity. Extractions may be carried out with a 1:1 ratio of phenol and chloroform rather than the separate components. This mixture appears to clear proteins from aqueous solutions with about the same efficiency as chloroform, but suffers the disadvantage of unnecessary exposure of RNA to oxidized phenolic compounds. The aqueous (upper) phase will contain the nucleic-acid fraction and can be removed most efficiently from underneath through the use of a hook-shaped Pasteur pipette (Fig. 1). The aqueous phase should be precipitated in

) Aqueous phase

Fig. 1. Hook-shaped Pasteur pipette. The viscous aqueous phase is drawn downward without disturbing the proteinaceous interface. Adapted from Schlief and Wensink (1981).

2 volumes of cold absolute ethanol and mixed several times by inversion after which it is chilled on crushed ice for 10 min. It is important to avoid the temptation to place the ethanolic precipitate on dry ice. Doing so will invariably decrease the yield (Zeugin and Hartley, 1985). Afterwards, the precipitated nucleic acids are collected by centrifugation at 12 000g for at least 15 min at 4 °C. The ethanolic supernatant is drawn off and the pellet is dried under vacuum. Traces of ethanol will interfere with subsequent solubilization of the pellet. Phenol used for the extraction of nucleic acids should be equilibrated in TBE buffer. This is done as follows. To a previously unopened 500 g bottle of (best reagent-quality) crystalline phenol, 50 mM TBE, pH 8.3 (Table I), is added until the bottle is full, and mixed gently until all of the phenol is in solution. 250 mg (0.05%) 8-hydroxyquinoline is added and the phases are allowed to separate at 4 °C. The aqueous (upper) phase is removed and discarded. The procedure is repeated once. The solution should be stored at -20 °C.

There are three reasonable approaches to the further purification of small RNAs from this point. The method of Kirby (1956, 1968), discussed in Section II.B, employs the selective precipitation of DNA as a means by which the aqueous nucleic-acid fraction may be enriched for RNAs. This is the most laborious approach, but results in excellent yields of RNA. Stepwise elution of RNA from DEAE-cellulose is both rapid and simple and results in very good yields of RNAs in the range of tRNA (75 bases) to 16S rRNA (1540 bases). Alternatively, if optimization of yield is not paramount, the sample may be resuspended in a small volume of sterile tracking-dye/loading-buffer and fractionated electrophoretically.

B. RNA extraction from eukaryotic cells

An efficient method for the extraction of total RNA from eukaryotic tissues has been described in detail by Kirby (1956, 1968). For description of cell disruption etc. the reader is referred to those papers. Part of the method described by Kirby (1956) is broadly applicable to preparative-scale purification of RNA from any source. This involves the selective precipitation of DNA from an aqueous nucleic-acid solution, thereby significantly increasing the amount of total RNA that can be loaded onto a column, gel, TLC plate, etc. A description of this technique follows.

The dried nucleic acid pellet is dissolved in distilled water and to it is added 2 volumes of redistilled 2-methoxyethanol (cellosolve), 2 volumes of 2.5 M potassium phosphate, dibasic, and 0.5 volume of 33% (v/v) phosphoric acid. This is mixed thoroughly for 10 min and centrifuged at 12 000g for 10 min at 4 °C. The aqueous (upper) of the three phases will contain the total RNA fraction. This is collected and precipitated by the addition of 2 volumes of cold absolute ethanol, followed by chilling on crushed ice as described above (Section II.A). After centrifugation, the RNA pellet will typically be saturated with (and usually covered by) several microlitres of potassium phosphate solution. Most of this can be removed using a Pasteur pipette drawn to a capillary. The RNA pellet is dissolved in a minimum volume of sterile distilled water and reprecipitated in cold ethanol.

C. DEAE-cellulose chromatography

The amount of any nucleic-acid preparation that can be fractionated on a polyacrylamide gel is limited by the maximum quantity that the gel matrix is able to sieve without severe loss of resolution. This is often only a hypothetical problem, since the total nucleic acid loaded onto a gel is often limited by its concentration and the total volume of the wells. For this reason, if yield is a consideration, it is profitable to remove chromosomal and plasmid DNA as well as monomers, dimers and very small nucleic-acid fragments, which are certain to represent a sizeable proportion of the total nucleic-acid preparation, before proceeding to fractionation by gel electrophoresis. DEAE-cellulose chromatography provides an excellent means for the removal of interfering oligomers. Its use, however, requires a conscientious pretreatment, which may be carried out months in advance, and the prepared DEAE-cellulose stock stored refrigerated in 50 mM TBE buffer. A stepwise description of this pretreatment (Peterson, 1980) is given in Table II.

TABLE II
Pretreatment of DEAE-cellulose

---

1. Suspend several grams of fresh DEAE-cellulose powder in 500 ml of 0.5 M NaOH. Let stand for 10 min. Dilute to 0.2 M NaOH with a solution of 1 M NaCl.
2. Filter through a Whatman No. 1 (or equivalent) filter using a Buchner funnel.
3. Rinse the DEAE-cellulose cake with a litre of distilled water.
4. Resuspend the DEAE-cellulose in 500 ml 0.5 M HCl.
5. Repeat steps 2 and 3.
6. Repeat steps 1, 2 and 3.
7. Resuspend DEAE-cellulose in 1 litre of distilled water.
8. Repeat steps 2 and 3.
9. Test pH of eluate using pH paper. Continue rinsing with distilled water until eluate reaches neutrality.
10. Completely resuspend DEAE-cellulose cake in 500 ml of 50 mM TBE buffer, pH 8.3.
11. Allow the larger cellulose particles to settle (approximately 15min), and remove fine particles by decanting.
12. Repeat steps 10 and 11 until all fine particles have been removed (typically 5 or 6 times).

Washed and TBE-equilibrated DEAE-cellulose (Cellex D, Bio Rad, Richmond, California) is carefully packed into a short wide silanized glass column or 10 ml sterile silanized plastic syringe barrel to a depth of 3–4 cm. This should be rinsed with 1 M NaCl, 7 M urea in 50 mM TBE (pH 8.3) and then equilibrated in 50 mM TBE (pH 8.3). The crude nucleic-acid solution is applied to the column. This is rinsed with several column volumes of 50 mM TBE buffer. Small fragments, 30 bases or less, can be removed by rinsing the column with 2 or 3 volumes of 0.2 M NaCl in 50 mM TBE. Afterwards, RNAs in the range of tRNA through 16S rRNA can be eluted stepwise with 0.5 M NaCl, 7 M urea in 50 mM TBE. It is essential that all solutions, including the nucleic-acid solution, be degassed prior to use. This can be achieved rapidly by connecting the vessel containing the solution to a vacuum line and tapping the wall of the vessel with a hard object several times. The nucleic-acid solution will be rather viscous and slow to load onto the column. If the solution is adequately degassed and the DEAE-cellulose properly pretreated so that fine particles have been removed, once the nucleic acid is loaded onto the column, washing and elution will proceed quickly. A few minutes of conscientious DEAE-cellulose preparation will save hours of frustration and wasted effort.

It is important to realize that there does not exist a simple linear relationship between molarity of NaCl and lengths of oligonucleotides that will be eluted (Gould and Matthews, 1967). This is due, in part, to the strong influence of secondary and tertiary structure on strength of binding of the phosphate backbone to the DEAE groups. Furthermore, the use of neither urea nor formamide, in the absence of heat, is sufficient to completely relax secondary structure in RNAs. Once eluted, the RNA should be precipitated in 2 volumes of cold absolute ethanol, followed by chilling on crushed ice and collection by centrifugation, as described above. Following removal of the ethanolic supernatant, the pellet should be dried under vacuum and resuspended in a tracking-dye/loading-buffer of the following composition: 10 M urea, 0.05% (w/v) xylene cyanol, 0.05% (w/v) bromophenol blue in 50 mM TBE, in preparation for purification by gel electrophoresis.

D.   Silanizing glass and plastic ware

All glassware used in the isolation and purification of RNAs should be silanized (Schlief and Wensink, 1981), and rinsed in glass-distilled or reagent-grade water. Afterward, glassware should be baked at 300 °C for 4 h. If desired, plastic micropipette tips and microfuge tubes may be silanized as follows. About 2 ml of a 1:1 ratio of chloroform and dichlorodimethylsilane (Sigma Chemicals, St. Louis, Missouri) is pipetted onto a watch glass placed in the bottom of a glass vacuum desiccator from which the desiccant has been removed. Eppendorf tubes and micropipette tips to be silanized are distributed inside, and a vacuum is applied. After 10–15 s the vacuum is abruptly released. This process is repeated about a dozen times, then the plastic ware is removed, rinsed thoroughly with distilled water, and autoclaved to sterilize.

III. Polyacrylamide-gel electrophoresis

A. A note on the use of BAC-acrylamide

The cross-linking agent routinely used in the casting of polyacrylamide gels suitable for electrophoresis is N,N'-methylene-bis-acrylamide (Bis). Once formed, however, it will not be possible to cleave the cross-link formed by Bis under conditions sufficiently mild to allow for the recovery of intact nucleic acids. For this reason, a thiol-soluble crosslinking agent, N,N'-bis-acrylylcystamine (BAC), was developed by Hansen (1981), and is excellent for the casting of preparative gels required for fractionation and purification of RNAs for sequence analysis. In order to ensure thiol-solubility of the gel, BAC-acrylamide gels must be polymerized in the presence of elevated levels of TEMED and at a temperature of at least 41 °C. Higher temperatures may be used, but polymerization may become inconveniently rapid. If it is not convenient to reset an incubator to 41–45 °C, the gel box may be warmed in a 37 °C incubator and the uncatalysed BAC-acrylamide heated to around 46 °C. We have used this method and consider it a satisfactory alternative. A method that eliminates the requirement for elevated temperatures has been discussed by Hansen (1981), and is summarized in the literature supplied by Bio Rad with their preparation of BAC. The use of lower temperatures has not been thoroughly investigated, so is not recommended at this time.

B. Fractionation of RNA species

For the purpose of isolation and purification of RNA species, 5% (w/v) acrylamide preparative stacking gels are prepared (see Table III) with the upper stack (approximately 30% of the volume) consisting of Bis-acrylamide and the lower stack consisting of thiol-soluble BAC-acrylamide (Hansen, 1981). Besides conserving BAC (which is expensive in comparison with Bis), the use of conventional (Bis) acrylamide in the upper stack facilitates the formation of clean, square-bottomed wells, since 5% BAC is sticky and tends to adhere to well formers (combs). The gel form (along with the degassed,

TABLE III

Polyacrylamide gels

The following recipies each make 100 ml of gel. Modify components proportionately for different volumes.

(1) *5% Bis-acrylamide gel*

    4.75 g acrylamide
    0.50 g methylene-bis-acrylamide
    0.10 g ammonium persulphate
    5.0 ml (20X) stock TBE buffer
    distilled water to make 100 ml

Degas thoroughly under vacuum and polymerize with 50–75 µl of TEMED.

(2) *10% BAC-acrylamide stock*

    95.5 g acrylamide
    4.5 g BAC-acrylamide
    distilled water to make 1 litre

(3) *5% BAC-acrylamide gel*

    50.0 ml (10%) stock BAC-acrylamide solution
    45.0 ml distilled water
    5.0 ml (20X) stock TBE buffer
    90.0 mg ammonium persulphate

Degas thoroughly under vacuum. Heat the gel box and unpolymerized gel to 41–45°C. Add 260 µl TEMEB to polymerize. Note that gel will polymerize in 30–45 s.

(4) *5% Bis-acrylamide denaturing gel*

    4.75 g acrylamide
    0.25 g methylene-bis-acrylamide
    50.00 g ultrapure urea
    0.10 g ammonium persulphate
    5.0 ml (20X) stock TBE buffer
    distilled water to make 100 ml

Filter (0.45 µm), degas thoroughly under vacuum, and polymerize with 18 µl of TEMED.

---

uncatalysed BAC-acrylamide) should be placed in a 41–45 °C incubator and left to equilibrate for approximately one hour. It is imperative that the apparatus be thoroughly warmed prior to pouring the gel.

Although the polymerization of BAC cross-linked acrylamide will proceed without apparent difficulty at temperatures less than 41 °C, the resulting gel will not be thiol-soluble. The BAC-acrylamide should be polymerized by addition of ammonium persulphate and TEMED, and poured to fill the bottom two thirds of the gel form. Polymerization should be allowed to proceed for at least 60 min at 41 °C or higher. After the BAC-acrylamide has completely polymerized, it may be removed from the incubator, and the upper Bis-acrylamide stack can be catalysed, initiated, and poured. It should be remembered that insufficiently degassed polyacrylamide solutions do not polymerize! A large (4 or 5 slot) preparative slot former should be inserted. Half an hour should be allowed for completion of polymerization.

Polyacrylamide gels should be pre-electrophoresed for at least 30 min at about half the running current. A good measure is to place 50 µl of tracking-dye/loading-buffer in one well and continue pre-electrophoresis until the bromophenol blue (lower band) has migrated approximately one third of the length of the gel. The actual current passed will depend on the geometry of the electrophoresis chamber and gel dimensions, but may be approximated by adjusting the current so that the glass plates warm only slightly. After pre-electrophoresis, the sample wells can be loaded with RNA dissolved in tracking-dye/loading-buffer, and electrophoresed at about $3 \, mA \, cm^{-1}$. As discussed above, the appropriate current may be determined empirically as that sufficient to warm the glass plates to approximately 55 °C. Electrophoresis of the RNA solution should be continued until the RNA of interest has entered the BAC-acrylamide. Under these conditions, tRNAS will be located about a third of the way, and 5S rRNA about four fifths of the way from the bromophenol blue to the xylene cyanol band (see Fig. 2). RNAs may be visualized by staining the gel in a $0.5 \, \mu g \, ml^{-1}$ solution of ethidium bromide for 15 min, rinsing in distilled water for 15 min, and viewing the gel on a UV transilluminator. It should be kept in mind that UV light is destructive to ethidium bromide stained nucleic acids, and exposure should be minimized as much as possible. A single electrophoretic purification may not yield well-resolved bands, but this is of little importance in a preparative run. If analytically pure RNA species are desired, the gel electrophoresis should be repeated.

IV. Agarose-gel electrophoresis

A. A note on the characteristics of agarose

Agarose is a linear galactan hydrocolloid component of agar. It is one of three galactans (the others are carrageenan and furcellaran), that are isolated from the agar-bearing seaweeds of the class Rhodophyta. Since agarose is a complex natural product, its composition has proven difficult to characterize. Actually, agarose appears to comprise a spectrum of compositions, ranging

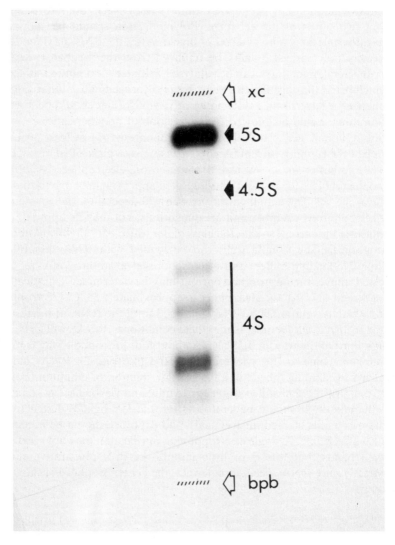

Fig. 2. Positions of xylene cyanol FF (xc) and bromophenol blue (bpb) relative to tRNA and 5S rRNA after electrophoretic separation on a 5% acrylamide denaturing gel.

from neutral to highly charged molecules (Duckworth and Yaphe, 1971). Owing to the complexity of the composition of agarose, as well as techniques employed in its extraction and purification, agarose has gained the reputation of being highly variable among lots and suppliers. As mentioned previously, there are limitations in the use of agarose for the isolation of nucleic acids for the purpose of genetic manipulations, since impurities in some lots may interfere with the action of various enzymes, typically restriction endonucleases, kinase and ligases.

Macromolecules can be separated on agarose on a basis of charge and/or molecular size. Separation solely by charge involves the unimpeded flow of the macromolecule in an electric field, whereas separation by size depends on the velocity of the macromolecule through the agarose gel matrix. Since the latter is a sieving process, the molecules are sorted by size, which is roughly proportional to molecular weight. Agarose is an excellent medium for the separation of nucleic acids greater than about 5 kilobase pairs, and can be used for separations of as little as 500 base pairs with decreasing resolution.

Unlike acrylamide, the use of agarose to the greatest benefit requires familiarity with several properties associated with it. These are (1) melting and gelling temperature, (2) gel strength and (3) electroendosmosis (EEO). The agarose gel matrix is maintained by hydrogen bonds. Differences in melting and gelling temperatures have been shown by Guiseley (1970) to be directly related to the methoxyl content of the agarose. Melting temperature may be an important factor if recovery of a particular oligonucleotide is to be attempted by melting the agarose gel plug. Guiseley (1976) discovered that gelling and melting temperatures can be lowered through the introduction of hydroxyethyl groups onto the agarose polymer. Several commercial preparations now employ this technique. Gel strength is mentioned since it may be desirable to separate RNAs under denaturing conditions. Urea and formamide, which are very effective in disrupting hydrogen bonding in nucleic acids, markedly reduce gel strength or can even inhibit formation of agarose gels. We have found that concentrations of urea greater than 2 molar (for agarose) or 1 molar (for NuSieve, see below) cause significant reductions in gel strength. Electroendosmosis (EEO) describes the characteristic net flow of water through agarose gels toward the cathode. EEO is expressed numerically: the higher the value, the greater the EEO. Agarose polymers contain anionic residues, mainly sulphate and pyruvate, with which are associated hydrated counterions. Once an electric field is applied to the agarose, these cations are drawn towards the cathode, carrying with them their water of hydration. Although this effect is used to enhance the resolution of cationic species, it is a nuisance in the separation of anionic species, such as nucleic acids. Therefore for nucleic-acid separations, low EEO agaroses should always be selected.

B. Fractionation of RNA species on agarose gels

Agarose-gel electrophoresis provides an inexpensive and highly reproducible means for the high resolution analysis of nucleic-acid fragments. Typical concentrations range from 0.7% to 1.2%, although concentrations from

0.1% to 2.5% find special application. In this range, agarose is capable of resolving nucleic acids from about 0.2 to 800 kilobase pairs. The use of field inversions can extend the separation farther upward, to the point of allowing the fractionation of intact chromosomal DNA (Schwartz and Cantor, 1984; Carle and Olson, 1985). Its use is straightforward and simple, and allows for extremely rapid analysis of genome structure.

Recently, a chemically modified and highly purified agarose was marketed (NuSieve, FMC Corporation, Rockland, Maine), which allows the separation of nucleic acids in the range of 50–1000 base pairs with excellent resolution. Employed as recommended, at a concentration of 4% (w/v), we have found this preparation capable of separating oligonucleotides as small as 100 base pairs with a resolution characteristic of polyacrylamide (Fig. 3). This can be very advantageous when a rapid screening technique is required that also has the resolution of acrylamide.

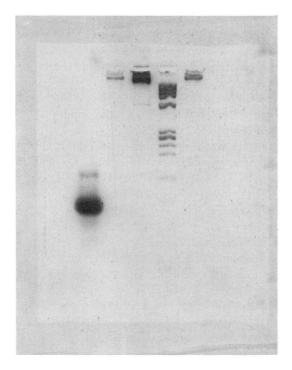

Fig. 3. Electrophoresis of nucleic acids on 4% NuSieve agarose (FMC Corp.). Lanes (L to R): 5S rRNA (note presence of concatemer); 16S rRNA; Sal I digest of bacteriophage lambda DNA; Hae III digest of bacteriophage ΦX174 DNA; partial nuclease S1 digest of 16S rRNA.

V. Recovery of RNA from gels

A. Recovery from liquified BAC-acrylamide

The RNA band(s) of interest are excised using a sterile blade and placed in a sterile silanized tube. The BAC-acrylamide is solubilized by addition of 5–10 ml of sterile 50 mM TBE and 50–100 µl of 2-mercaptoethanol. The mixture is agitated for several minutes. The RNA is recovered using DEAE-cellulose as described below. It is our experience that the duration of exposure of RNAs to mercaptoethanol should be limited. Although degradation of RNA has not been observed when exposed to mercaptoethanol for short periods, prolonged exposure (hours) does result in significant loss of yield. For this reason, the acrylamide–RNA solution should be kept on ice until applied to the DEAE column.

A DEAE-cellulose column is prepared as follows. A small plug of glass wool is placed aseptically in the bottom of a long-tip Pasteur pipette. Both the glass wool and the Pasteur pipette must be silanized and autoclaved. To this is added enough DEAE-cellulose slurry to form a bed of about 1 cm in height. This is prerinsed with approximately 1 ml of 1 M NaCl, 7 M urea in 50 mM TBE buffer, followed by equilibration with several millilitres of fresh TBE buffer. The solubilized gel solution containing the RNA is added to the DEAE-cellulose column and rinsed with 2 ml of fresh sterile TBE buffer followed by 2 ml of TBE buffer adjusted to the molarity of NaCl appropriate for the removal of small oligomers (see above). The RNA fraction of interest is then eluted with 0.5–1 ml of 0.5 M NaCl, 7 M urea in 50 mM TBE, added in aliquots of 0.1 ml (see Hansen, 1981). The eluate is collected as 500 µl aliquots in 1.5 ml Eppendorf tubes, 2 volumes of cold ethanol are added, it is chilled on crushed ice for 10 min and the RNA collected by centrifugation for 15–20 min in a microcentrifuge at 4 °C. The RNA thus recovered from the preparative electrophoresis should be dissolved either in sterile 10 mM EDTA, pH 7.0, and stored at −20 °C, or in 50–100 µl of tracking-dye/loading-buffer for repurification by gel electrophoresis.

Summary outline: extraction and purification of RNA

1. Wash and pellet cells from 500 ml of overnight broth culture.
2. Cell lysis by freeze–thaw or French pressure cell.
3. Bring lysate to 0.5 M NaCl.
4. Add 1 volume of chloroform, agitate several min.
5. Centrifuge at 12 000g for 10 min at 4 °C.
6. Collect the aqueous (upper) phase.
7. Precipitate nucleic acids in cold absolute ethanol, chill on ice.

8. Collect crude nucleic acid fraction by centrifugation as in step 5.
9. Dry on a vacuum line.
10. Proceed to step 11, 15 or 18 (see text).
11. Precipitation of DNA. Dissolve nucleic acid in distilled water.
12. Add 1 volume each of 2-methoxyethanol and 2.5 M K$_2$HPO$_4$ and 0.05 volume of 33% (v/v) phosphoric acid.
13. Agitate for several minutes.
14. Repeat steps 5–9.
15. DEAE-cellulose chromatography. Apply nucleic-acid solution to DEAE-cellulose column, wash with 2 volumes of (i) TBE, (ii) 0.2 M NaCl in TBE, elute with 0.5 M NaCl, 7 M urea in TBE.
16. Precipitate RNAs with 2 volumes of cold absolute ethanol, chill on ice.
17. Collect RNA by centrifugation (see step 5), dry on a vaccum line.
18. Resuspend RNA in tracking-dye/loading-buffer.
19. Fractionate RNA species on acrylamide/BAC-acrylamide stacking gel (see text, Table III).
20. Stain gel with ethidium bromide, visualize bands by UV.
21. Excise RNA band(s).
22. Solubilize excised gel plug with 2-mercaptoethanol.
23. Recover purified RNA on DEAE-cellulose.
24. Repeat steps 18–23 (or) proceed to step 25.
25. Dissolve RNA in 10 mM EDTA, pH 7.0, and store at $-20\,°C$.

B. Recovery from Bis-acrylamide

The occasion may arise (following the end-labelling step, for example) when it is necessary to recover small quantities of RNA species efficiently from conventional Bis-acrylamide gels. Thiol-soluble gels may be employed, but, owing to length of gel required, as well as rapidity of polymerization time (of the order of 1 min) they may be found to be less convenient than conventional Bis-acrylamide gels for the purification of end-labelled nucleic acids. The investigator will have to decide whether the superior resolution and recovery afforded by BAC-acrylamide offsets the increased difficulty of casting the very large gels necessary for purification of end-labelled oligonucleotides.

In order to ensure sufficient purification of the end-labelled oligonucleotide, a gel of at least 40 cm in length is desirable. This is especially true in the case of 3' end-labelled bacterial 5S rRNAs, since these often consist of a population of molecules having identical nucleotide base sequences, but varying in the number of pyrimidines (usually uridines) at the 3' terminus (Dams *et al.*, 1983). Resolution of RNAs of about 120 bases (in the case of 5S rRNAs), which vary by a single nucleotide base in length, is not a trivial exercise, and requires at least 30 cm of gel in order to resolve the species sufficiently.

Efficient elution of RNA species from conventional denaturing Bis-acrylamide gels may be accomplished as follows. The band of interest is excised using a sterile blade, and the gel slice is placed into a sterile 1 ml (blue) Eppendorf pipette tip that has been plugged with a small quantity of sterile silanized glass wool and heat-sealed at the tip. The gel slice is crushed to a paste along the walls of the pipette tip using a sterile silanized glass rod. The glass rod is rinsed into the gel paste with 300 μl of autoclave-sterilized 0.5 M ammonium acetate, 1 mM EDTA. Carrier tRNA is added to a ratio of about 10:1 (typically about 50 μg). The top of the pipette tip is sealed with parafilm and it is incubated overnight at room temperature. The RNA is recovered by carefully cutting off the heat-sealed tip using a sterile blade, and allowing the RNA solution to collect in a sterile 1.5 ml microcentrifuge tube. The contents of the pipette tip are rinsed with an additional 200 μl of ammonium acetate. The RNA is precipitated in 2 volumes of cold absolute ethanol, mixed several times by inversion, chilled on crushed ice for 10 min and collected by centrifugation for 15–20 min in a microcentrifuge at 4 °C. The RNA is resuspended in sterile 10 mM EDTA, pH 7.0, and stored at −20 °C.

C. Elution from agarose

Methods for the recovery of nucleic acids from agarose gels must meet four basic criteria. Specifically, they must (i) produce good yield, (ii) be free of contaminating substances that may interfere with subsequent enzymatic reactions, (iii) not result in damage to the nucleic-acid fragment, and (iv) be simple and reproducible. Obviously, no single methodology will meet all of these criteria equally well. Therefore it will be necessary to weigh the advantages and disadvantages of each, bearing in mind the eventual use for the recovered nucleic acid(s). Four methods for the recovery of nucleic acids from agarose gels will be discussed here. These are electroelution, gel melting with hot phenol, electrophoresis onto DEAE paper, and centrifugal filtration. Regardless of which method is ultimately selected by the investigator, it is critically important to employ a high-quality agarose. Even if the nucleic acids being separated are to be used for nothing more than photography of band positions with reference to a size standard, it will be worthwhile to select a molecular-biology-grade agarose that is lot-assayed by the manufacturer, such as GTC (genetic-technology grade) agarose (FMC Corporation, Rockland, Maine).

Agarose gels are generally run in one of several buffers, depending on the specific application, and choice of an appropriate electrophoresis buffer is another important consideration. For nucleic-acid separations, the two most commonly employed buffers are TBE (Tris–borate–EDTA), and TAE (Tris–acetate–EDTA). In fact, TBE is not a very good choice of buffer for agarose-gel electrophoresis, especially if nucleic acids are to be recovered from the gels. The use of borate buffers with agarose may lead to the formation of borate–agarose complexes, which not only increase electroendosmosis (EEO), but also interfere with the elution of nucleic acids from the agarose matrix (Sealy and Southern, 1982). Phosphate buffers are acceptable for most applications, although phosphates tend to coprecipitate with nucleic acids in the ethanol-precipitation step, and residual phosphate often interferes with enzymes. The buffers of choice for all agarose applications are the acetate buffers, Tris–acetate–EDTA (TAE), and sodium acetate–EDTA, at a pH range of 7.5–8.0. During electrophoresis, some of the acetate moiety will undergo electrolytic oxidation to carbonate, resulting in an increasing pH gradient. Usually this is not pronounced, nor does it generally interfere with most routine separations. Nevertheless, for lengthy electrophoretic separations, the buffer pH should be monitored periodically and replaced or recirculated as necessary. For most nucleic-acid separations, we have found a TAE (10 mM Tris, pH 7.8, 5 mM sodium acetate, 0.5 mM EDTA) buffer to be quite satisfactory.

The following, adapted from McDonell et al. (1977) describes a method for the electroelution of nucleic acids from agarose gels. Bands are visualized by staining with ethidium bromide ($0.5\,\mu g\,ml^{-1}$) and viewing on a UV transilluminator. The band is excised with a sterile scalpel blade and placed in a section of pretreated 10 mm dialysis tubing (molecular-weight cutoff of approximately 12 000 daltons) that has been knotted at one end. Enough electrophoresis buffer should be added to cover the gel slice completely, while keeping the volume to a minimum. The gel slice should float freely and not be constricted by the walls of the tubing. The free end of the dialysis bag should be knotted or clipped, care being taken not to trap any air. The sealed dialysis bag is oriented in the bottom of a horizontal electrophoresis chamber so that its long axis is parallel to the electrodes. Magnetic stirring bars are used to hold the bag in position. The nucleic acid electroelute is at $10–15\,V\,cm^{-1}$ for 30 min. It should be verified that the elution is complete using a hand-held UV light. When the nucleic acid is completely eluted from the agarose plug, the polarity of the current is reversed for 20 s to free the nucleic acid from the walls of the dialysis bag. The nucleic-acid solution is removed from the bag using a Pasteur pipette, and the bag rinsed once with fresh buffer. It is extracted twice with phenol and/or chloroform and precipitated with ethanol as described earlier.

Another way to extract nucleic acids from agarose gels is the hot-phenol method (Wieslander, 1979). For this method, a low-melting-temperature agarose should be used, although we have found that moderate-melting-range agaroses such as GTG-agarose (FMC Corporation) or Ultra-pure agarose (BRL, Gaithersburg, Maryland) are suitable. The nucleic-acid band of interest is located and excised as described above. It should be cut into small pieces on a square of parafilm, using a sterile scalpel blade. The gel pieces are transferred to a 1.5 ml Eppendorf tube and centrifuged for several seconds in a microcentrifuge in order to pack the gel fragments into the tube bottom. The gel fragments are covered with 0.5 M Tris-HCl, pH 8.0, and an equal volume of TBE-equilibrated phenol, and heated in a 68 °C water bath until the agarose has completely melted (about 10 min). They are mixed by gentle vortexing and chilled on crushed ice for 30 min. The phases are separated by centrifugation in a microcentrifuge for 5 min. The aqueous (upper) phase is transferred to a clean Eppendorf tube, with care being taken to avoid the interface, which contains the agarose. The residue is reextracted with TBE-equilibrated phenol and the aqueous phases are pooled. The pooled aqueous phase is phenol-extracted twice, and then ether-extracted. To the extracted aqueous phase, 0.1 volume of 3 M sodium acetate, pH 6.5, is added, mixed, and the nucleic acids precipitated in 2 volumes of cold absolute ethanol as described above.

A third method of extracting nucleic acids from agarose gels is by elution of nucleic acids that have been driven electrophoretically onto DEAE-paper (Dretzen et al., 1981). During elecrophoretic separation of the nucleic-acid fraction of interest, the DEAE-cellulose (Whatman DE81) paper is prepared by soaking it in 2.5 M NaCl for 1–2 h at 4 °C. Afterwards, the DEAE-paper is washed three times in sterile distilled water and equilibrated in electrophoresis buffer. With the aid of a transilluminator, incisions are made with a sterile scalpel blade immediately above and below the band to be eluted. A piece of pretreated DEAE-paper is inserted into each incision using one pair of forceps to hold the slit open and a second pair to insert the DEAE-paper. An interesting modification (Danner, 1982), is to position the DEAE-paper to the side of the band to be eluted, and turn the gel 90° in the chamber before applying the current. This not only results in concentrating the eluted sample, but also avoids the problem of contamination by other nucleic-acid fragments. The amount of time required to move the nucleic acid of interest onto the DEAE-paper must be determined empirically, and can be monitored easily using a hand-held UV light. After transfer the DEAE-paper is removed with forceps and rinsed in sterile distilled water. A small plug of sterile siliconized glass wool is placed in the bottom of a 0.7 ml Eppendorf tube and covered with 200 μl of elution buffer (20 mM Tris-HCl, pH 8.0, 2 mM EDTA, 1.5 M NaCl). This is centrifuged for 5 min in a microcentrifuge and the buffer is pipetted off. The DEAE-paper is transferred to the tube, 200 μl fresh elution buffer is added, and the tube is incubated at 37 °C for 1 h. A small hole is punched through the bottom of the tube using a hot 25-gauge hypodermic needle. The tube is quickly placed inside a sterile 1.5 ml Eppendorf tube and centrifuged for 5 min. The eluate is collected. 200 μl of fresh elution buffer is added and centrifuged for 5 min; the eluate is collected as above. The procedure is then repeated using 100 μl of fresh elution buffer. The eluates (total of 500 μl) are pooled. The nucleic-acid solution is extracted with 1 ml of water-equilibrated n-butanol. After centrifugation for 5 min, the butanol (upper) phase is discarded. The butanol extraction is repeated twice. The nucleic acids are precipitated in 2 volumes of cold absolute ethanol as described above.

A centrifugal-filtration method for the elution of nucleic acids from agarose gels was described by Zhu *et al.* (1985). First of all, the conical portion (lower third) is cut from a 1.5 ml Eppendorf tube and the apex pierced with a 25–gauge hypodermic needle. Next, a piece of nitrocellulose (or nylon) approximately 3 cm in diameter (wetted with elution buffer: 50 mM Tris-HCl, pH 7.5, 0.1% SDS) is cut and folded into the shape of a conical filter over the end of a glass rod. The glass rod is used to guide the filter into the conical piece of Eppendorf tube. The excess nitrocellulose membrane is trimmed with a sterile scalpel. The gel slice containing the nucleic acid of interest is placed in the conical tip/nitrocellulose, and the entire assembly put into another 1.5 ml Eppendorf tube. 200 μl of elution buffer is added and centrifuged for 10 min in a microcentrifuge. The nucleic acids are phenol- (or chloroform-) extracted, and precipitated in cold absolute ethanol as described above.

From our experience with each of the four methods described above, we have learned that different methods of recovery of nucleic acids from agarose gels cannot be expected to result in equivalent yields. This is due to differences in the number and kinds of manipulations required to elute and purify the nucleic acids. We offer the following observations on the methods discussed above.

The hot-phenol method has been reported to result in recoveries of 60–90% by Wieslander (1979), who used RNA eluted by this method as a probe in DNA–RNA hybridizations. We have been able to achieve about 50% yield; however, we have noted the presence of a smear of DNA associated with the sample well (Fig. 4). Possibly, some of the nucleic acid binds irreversibly to the agarose under these conditions.

Dretzen *et al.* (1981) achieved recoveries of 80% for fragments less than 2 kilobase in length using electrophoretic transfer of nucleic acids to, and subsequent elution from, DEAE-paper. We have obtained yields of less than 50% (Fig. 4). Danner (1982) observed that some loss of yield could be attributed to irreversible binding of nucleic acids to the DEAE-paper. This effect will tend to be more prominent as fragment length increases.

We have found that electroelution of nucleic acids from agarose gels results

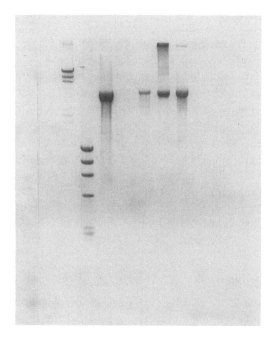

Fig. 4. Comparison of 4 methods for the elution of nucleic acids from agarose gels. Lane 1, Hind III digest of bacteriophage lambda DNA. Lane 2, Hae III digest of bacteriophage ΦX-174 DNA. Lanes 3–7, Sal I digest of pEMBL 8 + DNA: (L to R control); DNA recovered by centrifugal filtration method; DNA recovered by hot-phenol method; DNA recovered by electroelution. See text for discussion.

in the greatest yields (> 50%), with no indication of trauma to the molecules (Fig. 4). Additionally, this method is easily scaled up, and many samples can be processed simultaneously.

Our success with the centrifugal-filtration method (Zhu *et al.*, 1985) has been marginal (Fig. 4).

VI. End-labelling RNA

A. Methods

There are two practical methods for end-labelling RNA species with ^{32}P. One involves ligating [^{32}P]-cytidine-bis-phosphate (pCp) to the 3′ hydroxyl terminus of the RNA molecule, using T4 RNA ligase. The other involves the transfer of the gamma phosphate of [γ ^{32}P]-adenosine triphosphate (ATP) either to the dephosphorylated (direct reaction) or to the phosphorylated (exchange reaction) 5′ terminus of RNA, using polynucleotide kinase. Although dephosphorylation may be avoided in the labelling of either terminus, it is highly recommended since (1) phosphorylation of the 5′ terminus by the direct kinase reaction is much more efficient than the exchange reaction, and (2) failure to dephosphorylate the 5′ terminus of RNAs before ligation of pCp to the 3′-hydroxyl terminus will give rise to the formation of RNA concatemers, i.e. RNA species ligated end-to-end (Fig. 5). Usually, however, the efficiency of concatemer formation through the ligation of 5′-phosphoryl-RNAs is not great, and may not present a problem. The individual investigators should determine empirically whether or not to dephosphorylate a given RNA species. The unequivocal determination of the complete sequence will require construction of sequence ladders from both ends, requiring the eventual labelling of aliquots of RNA species on both termini, in turn.

B. Sequence extension

It is a characteristic of the mobilities of purines and pyrimidines through the matrix of thin polyacrylamide sequencing gels that the resolution of bands that comprise the sequence ladder begins to erode rapidly as the number of nucleotide bases drops below about eight in number. Therefore determination of terminal sequences is substantially more difficult than the determination of intervening sequences. An elegant solution to this problem is to ligate a short oligomer (e.g. polyadenine) to the 3′ or 5′ terminus of the RNA prior to end-labelling (see Luehrsen and Fox, 1981). This moves the true terminal sequence several bases from the end of the molecule, resulting in increased resolution (see Section XI.D). Unequivocal identification of the 3′ and 5′ termini involves thin-layer-chromatographic (TLC) analysis of exhaustive digests of the end-labelled species on PEI-cellulose (see Section VII).

C. Dephosphorylation of the 5′ terminus

In order to obtain high yields of end-labelled RNA by the forward (direct) phosphorylation of 5′ hydroxyls, the native 5′ phosphoryl terminus of RNAs must be dephosphorylated (Richardson, 1965; Lillehaug *et al.*, 1976). In the case of capped RNAs (mRNAs), an additional step, removal of the mGppX(n) cap must precede dephosphorylation. A rapid and satisfactory method for removal of the cap structure has been described by D'Alessio (1982).

We have found calf-intestinal (alkaline) phosphatase (CIP) to be far superior to bacterial alkaline phosphatase (BAP) for the dephosphorylation

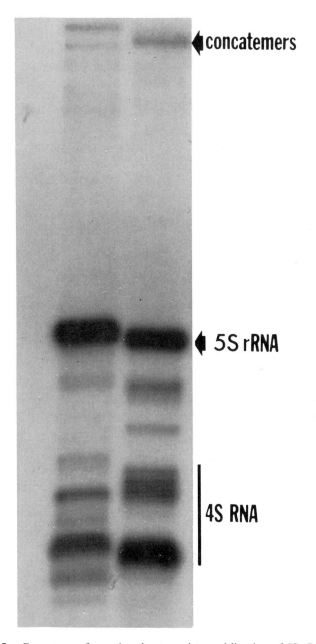

Fig. 5. Concatemer formation due to end-to-end ligation of 5S rRNAs.

of bacterial RNAs. Furthermore, highly purified i.e. molecular-biology grade, CIP is commercially available (see Appendix). Approximately 25 pmol (1 μg) of RNA is sufficient for a complete sequence analysis. With 250 μCi of [^{32}P]-ATP, end-label yields in excess of 10^7 cpm per μg RNA are typical.

Procedure summary: dephosphorylation

1. To an autoclave-sterilized microcentrifuge tube add 1 μg of uncapped RNA in 10 μl sterile distilled H_2O, 1 μl CIP (diluted to 0.3 U μl^{-1} with 50 mM Tris-HCl, pH 8.0, 1 mM $MgCl_2$), and 90 μl CIP buffer (50 mM Tris-HCl, pH 9.0, 1 mM $MgCl_2$, 1 mM spermidine).
2. Incubate for 30 min at 37 °C.
3. Extract RNA using a NENSORB 20 (or similar) column (or) proceed to step 4.
4. Add 100 μl of TBE-equilibrated phenol (described above), vortex briefly and separate phases by centrifugation for 5 min in a microcentrifuge at 4 °C.
5. Collect the aqueous (upper) phase in a sterile microcentrifuge tube and place on ice.
6. To the organic phase add 100 μl 50 mM TBE, vortex briefly and separate as in step 5.
7. Collect and pool aqueous phases.
8. To the pooled aqueous phases add 100 μl phenol solution, vortex and centrifuge and collect as above.
9. To the pooled phenol-extracted RNA solution add 0.5 ml of fresh diethyl ether.
10. Vortex briefly, centrifuge for several seconds and discard the organic (upper) phase. Repeat steps 9–10.
11. Place the extracted RNA on crushed ice and add 50 μl of 2 M sodium acetate (pH 5.5), vortex briefly and return to ice bath.
12. Precipitate the RNA with 2 volumes of cold absolute ethanol, mix by inversion and chill on crushed ice for 10 min.
13. Collect the RNA by centrifugation for 15 min in a microcentrifuge at 4 °C. *Note that the RNA pellet may not be visible: always orient the hinge of the microcentrifuge tube outwards so that the location of the pellet can be determined.*
14. Draw out the end of a Pasteur pipette over a flame and gently pipette off the ethanolic supernatant.
15. Carefully layer 300 μl cold absolute ethanol over the pellet, chill on crushed ice for 1 min, centrifuge, and discard the supernatant as described above (in step 13).

16. Place the microcentrifuge tube in a vacuum desiccator (or a stoppered sidearm flask) and dry the RNA under vacuum for several minutes.

D. Labelling the 5′ terminus

The following procedure is a modification of one described by D'Alessio (1982).

1. Resuspend the dephosphorylated RNA in 10 µl of spermidine buffer (10 mM Tris-HCl, pH 7.5, 1 mM spermidine, 1 mM EDTA).
2. Add 3 µl of 10X kinase buffer (0.5 M Tris-HCl, pH 9.0, 10 mM MgCl$_2$, 10 mM spermidine), and 5 µl of 10 µM ATP and 10 µl of distilled water. Place on ice.
3. Dry 250–500 µCi of [^{32}P]-ATP (in 50% ethanol) under a nitrogen jet. Alternatively, [^{32}P]-ATP packaged in tricine buffer may be used without prior drying.
4. Add the RNA solution to the [^{32}P]-ATP and carefully vortex. Return to crushed ice.
5. Add 30 U cloned T4 polynucleotide kinase (PNK) and incubate for 15 min at 37 °C.
6. Terminate the reaction by placing the mixture on ice and adding an equal volume of sterile 4 M ammonium acetate.
7. Extract the [^{32}P]-RNA using a NENSORB 20 (or similar) column, *or* proceed to step 8. *Note that if a NENSORB 20 (or similar column) is used, add 10 µg of phenol-extracted carrier tRNA after elution of RNA from the column.*
8. Add 10 µg phenol-extracted carrier tRNA. Precipitate the RNA with 2 volumes of cold absolute ethanol and mix by inversion. Chill on crushed ice for 10 min and collect the RNA by centrifugation for 15 min in a microcentrifuge at 4 °C.
9. Draw off the ethanolic supernatant using a drawn Pasteur pipette and discard it in radioactive waste.
10. Resuspend the RNA in 100 µl of cold 0.5 M sodium acetate by swirling.
11. Add 2 volumes of cold absolute ethanol, mix, chill, and collect as described above.
12. Carefully layer the pellet with 500 µl cold absolute ethanol, chill on crushed ice for 2 min and centrifuge for 1 min.
13. Draw off the (radioactive) ethanolic supernatant, and dry the [^{32}P]-RNA under vacuum for several minutes.

E. Labelling the 3′ terminus

As mentioned above, it is not always necessary to dephosphorylate RNAs prior to 3' end-labelling. Since RNA ligase is used in the 3' end-labelling technique, the decision whether or not to dephosphorylate the 5' terminus depends on the likelihood of significant concatemer formation through ligation of the 5' phosphate of one molecule to the 3' hydroxyl of another. The 5' and 3' termini of 5S rRNA, for example, terminate in a helical region with a 3' overhang. Concatemer formation during the 3' end-labelling of 5'-phosphoryl 5S rRNAs, although measurable (Fig. 5), does not present a serious problem.

1. To an autoclave-sterilized microcentrifuge tube add 1 μg RNA in 10 μl sterile distilled water, 2 μl of 10X ligase buffer (0.5 M HEPES, pH 7.5, 0.1 M MgCl$_2$, 33 mM dithiothreitol), 2 μl dimethyl sulphoxide (DMSO), 2 μl of 0.1 M ATP. Mix by swirling and place on ice.
2. Dry 500 μCi of [α ^{32}P]-cytidine-bis-phosphate (pCp) (packaged 1:1 in ethanol:water) under a nitrogen jet. Alternatively, [^{32}P]-pCp packaged in tricine buffer may be used without prior drying.
3. Add 10 U of T4 RNA ligase, mix by gentle swirling.
4. Incubate for 4–12 h at 4 °C.
5. Continue as described in the Section VI.D, beginning with step 6.

F. A note on the use of NENSORB 20 columns

Recently, a small disposable chromatographic column was developed to separate nucleic acids from protein, salts and other low molecular weight compounds, such as unincorporated radioactive monomers (Johnson *et al.*, 1986). The use of these columns eliminates the need for phenol (or chloroform) extractions, which are a major source of loss of yield. In our hands, these columns, marketed under the name NENSORB 20 (DuPont/NEN Products, Boston, Massachusetts), function flawlessly and permit the elimination of numerous purification steps ordinarily required after dephosphorylation, end-labelling, etc. We have found that the cumulative effect of the use of NENSORB 20 columns in our RNA purifications is as much as a 10-fold increase in yield of end-labelled RNA. They are limited only by their capacity of 20 μg total (nucleic acid + protein), and the requirement that samples must be free of SDS and/or organics when loaded onto the columns.

We have found the following conditions give very satisfactory results for the purification of tRNA, 5S rRNA and 16S rRNA (see package insert for general details).

1. Pack the NENSORB 20 column by tapping it lightly several times on a clean paper towel.

2. Rinse the column with 2ml of HPLC-grade absolute methanol using a sterile Pasteur pipette.

3. Equilibrate the column with 2 ml of 100 mM Tris-HCl, pH 7.7, 10 mM triethylamine (TEA), 1 mM EDTA, adding this while there is still a few microlitres of methanol above the bed.

4. Dilute the nucleic-acid sample 1 : 5 in equilibration buffer. Add this while there is still several microlitres of equilibration buffer over the bed.

5. Add approximately 0.5 ml of equilibration buffer (step 3) while there is still a few microlitres of sample over the bed.

6. Wash column with an additional 2 ml of equilibration buffer.

7. Elute sample by adding 2 ml of 50% (v/v) aqueous HPLC-grade methanol while there is still several microlitres of equilibration buffer over the bed (sample will elute in approximately 600 µl).

Notes

(1) Degas all solutions under vacuum before adding to column.

(2) Best results will be obtained from NENSORB 20 columns if each buffer (sample, etc.) is added to the column while there is still a small column (1 mm or so) of the previous buffer over the chromatographic bed. The inert polymer that comprises the solid support of these columns binds nucleic acids and proteins by hydrophobic interactions. The hydrophobicity of the column and support can assist in the inadvertent introduction of air into the chromatographic bed if a certain amount of care is not taken to avert it.

G. Electrophoretic purification of labelled RNA

In order to ensure sufficient purification of the end-labelled oligonucleotide, a gel of at least 40 cm length is desirable. This is especially true in the case of 3′ end-labelled bacterial 5S rRNAs, since these often consist of a population of molecules having identical nucleotide base sequences, but varying in the number of pyrimidine (usually uridine) residues at the 3′ terminus (see Dams et al., 1983). Resolution of 120-mers, which vary in length by a single nucleotide base, is not a trivial problem. Thirty centimetres or more of a denaturing 5% polyacrylamide gel is needed in order to sufficiently resolve the individual species.

A 5% polyacrylamide/8 M urea denaturing gel is prepared and pre-electrophoresed (Table III). The end-labelled RNA should be resuspended in approximately 50 µl of tracking-dye/loading-buffer in an autoclave-sterilized microcentrifuge tube. The [^{32}P]-RNA is loaded into a single well and the current adjusted so that the outer glass panel warms to about 55 °C. Electrophoresis is continued until the xylene cyanol (upper) band has travelled three quarters of the length of the gel. The glass plates are recovered, and the gel carefully covered with plastic wrap. The purified [^{32}P]-RNA is located by autoradiography.

VII. Terminal analysis

A. Identification of the 5′ terminus

5 000–20 000 cpm of 5′ [^{32}P-]RNA is exhaustively digested with nuclease Pl (refer to Table IVa) and chromatographed on a PEI-cellulose thin layer plate (with fluorescent indicator). Standards composed of the 4 common base monophosphates are spotted on the TLC plate and chromatographed in 0.25–1.0 M LiCl alongside the labelled digest, to serve as references. After chromatography is complete, locations of the reference monophosphates may be determined by shadow-casting the TLC plate with a hand-held UV light. Their positions should be marked on the TLC plate. Next, the plate is

TABLE IV
Terminal analysis by thin-layer chromatography (TLC)

(a) Identification of the 5′ terminus

1. Prechromatograph a PEI-cellulose TLC plate (with fluorescent indicator) in distilled water. Allow to air-dry.
2. In an autoclave-sterilized microcentrifuge tube, mix 20 000 cpm of 5′[^{32}P]-RNA, 1 μl of 0.2 M sodium acetate, pH 5.5, 10 U of nuclease Pl, and sterile water to make 10 μl.
3. Incubate at 37°C for 4–12 h.
4. Spot digest and reference mononucleotides on the PEI-cellulose TLC plate and develop in 0.25–1.0 M LiCl. Migration order is U > C > A > G (Randerath and Randerath, 1967).
5. Remove the TLC plate and air-dry. Locate reference bases with a hand-held UV light.
6. Expose the TLC plate to X-ray film for 2–6 h in order to locate the radioactive terminal nucleotide.

(b) Identification of the 3′ terminus

Proceed as described above for 5′[^{32}P]-RNA, except for step 2:
2. In an autoclave-sterilized microcentrifuge tube mix 20 000 cpm of 3′[^{32}P]-RNA, 1 μl of 0.25 M sodium citrate, pH 5.0, 3 U of RNase T2, and sterile water to make 10 μl.

---

autoradiographed overnight (or 2–4 h with intensification screens) to locate the position of the radioactive terminal base (Fig. 6). R_f values of nucleotide monophosphates on PEI-cellulose are 0.20, 0.15, 0.11 and 0.06 for UMP, CMP, AMP and GMP respectively developed in 0.25 M LiCl (0.74, 0.64, 0.52 and 0.40 for 1 M LiCl) (Randerath and Randerath, 1967).

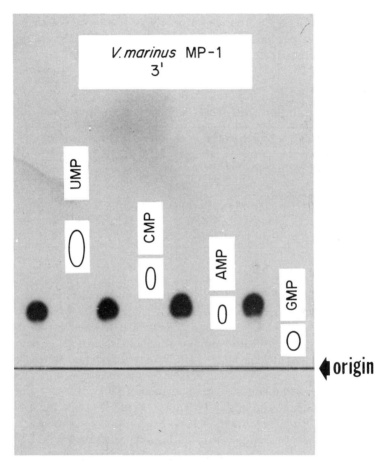

Fig. 6. Terminal analysis by thin-layer chromatography on PEI-cellulose. Positions of reference nucleotides are indicated. The origin is indicated with an arrow.

B. Identification of the 3′ terminus

3′ terminal follows the same rationale as 5′ terminal analysis, except that the enzyme T2 is substituted for P1 (refer to Table IVb).

VIII.   Notes on the enzymatic sequencing of RNA

The primary structure of RNAs that do not contain modified bases (bacterial 5S rRNAs, for example) may be determined readily by electrophoresis of limited enzymatic digests of separate aliquots on ultrathin denaturing polyacrylamide gels (Sanger and Coulsen, 1978). Commercially available enzymatic sequencing kits have provided the means by which highly repro- ducible sequence determinations of RNAs may be carried out routinely at a modest cost per base. In addition, a number of specific endoribonucleases have been described (Table V).

TABLE V

Partial listing of RNases useful in enzymatic sequencing

Ribonuclease	Source	Specificity		
B.c(ereus).	*Bacillus cereus*	Cp/N	Up/N	
M1	*Cucumis melo*	N/pA	N/pG	N/pU
Phy I	*Physarum polycephalum*	Ap/N	Gp/N	Up/N
Phy M	*Physarum polycephalum*	Ap/N	Up/N	
T1	*Aspergillus oryzae*	Gp/N		
U2	*Ustilago sphaerogena*	Ap/N		

Purines are particularly easy to identify enzymatically, since the enzymes Tl (Sato and Egami, 1957) and U2 (Uchida *et al.*, 1974), which clip at guanine and adenine respectively, are model RNases in that they are both stable and exhibit high degrees of specificity. However, enzymes with high specificities for cytidine and uridine have yet to be characterized. Therefore it is necessary to employ several RNases in concert in order to deduce the identity of pyrimidine bases in the sequence. Three of these—Phy M, specific for adenine and uridine (Donis-Keller, 1980), B.c., specific for pyrimidines (Lockard *et al.*, 1978), and M1, no attack at cytidine residues (Pharmacia Fine Chemicals, unpublished data)—are particularly useful. RNase CL3, which is commercially available from several sources, has a putative specifi- city for cytidine (Bogusky *et al.*, 1980; Levy and Karpetsky, 1980). There are, however, numerous exceptions to its specificity, which render its usefulness questionable. For example, CL3 will clip at uridines that are situated 5′ to adenines (Bogusky *et al.*, 1980). Because of the difficulty with which cytidine is distinguished from uridine by RNase CL3, and in light of the high specificity of RNase M1 for any base other than cytidine, we cannot recommend CL3.

Limited scission of the RNA backbone using RNases T1, U2, Phy M, and B.c. is straightforward and uncomplicated. These RNases produce nested sets of end-labelled 3' monophosphoryl RNAs (Table V), whose electrophoretic separation yields sequence ladders that are in register with each other, and may be read directly. This is not the case for RNase M1. The limited digest of [^{32}P]-RNA by RNase M1 unequivocally locates the position of cytidine residues through gaps in the sequence ladder, but the sequence ladder itself will not be in register with those produced by the other sequencing enzymes. RNase M1 cleaves the RNA backbone one base 3' to A, G, or U, so as to produce 5'-monophosphoryl RNAs. The net result of this is that, for 5' end-labelled RNAs, the M1 lane will appear one base longer at each position. In other words, moving it downwards one position would bring it in register with the other ladders. Curiously, the opposite case is not true for 3' end-labelled RNAs, where the ladders appear virtually in register. There is an additional consideration in the use of RNase M1, since it requires Zn^{2+}. Exposure to Zn^{2+} is very deleterious to RNA and should be minimized (Butzow and Eichhorn, 1975). This does not necessarily present a problem in sequencing reactions, but could be the cause of spurious chain scissions in the RNase M1 lane (MacDonell and Colwell, 1984).

IX.   Limited (or "single-hit") digests

The generation of a "sequence ladder" (Fig. 7), from which the nucleotide base sequence of RNA molecules may be read directly, depends on a set of conditions, one of which is adjustment of the ratio of enzyme (RNase) to substrate such that each end-labelled RNA molecule is clipped (on average) at one site. The consequence of such "single-hit" conditions is the generation of a nested set of fragments in which every possible end-labelled sequence is represented. These fragments can be separated in thin polyacrylamide sequencing gels, which are capable of resolving oligonucleotides that differ in length by a single nucleotide base. If the single-hit reactions are carried out using enzymes that are selective for specific bases, the result is the generation of nested sets of oligomers that bear the radioactive label at one terminus and the enzyme-specific base at the other. Those fragments with guanines at their unlabelled terminus, for example, will appear in the autoradiogram only in the gel lane corresponding to the RNase T1 digest, and so on. The only requirements are that the RNA molecules must be (1) homogeneous, (2) sufficiently pure and (3) uniquely end-labelled. A lane containing a limited alkaline hydrolysate of an aliquot of the end-labelled RNA is included as a means of marking each base position in the gel image. Electrophoresis, in adjacent lanes, of specific enzymatic digests of RNA carried out under

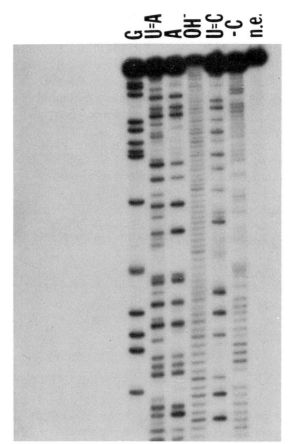

Fig. 7. Sequence ladder generated by the enzymatic method. Endoribonucleases corresponding to lanes (L to R): T1; Phy M; U2; (alkaline hydrolysis); B.c.; M1; control (no enzyme).

"single-hit" conditions results in a unique set of sequence ladders from which the RNA sequence may be read directly. The number of bases that can be determined from either end of the RNA is independent of the length of the molecule, and is a function of gel dimensions, acrylamide concentration, diffusion, etc. The practical limit of resolution, however, is approximately 174 bases from either terminus.

Adjustment of the enzyme-to-substrate ratio so as to achieve "single-hit" conditions is generally approached in one of two ways: (1) serial 10-fold dilutions of the enzymes to the proper titre, and (2) adjustment of substrate concentration through the addition of carrier tRNA. The latter method provides finer control over enzyme-substrate ratio than the serial-enzyme-dilution method.

Buffers required for sequence reactions and for diluting stock enzymes are listed in Table VI. The relative volumes of enzyme, RNA and tracking-dye/loading-buffer, as well as the duration and conditions of incubation have been described in a technical publication (Method E998: Sequencing RNA by the Enzymatic Method, Pharmacia Fine Chemicals, Milwaukee, Wisconsin).

TABLE VI
Buffers and reagents for enzymatic sequence analysis of RNA

Enzyme dilution buffers

RNases T1 and Phy M:	25 mM sodium citrate, pH 5.0, 7 M urea, 1 mM EDTA, 0.05% (w/v) xylene cyanol FF, 0.05% (w/v) bromophenol blue.
RNase U2:	25 mM sodium citrate, pH 3.5, 7 M urea, 1 mM EDTA, 0.05% (w/v) xylene cyanol FF, 0.05% (w/v) bromophenol blue.
RNase B.c:	25 mM sodium citrate, pH 5.0
RNase M1:	25 mM sodium citrate, pH 5.0, 1 mM EDTA.

Reaction buffers

Buffer I (T1, Phy M, M1):	25 mM sodium citrate, pH 5.0, 7 M urea, 1 mM EDTA, and 0.05% (w/v) each of xylene cyanol FF and bromophenol blue.
Buffer II (U2):	25 mM sodium citrate, pH 3.5, 7 M urea, 1 mM EDTA, and 0.05% (w/v) each of xylene cyanol FF and bromophenol blue.
Buffer III (B.c.):	25 mM sodium citrate, pH 5.0.

X. Autoradiography

There are two times when autoradiography will be necessary in the sequencing of RNAs. The first will occur during the purification of $[^{32}P]$-RNA by gel electrophoresis, and the second is necessary in order to develop the sequencing ladder. Kodak XAR films are excellent for autoradiography of ^{32}P. They may be developed with either D-11 or Kodak GBX developer.

A. Autoradiography of purified $[^{32}P]$-RNA

After purification of end-labelled RNA by gel electrophoresis, the RNA band must be located so that it can be excised from the gel. In this case, relatively large amounts of [^{32}P]-RNA are involved, and typical exposure times will range from 1 s to as much as 1 min.

Once the electrophoresis is complete, the gel (in its glass plates) is removed from the electrophoresis chamber and laid on a flat surface. The upper plate is gently prised from the gel using a spatula. The gel may adhere to the upper plate, in which case the entire assembly should be turned over. The glass plate is removed and the gel covered with plastic wrap. It may be expedient to trim the dimensions of the gel in order to make it more manageable, keeping in mind that portions of the gel are radioactive. Denaturing gels tend to shatter when sliced, but can be trimmed very efficiently with a pizza cutter. The gel is turned over onto a clean flat surface, plastic wrap down, and is gently freed from the remaining glass plate. A moistened spatula is helpful in freeing the edge of the gel from the plate. Once removed, the exposed gel is covered with plastic wrap. The wrapped gel is placed on a sheet of cardboard and, in a darkroom, a sheet of X-ray film is exposed by placing it directly on the wrapped gel. Since the developed film will serve as a template for locating the [^{32}P]-RNA, it is necessary to reposition the film precisely. One way to ensure repositioning of the gel is to pierce the film, gel and cardboard support in several locations, preferably near the corners, using a large-bore hypodermic needle, during the exposure. After development, the *image* of the radioactive band is carefully cut from the X-ray film, using a scalpel, and the film is realigned over the gel, using the needle holes as references. Using the film as a template, the ^{32}P-band is carefully excised with a sterile scalpel blade.

B.   Autoradiography of the sequence ladder

In the case of the imaging of fragments produced during sequencing reactions, very small quantities of [^{32}P]-RNA are often involved. The first consideration is whether or not to employ intensification screens in the autoradiography. Intensification screens will result in nearly a 10-fold enhancement of the radiographic image, but will cause a significant decrease in resolution of closely situated bands owing to parallax. A satisfactory autoradiogram of a sequencing gel requires about 100 000 cpm [^{32}P]-RNA per lane. With the use of intensifying screens, this may be reduced to about 10 000 per lane; however, the number of "readable" bases in the developed film will be reduced by about 40%. The decision whether or not to employ intensification screens will generally be dictated by the relative abundance of [^{32}P]-RNA being sequenced.

After completion of electrophoresis, the gel is removed from the gel box and wrapped in plastic. This is the most difficult part of the sequence determination, since thin denaturing sequencing gels are extremely delicate. Removal of the glass plates is approached as described above, except that much more care is required in freeing the gel from the second plate. This may be done as follows. The wrapped gel is placed on the edge of a flat surface (such as over the edge of a lab bench), plastic wrap down, so the gel protrudes several inches beyond the edge of the bench. The plastic wrap is grasped near a corner of the gel and pulled downwards (away from the glass plate). At the same time, the gel is gently eased away from the glass with a moistened spatula or thin plastic ruler. This should be done in such a way as to "unzip" the edge of the gel from the glass from one corner to the other. Once the edge of the gel is freed, the glass plate is slowly lifted away from the gel. The exposed side of the gel is wrapped and placed in a film cassette. Alternatively, if the gel is to be dried (this will increase the resolution somewhat) then, once the second glass plate has been removed, the exposed surface is covered with a heavy chromatographic paper such as Whatman 3MM, and dried in a gel dryer.

In a darkroom, the gel is covered with X-ray film, the film cassette closed, and exposed overnight at $-20\,°C$. If intensification screens are used, the film must be exposed at $-70\,°C$.

XI. Problems affecting the sequence ladder

A. Edge effects

This is synonymous with "smile" (Fig. 8). It is caused by the uneven build-up and dissipation of heat generated by resistance across the gel. Denaturing gels require elevated temperatures, typically 50–60 °C, to function optimally. The uneven accumulation of heat, with the centre reaching several degrees higher than the edges, produces the "smile" that is characteristic of polyacrylamide gels. There are several solutions to the problem. One of these is the purchase of a water- or buffer-cooled sequencing apparatus. By keeping the gel temperature constant over the entire gel surface, edge effects are virtually eliminated. The most drastic solution we have seen is the clamping of an aluminium plate to one of the glass plates to act as a heat sink. This also has the potential of turning an electrophoresis apparatus into an electrocution apparatus! A much more practical and cost-effective solution is to avoid using the 2 or 3 sample wells near either edge. In the majority of cases, edge effects impair only the aesthetic quality of the gel, but do not impair the ability to analyse it.

B. Bleached-out regions

There often occur, in enzymatic sequencing, regions of the sequence ladders in which bands appear to fade out relative to the alkaline hydrolysis lane

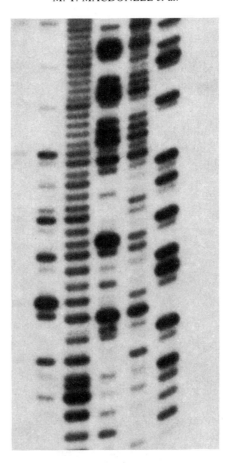

Fig. 8.   Edge effect. Uneven distribution of heat across the sequencing gel produces distortion or "smile".

(Fig. 9). This is usually due to secondary-structure interference with enzyme approach. In RNAs this effect is often associated with strong helical regions. This is a problem peculiar to enzymatic sequencing. We know of no simple effective measure that can be taken to counteract this problem. Although the reason is unclear to us, the bases on the side of the helix closest to the end-label are usually readable. Since the determination of a complete sequence requires the eventual labelling of both termini, in turn, it is our experience that all of the bases, even those in areas of substantial secondary structure, can be determined.

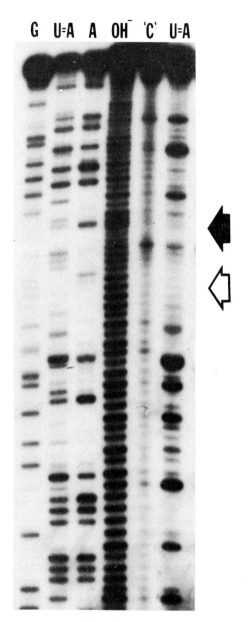

Fig. 9. Band compression and "bleaching". Band compression in the sequence ladder is indicated by a solid arrow. Bleached-out region is due to steric hindrance to enzyme approach (open arrow).

C. Dye interference

This occurs when oligonucleotides and dye molecules are forced to compete for pores in the gel matrix. It is often caused by too great a concentration of tracking dye. The dye most often associated with this effect is bromophenol blue, which migrates as a 11-mer in a 10% acrylamide denaturing gel (Table VII). The distortion caused by this effect may hamper the identification of bases at these positions (Fig. 10). Generally the best method of circumventing interference by tracking dye is to slightly alter the concentration of acrylamide in the gel, causing a shift in position of dye interference so that previously distorted bands may be identified.

TABLE VII

Migration (expressed as apparent base length) of xylene cyanol FF and bromophenol blue in conventional acrylamide sequencing gels

| | Denaturing polyacrylamide gel | | |
| | (% monomer) | | |
	5%	10%	20%
Xylene cyanol FF	150	55	28
Bromophenol blue	25	11	7

D. Distortion of sequence ladders near termini

This is probably the most frustrating problem encountered in sequence analysis, and is not restricted to enzymatic methods. Resolution of sequence ladder bands decreases markedly as the number of bases in the fragment approaches 1 (Fig. 11). This is due to increasing interaction between character of the nucleotide bases and the gel matrix. In the case of larger *n*-mers, where $n > 10$ bases, the relative contribution of the chemical composition of the component nucleotide bases becomes very small when compared to the contribution of the length of the oligomer. Since the effect derives from a relationship between base composition and base length, increasing the gel concentration is of little benefit. One solution, described by Luehrsen and Fox (1981), is to ligate a 5–10-base fragment, poly rA for example, to the terminus to be labelled. This results in the shifting of the region to be read into the range of longer-base-length fragments, thus markedly improving resolution.

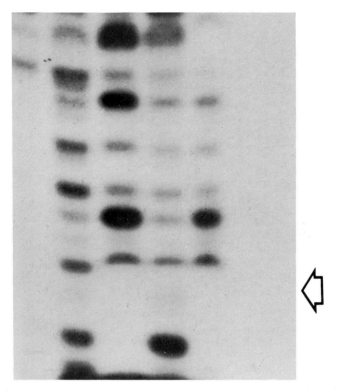

Fig. 10 Interference due to exclusion of RNA fragments from gel pores by bromophenol blue (arrow).

E. Band compression

This is evidenced by a dramatic change in spacing between bands, or the superimposition of two or more bands (Fig. 9). Band-compression effects occur as a result of the formation of secondary helices, a consequence of chain scisson during enzymatic degradation. This leads to the formation of spurious secondary structures as oligomers fold back upon themselves to form stable hairpins. Often it can be corrected by running the sequencing gel very warm (65–75 °C). Although the conventional wisdom suggests heating the digest to 90 °C and plunging it into an ice bath prior to loading, we have not found that this has a noticeable effect on this problem.

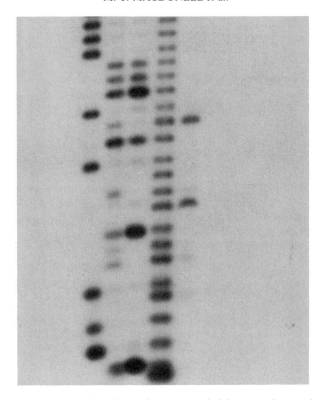

Fig. 11. Loss of resolution in sequence ladder near the terminus.

F. Extraneous bands

This is invariably due to heterogeneity in the RNA being sequenced. The criterion for purity of a particular RNA, i.e. the appearance of a discrete band on a polyacrylamide gel, ensures only that the sample contains molecules that are of a homogeneous length. The possibility nevertheless exists that two species, homogeneous in length but heterogeneous in sequence, have been end-labelled. There is no practical solution to this problem.

G. Simultaneous occurrence of bands in all lanes

This is evidence of contamination by a ribonuclease (Fig. 12). The situation may be salvageable, but will require that the source of the ribonuclease be identified. First, reagents, buffers, tracking dye and water involved in the sequence reaction are replaced from fresh sterile stocks. The sequence reactions are repeated and the gel is autoradiographed. If the problem

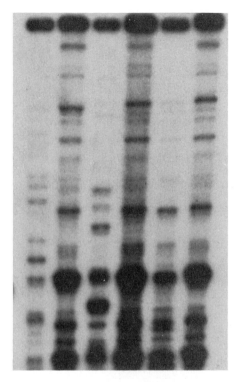

Fig. 12. Bands occurring in all lanes. The cause was inadvertent contamination by an exogenous RNase.

persists then either the contamination is in the [^{32}P]-RNA solution, or the [^{32}P]-RNA has already become degraded by the contaminating RNase. the purification by gel electrophoresis should then be repeated. If there is still a sharp band corresponding to the RNA sample, it should be re-extracted in fresh sterile buffer, and the RNA resuspended in fresh sterile EDTA.

H. Superimposed sequence ladders

In some cases, particularly when sequencing 3′ end-labelled bacterial 5S rRNAs, bands will appear in sequence ladders in pairs (Fig. 13). The occurrence of doublets, triplets, etc. is an indication of the existence of two or more end-labelled species that differ in length but not sequence (see Dams *et al.*, 1983). Bacterial 5S rRNAs that differ only by the number of pyrimidine residues (usually uridines) at the 3′ terminus are frequently encountered. This has no effect on the sequence analysis of 5′ end-labelled RNAs, but is a disaster when the label is attached to the 3′ terminus. The solution is the electrophoretic repurification of the [^{32}P]-RNA.

M. T. MACDONELL *et al.*

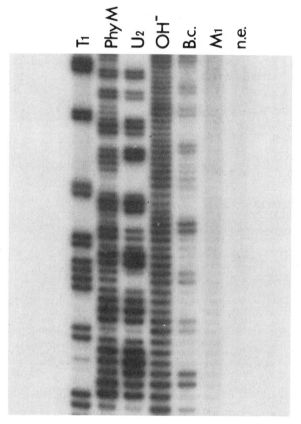

Fig. 13. Occurrence of superimposed sequence ladders due to the presence of a mixture of 119- and 120-base 5S rRNA molecules (see text for discussion).

I. Gap in the sequence ladder in all lanes

The occurrence of a gap at the same position in all lanes, including the alkaline hydrolysis lanes, is an indicator of 2-*O*-methylation of the ribose sugar. In this case, methods other than enzymatic ones will be necessary to identify the base (D'Alessio, 1982).

XII. Final thoughts on the use of thiol-soluble gels

To prepare an acrylamide gel that has been cross-linked by disulphide bonds, one can substitute BAC for Bis on a mole-for-mole basis, and polymerize the gel under appropriate conditions, using TEMED and persulphate as with Bis gels. The only difference in the polymerization procedure is the use of an increased quantity of TEMED, and polymerization at a controlled elevated temperature. Once polymerization is complete, the gels can be used exactly the same way as Bis gels. We have found the resolving properties of BAC gels to be superior to comparable Bis gels; they are often the electrophoretic medium of choice even if sample recovery is not desired. After electrophoresis, bands may be cut out of the gels and nucleic acids recovered by solubilizing the gel with mercaptoethanol. The liquefied gel can be applied to an ion-exchange column, which is washed with buffer to remove gel components. The nucleic-acid sample is then recovered in high yield by salt elution followed by ethanol precipitation. These procedures are simple and rapid, recoveries are excellent, and many samples can be processed at once. The recovered nucleic acids do not display abnormal properties in any of the subsequent chemical and enzymatic reactions that we have used.

There are a few minor disadvantages associated with the routine use of BAC-acrylamide. One is cost in comparison with Bis gels. A 100 ml BAC gel costs about a dollar for the BAC, compared with about 2 cents for an equivalent amount of Bis (1986 prices). However, considering the fact that it is common for an experimenter to commit samples that are the result of several days of work to a single gel, and that the convenience of recovery resulting from the use of BAC-acrylamide may reduce the time required for an experiment by several days, the cost consideration seems trivial.

A more substantive disadvantage in the use of BAC gels is that they require greater care in their polymerization if sample recovery is desired, although the excellent resolution is not particularly affected by the polymerization conditions. The chemistry of the disulphide bond is complex. Although it is relatively inert under the physiological conditions in cells and the conditions used for electrophoresis, the disulphide bond is sensitive to cleavage by nucleophiles and free radicals. Inasmuch as BAC gels are polymerized by a free-radical reaction, this creates a potential problem. If inappropriate polymerization conditions are used, the disulphide link can react, resulting in its cleavage and the production of a thiyl radical. This can, in turn, react with acrylamide, resulting in a sulphide–carbon bond instead of a disulphide bond. The former is not sensitive to mercaptoethanol, and gels in which this has occurred extensively do not solubilize. Fortunately, this spurious side-reaction can be suppressed by carrying out the polymerization reaction at an elevated temperature (41–45 °C). With appropriate attention to temperature, and the use of reagents that have not been abused by poor storage conditions, BAC gels are extremely dependable and easy to use.

XIII. Conclusion

Our approach to this chapter has been to provide the investigator involved with the sequence analysis of RNA with a "tool kit" of techniques, helpful hints, and recipes. In contrast with proteins, each of which provides a unique problem for separation and isolation, nucleic acids tend to have consistent properties. Thus the solution to many of the problems encountered in the isolation and purification of one species of nucleic acid will be applicable to the isolation and purification of another. Although the techniques discussed herein were designed for the manipulation of RNAs, most serve equally for the manipulation of DNAs. In other words, nucleic-acid techniques are highly portable from one system or project to another.

Acknowledgements

Support for this research was provided in part by NSF Grant BSR 84-01397, ONR Grant N00014-81-K-0638, EPA contract CR812246-01-0, Biomedical Research Support Grant RR-07042 to the University of Maryland, from the Division of Research Resources, NIH Public Health Service, and The University of Maryland Centre of Marine Biotechnology.

Appendix: Recommended sources of enzymes and reagents

Product	Recommended source
Enzymes	
Alkaline phosphatase (calf intestinal), (CIP), molecular-biology grade	Boehringer
T4 Polynucleotide kinase (cloned)	US Biochemicals
RNA ligase	New Products
Ribonuclease B.c.*	Pharmacia
RNase CL3	Pharmacia
RNase M1	Pharmacia
RNase Phy M*	Pharmacia
RNase T1*	Pharmacia
RNase U2*	Pharmacia
Nuclease P1	Boehringer
Nuclease S1	Boehringer
Nuclease T2	BRL
(* available in kit form)	
Chemicals and reagents	
Phenol (ultrapure)	BRL
m-Cresol	Sigma
8-hydroxyquinoline	Sigma

Tris base (Trizma base)	Sigma
Boric acid	Sigma
EDTA free acid	Sigma
Urea (ultrapure)	BRL
Trichloroacetic acid	Aldrich
Lithium chloride	Aldrich
Acrylamide (gel-electrophoresis grade)	BRL
N,N'-methylene-bis-acrylamide	BRL
N,N'-bis-acrylylcystamine (BAC)	Bio Rad
Adenosine triphosphate (ATP)	Sigma
Dimethyl sulphoxide (DMSO)	Baker
Spermine, Spermidine	Sigma
Dithiothreitol	Research Organics
HEPES	Research Organics
tRNA carrier (tRNA, RNase free)	Boehringer
PEI-cellulose TLC plates	American Scientific Prod.
Sodium pyrophosphate	Sigma
Xylene cyanol FF	Baker
Bromophenol blue	Baker
Ethidium bromide	Sigma

Hardware

X-ray film (XAR)	Kodak
Intensification screens (Cronex lightening plus)	Dupont
Sequencing apparatus (gel box)	BRL
Power supply (3000 V)	Bio Rad
Heat blocks	American Scientific Prod.

Radioactive nucleotides

[γ^{32}P]-ATP (packed in tricine buffer)	NEN Products
5'[^{32}P]-cytidine-bis-phosphate (in tricine)	NEN Products

References

Anker, H. S. (1970). *FEBS Lett.* **7**, 293.

Bogusky, M. S., Hieter, P. A. and Levy, C. C. (1980). *J. Biol. Chem.* **255**, 2160–2163.

Butzow, J. J. and Eichhorn, G. L. (1975). *Nature (London)* **254**, 358–359.

Carle, G. F. and Olson, M. V. (1985). *Proc. Natl. Acad. Sci. USA* **82**, 3756–3760.

D'Alessio, J. M. (1982). In *Gel Electrophoresis of Nucleic Acids*, (D. Rickwood and B. D. Hames, eds.), pp. 173–197. IRL Press, Oxford.

Dams, E., Londie, P., Cammarano, P., Vandenberghe, A. and DeWachter, R. (1983). *Nucl. Acids. Res.* **14**, 4667–4676.

Danner, D. B. (1982). *Anal. Biochem.* **125**, 139–142.

Donis-Keller, H. (1980). *Nucl. Acids. Res.* **8**, 3133–3142.

Dretzen, G., Bellard, M., Sassone-Corsi, P. and Chambon, P. (1981). *Anal. Biochem.* **112**, 295–298.

Duckworth, M. and Yaphe, W. (1971). *Carbohydr. Res.* **16**, 189–197.

Gould, H. and Matthews, H. R. (1967). *Separation Methods for Nucleic Acids and Oligonucleotides.* Elsevier/North-Holland, New York.

Guiseley, K. B. (1970). *Carbohydr. Res.* **13**, 247–256.

Guiseley, K. B. (1976). *US Pat.* 3 956 273.

Hansen, J. N. (1976). *Anal. Biochem.* **76**, 37–44.

Hansen, J. N. (1981). *Anal. Biochem.* **116**, 146–151.

Johnson, M. T., Read, B. A., Monko, A. M., Pappas, G. and Johnson, B. A. (1986). *Biotechniques* **4**, 64–70.

Kirby, K. S.(1956). *Biochem. J.* **64**, 405–408.

Kirby, K. S. (1968). *Meth. Enzymol.* **12B**, 87–99.

Levy, C. C. and Karpetsky, T. P. (1980). *J. Biol. Chem.* **255**, 2153–2159.

Lillehaug, J. R., Kleppe, R. K. and Klepp, K. (1976). *Biochemistry* **15**, 1858–1865.

Lockard, R. E., Alzner-DeWeerd, B., Heckman, J. E., MacGee, J., Tabor, W. and RajBhandary, U. L. (1978). *Nucl. Acids Res.* **5**, 37–56.

Luehrsen, K. R. and Fox, G. E. (1981). *J. Mol. Evol.* **17**, 52–55.

MacDonell, M. T. and Colwell, R. R. (1984). *FEBS Lett.* **175**, 183–188.

MacDonell, M. T., Morris, S. C., Ortiz-Conde, B. A., Pillidge, C. J. and Colwell, R. R. (1986). *J. Chromatogr.* **363**, 348–443.

McDonell, M. W., Simon, M. N. and Studier, F. W. (1977). *J. Mol. Biol.* **110**, 119–146.

O'Connell, P. B. H. and Brady, C. J. (1977). *Anal. Biochem.* **76**, 63–73.

Peterson, E. A. (1980). *Cellulosic Ion Exchangers.* Elsevier/North-Holland, New York.

Randerath, K. and Randerath, E. (1967). *Meth. Enzymol.* **12A**, 323–347.

Richardson, C. C. (1965). *Proc. Natl Acad. Sci. USA* **54**, 158–165.

Sanger, F. and Coulsen, A. R. (1978). *FEBS Lett.* **87**, 107–110.

Sato, K. and Egami, F. (1957). *J. Biochem.* **44**, 753–767.

Schlief, R. F. and Wensink, P. C. (1981). *Practical Methods in Molecular Biology.* Springer-Verlag, New York.

Schwartz, D. C. and Cantor, C. R. (1984). *Cell* **37**, 67–75.

Sealy, P. G. and Southern, E. M. (1982). In *Gel Electrophoresis of Nucleic Acids*, (D. Rickwood and B. D. Hames, eds.), pp. 39–76. IRL Press, Oxford.

Uchida, T., Bonen, L., Schaup, H. W., Lewis, B. J., Zablen, L. and Woese, C. R. (1974). *J. Mol. Evol.* **3**, 63–77.

Wieslander, L. (1979). *Anal. Biochem.* **98**, 305–309.

Zablen, L., Bonen, L., Meyer, R. and Woese, C. R. (1975). *J. Mol. Evol.* **4**, 347–358.

Zeugin, J. A. and Hartley, J. L. (1985). *Focus* **7**(4), 1–2.

Zhu, J., Kempenaers, W., Van der Straaten, D., Contreras, R. and Fiers, W. (1985). *Biotechniques* **3**, 1014–1016.

10
The Application of 16S rRNA Cataloguing and 5S rRNA Sequencing in Bacterial Systematics

GEORGE E. FOX

Department of Biochemical Sciences, University of Houston, University Park, Houston, Texas 77004, USA

ERKO STACKEBRANDT

Institut für Allegemeine Mikrobiologie, Universität Kiel, 23 Kiel, Federal Republic of Germany

I. Introduction

The fundamental concept of comparative biology is based on homologies. Since homologous molecules and organs descend from a common genetic origin, it is argued that homologies can be used to determine phylogenetic histories, which makes a classification of organisms on the basis of their natural relationships possible. In highly evolved eukaryotes, comparative anatomy and embryology, together with paleontological records, have successfully been used to establish phylogenetic lines of descent, which later were confirmed and broadened when the studies were extended to the molecular level.

In higher plants and animals, complex morphologies are often reflections of the genealogy of the organisms and not the result of convergent evolution. This is not the situation among the microorganisms. Morphological characteristics and physiological features cannot in general be used to derive phylogenetic relations. Similarly genealogical lines cannot be traced from the sparse fossil record. In the absence of suitable criteria, microbiologists have for the last 100 years been unable to decide which of the morphological and physiological features were homologous and which evolved by convergence.

Even at the beginning of the modern era of microbiology Cohn (1875) recognized these problems. He thus argued that if we were unable to trace back the genealogy of bacteria, this would prevent the establishment of a classification scheme analogous to that of the higher organisms. To allow identification and characterization of bacteria in the absence of such a scheme, Cohn (1872, 1875) and later Migula (1900) proposed a classification that was based on morphological criteria only. Cohn clearly pointed out that taxa, although named using Greek–Latin nomenclature, could not be considered phylogenetic units as their eukaryotic counterparts were. Nevertheless, van Niel (1946) claimed that Cohn failed to appreciate that morphological criteria were only useful for determinative microbiology. Cohn was not guilty of this charge—but others were, and, despite the early recognition of the fallacy, the descriptive part of bacterial taxonomy was frequently equated with phylogeny. This led to a "hierarchical" structuring of bacteria that changed during the coming years, whenever systematics was based on new criteria, for example physiology (Winslow and Winslow, 1908; Orla-Jensen, 1909) or a combination of various features (1st–7th editions of *Bergey's Manual*). The foreword of the 7th edition of *Bergey's Manual* summarizes the history of attempts to achieve a meaningful classification scheme, and subsequently, the editors of the 8th edition (Buchanan and Gibbons, 1974) finally resigned themselves to being unable to construct a completely hierarchical system on the basis of morphological and physiological features. Nevertheless, a few investigators have persisted, and, even in this decade, a "phyla" of the "kingdom Monera" has been proposed (Margulis and Schwartz, 1982) on the basis of characters whose phylogenetic significance have either not been proved or have already been dismissed.

With the onset of molecular biology, the situation has drastically changed. A whole new class of "characters" suddenly became available for study. The realization that macromolecular sequences retain a trace of the historical record came early (Crick, 1958; Zuckerkandl and Pauling, 1965a, b for example). With the successful demonstration that cytochrome c sequence comparisons could provide reasonable evolutionary trees for eukaryotes (Fitch and Margoliash, 1967), it was inevitable that molecular methods would be adapted to the immense problems of prokaryotic systematics.

Subsequently, many molecular methods have been used. These include direct sequencing of nucleic acids and proteins, semidirect methods, such as oligonucleotide and oligopeptide mapping, and indirect methods such as DNA/DNA hydbridization, DNA/RNA hybridization and determination of %G-C. Each of these approaches has proved useful in some aspects of systematics. To address the global question of a hierarchical arrangement of the taxa, however, not just any molecular method will work. It is essential that the method be sufficiently expedient that a large number of genera can be examined. At the same time, it is necessary that the method directly reflect differences at the sequence level. With the technology available in the last decade, the best methods for exploring phylogenetic relations among the microorganisms have proven to be 16S rRNA oligonucleotide cataloguing and 5S rRNA complete sequencing. As a result of the application of these methods, an extensive outline of hierarchical structure among the bacteria is available.

Now that the long-sought "natural" system of classification is feasible the microbiologist must rethink the goals of bacterial systematics. To abandon *Bergey's Manual* in favour of genealogical classification would be counter-productive. Yet to ignore the new information and insights cannot be valid either. It is essential then to consider how the new phylogenetic insights can be most productively interfaced with the existing physiological and morphological information.

In this review, we briefly discuss 5S rRNA sequencing and 16S rRNA oligonucleotide cataloguing methodologies and discuss in more detail the potential difficulties in properly interpreting 5S rRNA results, a neglected subject. We attempt to tabulate for the first time in one place, the literature pertaining to the bacterial genera that have been examined by molecular methods. We discuss briefly the new insights that 5S rRNA data provides for the eukaryotic microorganisms and outline the hierarchical view of prokaryotic evolution as seen by 16S rRNA cataloguing and briefly compare it with results obtained by other molecular methods in the case of Gram-negative eubacteria. The favourable results of these comparisons show why so much enthusiasm exists for the genealogies produced by these molecular methods. We present in some detail our views on how the existing knowledge of bacterial taxa can be best integrated with the emerging molecular data to produce a genealogically reasonable bacterial taxonomy. Finally, we discuss some trends that are likely to have significant impact on microbial systematics over the next few years.

II. Methods

A. 16S rRNA oligonucleotide cataloguing and complete sequencing

The essential goal of 16S rRNA cataloguing is to extract a large portion of the phylogenetic information contained in the 16S rRNA molecule without resorting to complete sequencing. This is accomplished by digesting the purified 16S rRNA completely with ribonuclease T_1, which is specific for guanosine residues. Each oligonucleotide that is produced by such a digestion is sequenced in its entirety and a tabulation, referred to as a catalogue, is made.

These catalogues are subsequently compared with one another in a binary fashion. A Jacard-type association coefficient is defined as follows (Fox et al., 1977):

$$S_{AB} = \frac{2N_{AB}}{N_A + N_B}$$

where N_A is the total number of residues in oligonucleotides of length at least L in catalogue A, N_B is the total number of residues in oligonucleotides of length at least L in catalogue B and N_{AB} is the total number of residues represented by all the coincident oligonucleotides between the two catalogues A and B of length at least L. The choice of L is governed by statistical considerations (Fox et al., 1977b), and is six for all but the most closely related organisms. A matrix of such S_{AB} values is constructed, and dendrograms are made by average linkage clustering (Anderberg, 1973) to display the relations between the individual strains.

Two experimental methods have been used to determine 16S rRNA catalogues. The original approach (HVE method) employed RNA that was uniformly labelled with ^{32}P in vivo. The oligonucleotides were separated by two-dimensional paper electrophoresis and located by autoradiography. Detailed protocols have been published (Uchida et al., 1974; Woese et al., 1976a). The current technology (TLC method) uses RNA that is labelled in vitro after digestion with ribonuclease T_1 and conducts the second dimension by thin-layer chromatography (Stackebrandt *et al.*, 1981a, 1982). This method offers the significant advantage that it is possible to work with any organism for which an amount of cells can be obtained. Detailed procedures are provided in a methodological paper by Stackebrandt *et al.* (1985). An alternative separation method is the use of two-dimensional gels (De Wachter and Fiers, 1982). This approach is widely used in fingerprinting virus genomic RNAs (see e.g. Trent *et al.*, 1983). We have tried this method (J. A. Grant, G. E. Fox and E. Stackebrandt, unpublished results) and found that it produces fingerprints of comparable but not significantly better quality than those obtained with the TLC method. Any group wishing to utilize the two-dimensional gel approach in 16S rRNA oligonucleotide cataloguing would find it necessary to modify the existing protocols for secondary and tertiary digests.

The data-analysis procedures have been described briefly above. The detailed procedures that are used in processing the data and many issues relating to the meaning and reliability of the S_{AB} values are discussed in detail in the methodological paper of Stackebrandt *et al.* (1985). A method for evaluating which branches are least certain has been described (Fox, 1985) and further discussion of the interpretation of the S_{AB} values is available (Kössel *et al.*, 1983; Fox, 1985).

Complete sequencing of the small subunit rDNA is increasingly common. It is generally assumed that the rDNA is not derived from a pseudogene or some other inactive structure. It would appear that this is usually a reasonable assumption. Such complete sequence data can be independently analysed or it can be degenerated to allow incorporation into the 16S rRNA catalogue data base. The methods that have been used for sequencing rDNA, to date, have been those which are essentially standard (see e.g. Hindley, 1983; Maxam and Gilbert, 1980).

B. 5S rRNA cataloguing and 5S rRNA sequencing

5S rRNA catalogues can be determined with essentially the same methods as used for 16S rRNA cataloguing. They are very fast and cheap to produce for a group that is already doing 16S rRNA cataloguing. Historically, they were successfully used to demonstrate the applicability of rRNA methods in systematics (Sogin *et al.*, 1972). Subsequently they have not been seriously used, though as indicated in Table I (p.439) a significant amount of information exists.

In fact it has been shown that 5S rRNA cataloguing can be a surprisingly effective tool when used in conjunction with 5S rRNA complete sequencing (Nicholson, 1982). When several 5S rRNA sequences are available for a single taxonomic group it is useful to determine a large number of 5S rRNA catalogues from additional species. The existing complete sequence data allow the assignment of essentially every large oligomer to its appropriate place in the sequence. In this way partial sequences can be constructed that typically contain 70–80 nucleotides. These can be analysed in conjunction with the available complete sequences in terms of % homology rather than S_{AB}. In this fashion a large portion of the information that would be available from complete sequences can be extracted quite quickly. Although this approach is unlikely to be used extensively in the future, those 5S rRNA catalogues that are currently in existence should be analysed in this way to further extend the relevant data base.

Complete sequencing of a small molecule such as 5S rRNA is easy in an age where hundreds of nucleotides of DNA sequences can be determined in one experiment. That this is in essence true is attested to by the fact that approximately 450 5S rRNA sequences have now been determined. Nevertheless, the neophyte should be advised that there are some difficulties. Appropriate technology is available and very well documented (Donis-Keller et al., 1977; Peattie, 1979; Donis-Keller, 1980; MacDonell et al., 1987— Chapter 9 of this volume), but, as is well known, it is not comparable in reproducibility or capability to modern DNA sequencing techniques. Also the molecules themselves, unlike restriction fragments, have biologically well-defined ends, which must be separately analysed. In addition, probably because of variations in processing, the 5 and/or 3 ends frequently exhibit length heterogeneities, which can cause gel-reading problems unless preliminary separations are first made. Internal microheterogeneities due to the presence of multiple 5S rRNA cistrons can also cause difficulties in the interpretation of gels.

Once sequences have been determined, they are aligned with existing sequences. This is straightforward, as long as one compares only 5S rRNAs from the same kingdom. Alignment difficulties due to apparent insertion or deletion events or disagreement with the concensus secondary structure models (for a detailed discussion see Fox, 1985) should be taken as a symptom of possible sequencing errors. Band compression, although well known, can be a subtle problem on RNA sequencing gels. A second set of gels with the labelled phosphate at the opposite end should be obtained in order to resolve such disagreements with the usual patterns. In any case, a high-quality sequence should always include gels reading in both directions. The aligned sequences are finally used to construct a tree. The number of alternative methods is rather large. An inexhaustive list of approaches used with 5S rRNA includes Hori (1975), Li (1981), Hinnebusch et al. (1981), Fitch (1981), Küntzel et al. (1983), Manske (1983) and, most recently, Hogeweg and Hesper (1984). The choice of method is a subject of continuing study, and none has as yet been convincingly established as the "best". We know that at least two authors—Li (1981) and Fitch (1981)—will gladly make FORTRAN computer programs available. It is likely that others would do so as well (see Sackin, 1987—Chapter 11 of this volume).

5S rRNA trees provide the usual concerns about evolutionary rates, etc., that affect the interpretation of any such tree. There are, however, some concerns that are peculiar to 5S rRNA sequencing studies. To begin with, it is often said that the structure of 5S rRNA is "universal" (De Wachter et al., 1982). What is meant, however, is that the structures are highly similar. It is quite clear (Fox, 1985) that there are meaningful differences in the secondary structures of 5S rRNAs from eubacteria, archaebacteria and eukaryotes. Even within the eubacteria (Delihas and Andersen, 1982; Stahl et al., 1984) and the archaebacteria (Fox et al., 1982) there are real structural variations. Because 5S rRNA is small, these differences affect a larger percentage of the molecule than do comparable structural variations in the larger 16S rRNA. As a result, these differences need to be considered in tree construction.

Why is this? Simply because if one is ever to find evolutionary rates that are uniform, it will intuitively be for sequence regions that are not undergoing structural evolution. As soon as the structure of an RNA domain is changed, the character of the evolutionary rate in that structural domain can be drastically changed. This is so because the original set of structural constraints may be more or less compatible with the acceptance of mutations than the new set. Thus it is formally valid to compare only those positions that are in structurally homologous regions.

In the case of 5S rRNA, it is usually argued that a major advantage is that trees can be constructed that simultaneously address prokaryotic and eukaryotic evolution. In principle this is true. In practice, recent trees that have been made (e.g. Küntzel et al., 1983) do not take the structural differences between the various types of 5S rRNA into account. Although these trees are not invalid, the branch points that separate different structural types must be interpreted cautiously. It should be noted that tree-constructing methods that weight positions according to nucleotide variability (Manske, 1983) may not be subject to this difficulty, because they are in effect ignoring positions where variability is high; for example including places where structural homology does not exist.

Another danger exists for global 5S rRNA trees and trees that encompass all eukaryotic 5S rRNA sequences. Gene expression in at least some eukaryotic 5S rRNAs has been found to be dependent on an internal control region (Bogenhagen et al., 1980; Sakonju et al., 1980; Ciberto et al., 1983a). In the case of Xenopus laevis oocytes, a protein factor initially binds to the 5S rDNA as part of the initiation of transcription, and later binds to the 5S rRNA product itself (Pelham and Brown, 1980). This internal control region in 5S rRNA has been found to be separable into "A" and "B" boxes

(Cliberto *et al.*, 1983a). The "A" box is further found to contain sequence homologies with other eukaryotic RNAs that are transcribed by RNA polymerase III (Cliberto *et al.*, 1983b). The bacterial 5S rRNA sequences apparently do not share these same sequence homologies. For essentially the same reasons as argued before, there may be problems in comparing positions that have a double function in one group of organisms and only a single function in the group of organisms it is compared with. Fortunately for phylogenetic work, this internal control region may only be found in the higher eukaryotes, and thus may not affect composite trees involving the lower eukaryotes and the bacteria.

A final remark concerns a minor difficulty that affects the use of 5S rRNA trees in eukaryotic systematics, namely the occurrence of multiple 5S rRNA types in some genera. Eukaryotic 5S rRNA genes are often found in multigene families and in some cases there are two or more of these families. In *Xenopus laevis*, for example, there is an oocyte 5S rRNA and a kidney cell 5S rRNA (Ford and Southern, 1973). These two *Xenopus laevis* 5S rRNAs differ by more nucleotides than either from its counterpart in the closely related *Xenopus borealis* (Korn and Brown, 1978; Brown *et al.*, 1978). When such multiple 5S rRNAs are encountered it is clear that one must be careful to use the equivalent ones in tree construction, or spurious results will be obtained.

C.   16S rRNA methods compared with 5S rRNA methods

Which rRNA method is best for work in molecular systematics? The answer historically has not been entirely clear-cut. 5S rRNA sequencing is certainly superior to the cataloguing approach for eukaryotes. The many base modifications and somewhat larger number of oligonucleotides make the cataloguing procedure far more time-consuming and laborious (Stöcklein *et al.*, 1983). With prokaryotes, 16S rRNA cataloguing is quite fast, and probably surpasses 5S rRNA sequencing in this respect. The greater number of laboratories able to determine 5S rRNA sequences is nevertheless beginning to tilt the balance the other way. Thus, while three laboratories have combined to generate approximately 450 catalogues, the 5S rRNA community has as a whole produced 450 sequences and is now rapidly gaining ground. Because the majority of these are from eukaryotes, the 16S rRNA cataloguing procedure will continue to provide a far more extensive data base for the prokaryotes over the next few years.

The issue of relative information content must also be considered. When they begin to become available in significant numbers, 16S rRNA sequences, which typically contain 1550 nucleotides, will provide almost a 13 to 1 advantage over complete 5S rRNA sequences. 16S rRNA catalogues typically address 600 positions, and thus have an 8-fold advantage in terms of bases examined over 5S rRNA catalogues, which access approximately 75 of the 120 nucleotides present in a 5S rRNA. These comparisons must be tempered, however. The tree ultimately obtained from complete 16S sequences will not be 13 times better! Indeed it is theoretically possible (but not likely) that it would be the same. As more nucleotide positions from structurally homologous regions are examined, the trees will become better defined, and if enough positions are included, they would presumably become stable. At that point additional sequence data would not be of significant value. Unfortunately, we do not have enough insight at this time to decide where this point is. It is conceivable that sequencing some portion of the 16S rRNA molecule may be essentially as useful as complete 16S rRNA sequencing. On the other extreme, it may prove essential to include 23S rRNA data as well.

A comparison of the utility of 16S rRNA catalogues and complete 5S rRNA sequences is not straightforward, but some observations can be made. Because eubacterial 5S rRNA contains approximately 30 Watson–Crick interactions in its secondary structure, the actual number of positions that are meaningful in tree construction is not more than 90. 16S rRNA also has numerous paired positions; hence one should wonder how frequently both bases involved in such pairing would be included in the oligonucleotide catalogues. Intuitively the answer is very few because the base paired regions contain large numbers of G-C pairs. When one side of a helix contains a larger oligomer, the other will only contain small oligomers that are not part of the catalogue. That this is so, has been shown for *E. coli* 16S rRNA, as is illustrated in the methodological review by Stackebrandt *et al.* (1985). Thus we see that the quality of the 16S rRNA cataloguing data is high, and the effective length of the 5S rRNA is not much longer than the number of positions that can be reached by cataloguing alone.

In spite of these arguments, it is not formally obvious how to demonstrate that 5S rRNA sequencing is less useful than 16S rRNA cataloguing. The two types of data are handled differently. The 5S rRNA sequences allow one to include positions in the analysis where sequence variation occurs, and is thus far superior to an S_{AB} type of analysis of 5S rRNA catalogue data. Does it approach 16S catalogue data? It has generally been argued that it does not — by Stackebrandt and Woese (1981a), for example. Perhaps the best indication is that global trees produced from 5S rRNA sequence data do not "seem as reasonable" as those obtained from 16S rRNA data, but this probably in part reflects inadequacies in the methods used for tree construction.

D. Hybridization methods

DNA–DNA hybridization and rRNA cistron similarity studies (DNA–rRNA hybridization) are two additional approaches using nucleic acids as phylogenetic probes. Neither method directly characterizes the sequence of DNA or RNA. Instead, the degree of relationship is analysed by measuring the extent to which nucleic acids from different sources are able to reassociate (expressed in terms of homologies or melting points of the heteroduplexes). In the notation of Ambler (1976), these are analogue rather than digital methods, and as a result both approaches have the disadvantage that the data are not cumulative. This makes comparison and use of data from different laboratories impossible without the inclusion of reference organisms.

The DNA–DNA hybridization method has the advantage that it represents an average of the entire genome. It is especially effective for close relationships (where 16S rRNA cataloguing, 5S rRNA sequencing and rRNA cistron similarity studies may fail) and it has a high cost-effectiveness. Comparative studies have shown that relationships among closely related organisms (S_{AB} values above 0.75) can be analysed more rapidly, less expensively and more reliably by DNA reassociation than by 16S rRNA cataloguing (Ludwig et al., 1981a; Schleifer and Stackebrandt, 1983; Stackebrandt et al., 1983a).

Cost-effectiveness and speed are advantages of rRNA similarity studies, compared with 16S rRNA cataloguing. Comparison of data obtained by both methods has shown a linear correlation above S_{AB} values of 0.45 (Fig. 1) (Byng et al., 1983; Johnson and Harich, 1983; Schleifer and Stackebrandt, 1983). The amount of scatter is such that it would be difficult to estimate particular S_{AB} values accurately from hybridization data. Thus it is possible only to merge the two types of data approximately. Though both methods use ribosomal RNAs as probes, the hybridization is less useful in sorting out deepest branchings within a kingdom and in detecting the exact order of branchings within major sublines. Nevertheless, this can be done (Tu et al., 1982). Another concern is that hybridization will fail to detect "fast molecular clocks" (Woese et al., 1984a, b; Stackebrandt and Woese, 1981a).

E. Summary

Despite their limitations, all of the nucleic-acid methods, taken together, represent powerful tools that are useful in assembling meaningful phylogenies of microorganisms. DNA–DNA hybridization makes an important contribution by allowing rapid identification of strains that are not sufficiently different to justify analysis by the slower but more powerful analytical methods. 16S rRNA cataloguing and 5S rRNA sequencing are both useful in establishing phylogenetic "skeletons". The cataloguing procedure may be more useful and represents an important set of data for the bacteria. Among the lower eukaryotes, 5S rRNA sequencing is, at present, the method of

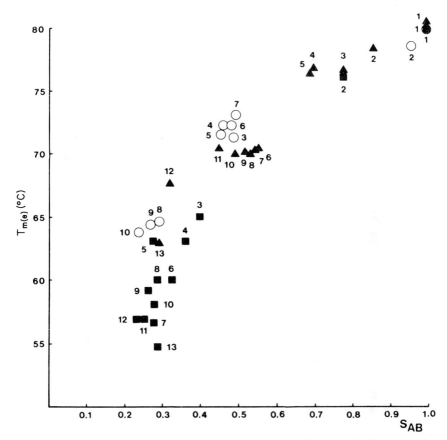

Fig. 1. Correlation between two parameters measuring phylogenetic distances, the S_{AB} values (unpublished data) and the $T_{m(e)}$ values derived from comparative analysis of oligonucleotides of the 16S rRNA and DNA–rRNA cistron similarity studies. The data included here are from three studies in which the reference organisms were *Kitasatoa kauaiensis* (black squares), *Streptococcus faecalis* (white circles) and *Agrobacterium tumefaciens* (black triangles). A positive linear correlation is seen between $T_{m(e)}$ and S_{AB} values within a region whose lower limits are defined by $T_{m(e)}$ values of 70 °C and S_{AB} values of 0.45. The identification of individual data points is given in Schleifer and Stackebrandt (1983), from which this figure has been reprinted with permission.

choice, and it is providing biologists new insights into the evolution of these organisms. RNA–DNA hybridization is valuable in filling in branches of phylogenetic trees, and can be used to identify misplaced stains that should be subjected to either 16S rRNA cataloguing or 5S rRNA sequencing.

Finally, complete sequencing of 16S rRNA will play an increasing role in the refinement of the earliest branching patterns.

III.   Existing molecular data—a key to the literature

As the number of papers containing molecular data pertaining to the phylogenetic position of various taxa grows, it is increasingly difficult for individul groups to keep track of it all. The task of the specialist who decides to study systematics is to locate quickly all of the molecular data pertaining to an individual taxon or groups of taxa, currently, a difficult task. In this section we make a first attempt to simplify matters by outlining the literature in each of the major areas pertaining to the molecular systematics of bacteria.

Table I (p. 439) provides specific references to the literature for those bacterial genera and species that have been investigated by one or more rRNA method. The table is arranged in accordance with the global 16S rRNA tree shown in Fig. 2. In those cases where the molecular data have been used to locate individual species of genera in separate parts of the tree, both genus and species are listed. In those cases where the genus has remained coherent, only the genus name is included. In these instances the reader must consult the primary literature to determine which species have been examined, which must be done in any event if information about specific strains is needed. In Table II (p. 450) we have tabulated correspondences between new and old names in all cases that we are aware of where organisms have been renamed since the original publication of 16S rRNA or 5S rRNA data. In the following paragraphs we make specific observations on the literature in each of the key areas.

For rRNA, the bulk of the data at present consists of complete sequences of small- and large-subunit RNAs, oligonucleotide catalogues of 16S rRNA, 5S rRNA complete sequences, 5S rRNA oligonucleotide catalogues and RNA–DNA hybridization data. The small rRNA (4.5S rRNA, 5S rRNA, and 5.8S rRNA) complete sequence data are conveniently summarized periodically by *Nucleic Acids Research*, to which the reader is referred for original sources of most 5S rRNA sequences. Recently published papers are referenced directly, in Table I, to the comprehensive list following the table.

The situation with larger rRNAs is similar. A collection of small subunit RNA sequences in aligned form has appeared (Huysmans and De Wachter, 1986) and may be obtained in machine-readable form. Sequences can also be obtained from the large data bases (i.e. EMBL and GENBANK) but these are not aligned and typically include sequences that have been published for

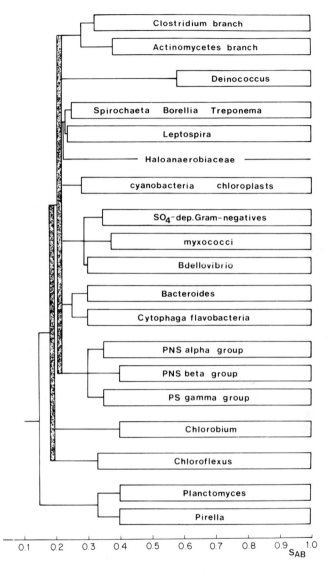

Fig. 2. Dendrogram of the eubacteria constructed by average linkage clustering (Anderberg, 1973) of S_{AB} values calculated from 16S rRNA catalogue data. The lower branchings are replaced by heavy lines to obscure branching patterns that are almost certainly meaningless. Ten major clusters are seen. In several cases two or three subclusters are also indicated. Thus the major group of Gram-negative bacteria is divided into alpha, beta and gamma groups. Each box on the dendrogram represents a number of species. The total number of strains included in the calculation exceeded 400.

some time. At present large subunit sequences are only obtainable through the large data bases and direct examination of the literature. The 1986 small subunit RNA collection included 9 archaebacterial sequences, 13 eubacterial sequences and 4 chloroplast sequences. Several additional bacterial sequences have now been published that were not included in the 1986 collection. These are *Bacteroides fragilis* and *Flavobacterium heparinum* (Weisburg *et al.*, 1985a), *Rochalimaea quintana* (Weisburg *et al.*, 1985b) and *Chlamydia psittaci* (Weisburg *et al.*, 1986). Phylogenetic trees which encompass eukaryotes, eubacteria, archaebacteria, organelles and eukaryotes have been constructed (MacCarroll *et al.*, 1983; Woese and Olsen, 1986).

The 16S rRNA oligonucleotide catalogue data are maintained in a specialized database by one of us (G.E.F.), and a collection of programs has been developed for extracting various types of information from this database (Sobieski *et al.*, 1984). (See also Sackin (1987)—Chapter 11 of this volume.) The published data can be obtained in machine-readable form upon request. The individual papers containing the original data are scattered throughout the literature, and are now summarized for the first time in Tables I and II. Important reviews providing an overall picture of phylogeny based on 16S rRNA cataloguing include Woese *et al.* (1978), Fox *et al.* (1980), Stackebrandt and Woese (1981a, 1984), Woese (1982, 1983). Key methodological papers include Uchida *et al.* (1974), Woese *et al.* (1976b, 1982), Fox *et al.* (1977), Stackebrandt *et al.* (1981a, 1985) and Hespell *et al.* (1984).

Although protein data are only peripheral to this review we have included in Table I a summary of the prokaryotic organisms for which at least one cytochrome *c* type or ferredoxin type has been sequenced. These data were obtained from the August 1986 version of the protein data base maintained by the National Biomedical Research Foundation at Georgetown University. The NBRF database may be consulted for original references as well as the sequence data.

IV.   Hierarchical structure of the prokaryotes

The first dendrograms summarizing prokaryotic phylogeny based on 16S rRNA oligonucleotide catalogues were published in 1980 (Fox *et al.*, 1980). At that time 170 individual catalogues were available. Two bacterial Ur-kingdoms; the Archaebacteria and the Eubacteria, had been described (Woese and Fox, 1977; Woese *et al.*, 1978) and some internal structure defined for each. Today more than 450 individual catalogues are in existence, and the general picture that was seen in 1980 is now much more detailed but in essence, remains unchanged. Overview dendrograms of the two Ur-kingdoms are shown in Figs 2 and 3.

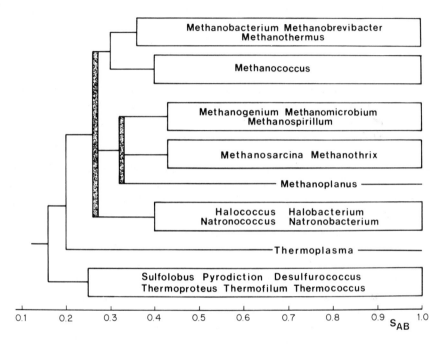

Fig. 3. Dendrogram of the archaebacteria constructed by average linkage clustering (Anderberg, 1973) of S_{AB} values calculated from 16S rRNA catalogue data. Two major groups are seen: the methanogen/extreme halophile group and the thermo-acidophiles. *Thermoplasma acidophilum* is essentially in-between the two groups, and so may be indicative of the presence of a third group, from which it is currently the only known isolate. The methanogen/extreme halophile group is shown in some detail so that the major genera can be localized. The dark bars serve to eliminate branchings that are not significant.

At the lower reaches of the figures, dark bars obscure individual branch-ings produced by the clustering algorithm. This is deliberate, since at these very low S_{AB} levels, the cataloguing procedure is unable to detect meaningful branching patterns. This device therefore leaves a number of clusters from a common branch. The inability of the S_{AB} method to resolve the earliest branchings gives 16S rRNA catalogue workers an operational definition for a bacterial Division or Phylum. (Eukaryotic systematists use the term "Division" for plants and "Phylum" for animals. Historically, "Division" has been commonly employed for bacteria and therefore is used here.)

Among the Archaebacteria, one such Division, the methanogens and extreme halophiles, were well characterized by 1980. In contrast, the evidence for a separate thermoacidophilic Division consisted of catalogues for two distantly related organisms, *Thermoplasma acidophilum* and *Sulfolobus acidocaldarius*. Subsequent cataloguing studies of a number of newly isolated thermoacidophilic archaebacteria (Woese *et al.*, 1984d) have provided data that establish a thermoacidophilic division of the archaebacteria. The taxomomic position of *T. acidophilum*, however, remains an enigma, since it does not group with the thermoacidophiles—perhaps an indication of a third division of archaebacteria.

Among the Eubacteria, the most significant findings since 1980 include formation of three new Divisions: the Bacterioides/Cytophaga group (Paster *et al.*, 1985); a heterogeneous cluster of sulphur-dependent eubacteria (Fowler, 1984), myxococci (Ludwig *et al.*, 1983), and bdellovibrios (Hespel *et al.*, 1984), and the *Planctomyces/Pirella* group (Stackebrandt *et al.*, 1984a). The latter are a most unusual group of eubacteria. The taxonomic status of three organisms (*Leptospira*, *Chlorobium* and *Chloroflexus*) and their position on the tree published since 1980 has been only partially clarified. Signature analysis (Woese *et al.*, 1982; Hespell *et al.*, 1984) suggests that *Leptospira* diverged very early from the spirochaetes. In addition, the genus *Haloanaerobium* (Oren *et al.*, 1984) shows affinity to the *Spirochaetes* and *Leptospiras*. Whether it proves useful ultimately to include all of these organisms within a single Division remains to be determined. Among the green photosynthetic bacteria, a few relatives have been found for *Chloroflexus* and *Chlorobium*. Not enough data are available to know whether these two photosynthetic bacteria represent one or two Divisions. The current view is that the archaebacteria contain at least two Divisions and the eubacteria approximately ten (Woese, 1985; Stackebrandt, 1985). As additional 16S rRNA cataloguing data are produced for additional genera, it is likely that more Divisions will be formed.

With the availability of rapid methods for DNA sequencing, it is certain that complete sequencing of 16S rRNA from key organisms will be used to decipher branching among the Divisions. Once it has been determined that two or more of the Divisions defined by 16S rRNA cataloguing are related, the nomenclatural problems will have to be solved. It may be appropriate to create higher taxa, such as Superdivisions or Kingdoms, for these groups to merge two or more Divisions into a single Division. These are of course not new problems, but what is new is that these issues can now be discussed from data for higher taxa, not just an individual genus or species.

V. Correlation of data obtained by molecular methods, concerning prokaryotic genealogy

A. General comments

Although the number of bacterial genera and species examined by 16S rRNA cataloguing and other molecular methods (see Table I) is large, the interested microbiologist who is not a systematist may ask whether the various sets of data really agree. Construction of joint, or "hybrid" trees using more than one type of molecular data and/or formal comparison of the extent of agreement between two trees, each based on a different type of molecular data, are non-trivial tasks, which are outside the scope of this review. Instead, evidence is presented showing that, although differing in detail, the various methods do tell a reasonably consistent story.

Because some of the molecular methods, especially protein sequencing, and rRNA cistron similarity studies, have been applied only to a limited selection of genera, it is not possible to compare "global" trees. Instead, we focus on comparisons for one phylogenetic group, the major order of the Gram-negative bacteria, which has been studied by 16S rRNA cataloguing, 5S rRNA sequencing, rRNA cistron similarity studies and cytochrome c sequencing. Not only have the same groups been studied, but, in many instances, the same species are included in several of the data sets. We begin the comparison by describing 16S rRNA results. Results from each of the other methods are also described and compared with those from 16S rRNA cataloguing studies.

B. Relationships among the purple photosynthetic bacteria and their non-phototrophic relatives as seen by 16S rRNA cataloguing

16S rRNA cataloguing of purple sulphur and non-sulphur eubacteria very early yielded results that indicated that these organisms are not closely related (Gibson et al., 1979). Although they belong in one of the main lines of descent of the Urkingdom Eubacteria (Fox et al., 1980), S_{AB} values of ca. 0.3 separated the three groups: the majority of purple non-sulphur bacteria, members of *Rhodocyclus* and the purple sulphur bacteria. These three groups were designated I, II and III by Gibson *et al.* (1979), but later changed to alpha, beta and gamma groups by Woese *et al.* (1984 a, b; 1985b). Subsequently, it became clear that each of the three groups contain non-phototrophic Gram-negative bacteria of various phenotypes. In many cases, aerobic, non-phototrophic species were found to be more closely related to phototrophic species, indicating that respiring Gram-negative bacteria should be considered descendents of the anaerobic phototrophs. More than 120 representatives of the three groups have now been investigated, and the clustering is as outlined in Fig. 4. The alpha group (I) contains the genera *Rhodospirillum, Rhodopseudomonas, Rhodobacter, Rhodophila* and *Erythrobacter* (see Table II for the traditional names), nitrogen-fixing bacteria (*Rhizobium, Agrobacterium, Bradyrhizobium*) and chemolithotrophic organisms (*Nitrobacter, Paracoccus*, manganese-oxidizers). In addition, certain spirilla and budding and/or appendaged bacteria (*Nitrobacter, Hyphomicrobium*, certain phototrophs, *Blastobacter, Prostecomicrobium*) and various other species are members of this group. The beta (II) group contains phototrophs of the genus *Rhodocyclus*, which, however, do not form a phylogenetically homogeneous genus. While *Rps. gelatinosa* is related to *Sphaerotilus, R. tenue*, a variety of pseudomonads (*Ps. acidovorans* branch) and *Thiospirillum intermedius*, show distinct relationship with members of *Aquaspirillum, Chromobacterium, Janthinobacterium* (*C. lividum*, see Table II), *Alcaligenes, Ps. cepacia* and certain gliding bacteria (*Vitreoscilla, Simonsiella*). A third sub-branch of the beta group contains the ammonium-oxidizing chemolithoautotrophs. Within the gamma (III) group, the purple sulphur bacteria of Chromatiaceae and Ectothiorhodospiraceae are specifically related, forming an individual subgroup, which, so far, does not contain a non-phototrophic representative. The gamma group comprises the terrestrial and marine enterobacteria, *Oceanospirillum, Legionella*, the fluorescent pseudomonads, *Xanthomonas* and gliding bacteria of the genera, *Beggiatoa, Leucothrix* and *Alysiella*.

C. Comparison of the 16S rRNA genealogy with 5S RNA sequences

Although the number of 5S rRNA sequences available for the purple photosynthetic bacteria and their relatives is small, compared with 16S rRNA catalogues, the major groupings are all represented. Thus it is possible to make direct comparisons. See Fig. 5 (Stahl *et al.*, 1984). The same three major groups can be observed. The alpha group includes *Rhodospirillum rubrum, Rhodobacter sphaeroides* (Villanueva *et al.*, 1985) and non-photosynthetic relatives, including *Paracoccus denitrificans*. The beta group also

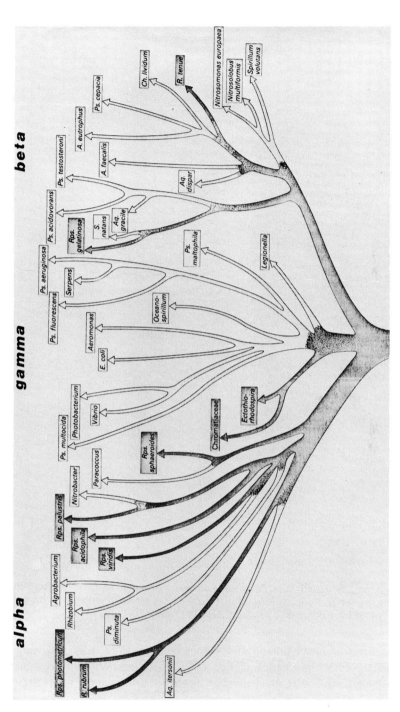

Fig. 4. Schematic drawing of specific phylogenetic relations between genera in the major group of Gram-negative eubacteria. The alpha, beta and gamma subgroups are indicated. The dark lines indicate photosynthetic branches. The figure was redrawn from a dendrogram based on 112 specific Gram-negative strains, and is reprinted with permission from Stackebrandt and Woese (1984).

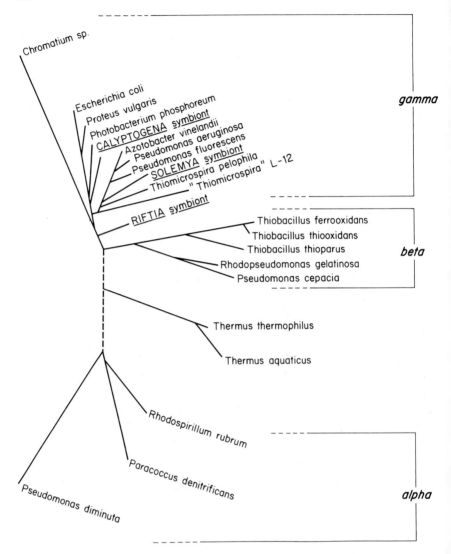

Fig. 5. A phylogenetic tree of the major Gram-negative taxa constructed from the available 5S rRNA complete sequences (Stahl *et al.*, 1984) is redrawn, with permission, to indicate the alpha, beta and gamma groupings.

includes *Rhodocyclus gelatinosa* and *Pseudomonas cepacia*, and the gamma group incorporates the enterics, vibrios and *Chromatium*. Within the gamma group, enough sequences are available that one can see some subclusters. These also correspond to the structure obtained by 16S rRNA cataloguing (Fig. 4).

The 5S rRNA data more than verifies conclusions drawn from the 16S rRNA data. Because enough data are available to define the main phylogenetic outline, the 5S rRNA data can be used to establish the phylogenetic position of several important strains not yet examined by 16S rRNA cataloguing. Thus the 5S rRNA database includes several *Thiobacillus* strains, and the tree shows this important genus in the beta group. Again, in the alpha group, the genealogical locations of several symbionts are established. In contrast, the genus *Thermus* is an enigma in that it falls in an intermediate position between the alpha and beta groups.

D. Comparison of the 16S rRNA genealogy with rRNA cistron studies

Figure 4 shows the branching pattern of the group of purple bacteria and their relatives determined from 23S/16S rRNA cistron similarity studies (see Table I for references). The clustering of organisms into three well-separated groups, i.e. "rRNA superfamilies", according to De Vos and De Ley (1983) renamed alpha, beta and gamma in Fig. 6, to facilitate comparison with the pattern depicted in Fig. 4, is in accord with the phylogenetic pattern based on 16S rRNA cataloguing data. The hybridization data, however, indicated that the members of the beta group are slightly more closely related to members of the gamma group than members of both groups are related to those of the alpha group.

The similarity of these branching patterns is not restricted to organisms defining the individual groups, but extends to internal branching structure as well. This is quite clear, for example, in the relationships of *Rhizobium/ Agrobacterium* (alpha group), enterobacteria/*Ps. fluorescens* (gamma group), and *Ps. acidovorans/Chromobacterium* (*Janthinobacterium lividum*) (beta group).

Although only a few representatives of the many species investigated by both cataloguing and hybridization are shown in Figs. 3 and 4, the excellent agreement reveals that, at this level of taxonomic relationship, both methods are equally useful. For taxonomic purposes, both methods are valuable tools, if one keeps in mind the limitations inherent in the hybridization approach discussed earlier (see also Stackebrandt and Woese, 1984).

E. Comparison of the 16S rRNA genealogy with cytochrome *c* data

One of the most revealing observations from Table I is the limited number of bacterial groups examined by protein sequencing. This picture would not be significantly changed by the inclusion of other proteins, because no other protein is sequenced for a significant number of bacterial genera. Even the large number of sequences from the cytochrome *c* type proteins and the

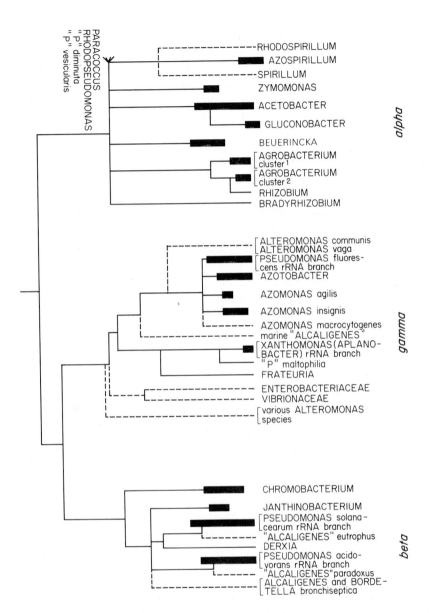

Fig. 6. Dendrogram displaying the relationship between the rRNA cistrons of various Gram-negative taxa based on $T_{m(e)}$ values. The figure is redrawn from De Vos and De Ley (1983). The dark bars indicate the extents of the individual branches. The dotted lines indicate branches that are to be described in detail in future publications. The major groups have been relabelled alpha, beta and gamma and their order of display changed to facilitate comparison with other figures in this chapter.

ferredoxins is somewhat deceiving. A large portion of these are in fact from eukaryotic organisms, and hence are not directly relevant here.

The ferredoxin database is most extensive for the cyanobacteria and cannot be directly compared with data obtained by the other methods, owing to the limited number of mutually investigated species. In the case of cytochrome c-like molecules there are enough data to effect a comparison for the purple photosynthetic bacteria. It has been argued (Dickerson, 1980; Woese *et al.*, 1980a) that, in this instance, the agreement is in fact excellent. The relevant trees include a 16S rRNA dendrogram (Woese *et al.*, 1980a), a dendrogram for the cytochrome c data calculated from the percentage of sequence homology and a subjectively constructed tree (Dickerson, 1980), which emphasizes the insertion/deletion events that have occurred during the evolution of the cytochrome.

If one examines these trees, one sees immediately that the alpha and beta subgroups are present in all of them and comprise the same organisms. Similarly, specific relations, *Rhodobacter sphaeroides* and *Rhodobacter capsulatus*, *Rhodocyclus tenuis* and *Rhodocylcus gelatinosa*, and *Rhodopseudomonas viridis* and *Rhodomicrobium vannielii*, are common to all the trees. Where the differences lie is primarily in the intermediate branchings. Thus the clustering of the cytochrome c_2 data puts *Rhodospirillum rubrum* in specific relation to the *Rb. sphaeroides* and *Rb. capsulatus*, whereas the 16S rRNA data do not. In this arrangement, the dendrogram fits exactly the data pertaining to membrane type and cell division mechanism.

It would also be expected that a logically constructed tree would account for the size changes encountered during the evolution of the cytochrome molecule. The third tree, constructed with this concept in mind, moves both *Rps. viridis* and *Rhodopseudomonas palustris* into the *Rhodobacter* group. This severely disrupts the agreement with the phenotypic factors in the case of *Rps. palustris*, which reproduces by budding and has intracytoplasmic membranes that are adjacent and parallel (i.e. lamellar) to the cytoplasmic membrane. It should be realized that several alternative evolutionary pathways can be proposed to account for the cytochrome size differences. For example, another reasonable interpretation of the insertion/deletion data is that the larger than normal insert in the 70's region of the cytochrome c_2 arose as a single event before and separately from the smaller insertion in the 70's region. With this proposal, one would maintain a topology that was identical with that provided by the simple clustering of the cytochrome c_2 data.

We see then that the cytochrome c and 16S rRNA data tells a very similar story, reassuring us that one can obtain good congruence between protein methods and rRNA methods. This does not, however, alter the fact that gene transfer can obscure relationships in the case of proteins. For example, an analysis of the cytochrome *c* data reveals a specific relationship between *Chromatium vinosum* and *Rhodospirillum tenue* (Dayhoff, 1983), which would be totally contradictory. Thus one must suspect gene transfer in that instance (Ambler *et al.*, 1979).

VI.   Bacterial systematics—towards a new system of classification incorporating genealogical data

With the emergence of a meaningful hierarchical structure for the prokaryotes, bacterial taxonomists must begin to consider how to best use this new information. Indeed, for the first time, taxonomists can obtain data to answer the question of whether or not a particular grouping is a Family, Order, or Class. It is essential to decide whether or not a genealogically based scheme can serve the needs of practical microbiology. In this section, these issues are discussed and examples from the Gram-positive bacteria are given showing how a practical, genealogically based scheme might be constructed.

For the working microbiologist reliable strain descriptions are necessary for communication, that is, to inform oneself and others whether organisms are the same or similar. For the foreseeable future, this kind of deterministic work will be done with phenotypic characters. Genetic studies, such as DNA–DNA hybridization, will provide genealogical coherence for a group of isolates, but will not replace phenotypic descriptions. Similarly, phenotypic characters, whether morphological (Micrococcaceae, Spirillaceae, Pseudomonadaceae), pigmentation (Chromobacterium, Flavobacterium), physiology (Nitrobacteraceae, Azobacteraceae), motility (Cytophagales, Beggiatoaceae) or the presence or absence of photosynthetic apparatus, have been shown not to be able to replace genealogical studies in describing taxa of higher ranks. Thus the practising microbiologist must also realize that genetic analysis must be done before a new group of strains are allocated to a described taxon or before a new taxon is created.

How is a genealogically based scheme incorporating phenotypic information to be constructed? It is desirable that nomenclature continue to follow guidelines adopted by microbiologists from eukaryotic systematics over a century ago. A fundamental difference, however, is the use of Greek–Latin nomenclature in the traditional, artificial system of prokaryotes and the new phylogenetic system. In the past, higher taxonomic ranks were often used without knowledge of natural relationships. In a phylogenetically based system, what will these ranks comprise? Murray (1974) uses the terms Kingdom, Division (= Phyla) and Class for the three highest taxa, followed by Families, Genera and Species. At present these ranks are sufficient for use with molecular data to construct a phylogeny of the prokaryotes. Thus there is no compelling reason to abandon these procedures, but the definitions will be substantially revised.

The finding that prokaryotes can be classified either as Eubacteria or Archaebacteria, both as unrelated to each other as either is to the eukaryotes (Woese and Fox, 1977) provides a logical basis for assigning the term Kingdom to these two largest taxa. The several major lines of descent constituting the Kingdoms of the Archaebacteria and Eubacteria respectively (see the earlier discussion on pp. 419–421) define operationally the Divisions, by which lower ranks can be assigned to subclusters, according to molecular genetic relationships.

In principle, assignment of isolates to the lower ranks might also be achieved by following strict operational rules. This is feasible because measures of genetic variation, such as % sequence homology, S_{AB} and T_{ME}, can be expected to have similar meaning in different bacterial groups. Thus it is appealing to select an arbitrary value or a range of values to correspond to each taxonomic level. Such an operational system has been proposed for the methanogenic bacteria (Balch et al., 1979).

When the phylogenetic coherency of the methanogenic bacteria was discovered, the situation was relatively uncomplicated. The small number of species, together with their relatively distant relationships, allowed the use of S_{AB} values for defining taxa (Balch et al., 1979): Orders, Families, Genera, Species and Strains were defined by ranges of S_{AB} values of 0.22–0.28, 0.34–0.36, 0.46–0.51, 0.55–0.66 and 0.84–1.0 respectively. Morphological features and chemical analysis of cell constituents were used to describe individual organisms at the genus level, while the rather large phenotypic heterogeneity, observed for some families was not taken as sufficient evidence for subdividing taxa. This strategy was continued when the genetic heterogeneity of a second, large group of Archaebacteria, the thermoacidophilic sulphur-dependent Division was discovered (Tu et al., 1982; Woese et al., 1984d). To date, the system appears to be working, but not without problems for those who discover new isolates and wish to determine where they properly belong. The availability of an immunological test (Conway de Macario et al., 1982; Macario and Conway de Macario, 1983) has helped. In the future, as more data accumulate, it is possible that practical problems will develop.

The situation is completely different within the Kingdom Eubacteria. Not only are a larger number of taxa described than for the Archaebacteria, but the former carry the century-old traditions of bacterial classification, in which, for various reasons (e.g. ease of determination), emphasis is placed on selected phenotypic traits for defining groups. Many characteristics define phylogenetically coherent taxa, while others do not. What is new is that the molecular data permit decisions to be made as to which of the phenotypic traits are phylogenetically meaningful. By preserving such coherent groups in the genealogy, it is both more familiar and more useful in deterministic work than a phylogeny based on operational definitions alone would be. Thus operational definitions of taxa do not serve well for the Eubacteria at this time for defining taxa below the rank of Division. An exception is for defining species boundaries where DNA–DNA hybridization provides a widely accepted criterion. Instead, we advocate a system where phylogenetic data are used in conjunction with selected phentotypic data to define taxa.

In this scheme, the most appropriate definitions of rank below the level of Division depend upon a variety of parameters, for example the phylogenetic depth of the entire Division, the number of sub-branches and organisms investigated and their phenotypic variability. In those Divisions where results of phylogenetic analyses reveal distinct clustering of phenotypical homogeneity decisions concerning ranks will be easier (e.g. *Deinococcus, Planctomyces, Pasteuria*) than for those in which results of phylogenetic analysis reveal clusters of organisms with a broad range of phenotypic characters (e.g. purple bacteria, Gram-positive eubacteria, cyanobacteria or the Bacteroides–Cytophaga group).

Whatever the choice, if the definitions are locally consistent and employ the best available genealogical data, the entire nomenclature system will be improved over time, as new information accumulates. Names and rankings of given taxa may change as results of new phylogenetic analyses become available or when phenotypic studies of new or known isolates indicate rearrangements. Unlike the traditional system, in which rearrangements were made by combining taxa of different phylogenetic origin, only the ranks but not the overall genealogical pattern will be changed in the phylogenetically based classification.

To illustrate the practical difficulties that necessitate a combined approach, Gram-positive bacteria offer a good example. These bacteria, with the exception of the genera *Deinococcus* and *Ornithinobacter*, represent one of the major Divisions of the Eubacteria. They can be separated into two groups: those with a DNA $G+C$ content of more than 55 mol% and those with lower values. This distinction, at present, is meaningful genealogically and provides two sublines at the rank of Class. Within each there are a variety of subclusters which must be structured. Figs. 7–9 illustrate alternative ways in which this might be accomplished for the actinomycetes and their relatives.

In Fig. 7 emphasis is placed on the strict use of S_{AB} values, in that, starting with the lowest values, a range of *ca.* 0.05 defines the rank of taxa. In doing so, two orders "Bifidobacteriales" and "Actinomycetales", emerge, with the former containing one Family and one genus. The latter order would contain two Families (separated by a range of S_{AB} values between 0.475 and 0.525). While the situation for the Propionibacteriaceae is clear-cut that of the

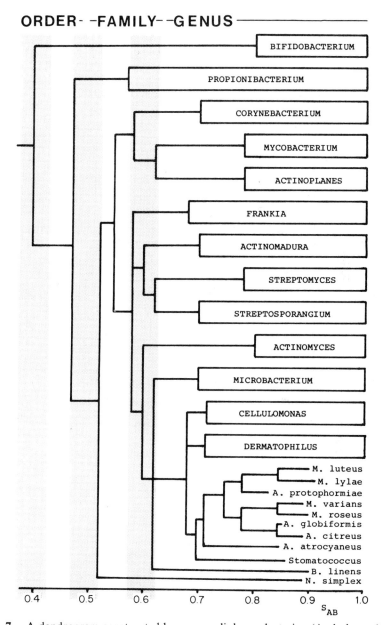

ORDER─ ─FAMILY─ ─GENUS ─────────

	BIFIDOBACTERIUM
	PROPIONIBACTERIUM
	CORYNEBACTERIUM
	MYCOBACTERIUM
	ACTINOPLANES
	FRANKIA
	ACTINOMADURA
	STREPTOMYCES
	STREPTOSPORANGIUM
	ACTINOMYCES
	MICROBACTERIUM
	CELLULOMONAS
	DERMATOPHILUS

M. luteus
M. lylae
A. protophormiae
M. varians
M. roseus
A. globiformis
A. citreus
A. atrocyaneus
Stomatococcus
B. linens
N. simplex

0.4   0.5   0.6   0.7   0.8   0.9   1.0
S_{AB}

Fig. 7. A dendrogram constructed by average linkage clustering (Anderberg, 1973) of S_{AB} values calculated from 16S rRNA catalogue data is shown for the actinomycetes and their relatives (high-%G-C Gram-positive bacteria). The various subclusters are shown schematically, with the exception of the *Micrococcus/Arthrobacter* group, which is shown in full detail. This figure shows the consequence of defining taxonomic levels by strict S_{AB} ranges from the highest level to the lowest. The problems with this approach are discussed in the text.

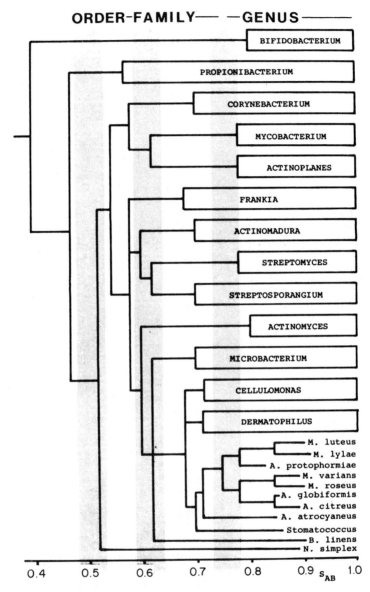

ORDER–FAMILY— —GENUS———

- BIFIDOBACTERIUM
- PROPIONIBACTERIUM
- CORYNEBACTERIUM
- MYCOBACTERIUM
- ACTINOPLANES
- FRANKIA
- ACTINOMADURA
- STREPTOMYCES
- STREPTOSPORANGIUM
- ACTINOMYCES
- MICROBACTERIUM
- CELLULOMONAS
- DERMATOPHILUS
- M. luteus
- M. lylae
- A. protophormiae
- M. varians
- M. roseus
- A. globiformis
- A. citreus
- A. atrocyaneus
- Stomatococcus
- B. linens
- N. simplex

0.4   0.5   0.6   0.7   0.8   0.9 S_{AB} 1.0

Fig. 8. The same dendrogram as in Fig. 7. In this case an attempt has been made to define taxa in accordance with strict S_{AB} ranges, beginning with the Genus and working back to Family and Order. The problems of this approach are discussed in the text.

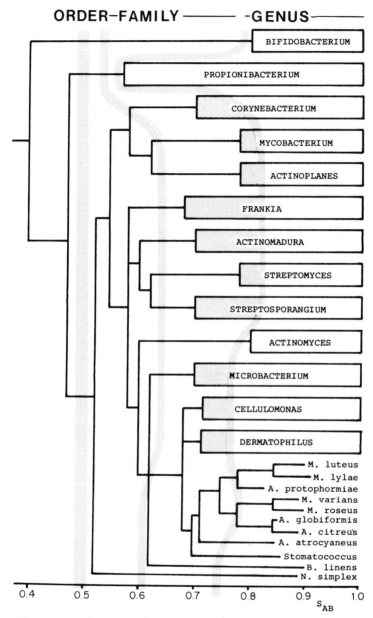

ORDER–FAMILY ——— –GENUS—

BIFIDOBACTERIUM

PROPIONIBACTERIUM

CORYNEBACTERIUM

MYCOBACTERIUM

ACTINOPLANES

FRANKIA

ACTINOMADURA

STREPTOMYCES

STREPTOSPORANGIUM

ACTINOMYCES

MICROBACTERIUM

CELLULOMONAS

DERMATOPHILUS

M. luteus
M. lylae
A. protophormiae
M. varians
M. roseus
A. globiformis
A. citreus
A. atrocyaneus
Stomatococcus
B. linens
N. simplex

0.4   0.5   0.6   0.7   0.8   0.9   1.0
S_{AB}

Fig. 9. The same dendrogram as in Fig. 7. In this instance the terms Genus, Family and Order are defined by a flexible approach that tempers the S_{AB} evidence with known phenotypic properties. This produces taxa that maintain consistency with the phylogenetic results and can be described by phenotypic properties as well. The merits of this approach are discussed in the text.

Actinomycetaceae is more difficult. By strict application of S_{AB} values, most of the newly defined genera comprise a collection of traditional genera of various phenotypes (e.g. *Actinoplanes, Ampullariella, Dactylosporangium* and *Micromonospora*, or *Microbacterium, Curtobacterium, Aureobacterium*, or *Mycobacterium, Nocardia, Rhodococcus*, or *Arthrobacter, Micrococcus, Stomatococcus* and so on). This approach would result in a rearrangement of established names that would be confusing and impractical. Even the introduction of additional terms, such as Suborder or Subfamily, improves the situation only slightly.

In Fig. 8 an alternative operational strategy is depicted. Here the delineation of taxa begins by using S_{AB} values to define genera. Values of *ca.* 0.75 offer a good choice, because such values are frequently found for remotely related species of traditionally defined genera and are likely to be a good indication of a lower boundary for a genus within the genealogical time period. The number of genera thus defined would be approximately the same as in the traditional system, but the number of Families, relating genera at the next lower branching point, would be markedly increased.

The same conclusions would be drawn for an Order. Such an inflexible use of S_{AB} values for defining taxa results in genera comprising similar phenotypes that are members of different Families, or genera with different phenotypes but high S_{AB} values within the same genus. An example is the union of *Cellulomonas* and *Oerskovia*, joined into a single genus because of high S_{AB} (Stackebrandt *et al.*, 1983e). Members of the two original genera can be distinguished easily by morphological and biochemical features. The proposal for a single genus was originally made because some members of the related genus *Arthrobacter* exhibited even lower S_{AB} values than for species of *Cellumonas* and *Oerskovia*. Thus it was argued that species of the latter two genera actually belonged in one phylogenetic taxon, comparable to *Arthrobacter*. This union, although reasonable from a genealogical point of view, is not practical and is an example of a failed attempt to use phylogenetic data to improve classification of the bacteria.

In view of these problems, it is clear that strict applications of S_{AB} values for defining taxa will create problems. How can a more flexible scheme be obtained? To begin with, ranks can be defined by a broad and variable range of S_{AB} values. The ranges can be adjusted, case by case, to coincide with phenotypic characteristics consistent with the genealogical data. If the various ranks are retained so as to be roughly comparable and follow the usual hierarchy, a consistent genealogy of the organisms can be developed. Thus one would not propose changing names of established genera because of S_{AB} value alone, as long as the cluster remains phylogenetically coherent, i.e. homogeneous. If, as in the case of *Arthrobacter*, individual members of a genus are found in disparate parts of the genealogical tree then, despite phenotypic similarities, the genus would be split and some members placed either into a new genus or an existing genus.

This flexible approach is illustrated in Fig. 9, where assignment of Order is not exclusively determined by the range of S_{AB} values but is also based on differences observed in physiology, i.e. growth requirement for oxygen. Thus three Orders can be proposed: anaerobic bifidobacteria; facultative propionibacteria; and (mostly) aerobic actinomycetes. The substructure of the latter basically would follow phylogenetic traits, with resulting separation into Families. The various common phenotypic characteristics make this attractive. A different interpretation of the importance of certain characters, on the other hand, would lead to different hierarchic definitions. Similarly, the range of S_{AB} values, now used to separate Families, could be extended to both higher and lower values, since the strategy allows a flexible delineation.

When the classification of the Actinomycetes and their relatives outlined here (Fig. 9 and Table III, see p. 451) is compared with the classification of these organisms given in *Bergey's Manual* (Buchanan and Gibbons, 1974) the overall picture, with respect to individual genera and definition of the Order, is not drastically changed. The most important differences are the exclusion of the genera *Bifidobacterium* and *Thermoactinomyces* and the inclusion of the coryneforms in the genealogically defined Order Actinomycetales. At the intermediate taxonomic ranks the hierarchy is, however, significantly different. The Propionibacteriaceae, believed to be less closely related to the Actinomycetes in the traditional system, are elevated to Order. Almost none of the traditionally defined families remain unchanged. Except for the Mycobacteriaceae and Streptomycetaceae, all families are redefined. Dramatic examples are the Actinoplanaceae and Micromonosporaceae. At the intrageneric level much work has been done in the past, especially in nucleic-acid homology studies, while morphologically, several poorly defined genera have been recognized as heterogeneous for many years. In most of these cases the various subgroups could not be classified with confidence. With a genealogically based system, the heterogeneous genera *Micrococcus, Corynebacterium, Brevibacterium* or *Actinomadura* can be defined more accurately. Misclassified strains are transferred to other taxa or, if an appropriate placement is not yet clear, they are listed by their original name as species or genera of uncertain affiliation.

It is explicitly part of the proposed strategy that the taxonomic levels of various clusters can be altered as new data are gathered. It is essential only that the taxa thereby created be phylogenetically homogeneous and reasonably comparable. It will inevitably be observed that such adjustments would be facilitated by the use of additional terms such as Suborder and Superfamily to reflect reality, i.e. to treat essentially continuous data in a discrete fashion. In fact one could employ a very large number of such terms to provide flexibility. In practice an increase in the number of high-order taxa may not be necessary, as a reasonable scheme at present can be achieved within each Division based on Class, Order, Family, Genus and Species.

Table III (p 451) provides the outline of a genealogical classification for a Division comprising the Gram-positive bacteria. It was developed by the same flexible incorporation of phenotypic and phylogenetic data as outlined above for the Actinomycetales. A formal proposal is not intended but instead, this scheme should serve as a starting point for discussion. To achieve a useful integration of results into microbial taxonomy requires participation of the much larger community of practitioners.

VII. Future directions

The success of the oligonucleotide cataloguing approach has solidified the position of rRNA as a most useful molecule for systematic studies. It is clear that, in the near future, substantial effort will be focused on complete rRNA sequencing. Although comparative work of this type is feasible by existing techniques, it is too tedious to do the extensive investigations that need to be done. It is essential to develop specialized sequencing procedures that compare favourably in cost and speed with the existing cataloguing methods.

One promising approach (C.R Woese, personal communication) is to optimize the dideoxy sequencing system by the use of specialized synthetic primers. Because much is known about conserved positions in 16S rRNA, it is possible to identify stretches of 15–20 bases that are essentially invariant in major taxa: eubacteria, archebacteria and eukaryotes. These conserved regions are found throughout the RNA, and complimentary synthetic DNA primers can be readily synthesized. In principle, then, one can use primers to regularly reinitiate the dideoxy method to move along the cloned rDNA from end to end in 300–500 nucleotide increments. In this manner a cloned 16S rRNA gene can be rapidly and accurately sequenced.

The likely successor to the cataloguing methodology is a related approach in which 16S rRNAs are rapidly partially sequenced (Qu et al., 1983; Lane et al., 1985). This method uses oligodeoxynucleotides that are complementary to selected areas of 16S rRNA as primers for reverse transcriptase. A cDNA is then synthesized in the presence of dideoxynucleotides as in enzymatic sequencing of DNA. As a result the sequence is obtained directly from the RNA template without the need for any cloning steps. In principle then 16S rRNA sequencing becomes comparable to hybridization studies in terms of the cost and the amount of experimental effort required. A set of standard primers can be used to sequence the same sequence regions from all the strains included in a particular study. Typically these regions together will cover from 800 to 1400 positions depending on how many primers are used.

The reverse transcriptase partial sequencing technology is currently being employed in a number of laboratories an a rush of new results will soon be forthcoming. In the long view it appears that this technology has the potential to make a major contribution in the establishment of a molecular phylogeny for bacteria. In the immediate future however this new methodology is likely to cause some difficulties in both data analysis and data processing. Our experience with reverse transcriptase sequencing (Lau *et al.*, 1987) suggests that considerable uncertainty exists regarding the sequence at many positions due to premature stops and other artifacts.

A conservative approach in interpreting reverse transcriptase sequencing data is strongly recommended. Sequences in local regions that do not agree with known secondary structure constraints for that region should not be reported unless they are unequivocal as they are otherwise very suspect. In this regard novices should be advised that there will even be a few cases in which bands exhibit inverted mobilities causing misinterpretation if secondary structure is ignored. More generally we would recommend reporting the full ambiguity at each position rather than the most likely base with an overall error estimate. This results in a much less attractive publication (i.e. disinterested parties will wonder why the sequence was so bad) which is actually far more useful. This is because certain positions have substantial phylogenetic signature value (Woese, 1987) which can only be taken advantage of if the status of these individual positions is unequivocally presented in the new data.

The reverse transcriptase data will also raise questions of data storage and sharing. The great value of this type of data is that any new partial sequence can immediately be compared to all previously published data. This however ceases to be true if the sequence data do not get published. Thus until such data are automatically placed in a publicly available database in aligned form, it is essential that they be included in original journal articles. It will also be necessary to work out detailed procedures for intercomparing partial sequences, catalogues and full sequences so that the earlier work need not be needlessly repeated.

Another area of likely future development is microbial ecology. The widespread application of rRNA techniques to bacterial genera is having the effect of creating a potentially very useful database. Already 5S rRNA sequencing has been applied to natural populations to discover the phylogenetic position of organisms that cannot as yet be cultured in the laboratory (Stahl *et al.*, 1984). With the knowledge now available about oligonucleotide signatures (Woese *et al.*, 1982; Hespell *et al.*, 1984; G. E. Fox, E. Stackebrandt and C. R. Woese, unpublished results) it would not be surprising if a system employing specific probes for various genera or species were developed.

Acknowledgements

This work was made possible by grants from the North Atlantic Treaty Organization (G.E.F. and E.S.), the Deutsche Forschungs Gemeinschaft and Gesellschaft für Biotechnologische Forschung m.b.H, Stöckheim (E.S) and the National Aeronautics and Space Administration (NSG #7440 to G.E.F.). We also would like to thank Professor O. Kandler for helpful discussions on possible names for higher taxa in the Gram-positive bacteria.

TABLE I

Bacterial genera that have been examined by 16S rRNA Cataloguing or SS rRNA sequencing

The numbers in each column indicate the entry in the reference list at the end of the table, where the original information can be found. In some instances the number is replaced by a symbol. The meanings of these are as follows: uW, unpublished 5S sequence or 16S rRNA catalogue from Dr Carl Woese's laboratory; ucW, unpublished 5S rRNA catalogue from Dr Carl Woese's laboratory; uF, unpublished 5S rRNA sequence from Dr George Fox's laboratory; uS, unpublished 16S rRNA catalogue from Dr Erko Stackebrandt's laboratory; uST, unpublished 5S rRNA sequence provided by Dr David Stahl of the University of Illinois. When individual organisms are suspected of being rather unlike others in the same genus they are listed by both genus and species.

	16S rRNA cataloguing	23/16S rRNA homologies	5S rRNA sequences	Cytochrome c sequences	Ferredoxin sequences
EUBACTERIA					
Gram-positive					
Bacillus	1, 2, uW		73, c75		88
Sporolactobacillus	2		c75		
Sporosarcina	3		c75		
Fillibacter			93		
Thermoactinomyces	4				
Planococcus	5				
Staphylococcus	5, 6	42, 43, 44	76		
Brochothrix	7				
Listeria	7				
Bacillus polymyxa	uW		ucW		
Bacillus alvei	uW		ucW		
Enterococcus	8	45, 46	73		
Streptococcus	8	45, 46, 72	73		
Aerococcus	uS				
Gemella	uS				
Bacillus acidocaldarius	uW				
Lactobacillus	9		73		
Pediococcus	9		73		
Leuconostoc	9				
Kurthia	10				
Clostridium group I	11, 12, uW	47, 48, 72	73, uD		
Sarcina ventriculi	uW				88

TABLE I *continued*

	16S rRNA cataloguing	23/16S rRNA homologies	5S rRNA sequences	Cytochrome *c* sequences	Ferredoxin sequences
Clostridium group II	11	47, 48, 72	c77, uD		
Eubacterium tenue	11	48, 72			
Peptostreptococcus anaerobius	uS				
Clostridium group III	uW	47	78		
Peptococcus glycinophilus	12				
Desulfotomaculum	13				
Ruminococcus	uW				
Peptococcus aerogenes	uW		87		
Megasphaera			94		88
Selenomonas			94		88
Sporomusa			94		88
Clostridium thermoaceticum	12				
Clostridium thermosaccharolyticum	uW	47	uW		88
Thermoanaerobium	uW				
Acetogenium	12				
Acetobacterium woodi	11, 12	48			
Eubacterium limosum	11, 12	48			
Clostridium barkeri	11, 12	47			
Mycoplasma	14		73		
Spiroplasma	14		73		
Acholeplasma	14		73		
Ureaplasma			73		
Anaeroplasma			73		
Clostridium innocuum	14	47	73		
Clostridium ramosum	14	47, 48	73		
Lactobacillus catenaforme	uS				
Erysipelothrix	uS				
Lactobacillus minutus	uS				

Actinomycetes branch

Arthrobacter	5, 15, 16		
Micrococcus	5, 15	49	73
Stomatococcus	uS		
Dermatophilus	17		
Cellulomonas	4, 15, 19		
Oerskovia	18, 19		
Promicromonospora	19		
Brevibacterium	15		
Microbacterium	15	50	
Curtobacterium	15	50	
Aureobacterium		50	
Agromyces		50	
Actinomyces	4	51	ucS
Actinomadura	20	51	
Nocardiopsis	20	51	
Planomonospora		52	
Planobispora		52	
Streptosporangium	19	52	
Thermomonospora	19	52	
Streptomyces	4, 19	52	73
Kitasatoa	19	52	
Chainia	19	52	
Elytrosporangium	19	52	
Microellobosporia	19	52	
Streptoverticillium	19	52	
Ampullariella	18, 19	52	
Actinoplanes	18, 19	52	
Amorphosporangium		52	
Dactylosporangium	4, 19	52	
Micromonospora	4, 19	52	
Frankia	uS		
Geodermatophilus	17, 19		
Nocardioides	15		ucS

TABLE 1 *continued*

	16S rRNA cataloguing	23/16S rRNA homologies	5S rRNA sequences	Cytochrome c sequences	Ferredoxin sequences
Corynebacterium	15, 19		uD		
Mycobacterium	4, 15, 19				
Nocardia	4, 15, 19				
Rhodococcus	15	53	106		
Bifidobacterium	4				
Propionibacterium	4				
Deinococcus branch					
Deinococcus	21		uSt		
Ornithinobacter	uS				
Spirochaetes branch					
Spirochaeta	22		ucW, uSt		
Borrelia	22		uSt		
Treponema	22		uF		
Leptospira	22				
Haloanaerobium	23				
Haloanaeromicrobium	23				
Clostridium lortetii	uS				
Cyanobacteria/Chloroplast branch					
Nostoc	24				88
Fischerella	24				
Prochloron	25		73		
Spirulina	95			88	88
Aphanocapsa	24				
Agmenellum	24			88	
Synechococcus	24		73		88
Anacystis	24		73		88

Oscillatoria

Anabaena   88   88

Chloroplasts of:

			c80	
Porphyridium	24			
Chlamydomonas	25			
Zea Mays	26			
Lemna	uW		73	
Spinacia			73	
Vicia			73	
Nicotiana			73	
Dryopteris, Spirodela			73	
Marchantia			73	
Euglena	24		73	

Myxobacteria/Bdellovibrio/S-dependent eubacteria branch

			ucW	
Bdellovibrio	27		ucW	
Myxococcus	28			
Stigmatella	28			
Cystobacter	28			
Sorangium	28			
Nannocystis	28			
Desulfovibrio	13			88
Desulfobacter	13			87
Desulfococcus	13		uF	88
Desulfobulbus	13			
Desulfosarcina	13			
Desulfonema	13		uF	88
Desulfuromonas	13			

Bacteroides/Cytophaga branch

Bacteroides	29	76	uF	
Fusobacterium	29			
Cytophaga	29			

TABLE I continued

	16S rRNA cataloguing	23/16S rRNA homologies	5S rRNA sequences	Cytochrome c sequences	Ferredoxin sequences
Sporocytophaga	29				
Flavobacterium	29	54			
Flexibacter	29				
Saprospira	29, 95				
Haliscomenobacter	29				
Chlorobium branch					
Chlorobium	96		uF	88	88
Chloroherpeton	96				
Prosthecochloris	96		uF	88	
Chloroflexus branch					
Chloroflexus	96		ucW		
Herpetosiphon	95, 96		108		
Thermomicrobium roseus	96				
Planctomyces branch					
Planctomyces	41, 102				
Pirella	41, 102				
Gemmata	101				
Purple-bacteria branch					
Alpha group					
Rhodopseudomonas viridis	30, 31			88	
Rhodomicrobium	30, 31			88	
Agrobacterium	31	55, 56		88	
Rhizobium	31, 97	55, 56, 82 84	uD		
Brucella	98				
Blastobacter	uS				
Prosthecomicrobium					
Rhodopseudomonas palustris	30, 31	56, 82	105	88	88
Bradyrhizobium	97				

Nitrobacter	31, 32			88	
Rhodopseudomonas acidophila	31			88	
Protomonas	uS		105	88	
Rhodobacter	30, 31		73	88	
Gemmobacter		98			
Paracoccus	31		73	88	
Manganese oxidizer	31				
Stella	99				
Rhodospirillum	30		73	88	
Aquaspirillum itersonii	31, 33	58			88
Azospirillum brasilense	31, 33	56, 74			
Rhodophila globiformis	31				
Pseudomonas diminuta	31, 34	56, 57	uF		
Phenylobacterium immobile	31, 35				
Hyphomicrobium	uS				
Erythrobacter	31		105		
Acetobacter		56, 59			
Gluconobacter		56, 59			
Zymomonas		56			
Beijerincka		56, 63			
Beta group					
Rhodocyclus gelatinosus	30		73	88	
Sphaerotilus	36				
Comamonas	36				
Aquaspirillum gracile	33, 36	58			
Pseudomonas: acidovorans branch	34, 36	56, 57, 86	uD		
Thiospirillum intermedius	36				
Aquaspirillum	33, 36	58	73		
Chromobacterium	36	56, 60			
Kingella	90				
Neisseria	90				
Thiospirillum denitrificans	36				
Bordetella	83				
Alcaligenes faecalis	36	56	uD	88	

TABLE I *continued*

	16S rRNA cataloguing	23/16S rRNA homologies	5S rRNA sequences	Cytochrome *c* sequences	Ferredoxin sequences
Pseudomonas:					
solanacearum branch	33, 36	56, 57, 86	uF, uD	88	
Alcaligenes eutrophus	36	56			
Derxia		56			
Janthinobacterium	36	56, 60			
Rhodocyclus tenuis	30		78	88	
Vitreoscilla	95		78		
Simonsiella	uS		73		
Thiobacillus	36				
Nitrosospira	36				
Nitrosolobus	36				
Nitrosovibrio	36				
Nitrosococcus	36				
Nitrosomonas	36				
Spirillum volutans	33, 36				
Gamma group					
Chromatium	30, 37, 38		ucW	88	87
Amoebobacter	38				
Lamprocystis	37, 38				
Thiocapsa	37, 38				
Thiocystis	37, 38				
Thiospirillum	37, 38				
Thiodictyon	37, 38				
Ectothiorhodospira	37, 39	91	107	88	
Escherichia	37	61, 62	73		
Salmonella		61	c77		
Klebsiella		61	c77		
Enterobacter	37	62			
Serratia	37	61, 62	c77		
Proteus	37	62	73, c77		

Yersinia	37		ucW		
Erwinia		61	c77		
Aeromonas	37	62			
Pasteurella	37				
Photobacterium	37	62	73		
Vibrio	37	62	73, 104, 105		
Calyptogenena symbiont					
barophilic eubacterium			73		
Beneckea		62			
Alteromonas	37	56, 85			
Oceanospirillum	33, 37	58	uF		
Bacteroides amylophilus	37				
Flavobacterium halmephilum	37	54			
Halomonas	37		ucW		
Xanthomonas	34, 37	56			
Lysobacter	37				
Frateuria		56			
Pseudomonas:					
fluorescens branch	34, 37	56, 57, 86	73	88	
Thiomicrospira			73	88	
Solemya symbiont			73	88	
Thiothrix			78		
Azotobacter		56, 63	73		88
Azomonas		56, 63			
Legionella	40	103			
Acinetobacter	37	81	73		
Alysiella	uS				
Leucothrix	37, 95		78		
Beggiatoa	37, 95		78		
Vitreoscilla beggiatoides					
Of uncertain affiliation					
Thermus	100		73		88
Rifia symbiont			85		
Thiovulum			78		

TABLE I continued

	16S rRNA cataloguing	23/16S rRNA homologies	5S rRNA sequences	Cytochrome c sequences	Ferredoxin sequences
ARCHAEBACTERIA					
Methanogens and halophiles					
Methanobacterium	66, 65	70, 71	111, uF		
Methanobrevibacter	66, 65		73		
Methanothermus	uW	70, 71			
Methanococcus	66	70, 71	73, 110		
Methanogenium	66, 65	70, 71	uF		
Methanomicrobium	66		uF		
Methanospirillum	66, 65		73		
Methanosarcina	66, 65	70, 71	111		88
Methanothrix	67				
Methanoplanus	uW	70, 71			
Halococcus	uW	70, 71, 92	73		
Halobacterium	68, 102	70, 71, 92	73		88
Natronococcus		92			
Natromonobacterium	uW	92			
Thermoplasma	14	70, 71	73		88
Thermoacidophiles					
Sulfolobus	69	70, 71	73		88
Thermoproteus	69	70, 71			
Thermofilum		70, 71			
Desulfurococcus		70, 71			
Thermococcus		70			
Thermodiscus		70			
Pyrodictium	uS	71	uSt		

References

1, Woese et al. (1976a); 2, Fox et al. (1977b); 3, Pechman et al. (1976); 4, Stackebrandt and Woese (1981b); 5, Stackebrandt and Woese (1979); 6, Ludwig et al. (1981a); 7, Ludwig et al. (1984b); 8, Ludwig et al. (1985b); 9, Stackebrandt et al. (1983d); 10, Ludwig et al. (1981b); 11, Tanner et al. (1981); 12, Tanner et al. (1982); 13, Fowler et al. (1986); 14, Woese et al. (1980b); 15, Stackebrandt et al. (1980); 16, Stackebrandt et al. (1983f); 17, Stackebrandt (1983c); 18, Stackebrandt et al. (1981b); 19, Stackebrandt et al. (1983a); 20, Fowler et al. (1985); 21, Brooks et al. (1981); 22, Paster et al. (1984); 23, Oren et al. (1984); 24, Bonen et al. (1979); 25, Seewaldt and Stackebrandt (1982); 26, Schwarz and Kössel (1980); 27, Hespell et al. (1984); 28, Ludwig et al. (1983); 29, Paster et al. (1985); 30, Gibson et al. (1979); 31, Woese et al. (1984a); 32, Seewaldt et al. (1982); 33, Woese et al. (1982); 34, Woese et al. (1984c); 35, Ludwig et al. (1984); 36, Woese et al. (1984b); 37, Woese et al. (1985); 38, Fowler et al. (1984); 39, Stackebrandt et al. (1984b); 40, Ludwig and Stackebrandt (1983); 41, Stackebrandt et al. (1984a); 42, Kilpper et al. (1980); 43, Kilpper-Bälz and Schleifer (1981); 44, Mordarski et al. (1981); 45, Garvie and Farrow (1981); 46, Kilpper-Bälz et al. (1982); 47, Johnson and Francis (1975); 48, Johnson and Harich (1983); 49, Stackebrandt et al. (1983b); 50, Döpfer et al. (1982); 51, Fischer et al. (1983); 52, Stackebrandt et al. (1981b); 53, Mordarski et al. (1980); 54, Bauwens (1980); 55, De Smedt and De Ley (1977); 56, De Vos and De Ley (1983); 57, Palleroni et al. (1973); 58, Pot et al. (1984); 59, Gillis and De Ley (1980); 60, De Ley et al. (1978); 61, De Smedt and De Ley (1979); 62, Baumann and Baumann (1976); 63, De Smedt et al. (1980); 64, Balch et al. (1977); 65, Fox et al. (1977a); 66, Balch et al. (1979); 67, Stackebrandt et al. (1982); 68, Magrum et al. (1978); 69, Woese et al. (1984d); 70, Tu et al. (1982); 71, Stetter and König (1983); 72, Kilpper-Bälz and Schleifer (1984); 73, Erdmann et al. (1986); 74, Falk et al. (1986); 75, Woese et al. (1976b); 76, Johnson and Harich (1986); 77, Sogin et al. (1972); 78, Stahl et al. (1987); 79, Sutton and Woese (1975); 80, Corry et al. (1974); 81, Van Landschoot et al. (1986); 82, Jarvis et al., (1986), 83, De Ley et al. (1986); 84, De Ley et al. (1987); 85, Van Landschoot and De Ley (1983); 86, De Vos et al. (1985); 87, Plas et al., (1986); 88, August 1986 data tape, National Biomedical Research Foundation at Georgetown University; 89, Nicholson and Fox (1983); 90, Rosen et al. (1986); 91, Ivanova et al. (1985); 92, Ross and Grant (1985); 93, Clausen et al. (1985); 94, Stackebrandt et al. (1985b); 95, Reichenbach et al. (1986); 96, Gibson et al. (1985); 97, Hennecke et al. (1985); 98, Rothe et al. (1987); 99, Fischer et al. (1985); 100, Hensel et al. (1986); 101, Stackebrandt et al. (1986); 102, Magrum et al. (1978); 103, MacDonell and Colwell (1987); 104, Pillidge et al., (1987); 105, MacDonell et al. (1986); 105, Kato and Komagata (1986); 106, Park et al. (1987); 107, Van den Eynde, H. et al., (1987a); 108, Van den Eynde et al. (1987b); 109, Specht et al. (1986); 110, Willekens et al. (1986a); 111, Willekens et al. (1986b). 112, Stahl et al. (1987).

TABLE II

Partial list of genera and species that have been validly renamed simultaneously with or after publication of 16S rRNA catalogues or 5S rRNA sequences

New name	Old name	Reference
Eubacteria		
Ruminobacter amylophilus	*Bacteroides amylophilus*	Stackebrandt and Hippe (1986)
Enterococcus faecalis	*Streptococcus faecalis*	Schleifer and Kilpper-Bälz (1984)
Staphylococcus saccharolyticus	*Peptococcus saccharolyticus*	Kilper-Bälz and Schleifer (1981)
Stomatococcus mucilaginosus	*Micrococcus mucilaginosus*	Bergen and Kocur (1982)
Cellulomonas turbata	*Oerskovia turbata*	Stackebrandt et al. (1983b)
Cellulomonas cartae	*Nocardia cellulans*	Stackebrandt et al. (1983f)
Rhodococcus fascians	*Corynebacterium fascians*	Goodfellow (1984)
Nocardioides simplex	*Arthrobacter simplex*	O'Donnell et al. (1982)
Deinococcus radiodurans	*Micrococcus radiodurans*	Brooks and Murray (1981)
Deinococcus radiophilus	*Micrococcus radiophilus*	
Deinococcus radiopygans	*Micrococcus roseus* UWO 294	Brooks and Murray (1981)
Synechococcus strain ATCC 27144	*Anacystis nidulans* PCC 6301	Rippka et al. (1979)
Rhodobacter sphaeroides	*Rhodopseudomonas sphaeroides*	Imhoff et al. (1984)
Rhodobacter capsulatus	*Rhodopseudomonas capsulata*	Imhoff et al. (1984)
Rhodophila globiformis	*Rhodopseudomonas globiformis*	Imhoff et al. (1984)
Rhodocyclus tenuis	*Rhodospirillum tenue*	Imhoff et al. (1984)
Rhodocyclus gelantinosus	*Rhodopseudomonas gelatinosa*	Imhoff et al. (1984)
Xanthomonas maltophilia	*Pseudomonas maltophilia*	Swings et al. (1983)
Janthinobacterium lividum	*Chromobacterium lividum*	De Ley et al. (1978)
Vibrio harveyi	*Beneckea MAV*	Baumann et al. (1980), MacDonell and Colwell (1985)
Photobacterium phosphoreum	*Photobacterium 8265*	Baumann et al. (1980),
Vibrio fischeri ATCC 15382	*Vibrio logei*	Baumann et al. (1980), MacDonell and Colwell (1985)
Archaebacteria		
Methanobrevibacter ruminantium	*Methanobacterium ruminantium*	Balch et al. (1979)
Methanobrevibacter arboriphilicus	*Methanobacterium arboriphilum*	Balch et al. (1979)
Methanomicrobium mobile	*Methanobacterium mobile*	Balch et al. (1979)

Table III

Possible hierarchical structure for the Gram-positive bacteria

Division: Gram-positive
  Class 1: Clostridia
    Order 1: Clostridiales
      Family 1: Clostridiaceae I
        Genera: *Clostridium butyricum* and relatives
                (Group I according to Johnson and Francis, 1975)
                Sarcina
      Family 2: Clostridiacea II
        Genera: *Clostridium lituseburense* and relatives
                (Group II according to Johnson and Francis, 1975)
                Peptostreptococcus anaerobius, Eubacterium tenue
      Family 3: Clostridiaceae III
        Genera: *Clostridium sphenoides* and relatives
    Order 2: Desulfotomaculales
      Family 1: Desulfotomaculaceae
        Genera: *Desulfotomaculum, Ruminococcus*
                uncertain affiliation: *Peptococcus aerogenes*
    Order 3: Mycoplasmatales
      Family 1: Mycoplasmataceae (true mycoplasma)
        Genera: *Mycoplasma, Spiroplasma, Acholeplasma, Anaeroplasma,*
                Ureaplasma
      Family 2: Clostridiaceae IV
        Genera: *Clostridium innocuum, Clostridium ramosum, Lactobacillus*
                catenaforme, Erysipelothrix
    Order 4: Acetobacteriales
      Family 1: Acetobacteriaceae
        Genera: *Acetobacterium, Eubacterium*
      Family 2: Thermoanaerobiaceae
        Genera: *Thermoanaerobium, Acetogenium, Clostridium thermoaceticum*
                and relatives
    Order 5: Bacillales
      Family 1: Bacillaceae
        Genera: *Bacillus, Straphylococcus, Brochothrix, Listeria, Gemella*
      Family 2: Streptococcaceae
        Genera: *Streptococcus, Enterococcus*
      Family 3: Lactobacillaceae
        Genera: *Lactobacillus, Pediococcus, Leuconostoc*
    Of uncertain affiliation: *Aerococcus, Kurthia*
  Of uncertain affiliation: *Lactobacillus minutus*
  Class 2: Actinomycetes
    Order I: Bifidobacteriales
      Family 1: Bifidobacteriaceae
        Genus: *Bifidobacterium*
    Order 2: Propionibacteriales
      Family 1: Propionibacteriaceae
        Genus: *Propionibacterium*
    Order 3: Actinomycetales
      Family 1: Actinomycetaceae
        Genus: *Actinomyces*

Family 2: Corynebacteriaceae
   Genus: *Corynebacterium*
Family 3: Mycobacteriaceae
   Genera: *Mycobacterium, Nocardia, Rhodococcus*
Family 4: Actinoplanaceae
   Genera: *Actinoplanes, Ampullariella, Amorphosporangium,*
      Dactylosporangium, Micromonospora
Family 5: Frankiaceae
   Genera: *Frankia, Geodermatophilus*
Family 6: Actinomaduraceae
   Genera: *Actinomadura, Microtetraspora, Thermomonospora*
Family 7: Streptomycetaceae
   Genera: *Streptomyces, Chainia, Kitasatoa, Streptoverticillium,*
      Elytrosporangium, Microellobosporia
Family 8: Streptosporangiaceae
   Genera: *Streptosporangium, Planomonospora, Planobispora, Nocardiopsis,*
      "Actinomadura" pusilla and relatives.
Family 9: Microbacteriaceae
   Genera: *Microbacterium, Curtobacterium, Aureobacterium, Agromyces*
Family 10: Arthrobacteriaceae
   Genera: *Arthrobacter, Micrococcus* I, II, III, *Cellulomonas/Oerskovia,*
      Promicromonospora, Stomatococcus, Brevibacterium,
      Dermatophilus
Of uncertain affiliation: *Nocardioides simplex*

References

Ambler, R. P. (1976). In *Structure Function Relationships of Proteins* (R. Markham and R. W. Horne, eds.), pp. 1–14. Elsevier–North Holland, Amsterdam.

Ambler, R. P., Daniel, M., Meyer, T. E., Bartsch, R. G. and Kamer, M. D. (1979). *Biochem. J.* **177**, 819–823.

Anderberg, M. R. (1973). *Cluster Analysis for Applications.* Academic Press, New York.

Balch, W. E., Magrum, L. J., Fox, G. E., Wolfe, R. S. and Woese, C. R. (1977) *J. Mol. Evol.* **9**, 305–311.

Balch, W. E., Fox, G. E., Magrum, L. J., Woese, C. R. and Wolfe, R. S. (1979) *Microbiol. Rev.* **43**, 260–296.

Baumann, L. and Baumann, P. (1976) *Microbios. Lett.* **3**, 11–20.

Baumann, P., Baumann, L., Bang, S. S. and Woolkalis, M. J. (1980). *Curr. Microbiol.* **4**, 127–132.

Bauwens, M. (1980). *Antonie van Leeuwenhoek* **46**, 95.

Bergan, T. and Kocur, M. (1982). *Int. J. Syst. Bacteriol.* **32**, 374–347.

Bogenhagen, D. F., Sakonju, S. and Brown, D. D. (1980). *Cell* **19**, 27–35.

Bonen, L., Doolittle, W. F. and Fox, G. E. (1979). *Can. J. Biochem.* **57**, 879–888.

Brooks, B. W. and Murray, R. G. E. (1981). *Int. J. Syst. Bacteriol.* **31**, 353–360.

Brooks, B. W., Murray, R. G. E., Johnson, J. L., Stackebrandt, E., Woese, C. R. and Fox, G. E. (1980). *Int. J. Syst. Bacteriol.* **30**, 627–646.

Brown, D. D., Birkenmeier, E. H., Doering, J. L., Fedoroff, N. U., Jordan, E., Korn, L. J. and Peterson, R. (1978). *Carnegie Institute Yearbook.*

Buchanan, R. E. and Gibbons, N. E. (1974). *Bergey's Manual of Determinative Biology,* 8th edn. William and Wilkins, Baltimore.

Byng, G. S., Johnson, J. L., Whitaker, R. J., Gherna, R. L. and Jensen, R. A. (1983). *J. Mol. Evol.* **19**, 272–282.

Clausen, V., Jones, G. and Stackebrandt, E. (1985). *J. Gen. Microbiol.* **131**, 2659–2663.
Cliberto, G., Castagnoli, L. and Cortese, R. (1983a). *Curr. Top. Dev. Biol.* **18**, 59–87.
Cliberto, G., Raugei, G., Costanzo, F., Dente, L. and Cortese, R. (1983b). *Cell* **32**, 725–733.
Cohn, F. (1872). *Beitr. Biol. Pfl.* **1**, 127–224.
Cohn, F. (1875). *Beitr. Biol. Pfl.* **3**, 141–208.
Conway, de Macario, E., Macario, A. J. L. and Wolin, M. J. (1982). *J. Bacteriol.* **149**, 320–328.
Corry, M. J., Payne, P. I. and Dyer, T. A. (1974). *FEBS Lett.* **46**, 67–70.
Crick, F. M. C. (1958). *Symp. Soc. Exp. Biol.* **12**, 138–163.
Dayhoff, M. O. (1978). *Atlas of Protein Sequence and Structure*, Vol. 5, Suppl. 3. National Biomedical Research Foundation, Washington, D.C.
Dayhoff, M. O. (1983). *Precambrian Res.* **20**, 299–318.
De Ley, J., Segers, P. and Gillis, M. (1978). *Int. J. Syst. Bacteriol.* **28**, 154–168.
De Ley, J., Segers, P., Kersters, K., Mannheim, W. and Lievens, A. (1986). *Int. J. Syst. Bacteriol.* **36**, 405–414.
De Ley, J., Mannheim, W., Segers, P., Lievens, A., Denijn, M., VanHoucke, M. and Gillis, M. (1987). *Int. J. Syst. Bacteriol.* **37**, 35–42.
Delihas, N. and Andersen, J. (1982). *Nucl. Acids Res.* **10**, 7323–7344.
De Smedt, J. and De Ley, J. (1977). *Int. J. Syst. Bacteriol.* **27**, 222–240.
De Smedt, J. and De Ley, J. (1979). *Int. J. Syst. Bacteriol.* **29**, 183–187.
De Smedt, J., Bauwens, M., Tytgat, R. and De Ley, J. (1980). *Int. J. Syst. Bacteriol.* **30**, 106–122.
De Vos, P. and De Ley, J. (1983). *Int. J. Syst. Bacteriol.* **33**, 487–509.
De Vos, P., Goor, M., Gillis, M. and De Ley, J. (1985). *Int. J. Syst. Bacteriol.* **35**, 169–184.
De Wachter, R. and Fiers, W. (1982). In *Gel Electrophoresis of Nucleic Acids* (D. Rickwood and B. D. Hines, eds.), p. 77. IRL Press, Oxford.
De Wachter, R., Chen, M. W.and Vandenberghe, A. (1982). *Biochimie* **64**, 311–329.
Dickerson, R. E. (1980). *Nature (London)* **283**, 210–212.
Donis-Keller, H. (1980). *Nucl. Acids Res.* **8**, 3133–3142.
Donis-Keller, H., Maxam, A. and Gilbert, W. (1977). *Nucl. Acids Res.* **4**, 2527–2538.
Döpfer, H., Stackebrandt, E. and Fiedler, F. (1982). *J. Gen. Microbiol.* **128**, 1697–1708.
Erdmann, V. A., Wolters, J., Huysmans, E. and De Wachter, R. (1985). *Nucl. Acids Res. Suppl.* **13**, r105–r153.
Falk, E. C., Johnson, J. L., Baldani, V. L. D., Dobereiner, J. and Krieg, N. R. (1986) *Int. J. Syst. Bacteriol.* **36**, 80–85.
Fischer, A., Kroppenstedt, R. M. and Stackebrandt, E. (1983). *J. Gen. Microbiol.* **129**, 3433–3446.
Fischer, A., Roggentin, T., Schlesner, H. and Stackebrandt, E. (1985). *Syst. Appl. Microbiol.* **6**, 43–47.
Fitch, W. M. (1981). *J. Mol. Evol.* **18**, 30–37.
Fitch, W. M. and Margoliash, E. (1967). *Science* **155**, 279–284.
Ford, P. J. and Southern, E. M. (1973). *Nature New Biol.* **241**, 7–12.
Fowler, V. J. (1984). Phylogenetic analysis of the phototrophic purple sulfur bacteria and dissimilarity sulfate-reducing bacteria. Ph.D. thesis, Technical University, Munich, FRG.
Fowler, V. J., Pfenning, N., Schubert, W. and Stackebrandt, E. (1984). *Arch. Microbial.* **139**, 382–387.
Fowler, V. J., Ludwig, W. and Stackebrandt, E. (1985). In *Chemical Methods in Bacterial Systematics* (M. Goodfellow and D. Minnikin, eds.), pp. 17–40. Academic Press, London.

Fowler, V. J., Widdel, F., Pfennig, N., Woese, C. R. and Stackebrandt E. (1986). *Syst. Appl. Microbiol.* **8**, 32–41.

Fox, G. E.(1985). In *The Bacteria*, Vol. 8 (I. C. Gunsalus, ed.). Academic Press, New York.

Fox, G. E., Magrum, L. J., Balch, W. E., Wolfe, R. S. and Woese, C. R. (1977a). *Proc. Natl Acad. Sci. USA* **74**, 4537–4541.

Fox, G. E., Pechman, K. J. and Woese, C. R. (1977b). *Int. J. Syst. Bacteriol.* **27**, 44–57.

Fox, G. E., Stackebrandt, E., Hespell, R. B., Gibson, J., Maniloff, J., Dyer, T. A., Wolfe, R. S., Balch, W. E., Tanner, R. S., Magrum, L. J., Zablen, L. B., Blakemore, R., Gupta, R., Bonen, L., Lewis, B. J., Stahl, D. A., Luehrsen, K. R., Chen, K. N. and Woese, C. R. (1980). *Science* **209**, 457–463.

Fox, G. E., Luehrsen, K. R. and Woese, C. R.(1982). *Zbl. Bakteriol. Hyg. I. Abt. Orig.* **C3**, 330–345.

Garvie, E. J. and Farrow, J. A. E. (1981). *Zbl. Bakterio. Hyg. I. Abt. Orig.* **C2**, 299–310.

Gibson, J., Stackebrandt, E., Zablen, L. B., Gupta, R. and Woese, C. (1979). *Curr. Microbiol.* **3**, 59–66.

Gibson, J., Ludwig, W., Stackebrandt, E. and Woese, C. R. (1985). *Syst. Appl. Microbiol.* **6**, 152–156.

Gillis, M. and De Ley, J. (1980). *Int. J. Syst. Bacteriol.* **30**, 7–27.

Goodfellow, M. (1984). *Syst. Appl. Microbiol.* **5**, 225–229.

Hennecke, H., Kaluza, K., Thony, B., Fuhrmann, M., Ludwig, W. and Stackebrandt, E. (1985). *Arch. Microbiol.* **142**, 342–348.

Hensel, R., Demharter, W., Kandler, O., Kroppenstedt, R. M. and Stackebrandt, E. (1986). *Int. J. Syst. Bacteriol.* **36**, 444–453.

Hespell, R. B., Paster, B. J., Macke, T. J. and Woese, C. R. (1984). *Syst. Appl. Microbiol.* **5**, 196–203.

Hindley, J. (1983). *DNA Sequencing.* Elsevier Biomedical Press, Amsterdam.

Hinnebusch, A. G., Klotz, L. C., Blanken, R. L. and Loeblich, A. R. (1981). *J. Mol. Evol.* **17**, 334–347.

Hogeweg, P. and Hesper, B. (1984). *J. Mol. Evol.* **20**, 175–186.

Hori, H. (1975). *J. Mol. Evol.* **7**, 75–86.

Huysmans, E. and De Wachter, R. (1986). *Nucl. Acids Res. Suppl.* **14**, r73–r118.

Imhoff, J. F., Trüper, H. G. and Pfennig, N. (1984). *Int. J. Syst. Bacteriol.* **34**, 340–343.

Ivanova, T. L., Turova, T. P. and Antonov, A. S. (1985). *Arch. Microbiol.* **143**, 154–158.

Jarvis, B. D. W., Gillis, M. and De Ley, J. (1986). *Int. J. Syst. Bacteriol.* **36**, 129–138.

Johnson, J. L., and Francis, B. S., (1975) *J. Gen. Microbiol.* **9**, 111–120.

Johnson, J. L. and Harich, B.(1983). *Curr. Microbiol.* **9**, 111–120.

Johnson, J. L. and Harich, B. (1986). *Int. J. Syst. Bacteriol.* **36**, 71–79.

Kato, S. I. and Komagata, K. (1986). *Nucl. Acids Res.* **14**, 4371.

Kilpper, R., Buhl, U. and Schleifer, K. H. (1980). *FEMS Microbiol. Lett.* **8**, 205–210.

Kilpper-Bälz, R. and Schleifer, K. H. (1981). *FEMS Microbiol. Lett.* **10**, 357–362.

Kilpper-Bälz, R. and Schleifer, K. H. (1984). *FEMS Microbiol. Lett.* **24**, 355–364.

Kilpper-Bälz, R., Fischer, G. and Schleifer, K. H. (1982). *Curr. Microbiol* **7**, 245–250.

Korn, L. J. and Brown, D. O. (1978). *Cell* **15**, 1145–1156.

Kössel, H., Edwards, K., Fritzsche, E., Koch, W. and Schwarz, Zs. (1983). In *Proteins and Nucleic Acids in Plant Systematics* (U. Jensen and D. E. Fairbrothers, eds.), pp. 36–57. Springer-Verlag, Berlin.

Küntzel, H., Piechulla, B. and Hahn, U. (1983). *Nucl. Acids Res.* **11**, 893–900.

Lane, D. J., Pace, B., Olsen, G. J., Stahl, D. A., Sogin, M. L. and Pace, N. R. (1985). *Proc. Natl. Acad. Sci. USA* **82**, 6955–6959.
Lau, P. P., Debrunner-Vossbrinck, B., Dunn, B., Miotto, K., MacDonnell, M. T., Rollins, D. M., Pillidge, C. J., Hespell, R. B., Colwell, R. R., Sogin M. L. and Fox, G. E. (1987). *Syst. Appl. Microbiol.* (in press).
Li, W. H. (1981). *Proc. Natl Acad. Sci. USA* **78**, 1085–1089.
Ludwig, W. and Stackebrandt, E. (1983). *Arch. Microbiol.* **135**, 45–50.
Ludwig, W., Schleifer, K. H., Fox, G. E., Seewaldt, E. and Stackebrandt, E. (1981a). *J. Gen. Microbiol.* **125**, 357–366.
Ludwig, W., Schleifer, K. H. and Stackebrandt, E. (1981b). *FEMS Microbiol. Lett.* **10**, 193–197.
Ludwig, W., Schleifer, K. H., Reichenbach, H. and Stackebrandt, E. (1983). *Arch. Microbiol.* **135**, 58–62.
Ludwig, W., Eberspächer, J., Lingens, F. and Stackebrandt, E. (1984a). *Syst. Appl. Microbiol.* **5**, 241–246.
Ludwig, W., Schleifer, K. H. and Stackebrandt, E. (1984b). *FEMS Microbiol. Lett.* **25**, 199–204.
Ludwig, W., Seewaldt, E., Killper-Bälz, R., Schleifer, K. H., Magrum, L. J., Woese, C. R., Fox, G. E. and Stackebrandt, E. (1985). *J. Gen Microbiol.* **131**, 543–551.
Macario, A. J. L. and Conway De Macario, E. (1983). *Syst. Appl. Microbiol* **4**, 451–458.
MacCarroll, R., Olsen, G. J., Stahl, Y. D., Woese, C. R. and Sogin, M. L. (1983). *Biochemistry* **22**, 5858–5868.
MacDonell, M. T. and Colwell, R. R. (1987). *Nucl. Acids Res.* **15**, 1335.
MacDonell, M. T., Swartz, D. G., Ortiz-Conde, B. A., Last, G. A. and Colwell, R. R. (1986). *Microbiol. Sci.* **3**, 172–178.
MacDonell, M. T., Hansen, J. N. and Ortiz-Conde, B. A. (1987). *Meth. Microbiol.* **19**, 357–404 (this volume).
Magrum, L. J., Luehrsen, K. R. and Woese, C. R. (1978). *J. Mol. Evol.* **11**, 1–8.
Manske, C. L. (1983). The application of information theory to: the comparative sequence analysis of 5S rRNA, computer simulations of molecular evolution and methods of construction phylogenetic trees from nucleotide sequences. Phylogenetic Ph.D. dissertation, University of California at Davis.
Margulis, L. and Schwartz, K. V. (1982). *Five Kingdoms.* W. H. Freeman, San Francisco.
Maxam, A. M. and Gilbert, W. (1980). *Meth. Enzymol.* **65**, 499–560.
Migula, W. (1900). *Specielle systematik der bakterien.* Gustav Fischer, Jena.
Mordaski, M., Goodfellow, M., Tkacz, A., Pulverer, G. and Schaal, K. P. (1980). *J. Gen. Microbiol.* **118**, 313–319.
Mordaski, M., Tkacz, A., Goodfellow, M., Pulverer, G., Peters, G. and Schmacher-Perdreau, F. (1981). *FEMS Microbiol. Lett.* **11**, 159–163.
Murray, R. G. E. (1974). In *Bergey's Manual of Determinative Bacteriology* (R. E. Buchanan and N. E. Gibbons, eds.), pp. 4–9. Williams and Wilkins, Baltimore.
Nicholson, D. E. (1982). Structure of 5S ribosomal RNA from Halobacteriacerae. Ph.D. dissertation, University of Houston.
Nicholson, D. E. and Fox, G. E. (1983). *Can. J. Microbiol.* **29**, 52–59.
O'Donnell, A. G., Goodfellow, M. and Minnikin, D. E. (1982). *Arch Microbiol.* **133**, 323–329.
Oren, A., Paster, B. J. and Woese, C. R. (1984). *Syst. Appl. Microbiol.* **5**, 71–80.
Orla-Jensen (1909). *Zbl. Bakteriol. Parasitenk. Infektionskr. Hyg. Abt. II* **22**, 97–98, 305–346.
Oyaizu, H. and Woese, C. R. (1985). *Syst. Appl. Microbiol.* **6**, 257–263.

Palleroni, N. J., Kunisawa, R., Cotopoulou, R. and Doudoroff, M. (1973). *Int. J. Syst. Bacteriol.* **23**, 333–339.

Park, Y. H., Hori, H., Suzui, K. I., Osawa, S. and Komagata, K. (1987). *Nucl. Acids Res.* **15**, 365.

Paster, B. J., Stackebrandt, E., Hespell, R. B., Hahn, C. M. and Woese, C. R. (1984). *Syst. Appl. Microbiol.* **5**, 337–351.

Paster, B. J., Ludwig, W., Weisburg, W. G., Stackebrandt, E., Hespell, R. B., Hahn, C. M., Reichenback, H., Stetter, K. O. and Woese, C. R. (1985). *Syst. Appl. Microbiol.* **6**, 34–42.

Peattie, D. A. (1979). *Proc. Natl Acad. Sci. USA* **76**, 1760–1764.

Pechman, K. J., Lewis, B. J. and Woese, C. R. (1976). *Int. J. Syst. Bacteriol.* **26**, 305–310.

Pelham, H. R. B. and Brown, D. D. (1980). *Proc. Natl. Acad. Sci. USA* **77**, 4170–4174.

Pillidge, C. J., MacDonell, M. T. and Colwell, R. R. (1987). *Nucl. Acids Res.* **15**, 1879.

Pot, B., Gillis, M., Aerts, C. and De Ley, J. (1984). Abstract of FEMS Symp. on the Evolution and Phylogeny of Prokaryotes, Munich, FRG.

Qu, L. H., Michot, B. and Bachellerie, J.-P. (1983). *Nucl. Acids Res.* **11**, 5903–5920.

Reichenbach, H., Ludwig, W. and Stackebrandt, E. (1986). *Appl. Microbiol.* **145**, 391–395.

Rippka, R., Deruelles, J., Waterbury, J. B., Herdman, M. and Stanier, R. Y. (1979). *J. Gen. Microbiol.* **111**, 1–61.

Ross, H. N. M. and Grant, W. D. (1985). *J. Gen. Microbiol.* **131**, 165–173.

Rossau, R., Van Landerschoot, A., Mannheim, W. and De Ley, J. (1986). **36**, 323–332.

Rothe, B., Fischer, A., Hirsch, P., Sittig, M. and Stackebrandt, E. (1987) *Arch. Microbiol.* **147**, 92–99.

Sackin, M. J. (1987). *Meth. Microbiol.* **19**, 000–000 (this volume).

Sakonju, S., Bogenhagen, D. F. and Brown, D. D. (1980). *Cell* **19**, 13–25.

Schleifer, K. H. and Kilpper-Bälz, R. (1984). *Int. J. Syst. Bacteriol.* **34**, 31–34.

Schleifer, K. H. and Stackebrandt, E. (1983). *Ann. Rev. Microbiol.* **37**, 143–187.

Seewaldt, E. and Stackebrandt, E. (1982). *Nature (London)* **295**, 618–620.

Seewaldt, E., Schleifer, K. H., Bock, E. and Stackebrandt, E. (1982). *Arch. Microbiol.* **131**, 287–290.

Sobieski, J., Chen, K. N., Filiatreau, J., Pickett, M. and Fox, G. E. (1984). *Nucl. Acids Res.* **12**, 141–148.

Sogin, S. J., Sogin, M. L. and Woese, C. R. (1972). *J. Mol. Evol.* **1**, 173–184.

Stackebrandt, E. (1985). In *The Evolution of Prokaryotes* (K. H. Schleifer and E. Stackebrandt, eds.). Academic Press, London.

Specht, T., Hartmann, R. K., Ulbrich, N. and Erdmann, V. A. (1986). *Nucl. Acids Res.* **14**, 4693.

Stackebrandt, E. and Hippe, H. (1986). *System. Appl. Microbiol.* **8**, 204–207.

Stackebrandt, E. and Woese, C. R. (1979). *Curr. Microbiol.* **2**, 317–322.

Stackebrandt, E. and Woese, C. R. (1981a). *Symp. Soc. Gen. Microbiol.* **32**, 1–31.

Stackebrandt, E. and Woese, C. R. (1981b). *Curr. Microbiol.* **5**, 131–136.

Stackebrandt, E. and Woese, c. r. (1984). *Microbiol. Sci.* **1**, 117–122.

Stackebrandt, E., Lewis, B. J. and Woese, C. R. (1980). *Zbl. Bakt. Hyg. I. Abt. Orig.* **C2**, 137–149.

Stackebrandt, E., Ludwig, W., Schleifer, K. H. and Gross, H. J. (1981a). *J. Mol. Evol.* **17**, 227–236.

Stackebrandt, E., Wunner-Füssl, B., Fowler, V. J. and Schleifer, K. H. (1981b). *Int. J. Syst. Bacteriol.* **31**, 420–431.

Stackebrandt, E., Seewaldt, E., Ludwig, W., Schleifer, K. H. and Huser, B. A. (1982). *Zbl. Bakt. Hyg. I. Abt. Orig.* **C3**, 90–100.
Stackebrandt, E., Ludwig, W. Seewaldt, E. and Schleifer, K. H. (1983a). *Int. J. Syst. Bacteriol.* **33**, 173–180.
Stackebrandt, E., Scheuerlein, C. and Schleifer, K. H. (1983b). *Syst. Appl. Microbiol.* **4**, 207–217.
Stackebrandt, E., Kroppenstedt, R. M. and Fowler, V. J. (1983c). *J. Gen. Microbiol.* **129**, 1831–1838.
Stackebrandt, E., Fowler, V. J. and Woese, C. R. (1983d). *Syst. Appl. Microbiol.* **4**, 326–337.
Stackebrandt, E., Seiler, H. and Schleifer, K. H. (1983e). *Zbl. Bakteriol. Hyg. I. Abt. Orig.* **C3**, 401–409.
Stackebrandt, E., Fowler, V. J., Fiedler, F. and Seiler, H. (1983f). *Syst. Appl. Microbiol.* **4**, 470–486.
Stackebrandt, E., Ludwig, W., Schubert, W., Klink, F., Schlesner, H., Roggentin, T. and Hirsch, P. (1984a). *Nature (London)* **307**, 735–737.
Stackebrandt, E., Fowler, V. J., Schubert, W. and Imhoff, J. F. (1984b). *Arch. Microbiol.* **137**, 366–370.
Stackebrandt, E., Ludwig, W. and Fox, G. E. (1985a). *Meth. Microbiol.* **8**, 75.
Stackebrandt, E., Pohla, H., Kroppenstedt, R., Hippe, H., and Woese, C. R. (1985b). *Arch. Microbiol.* **143**, 270–276.
Stackebrandt, E., Fischer, A., Hirsch, P., Roggentin, T., and Schlesner, H. (1986a). *Endocyt. C. Res.* **3**, 29–40.
Stackebrandt, E., Wehmeyer, U., and Liesack, W. (1986b). *FEMS Microbiol. Lett.* **37**, 289–292.
Stahl, D. A., Lane, D. J., Olsen, G. J. and Pace, N. R. (1984). *Science* **224**, 409–411.
Stetter, K. O. and König, H. (1983). *Sci. Am* **83**.
Stahl. D. A., Lane, D. J., Olsen, G. J., Heller, D. J., Schmudt, T. M. and Pace, N. R. (1987). *Int. J. Syst. Bacteriol.* **37**, 116–122.
Stöcklein, L., Ludwig, W., Schleifer, K. H. and Stackebrandt, E. (1983). In *Proteins and Nucleic Acids in Plant Systematics* (U. Jensen and D. E. Fairbrothers, eds.), pp. 58–62. Springer-Verlag, Berlin.
Sutton, L. A. and Woese, C. R. (1975). *Nature (London)* **256**, 64–66.
Swings, J., De Vos, P., Van den Mooter, M. and De Ley, J. (1983). *Int. J. Syst. Bacteriol.* **33**, 409–413.
Tanner, R. S., Stackebrandt, E., Fox, G. E. and Woese, C. R. (1981). *Curr. Microbiol.* **5**, 35–38.
Tanner, R. S., Stackebrandt, E., Fox, G. E. and Woese, C. R. (1982). *Curr. Microbiol.* **7**, 127–132.
Trent, D. W., Grant, J. A., Vorndam, A. V. and Monath, T. P. (1981). *Virology* **114**, 271–284.
Trent, D. W., Grant, J. A. Rosen, L. and Monath, T. P. (1983). *Virology* **114**, 319–332.
Tu, J., Prangishvilli, D., Huber, H., Wildgruber, G, Zillig, W. and Stetter, K. O. (1982). *J. Mol. Evol.* **18**, 109–114.
Uchida, T., Bonen, L., Schaup, H. W., Lewis, B. J., Zablen, L. and Woese, C. R. (1974). *J. Mol. Evol.* **3**, 63–77.
Van den Eynde, H., Imhoff, J. F. and De Wachter, R. (1987a). *Nucl. Acids Res.* **15**, 367.
Van den Eynde, H., Stackebrandt, E. and De Wachter, R. (1987b). *FEBS Lett.* **215**, 301–303.
Van Landschoot, A. and De Ley, J. (1983). *J. Gen. Microbiol.* **129**, 3057–3074.

Van Landschoot, A., Rossau, R. and De Ley, J. (1986). *Int. J. Syst. Bacteriol.* **36,** 150–160.

van Niel, C. B. (1946). *Cold Spring Harbor Symp. Quant. Biol.* **11,** 285–301.

Villanueva, E., Luehrsen, K. R., Gibson, J., Delihas, N. and Fox, G. E. (1985). *J. Mol. Evol.* **22,** 46–52.

Weisburg, W. G., Oyaizu, H., Oyaizu, H. and Woese, C. R. (1985a). *J. Bacteriol.* **164,** 230–236.

Weisburg, W. G., Woese, C. R., Dobson, M. E. and Weiss, E. (1985b). *Science* **230,** 556–558.

Weisburg, W. G., Hatch, T. P. and Woese, C. R. (1986). *J. Bacteriol.* **167,** 570–574.

Willekins, P., Stetter, K. O., Vandenberghe, A., Huysmans, E. and De Wachter, R. (1986a). *FEBS Lett.* **204,** 273–278.

Willekins, P., Huysmans, E., Vandenberghe, A. and De Wachter, R. (1986b). *Syst. Appl. Microbiol.* **7,** 151–159.

Winslow, C. E. A. and Winslow, A. R. (1908). *The Systematic Relationships of the Coccaceae.* Wiley, New York.

Woese, C. R. (1982). *Zbl. Bakteriol. Hyg. I. Abt. Orig.* **C3,** 1–17.

Woese, C. R. (1983). In *Evolution from Molecules to Men* (D. S. Bendall, ed.), pp. 209–233. Cambridge University Press, Cambridge.

Woese, C. R. (1985). In *The Evolution of Prokaryotes* (K. H. Schleifer and E. Stackebrandt, eds.). Academic Press, London.

Woese, C. R. (1987) *Microbial Reviews* in press.

Woese, C. R. and Fox, G. E. (1977). *Proc. Natl Acad. Sci. USA* **74,** 5088–5090.

Woese, C. R. and Olsen, G. J. (1986). *Syst. Appl. Microbiol.* **7,** 161–177.

Woese, C. R., Sogin, M., Stahl, D., Lewis, B. J. and Bonen, L. (1976a). *J. Mol. Evol.* **7,** 197–213.

Woese, C. R., Luehrsen, K. R., Pribula, C. D. and Fox, G. E. (1976b). *J. Mol. Evol.* **8,** 143–153.

Woese, C. R., Magrum, L. J. and Fox, G. E. (1978). *J. Mol. Evol.* **11,** 245–252.

Woese, C. R., Gibson, J. and Fox, G. E. (1980a). *Nature (London)* **283,** 212–214.

Woese, C. R., Maniloff, J. and Zablen, L. B. (1980b). *Proc. Natl Acad. Sci. USA* **77,** 494–498.

Woese, C. R., Blanz, P., Hespell, R. B. and Hahn, C. M. (1982). *Curr. Microbiol.* **7,** 119–124.

Woese, C. R., Stackebrandt, E., Weisburg, W. G., Paster, B. J., Madigan, M. T., Blanz, P., Fowler, V. J., Hahn, C. M., Blanz, P., Gupta, R., Nealson, K. H. and Fox, G. E. (1984a). *Syst. Appl. Microbiol.* **5,** 315–326.

Woese, C. R., Weisburg, W. G., Paster, B. J., Hahn, C. M., Tanner, R. S., Krieg, N. R., Koops, H.-P., Harms, H. and Stackebrandt, E. (1984b). *Syst. Appl. Microbiol.* **5,** 327–336.

Woese, C. R., Blanz, P. and Hahn, C. M. (1984c). *Syst. Appl. Microbiol.* **5,** 179–195.

Woese, C. R., Gupta, R., Hahn, C. M., Zillig, W. and Tu, J. (1984d). *Syst. Appl. Microbiol.* **5,** 97–105.

Woese, C. R., Debrunner-Vossbrinck, B. A., Oyaizu, H., Stackebrandt, E., and Ludwig, W. (1985a). *Science* **229,** 762–765.

Woese, C. R., Weisburg, W. G., Hahn, C. M., Paster, B., Zablen, L. B., Lewis, B. J., Macke, T. J., Ludwig, W. and Stackebrandt, E. (1985b). *Syst. Appl. Microbiol.* **6,** 25–33.

Zuckerkandl, E. and Pauling, L. (1965a). In *Evolving Genes and Proteins* (E. H. Bryson and H. J. Vogel, eds.), pp. 97–106. Academic Press, New York.

Zuckerkandl, E. and Pauling, L. (1965b). *J. Theor. Biol.* **8,** 357–366.

11
Computer Programs for Classification and Identification

M. J. SACKIN

Department of Microbiology, University of Leicester, Leicester LE1 7RH, UK

METHODS IN MICROBIOLOGY
VOLUME 19 ISBN 0–12–521519–3

I. Scope

This chapter is meant to help potential users to find out which programs to use for performing classification and identification on microbiological data. I have accumulated information on many programs, but have no doubt overlooked some. I apologize in advance for that.

I recommend the following procedure for finding an appropriate program. Use Table I (p. 487) to find which programs contain the features of interest. Section II explains the abbreviated terms used in Table I. Then turn to Section III for fuller details of the programs in question. Section III mentions all the features in Section II, where known, that are present in each program, plus some other features.

The "other remarks" section, where present, at the end of each program description in Section III may help in choosing from among those programs that contain all features required. There may be many such programs to choose from.

Much difficulty in understanding program documentation arises through the proliferation of roughly synonymous terms. Table II (p. 490) is designed to help in this area, and it serves also to indicate, for each set of synonymous terms, which term or terms will be used throughout this chapter.

The chapter makes no attempt to describe the methods involved, but some indication of less common methods is given, and the references in Sections II and III may be of some use.

I have tried to cover programs to analyse all the types of microbiological data corresponding to the different levels of genetic expression, as given by Norris (1980). However, as indicated in Table I, the vast majority of the programs allow data only in the form of a data table or matrix of OTUs (Operational Taxonomic Units; Sneath and Sokal, 1973) by characters, although there are programs for various other types of data also.

For more details of data processing on pyrolysis gas chromatography, pyrolysis mass spectroscopy and direct-probe mass spectroscopy see Gutteridge (1987—Chapter 6 in this volume), Wieten et al. (1983), Shute et al. (1984), Gutteridge and Puckey (1982), Stern (1982) and Alderson (1985).

Details not covered in this chapter include whether a program allows deletion (masking) of selected OTUs or characters. Most do, but this feature can also sometimes be more or less conveniently done by on-line editing, without recourse to the program. Also, much detail on the output has been omitted, such as whether the program draws a neat dendrogram on a plotter. Again, many programs do, but usually the user will, if necessary, be able to incorporate this feature himself, either by programming or by acquiring an existing program and interfacing it with existing software. Less-numerate users may need help from their computer laboratory or, if they have one, from a tame computing colleague.

A large area that has been omitted is the accuracy with which the programs perform their calculations and, indeed, the extent to which they have been tested, and generally how well they monitor their own performance. This would require detailed working experience of each program, a huge task. However, there is some coverage, albeit rather sketchy, of the extent to which the programs perform data-error checking, based mainly on the briefest of information from the programmers, and this may give some indication of how well the programs live up to what they claim to do.

A general guideline in producing this chapter has been the excellent, and entertaining, consumer reports of Blashfield and Aldenderfer (Blashfield, 1976a, b, 1977a, b; Blashfield and Aldenderfer, 1977; Aldenderfer, 1977). These authors stress the importance of error checking by the program and the very poor quality of this feature which they found. Some of the information in these articles is now out of date, but much is still useful. The data verification in some programs has since been considerably improved.

Warning: many programs are the single-handed work of research scientists. There are unlikely to be facilities for the widespread dissemination of these programs. I have tried to give some idea of the availability of each program as far as possible. Also, the amount of detail made available varies from program to program. On the whole, the more detail, the more readily available the program.

An additional warning: despite all efforts, it is virtually certain that errors will occur in the program descriptions. It is more likely that features have been wrongly omitted than wrongly claimed to be present.

Finally, it is intended that this chapter bring some focus to the variety of content and approach of the programs.

II.   Abbreviations

The following abbreviations are used throughout Section III and in Table I.

A.   Types of data

$t \times n$ data table or matrix of OTUs $\times$ characters (after Sneath and Sokal, 1973)

id mx   identification matrix. See Section II.G. below for definition.

unk(s)   unknown(s), usually strain(s) to be identified against an identification matrix.

B.   Characters and character types

ch(s)   character(s).

NC	missing data ("No comparison": Sneath and Sokal, 1973).
bin	binary characters.
ql	qualitative (non-ordered multistate) characters.
qn	quantitative (ordered multistate) characters
ch trsfn(s)	character transformation(s).

C. Resemblance coefficients

Note: no distinction is made between a coefficient and its complement. Thus S_{SM} and $1 - S_{SM}$ are both referred to as S_{SM}.

sim	similarity or dissimilarity, to include association, distance, correlation, in fact any resemblance coefficients.
sim mx	similarity matrix.
sim mces	similarity matrices.
assoc.	association, i.e. similarity based on binary characters.
coeff.	coefficient.
S_{SM}	simple matching coefficient (Sneath and Sokal, 1973, p. 132).
S_J	Jaccard coefficient (Sneath and Sokal, 1973, p. 131).
D_P	pattern difference coefficients (Sneath and Sokal, 1973, p. 176; Sackin, 1981).
S_G	Gower's similarity coefficient as in Gower (1971), or a close approximation to it. It is a generalization of Manh (see below) to allow (i) ignoring of matching zeros in selected characters and (ii) the use of qualitative characters. It is thus also a generalization of S_{SM} and of S_J. It thus allows binary, qualitative and quantitative characters. As implemented in GENSTAT (program 21) it is also a generalization of d (below).
d	Euclidean (Pythagorean) distance or taxonomic distance (= Euclidean distance divided by numbers of characters) or their squares.
Manh	Manhattan distance (Sneath and Sokal, 1973, p. 125) or mean character difference (= Manh divided by number of characters) (Sneath and Sokal, 1973, p. 123).
Mink	all Minkowski distances (Sneath and Sokal, 1973, p. 125). Includes Manh and d as special cases.
$\cos \theta$	cosine of angle subtended at origin of character space (but sometimes e.g. at grand centroid) by the two OTU vectors under comparison.
r	Pearson product-moment correlation coefficient (widely referred to as *the* correlation coefficient).
D	Mahalanobis generalized distance or its square.

D. Clustering

Definitions or descriptions of all the methods are in Sneath and Sokal (1973).

cl(s)	cluster(s).
hier.	hierarchical.
agglom.	agglomerative.
SL	single linkage.
CL	complete linkage.
UPGMA	unweighted average linkage.
WPGMA	weighted average linkage.
UPGMC	centroid clustering (sorting).
WPGMC	median clustering (sorting).
av. l.	average linkage (not specified whether weighted or unweighted but more likely to be unweighted).
L & W gen.	Lance and Williams (1966) generalized sorting. Includes SL, CL, UPGMA, WPGMA, UPGMC, WPGMC as special cases.
L & W flex.	Lance and Williams (1966, 1967a) flexible (or β-flexible) sorting. Special case of L & W gen. Includes WPGMA as special case but not SL, CL, UPGMA, UPGMC, WPGMC.
Ward	Ward (1963) minimum error sum of squares clustering, also described by Wishart (1969).
B_k	Jardine and Sibson (1968) B_k clustering.
MST	minimum spanning tree.
it. rel.	iterative relocation. See Blashfield (1977a) for review of programs in this area.

E. Goodness of clustering

coph. corr.	cophenetic correlation (Sneath and Sokal 1973, p. 278).

F. Ordination

PCA	principal components analysis.
PCD	principal coordinates analysis.
CVA	canonical variate analysis.
DA	discriminant analysis.
QDA	quadratic discriminant analysis.
FA	factor analysis.
MDSCAL	multidimensional scaling or non-linear mapping.
ADDPT	add a point to a PCA or PCD (Gower, 1968).

G. Identification

See also D in Section II.C above and CVA, DA and QDA in Section II.F
above.

Willcox   Bayesian method, as in Willcox *et al.* (1973), on unknowns
             scored as binary characters in relation to a stored identification
             matrix (next entry). Most programs with this option provide
             good back-up, for example a list of test results (character values)
             on the unknown that conflict with the best identification, list of
             the most promising tests, not so far done, which might improve
             the identification.

id mx   identification matrix, viz a group × character table of each
             character value in a collection of groups. Usually the characters
             are binary (presence/absence), and each entry is an estimate of a
             probability that a member of the group exhibits the "presence"
             state for the character. In this context the characters are usually
             referred to as tests and the character values as test results.

unk(s)   unknown(s), usually strain(s) to be identified against an id mx.
             Typically not all the tests in the id mx have been carried out on
             the unknown.

H. Computing

er chk   data-error checking.
FTN4   FORTRAN IV.
FTN77   FORTRAN 77.
prog.   program.
progr(s)   programmer(s).
enq   enquire.
docs   documentation.
W   write-up or user handbook.
P   publication(s).
L   program listing
MT   magnetic tape.
FD   floppy disc.

III.   Program details

Program details, where available, are given in the following order, each
group of details being followed by a semicolon:

program number (same numbering as in Table I) and program title;
name and address of programmer;
where to enquire about the program (if different from programmer);
computer(s) and operating system(s);
programming language(s);
machine dependence;
data-error checking;
program options (same order as in Table I):
  types of data (e.g. $t \times n$). (Note that many programs allow intermediate
  output and re-input of similarity matrices and other data. In general this
  is not mentioned here. Also, many programs read a group membership
  list for subsidiary processing only, for example computing mean inter-
  and intra-group similarities. This is also usually not mentioned here, but
  the processing options are mentioned as "other options" or in "other
  remarks".);
  whether missing data (NC) allowed;
  types of character that are allowed (usually omitted: clear from the
  context, especially from choice of similarity coefficients allowed by the
  program);
  similarity coefficients;
  clustering methods;
  options to test goodness of clustering in the data (e.g. cophenetic
  correlation);
  ordination options;
  identification options;
  other options;
documentation available, including publications, write-up/user handbook, magnetic tape, floppy disc;
cost of program;
other remarks.

A. Packages

This section outlines large taxonomic programs or suites of programs, which
contain a broad range of options. Although classification, that is the
formation of groups or hierarchies, forms the core of these packages, they all
contain a wide range of other options such as principal components analysis
or identification. The distinction between the packages and the programs in
Section III.B below is not clear-cut, but in general the programs there are
more specialized and have fewer options.

1. NUMIPAK; A. Stott and M. Goodall, Microbiology Department,

Monash University, Clayton, Victoria 3168, Australia; DEC VAX under VMS; BASIC; machine dependence slight; er chk: some; $t \times n$, electrophoretic traces; no NC; bin, qn; S_{SM}, S_J, D_P on bin chs (Sneath and Sokal, 1973), S_G (but may only be Manh), (for trace data) d or cosine coefficients on traces in optimum alignment obtained by linearly transforming the readings of one trace relative to the other; SL, CL, UPGMA; coph. corr.; Willcox; prog. PROMOST to find OTUs within m (bin) chs of unk; prog. PROSORT to find sets of identical OTUs; W, P: for background to trace comparisons see Feltham and Sneath (1979), ?FD; highly interactive and user-friendly, with good output on inter- and intra-cluster properties.

2.　No overall name; D. H. Colless, CSIRO Division of Entomology, PO Box 1700, Canberra City, ACT 2601, Australia; DEC PDP11/60 under RXS-11M; FTN77; machine dependence slight; er chk: very little; $t \times n$, trees; NC; bin, ql, qn; ch trsfns; (prog. PSIM) many sim coeffs including Mink, Canberra metric (Lance and Williams, 1967b), r, Farris "special similarity"; (prog. PCLASS) L & W gen. sorting, also a "variable" strategy with optional variation in gamma; (prog. ATREE) checks all comparisons of four OTUs for additivity (4-point metric), accumulates and averages deviations, and corrects matrix at the end, iterates, giving unique dendrogram (via e.g. distance Wagner); (prog. PHD) hier. clustering by maximizing a predictive index (Colless, 1984); (progs NWAG, PENDEK) Wagner trees, "Farris-optimized", including (prog. NSWAP) "nearest-neighbour single-branch swapping" and (prog. RADIX) relocation of root at midpoint of (a) median internode or (b) longest path on tree; (prog. MOTOR) from dendrogram finds "moats", i.e. steps between forks on the dendrogram or weighted (metric) tree; (prog. COHEST) computes intragroup pairwise distance statistics; (prog. DIFMAT) compares two distance matrices by average difference, Prager and Wilson (1978) F, Fitch·and Margoliash S.D., corr. coeff.; (prog. TREDIF) compares trees by computing number of shared components (subsets), equivalent to number of forks in strict consensus tree (Sokal and Rohlf, 1981; Sackin, 1985); MT or preferably FD (DECFILES 11, double density), free, L which include fairly detailed comments; programs designed primarily for own use, so no claims to be particularly user-friendly.

3.　No overall package name; progrs G. F. Estabrook, K. L. Fiala, C. A. Meacham and others; enq G. F. Estabrook, University of Michigan Herbarium, Ann Arbor, Michigan 48109, USA; IBM 360; FTN4; machine dependence slight; $t \times n$, ch state trees; no NC; (prog. SIMGRA) S_G but coeff extended to allow user-supplied sim values between each pair of states of ql chs (called matrix chs) (see also prog 8 below), (prog. MINK) Mink; (prog. LANCE) L & W gen. sorting, (prog KMEANS) it. rel., (prog. PRESERVE) finds best partitionings of the OTUs into two groups by use of information theoretic criteria (Estabrook, 1971), ql chs assumed; (prog. WITHINA) 1-way analysis of variance to compare variability of chs within OTUs to variability among OTUs, starting from several representatives of each OTU (same number of representatives for each OTU); (progs CLINCH, FAC-TOR, POTENTIAL, COMPROB) from $t \times n$ and hypothetical ch state evolutionary trees, finds sets of mutually compatible and incompatible chs and computes probabilities that sets of chs are mutually compatible; W, MT (3/4 in. × 1200 ft); $50; elegant prog. design and presentation, especially CLINCH, and good for teaching as well as research purposes.

4.   NTZ, D INDEX; progr (prog. NTZ) L. J. Wuest, R. R. #1, Cross Creek, N. B. E0H 1E0, Canada, (prog. D INDEX) C. Wilbur, Computer Centre, University of Windsor, Windsor, Ont. N9B 3P4, Canada; enq M. A. Holder-Franklin, Department of Biology, University of Windsor, Windsor, Ont. N9B 3P4, Canada; IBM 370/3031 under MVS; (NTZ) WATFIV (dialect of FORTRAN), (D INDEX) FORTRAN G; very machine-depen-dent; (prog. NTZ) er chk: yes; $t \times n$; NC; S_{SM}; SL, CL, UPGMA; (prog. D INDEX) uses id mx to obtain Gyllenberg (1963) discrimination measures C, q_0, q_1, R (also in Sneath and Sokal, 1973, pp. 384–385) for each ch; progs primarily for own research use on bacterial population shifts. NTZ is a development from NTSYS (prog. 12) with unwanted features (e.g. dendro-gram) omitted, but it contains extensive output on cluster properties and interrelationships.

5.   TAXAN; R. B. Ivimey-Cook, Department of Biological Sciences, University of Exeter, Prince of Wales Road, Exeter EX4 4PS, UK; ICL System 4; FTN4; machine dependence "too much" according to R. B. Ivimey-Cook; er chk: some; $t \times n$; NC; S_{SM}, S_J, other assoc. coeffs, D_P on bin chs (Sneath and Sokal, 1973), S_G,d, cos θ, r, other coeffs on qn chs; UPGMA, WPGMA; PCA, PCD, FA; computer and hence programs are obsolescent, but may be updated. Derives from earlier version of TAXPAK (prog. 15 below).

6.   D.A.C.L. 82 (Data Analysis and Cluster Analysis); M. Jambu and M.-O. Lebeaux, CNET-PAA/TIM/MTI, 38–40 rue du Général Leclerc, 92131 Issy-Les-Moulineaux, France; IBM and DEC VAX (English version), H-B Multics and GCOS (French version); FTN4; very machine-independent; $t \times n$; no NC; bin, qn; ch trsfns; S_{SM}, S_J, other assoc. coeffs, d, χ^2 distance, mutual information distance; SL, CL, UPGMA, UPGMC, WPGMC, Ward, other minimum within-group hier. clustering methods, MST, it. rel. suitable for very large data sets (two methods); PCA, FA; compare classification with

PCA and FA; add points to a cl analysis; test stability of clustering by Monte Carlo simulations; MDSCAL; P: full details in Jambu and Lebeaux (1983), MT with input and output examples; free to research and academic institutes, $500 to private institutes; much unfamiliar terminology makes Jambu and Lebeaux (1983) very hard to follow.

7. CLUSTRIT; L. P. Lefkovitch, ESRI, Agriculture Canada, Heritage House, C.E.F., Ottawa, Ontario K1A 0C6, Canada; IBM 370/160; FORTRAN plus 3 assembler routines; very machine-independent except for the assembler routines; er chk: yes; $t \times n$; NC; S_{SM}, S_J, 14 other assoc. coeffs, S_G, Lefkovitch's own coeff. for mixed data. All coeffs can be transformed in one of 7 ways; L & W gen. sorting, MST, sequential divisive method based on MST, (unpublished) iterative centroid clustering procedure in principal coordinate space, principal coordinate clustering; Frobenius norm and trace sigma methods of cluster optimization; many non-hier. and miscellaneous methods; many ways of displaying properties of resulting classifications; scope for user to incorporate his own methods; W which contains references to the methods, MT; free under certain conditions—not for commercial distribution; developed primarily as a research tool.

8. R; progr. A Vaudor, Département de Sciences Biologiques, Université de Montréal, C.P. 6128, Succ. A, Montréal, Québec H3C 3J7, Canada; enq P. Legendre, same address as progr; CDC CYBER under NOS or NOS/BE; PASCAL 6000, header prog., if used, in CYBER control language (CCL); machine dependence very slight; er chk: extensive; $t \times n$; NC; ch trsfns; 49 sim coeffs, possibly more than in any other prog., all in Legendre and Legendre (1983). Assoc. coeffs include S_{SM}, S_J, coeffs on mixed data include S_G and a coeff (Estabrook and Rogers, 1966) which is as in SIMGRA in prog. 3 above for ql chs and for qn chs allows the user to specify for each ch the largest ch value difference for which some similarity is allowed. There are two probabilistic sim coeffs, one based on χ^2, and Orlóci's (1978) version of the probabilistic sim coeff. of Goodall (1964, 1966), the general principle being to weight ch state matches by the rarity of the corresponding states over the rest of the OTUs under study. Also: d, chord distance, arc distance or geodesic metric (both the chord and the arc are between the pair of OTU vectors, scaled to unit length, subtended at the origin of the ch space), Mink, Canberra metric (Lance and Williams, 1967b), r, and other measures; SL, porportional link, CL, L & W gen. sorting, chronological clustering (with a time contiguity constraint: Legendre et al., 1985), non-hier. CL clustering, chain of primary connections (dendrites) (polythetic divisive clustering); coph. corr. (Pearson and Kendall versions), Gower's distance; PCA, PCD;

W: documentation file, in French, P: Legendre and Legendre (1983) (but not all details covered in this book), MT; $50; prog. runs interactively. Prog. also has options geared to ecological studies. Book includes very useful French–English glossary of technical terms.

9. No overall package name; I. C. Lerman and colleagues, Institut de Recherche en Informatique et Systèmes Aléatoires, Campus Universitaire de Beaulieu, Avenue du Général Leclerc, 35042 Rennes Cedex, France; FOR-TRAN, probably FTN4; (prog. CAHM1) hier. clustering program; $t \times n$; see W for details of similarity and clustering; W, P: Lerman (1981); (prog. MPATD) non-hier. partitioning method around nuclei (poles d'attraction) chosen by the prog. to optimize the partition; W, P: Lerman (1981), Leredde (1979); (various progs) collection of progs to examine the results of a classification; P: Lerman (1981, 1982); coverage of the programs hampered by difficulties understanding French.

10. No overall prog. name; L. Orlóci and colleagues, Department of Plant Sciences, University of Western Ontario, London, Ontario N6A 5B7, Canada; (progs INIT and 10 others) progr O. Wildi, Swiss Federal Institute of Forestry Research, CH 8903 Birmensdorf, Switzerland; enq 0. Wildi; PDP 10, CDC CYBER; FTN4, FTN77; machine dependence very slight; er chk: yes; $t \times n$; no NC; ch trsfns; d, r, van de Maarel's coeff. (see Table II: reduces to S_J if chs are bin) and others; SL, CL, av. l., Ward; PCA, PCD; DA, simple identification by matching unk to nearest group; P: Wildi and Orlóci (1983), more detail on methods in Orlóci (1978), MT; original application is analysis of vegetation data; (progs CORRELATION, ALC, TREE) progr L. Orlóci; enq L. Orlóci; Apple II series; Applesoft BASIC; machine dependence very slight; er chk: yes; $t \times n$; no NC; r; av. l.; P: Orlóci and Kenkel (1983), FD; (progs SIMMAT, ALC4, DISCOM) progr L. Orlóci and S. S. Shaukat, address as L. Orlóci above; DECsystem 10, PDP 10; BASIC; machine dependence very slight; er chk: none; $t \times n$, trees; no NC; Manh, r; UPGMA, WPGMA, UPGMC, WPGMC; compares sim mces, cophenetic matrices and topological matrices by the measures in Rohlf (1974); L, MT.

11. MINT; F. J. Rohlf, Department of Ecology and Evolution, State University of New York at Stony Brook, Stony Brook, NY 11794, USA; most minicomputers and larger systems, perhaps even a microcomputer with a hard disc; FORTRAN; machine dependence very slight; er chk: limited; $t \times n$; NC; ch trsfns; S_{SM}, S_J and other assoc. coeffs, Manh, d, r; SL, UPGMA, L & W flex. sorting and other hier. clustering methods, L*-clusters (Jardine and Sibson, 1971), MST; coph. corr.; PCA; W, MT; $35 plus cost of 200 ft

MT; probably more options than given here or in Table I—further details from F. J. Rohlf. Designed with emphasis on ease of implementation on a wide variety of computers. See NTSYS (prog. 12).

12. NTSYS; F. J. Rohlf, address as in prog. 11 above; UNIVAC1100, IBM 370/VM, VAX 11/780 under VMS, and others; machine dependence slight: needs modifications in 6 basic subroutines for different host systems; er chk: limited; $t \times n$; NC; ch trsfns; many assoc. coeffs, d, r; probably SL, CL, UPGMA, WPGMA, UPGMC, WPGMC and others; coph. corr.; probably PCA, PCD, FA; DA; (soon) tree comparisons based on strict consensus trees (Day, 1985); W, MT; $60 plus cost of 600 ft MT; probably many more options than given here or in Table I—further details from F. J. Rohlf. One of the earliest large numerical taxonomy systems. Larger systems than MINT (mini NTSYS) (prog. 11).

13. TAXON; D. Ross and colleagues, CSIRO Computing Research, 306 Carmody Road, St Lucia, Q4067, Australia; CDC CYBER 76 under SCOPE, CDC CYBER 835 under NOS; FTN77 plus minimal assembly code; machine dependence very slight: slow FTN77 versions of the assembly code routines are available; er chk: extensive; $t \times n$; NC; all ch types; S_{SM}, S_J, S_G, d, Manh, (soon) Mink, Canberra metric (Lance and Williams, 1967b), information statistic (on ql chs), Levenshtein metric (Lu and Fu, 1978), (soon) Goodall (1964, 1966) probabilistic coeff.; SL, CL, UPGMA, WPGMA, UPGMC, WPGMC, L & W flex. sorting, Ward, Burr (1970) (a minimal incremental sum of squares method, normally for Euclidean metric only), also information analysis (agglom. method) (Lance and Williams, 1967b), non-hier. methods including it. rel. and (soon) Jancey–True groups (d'après Orlóci), divisive clustering (many varieties), MST; PCA, PCD, ordination by detrended correspondence analysis to avoid (1) the frequent "arch" or "horseshoe" problem (see also prog. 47) due to quadratic dependency of the second axis on the first axis and (2) the compression of the axis ends. Optionally allows reciprocal averaging (Hill and Gauch, 1980); simple comparison (contingency table) between two groupings; properties of groups and relationships between groups; W (microfiche), MT; $50 as cost of MT. Licence agreement required; W is long but extremely clear. Prog. has great flexibility and is very rich in utility progs and options. Allows sensible default options wherever possible. Embodies most of the method of W. T. Williams, G. N. Lance and colleagues in Southampton, UK and Canberra, Australia, but has absorbed, or is planning to absorb, progs from many other sources. Includes PHYLIP (prog. 53) and allows data in DELTA format (see progs 41, 42).

14.   CLASP; G. J. S. Ross, Statistics Department, Rothamstead Experimental Station, Harpenden, Herts AL5 2JQ, UK; ICL 4–70, DEC VAX under VMS; FTN4; uses short integers—EBCDIC or ASCII codes—and random-number generator; er chk: some; $t \times n$; NC; ch trsfns; S_{SM}, S_J, Manh, d, weighted coeffs; SL, CL, av. l., UPGMC, WPGMC, MST, it. rel; PCD; identification by (i) ranked sims with standard groups, (ii) ADDPT, (iii) dichotomous branching on information criterion; batch keys for bin data— minimum number of chs needed to distinguish all OTUs; bin key based on reducing information; many options for displaying cluster properties and relationships between original chs and principal coordinate axes; W, prog. distributed under licence, annual cost according to type of user (up to £200); prog. has same origin as the taxonomic parts of GENSTAT (prog. 21), with which it shares many features.

15.   TAXPAK; M. J. Sackin and colleagues, Department of Microbiology, University of Leicester, Leicester LE1 7RH, UK; DEC VAX under VMS, older version on ICL 1900 series; FTN77 (but 1900 version is in ALGOL 60); machine dependence very slight; er chk: extensive; $t \times n$; NC; ch trsfns; S_{SM}, S_J, other assoc. coeffs, D_P including on qn chs (Sackin, 1981), S_G, d, r, Manh, $\cos \theta$ and other coeffs; SL, UPGMA, WPGMA (soon: CL, UPGMC, WPGMC, Ward), (soon) MST; coph. corr.; PCA, PCD; properties of groups and relationships between groups; W (soon), MT; allows user to add more sim coeffs and hier. clustering methods. Allows construction of id mx for use by (i) SAKID (prog. 37), (ii) the identification progs and mx evaluation progs of P. H. A. Sneath (progs 39, 55 respectively).

16.   Facom OSIV/X8, Mulva/X; T. Sekine, Daito Bunka University Computer Center, Takashima-Daira, Itabashi, Tokyo, Japan; er chk: yes; $t \times n$; ?no NC; d, r, D; SL, CL, UPGMA, WPGMA, Ward; details incomplete— probably more options available, including a measure of goodness of clustering.

17.   CAVE; progr G. Ohmayer, Datenverarbeitungsstelle, Tu München, D-8050 Freising-Weihenstephan, W. Germany; enq H. Seiler, Süddeutsche Versuchs- und Forschungsanstalt für Milchwirtschaft, D-8050 Freising-Weihenstephan, FRG; IBM 3081 under OS/MVS, CDC CYBER 175 under NOS; FTN4; machine dependence slight; er chk: no; $t \times n$; no NC; d, Mink; SL, CL, av. l., UPGMC, WPGMC, Ward, k-diameter clustering (varies from CL to SL as k increases: Ohmayer et al., 1980); MDSCAL, for aid in drawing 2-dimensional "linkage maps" (Ohmayer et al., 1980); W, MT; cost of MT.

18. DUST; S. T. C. Weatherup, Biometrics Division, Agriculture and Food Science Centre, department of Agriculture (NI), Newforge Lane, Belfast BT9 5PX, Northern Ireland; DEC VAX under VMS; FTN77; machine dependence slight; er chk: some; $t \times n$; NC; S_G, Manh, D; SL, CL, UPGMA, WPGMA, UPGMC, WPGMC, L & W flex. sorting, Ward; coph. corr.; PCA, PCD; CVA; univariate analysis of variance; W, P: Weatherup (1980), MT; prog. also contains options for multivariate analyses of plant variety distinctness, uniformity and stability trials (DUST), for which the prog. system was originally devised.

19. ARTHUR plus Biomol. routines; progr and enq; (i) ARTHUR: Infometrics, P.O.B. 25808, Seattle, Wa 98125, USA, (ii) Biomol routines: G. B. Eijkel, FOM Institute for Atomic and Molecular Physics, Kruislaan 407, 1098 SJ Amsterdam, Netherlands; CDC CYBER 170–750 under NOS/BE; FTN4 and FTN77; machine dependence very slight; er chk: yes; $t \times n$; NC; all ch types; ch trsfns; d, with allowance for ch weighting according to constancy within OTU replicates; SL, CL, UPGMC, MST; PCA; DA by double stage PCA (Hoogerbrugge *et al.*, 1983); MDSCAL; W, P (below); cost of ARTHUR is about $750; prog. usage at FOM is for results of pyrolysis of complex organic samples, e.g. intact bacterial cells or cellular fractions, and subsequent mass-spectrometric analysis of the volatile, ionized fragments. Ch selection is performed by F-test on between/within variance ratio of ch over replicates of each OTU. The F values are the optional weights allowed in computing d above. For entry into the field see Wieten *et al.* (1983) and Wieten (1983), which contains other publications bound in it. See also Section I above.

20. BMDP; progr L. Engelman and many others, under the chief editorship of W. J. Dixon; enq: BMDP Manual from University of California Press, 2223 Fulton Street, Berkeley, CA 94720, USA and from University of California Press Ltd, 37 Dover Street, London W1X 4HQ, UK. Also, from BDMP Statistical Software, P.O. Box 24A26, Los Angeles, CA 90024, USA: (1) 140-page BMDP User's Digest, (2) BMDP Pocket Guide, (3) BMDP Reference Card; implementations on most mainframe computers; FOR-TRAN; er chk: extensive; (prog. P1M: Cluster Analysis of Variables) $t \times n$; no NC; qn; r, |r|, arcos r, arcos |r|; SL, CL, UPGMA but with different averaging formula if arcos coeffs being used; printer output includes sim mx with dendrogram superimposed; (prog. P2M: Cluster Analysis of Cases) $t \times n$; no NC; qn; (with optional trsfns to z scores) d, Mink, (for cases where data values are counts, i.e. frequencies) χ^2, φ^2; SL, pseudo-nearest neighbour algorithm (i.e. $1 \leqslant k \leqslant 10$ OTUs must cover intersection of two hyperspheres before corresponding pair of cls join. k = 1 is SL), UPGMC; (prog. P3M:

Block Clustering) $t \times n$; bin, ql; clusters OTUs and chs simultaneously; (prog. PKM: K-means Clustering of Cases) it. rel.; output includes elegant pairs of histograms displaying distances from cl centroid of (a) members of the cl (b) members of the other cls, incorporating cl labels; (prog. P4M) FA; (prog. P7M) stepwise DA; (prog. P8M) Boolean FA; (all progs) W: see above, MT; BMDP is a wide-ranging statistical package, originally developed for medical purposes. The manual is extremely clear and helpful as is the design and scope of the prog. output, but many combinations of options commonly used in microbiological applications are not available, e.g. S_{SM} and UPGMA.

21. GENSTAT; progr: various, under J. A. Nelder, Statistics Department, Rothamstead Experimental Station, Harpenden, Herts AL5 2JQ, UK. Numerical taxonomic parts are by J. C. Gower and G. J. S. Ross (see also prog. 14); enq: (i) GENSTAT manuals from Director, Program Library Unit, 18 Buccleuch Place, Edinburgh, EH8 9LN, UK, (ii) enquiries on the distribution of software and subject matter of the manuals to GENSTAT Secretary, Statistics Department, Rothhamstead Experimental Station, Harpenden, Herts AL5 2JQ, UK; many mainframe computers; FORTRAN; er chk: some; $t \times n$; NC; S_G with extensions, allowing (i) option to ignore matching zeros in qn chs, (ii) qn Pythagorean chs whose contribution to sim is proportional to 1-*squared* ch difference, d, (d^2 is case of all chs being qn Pythagorean), D; SL, CL, UPGMA, UPGMC, WPGMC (note: clustering is with finite threshold steps), MST, it. rel.; PCA, PCD; CVA; identification by ADDPT; many options to display cluster properties; W (see above), MT; GENSTAT is a wide-ranging statistical package. The taxonomic parts of GENSTAT have the same origin as CLASP (prog. 14).

22. CLUSTAN; progr D. P. C. Wishart and colleagues, 16 Kingsburgh Road, Edinburgh EH12 6DZ, UK; enq: (i) manual from Program Library Unit, 18 Buccleuch Place, Edinburgh EH8 9LN, UK or from CLUSTAN, 16 Kingsburgh Road, Edinburgh EH12 6DZ, UK, (ii) expected German translation of manual from J. B. Schäffer, Institut für medizinische und Systemforschung, Gesellschaft für Strahlen und Umweltforschung MBH, D-8042 Neuherberg, Ingolstädter Landstraße, FRG, (iii) use of CLUSTAN: J. T. Henderson, Computing Laboratory, University of St Andrews, North Haugh, St Andrews, KY16 9SZ, UK; implementations on most mainframe computers; FTN4 and FTN77; machine dependence very slight; er chk: extensive; $t \times n$; no NC (but expected soon); bin, qn; ch trsfns, including conversion from raw chs to principal axes by preliminary PCA; S_{SM}, S_J, squared D_p on bin chs (Sneath and Sokal, 1973), many other assoc. coeffs, d, r, cos θ, sim ratio (same as van der Maarel's coeff. in prog. 10: reduces to S_J if

chs are bin), information gain statistic, and others, easy provision for user's own coeff; SL, CL, UPGMA, WPGMA, UPGMC, WPGMC, L & W flex. sorting, Ward, MST, it. rel., mode analysis: building up clusters around densest areas of points, both both monothetic and polythetic forms of divisive clustering, B_K; coph. corr. and all the measures of Jardine and Sibson (1971) for comparing a sim mx and a dendrogram or comparing two dendrograms; find most likely number of clusters; PCA (see also ISDC in progs 26 below); DA; maximum likelihood identification (as prog. 45 below); MDSCAL; exceptionally versatile plotting routines for 2-dimensional data representation, allowing display of cl membership, significant inter-cl links, cl radii and cl outlines; W (see above), MT under licence—fee according to nature of installation; extremely helpful manual, with details of the many available error messages, suggested default options according to size of data, recommendations on the usage of each feature including every sim coeff in the prog. and on suitable combinations of sim coeffs and clustering options and their effects, and comprehensive references to all methods in the prog. Allows ready interface with other packages and with user's own progs (see e.g. progs 26 and 29 below). Probably by far the most widespread taxonomic package. There is a PASCAL conversational preprocessor (CLUSCOM), which can be set up to give messages in any language.

23.   HIERPAK; R. J. White, Biology Department, The University, Southampton SO9 5NH, UK; ICL 2970 under VME/B; FTN4; machine dependence minimal; er chk: some; $t \times n$; no NC; bin, qn; sum of squares (sim); divisive clustering, several options (Lambert *et al.*, 1973) including monothetic and several polythetic methods, also a non-hier. method; PCA; W, MT, paper tape (8-track, ASCII); £20–£30. Send back any MT; prog. originally intended for vegetation data, viz presence/absence of plant species (chs) in vegetation quadrats (OTUs).

24.   No overall package name; H. R. Saunders and G. L. Smith, National Collections of Industrial and Marine Bacteria Ltd, Torry Research Station, PO Box 31, 135 Abbey Road, Aberdeen AB9 8DG, UK; IBM 1130; FTN4; considerable machine dependence; $t \times n$; ?no NC; S_{SM}, S_J, r, cos θ and degree of overlap for gas–liquid chromatography data; SL, CL, UPGMA; output includes a "deltagram", which is a simplified dendrogram in which each group is represented by a triangle, as well as ordinary dendrograms; cluster properties including calculating id mx; prog. obsolete with demise of IBM 1130 at Aberdeen.

B.   Other programs that include taxonomy

See comments at the start of Section II.A above.

25. Several progs; P. Laban, Laboratoire de recherche API, La Balme Les Grottes, 38390 Montalieu Vercieu, France; (progs LINKA, LINKS) DEC PDP 11/03 and PDP 11/23; FORTRAN; machine dependence slight; $t \times n$; no NC; d; SL, av. 1.; (prog. APILAB) progr P. Laban, M. Colla; enq P. Laban, as above; APPLE IIe, Commodore, DEC PDP 11/03, PDP 11/23; FORTRAN, BASIC; machine dependence slight; id mx and unks; identification; W, FD.

26. Various progs; T. N. Bryant, Medical Faculty, South Academic Block, Southampton General Hospital, Southampton SO9 4XY, UK; PRIME 750 under PRIMOS Rev. 19.2; FTN4 except where otherwise indicated; uses PRIME applications library for some VDU input/output and file operations; (prog. PCNA) PCA, PCD; (prog. GPROPS) $t \times n$ and group membership; bin, qn; NC; ch trsfns; cluster properties including, for bin chs, calculating id mx; (prog. OVERCLUST) $t \times n$ and group membership; finds overlap between groups. As OVCLUST (prog. 55 below); (prog. OVERMAT, in BASIC) finds overlap between groups in an id mx (as prog. 55 below); (progs GBEST, BEST) id mx; finds best tests (chs) either to separate a specified taxon from all the others or to try to distinguish between all pairs of taxa; (prog. BACTID) id mx and unks; Willcox; (prog. IDSC) similar to MOST-TYP (prog. 55) but with choice of options for id mx entries of .5; (prog. IDEN, in FTN77) id mx plus unk generated by computer; this is a teaching exercise in identification. The unk is the most typical possible member of a taxon, as in prog. IDSC above and MOSTTYP (prog. 55), but the user is not told which taxon. The prog. allows the user to try and make an identification after having asked the computer for as few of the unk's test results as possible (Bryant and Smith, 1979); W, MT; several of the above progs are designed as being supplementary to CLUSTAN (prog. 22 above). Prog. PCNA allows more chs than the PCA option in CLUSTAN.

27. TAXMAP; progr J. W. Carmichael, 31–4 RR1, Fanny Bay, B.C. V0R 1W0, Canada; enq Program Librarian, Computing Services, University of Alberta, Edmonton, Alberta T6G 2H1, Canada; FTN4; machine dependence minimal; er chk: some; $t \times n$; NC allowed but not recommended; all ch types; Manh- or S_G-type coeff, but always counting matching zeros and with option to weight the chs according to their relative information content; builds up clusters by empirically derived non-hier. method and plots them as taxometric maps; much detail on cluster structure and interrelationships; W, P: theoretical basis of TAXMAP is described in Carmichael *et al.* (1965, 1968) and Carmichael and Sneath (1969); $25 for the tape, including handling charge and postage; prog. is an interesting attempt to simulate the kind of groups that a person may build intuitively.

28. BOLAID; A. V. Hall, Bolus Herbarium, University of Cape Town, 7700 Rondebosch, South Africa; Sperry (UNIVAC) 1106; FORTRAN; Machine dependence slight; er chk: none; $t \times n$; NC; all ch types; ch trsfns; relative homogeniety coeff, which is used for clustering like information statistic and/or for a centroid method of clustering; measures peculiarity indices (Hall, 1965) of taxa, interrelationships between groups and coeffs for a descriptive function based on the amount of homogeneity disturbance on linkage; constructs dichotomous key; P: Hall (1973).

29. PLOTMAT and other progs.; K. K. Kersters, Laboratorium voor Microbiologie en Microbiele Genetica, Rijksuniversiteit-Gent, B-9000, Ledeganckstraat 35, Belgium; Siemens 7541 under BS 2000; FTN4; machine dependence very slight; er chk: some; $t \times n$; NC; S_{SM}, S_J, S_G, Canberra metric (Lance and Williams, 1967b), r; plots shaded sim mx; L, MT; sim mx is suitable as input to CLUSTAN (prog. 22 above).

30. Hierarchical Clustering Program, K-means Clustering Program; progr G. W. Milligan, Academic Faculty of Management Sciences, Ohio State University, 356 Hagerty Hall, 1775 College Road, Columbus, OH 43210, USA.; enq Ohio State University Data Center, College of Administrative Science, 16 Hagerty Hall, 1775 College Road, Columbus, OH 43210, USA; FTN4; machine dependence very slight; er chk: little; (Hier. Clustering Prog.) $t \times n$; no NC; d; SL, CL, UPGMA, WPGMA, UPGMC, WPGMC, L & W flex. sorting, Ward, allowance for user-specified clustering method; for all clustering levels, computes point-biserial goodness of fit and tests significance by Monte Carlo clusterings on random data; computes cluster centroids as possible starting points for K-means Clustering Prog.; (K-means Clustering Prog.) $t \times n$; it. rel.; output includes point biserial goodness of fit; W, P: Milligan and Sokol (1980), Anderberg (1973) (for k-means method), L with sample input and output, MT, cards, $15 (MT or cards); general scheme is to perform initial hier. clustering, with UPGMA as favoured clustering option, and then to use the k-means prog. to adjust the clusters to give clusters that are more stable against perturbations in the data, albeit at the expense of complete hierarchicalness.

31. TAXAN, IGPS3; enq R. R. Colwell, Central Administration, University of Maryland, Adelphi, MD 20783, USA; UNIVAC 1108; FTN4; $t \times n$; NC; S_J; UPGMA; properties of groups; progs developed from earlier versions of TAXPAK (prog. 15 above).

32. Various progs; M. I. Krichevsky and colleagues, Microbial Systematics Section, National Institute of Dental Research, Bethesda, MD 20205, USA;

$t \times n$; S_{SM}, S_J, UPGMA; properties of groups; Willcox; progs developed from earlier versions of TAXPAK (prog. 15 above). Details incomplete.

C. Programs for taxonomy based on electrophoretic traces

See also progs 1, 24 and Section I above.

33. TRACETAX, PAGETAX; P. J. H. Jackman, Division of Microbiology, AFRC Institute of Food Research, Colney Lane, Norwich NR4 7UA, UK; (prog. TRACETAX) COMMODORE 3032/3040 under DOS 1 or DOS 2; COMMODORE BASIC 3.00 or 4.00 with some machine code subroutines; an all-BASIC version is very machine-independent; er chk: none; traces, e.g. densitometer scans of electrophoretic protein patterns or gas–liquid chromatography traces, coded as a series of height values at constant time intervals, which have normally been converted into this form by an analog-to-digital converter (see also PAGETAX below); no NC; traces are smoothed and background is removed. Background is defined as a proportion of a coarsely smoothed version of the trace. For S_{Dice} the heights are converted to bin: peak present/absent; r, S_{Dice} (Sneath and Sokal (1973, p. 131): S_{Dice} prevents swamping by the largest peaks, which sometimes occurs with r), each coeff value chosen at the position of best alignment between the two traces that the prog. finds; UPGMA; W, P: Jackman et al. (1983) for use of r, Jackman (1983) for use of S_{Dice}, L: included in P, or from progr, FD; (prog. PAGETAX: PAGE stands for polyacrylamide gel electrophoresis) SAGE IV and SIRIUS computers, each under UCSD-p-system; USCD PASCAL; machine dependence minimal over all machines running USCD-p-system version IV, but with variation in graphics according to graphics facilities on given machine; er chk: none; data as TRACETAX but allows automatic recording of gels with the Joyce Loebl Chromoscan 3 or LKB Ultrascan densitometers; no NC; makes correction of gel-to-gel variation based on reference patterns by interpolation in segments; r; UPGMA; output as colour high resolution graphics; P: Jackman (1985), L, FD; identification methods under development.

34. BIOSYS-1; D. L. Swofford, Section of Economic Entomology, State Natural History Survey Division, 607 East Peabody Drive, Champaign, IL 61820, USA and R. B. Selander, Department of Genetics and Development, University of Illinois, Urbana, IL 61801, USA; most or all machines supporting full ANSI FTN77; FTN77; machine dependence minimal; $t \times n$; here gene × locus, each entry being genotype. Up to 10 alleles per locus. Prog. is designed for biochemical population geneticists to analyse electrophoretically detectable allelic variation; allows computation of allele (electromorph)

frequencies, measures of genetic variability, conformity test to Hardy–Weinberg equilibrium state, F-tests for analysis of population structure, χ^2 test of interpopulation heterogeneity; various measures of genetic sim; UPGMA, WPGMA: coph. corr. and F values of Prager and Wilson (1978); Wagner trees and networks; W, P: Swofford and Selander (1981), MT, cards, L, test data; see also progs 51, 58.

D. Programs for identification only

These are identification programs which do not contain options for classification. Progs 35–40 use Bayesian methods, progs 41–43 are key-generating programs, and progs 44–46 are other identification progs. See Table I for other progs that contain identification options in them.

35.   Identification of β-galactosidase positive enterobacteria; progr B. Lefebvre, IUT "A" de Lille I, BP 179, 59653 Villeneuve d'Ascq Cedex, France; enq INSERM U. 146, 369 rue Jules Guesde, BP 39, 59651 Villeneuve d'Ascq Cedex, France; ISTC 5000 microcomputer under CPM; FORTRAN; machine dependence very slight; er chk: yes; id mx and unks; Willcox.

36.   ONTRACK; progr W. E. Rypka and R. G. Babb, Section of Microbiology, Lovelace Medical Center, 5400 Gibson Blvd SE, Albuquerque, NM 87108, USA; enq E. W. Rypka; Hewlett-Packard 9845 and 9836; BASIC AP2–1, also a FORTRAN version; machine dependence minimal; er chk: yes; taxon × ch table, all chs bin, entries negative, variable, positive, missing; finds successive most discriminating chs to use for identification of an unk; performs identification by a Bayesian method but which allows missing entries in the id mx; P: Rypka *et al.* (1982a, b), MT, FD, cassette; uses much terminology from mathematical logic and cybernetics, for example, for different categories of ch according to their discriminatory power or, if none, their degree of redundancy.

37.   SAKID; M. J. Sackin, Department of Microbiology, University of Leicester, Leicester LE1 7RH, UK; also, variants of the prog. by R. K. A. Feltham, Public Health Laboratory, Leicester Royal Infirmary, Leicester LE1 5WW, UK; DEC VAX under VMS; FTN77; machine dependence minimal; er chk: some; id mx and unks; Willcox with option for prior probabilities of each taxon; two versions: SAKID1 reads unks from a file, SAKID2 reads each unk interactively in response to prompts at the terminal. SAKID1 would generally be used if there are many unks; prog. design and style of output derive ultimately from prog. MICRO by Friedman *et al.*

(1973), but their identification formula is different; W, L, MT; id mx may be generated by prog. TAXPAK (prog. 15 above).

38. POCKID/HP, POCKID/YI, IDES; progr (POCKID/HP) J. Schindler, Department of Medical Microbiology and Immunology, Faculty of Medicine, Charles University, Studničkova 2, CS 12800 Prague 2, Czechoslovakia, (POCKID/TI and IDES) Z. Schindler, Podbadska 6, 16000 Prague 6, Czechoslovakia; enq J. Schindler; (POCKID/HP) Hewlett-Packard 41C, (POCKID/TI) Texas Instruments 59, (IDES) Hewlett-Packard 85; (POCKID/HP and POCKID/TI) assembly code, (IDES) BASIC; (POCKID/HP and POCKID/TI) very machine-dependent, (IDES) moderately machine-dependent; er chk: some (IDES only); id mx and unks; Willcox; W, P: Schindler and Schindler (1983) for use of POCKID/HP, (POCKID/HP and POCKID/TI) magnetic cards, (IDES) magnetic tape cartridge.

39. MATIDEN, IDENMIX; P. H. A. Sneath, Department of Microbiology, University of Leicester, Leicester LE1 7RH, UK; DEC VAX under VMS; BASIC; machine dependence minimal; er chk: little; id mx and unks; identification options for both progs are (i) Willcox, (ii) taxonomic distance d from unk to taxon centroids, (iii) standard error score of d, s.e.(d). If $\bar{d}$ is the mean distance of the members of a taxon from their centroid then s.e.(d) s.e.(d) is the number of standard deviations by which the unk is further from the taxon centroid than $\bar{d}$. Thus s.e.(d) = 4 places the unk probably much further out than one would expect for a member, whereas s.e.(d) = -2 places it unusually close to the centroid even for a member, (iv) Gaussian integral of s.e.(d), giving a measure of the likelihood of taxon membership, (v) pattern difference, modified from the Sneath (1968) D_p, of the unk from the taxon centroid; the difference between the two programs is that MATIDEN compares the unk with each taxon in turn in the usual way, but IDENMIX compares the unk with all pairwise mixtures of taxa on the basis that the unk is a mixture of two bacterial cultures. It assumes that the mixture will be positive for a ch if one or both of the two components gives a positive result; W, P: (for MATIDEN) Sneath (1979d), L, MT; id mx may be generated by prog. TAXPAK (prog. 15 above). See progs 55 for progs to evaluate the quality of an id mx.

40. IDPROF; progr W. F. Willemse-Collinet, Th. F. J. Tromp and T. Huizinga; enq Th. F. J. Tromp or T. Huizinga, Department of Pharmacotherapy and Dispensing Division, Pharmaceutical Microbiology, University of Groningen, Antonius Deusinglaan 2, Groningen, Netherlands; CDC CYBER 74–18; FTN4; id mx and unks; Willcox but with different normalization (denominator of identification score), giving a score of 1 to any taxon

for which the unk has the more probable state on all the chs on which it has been tested; P: Willemse-Collinet *et al.* (1980).

41. KEY; M. J. Dallwitz, CSIRO Division of Entomology, G.P.O. Box 1700, Canberra, ACT 2601, Australia; DEC VAX under VMS, DEC PDP 11 under RXS 11, CDC CYBER 76, UNIVAC; FTN4; standard version available (with reduced capability), plus special versions for the above computers; er chk: extensive if read data via CONFOR (below), otherwise fair; taxon descriptions in the form of a taxon × ch table, allowing bin, ql and qn chs, in which each entry may be a single numeric value (for a ch that is constant within a taxon), several values, a range of values, any combination of these, or "v", meaning "variable", with extensive provision for verbal descriptions of the ch states. Recommended to use DELTA format (DEscription Language for TAxonomy) (Dallwitz, 1980) and convert it to KEY format by prog. CONFOR; prog. KEY is a non-probabilistic key-generating prog., with options to minimize its total cost by (i) reading in ch reliabilities (high reliability corresponds to low cost), (ii) reading in taxon weights or abundances so that as far as possible the shortest paths on the key are for the most abundant taxa; W, P: Dallwitz (1974), MT; documentation is extremely clear and brief. A program PABTRAN (progr J. P. Higgins, same address, enq M. J. Dallwitz) with similar input to KEY produces a card polyclave. DELTA format is also allowed by progs 13, 42.

42. KEYGEN; R. J. Pankhurst, Department of Botany, British Museum (Natural History), Cromwell Road, London SW7 5BD, UK; any mainframe or mini- or (probably) large microcomputer; FTN4 (FTN77 soon); machine dependence very slight; er chk: extensive; taxon descriptions, which may be in full DELTA format (see prog 41 above); KEYGEN is a non-probabilistic key-generating prog. with options for ch weights (to control the order in which the prog. selects chs), taxon weights (so that as far as possible the most highly weighted taxa key out along the shortest paths), conditional chs, i.e., option to disallow selected combinations of ch states, partial keys (where not all taxa are distinct); there is also an on-line identification prog. that reads unks one ch at a time and compares them with taxa stored in DELTA format. A BASIC version of this prog. exists for use on microcomputers. There is a prog. for identification by matching, i.e. calculation of sims of unks to taxa, two progs for diagnostic descriptions (Pankhurst, 1983), viz finding sets of the chs whose values, taken together, within a taxon are different from those in all other taxa, and there is a prog. for punching polyclaves onto punched cards. There is also a prog. to calculate a sim mx suitable for input to CLUSTAN (prog. 22 above) from data in DELTA

format, and a prog. to translate from DELTA format to PAUP format (see prog. 51 below); P: Pankhurst (1978, 1983), W, L, MT, probably FD or paper tape; media costs; all documentation is very clear.

43.   GENKEY; R. W. Payne, Statistics Department, Rothamstead Experimental Station, Harpenden, Herts AL5 2JQ, UK; ICL 4/70 and 1900, DEC VAX under VMS, Prime, IBM, CDC 7600 and 6400; FTN4; machine dependence slight: utilities must be provided for character handling and for operations on bit patterns (AND, OR etc.); taxon descriptions in the form of a taxon × ch table, allowing bin and ql chs, in which each entry may be a single value, for a ch that is constant within a taxon, or, for non-constant chs, a set of probabilities of each ch state within a taxon; GENKEY can construct probabilistic or non-probabilistic keys, diagnostic tables or polyclaves. Keys once constructed can be extended to include new taxa or to take account of further chs. Also, keys and diagnostic tables can be constructed to identify genera based on information about the species (Payne et al., 1982). Key-generating options include costs or convenience weighting of chs and prior probabilities or importance weightings of the taxa. Prog. also prints irredundant test sets, i.e. sets of tests (chs) that can identify all of the taxa and that contain no redundant tests; P: Payne (1978), Payne et al. (1982) and many more papers dealing with aspects of the methods and their use on yeasts, W, MT.

44.   Autokey; R. A. Hellenthal, Biology Department, University of Notre Dame, IN 46556, USA; IBM 370 series with TSO (Time-Sharing Option), CDC CYBER series under NOS, UNIVAC 1100 series, Radio Shack Color Computer; FTN4 and FTN77 (mainframe versions), BASIC (micro versions); machine dependence slight for mainframe versions, moderate for micro versions; er chk: yes, by separate prog.; taxon × ch table, all chs bin, entries negative, variable, positive, missing; identifies by requesting ch values of unk one ch at a time; W; prog. is conversational and very user-friendly. Prog. optimizes the order in which it requests ch values on the unk, but W does not give the algorithm. Author claims good results for insects, but less good for microbial organisms and higher plants.

45.   NORMIX; prog. John Wolfe, US Naval Personnel Research Laboratory, San Diego, CA, USA; enq John Wolfe or B. S. Everitt, Biometrics Unit, Institute of Psychiatry, De Crespigny Park, Denmark Hill, London SE5 8AF, UK; CDC 6600; FORTRAN; machine dependence very slight; er chk: none; $t \times n$ and number(s) of groups; no NC; qn; fits mixtures of multivariate normal distributions. Includes likelihood ratio test for number of groups,

probabilities of group membership for each OTU and discriminant function plots; MT; this prog. has been incorporated into CLUSTAN (prog. 22 above).

46. No prog. name(s); H. Chernoff, Department of Statistics, Stanford University, Stanford, CA 94305, USA; APL; $t \times n$; no NC; two progs to find the best linear and best quadratic classifiers for separating two multivariate normal populations, given their means and covariances. They also evaluate a distance which generalizes Mahalanobis D for populations with non-identical covariance mces; P: Chernoff (1979).

E. Programs for ordination only

See also Table I, under PCA, PCD, CVA and DA, FA, and ADDPT, for other progs which contain ordination options in them. The coverage here does not claim to be complete but is concentrated on progs used for microbiological applications and on taxonomy progs that contain ordination options in them.

47. Step-across, Step-along; M. H. Williamson, Department of Biology, University of York, YO1 5DD, UK; DEC-10, TOPS-10; (both progs) BASIC, PASCAL, (Step-across only) FTN4, FTN77; uses NAG library for latent roots and vectors; er chk: no; $t \times n$; no NC; (Step-across) bin, (Step-along) qn; PCD with preliminary transformation to remove "horseshoe" effect to which bin data and data with many zeros generally are prone. Uses S_J in Step-across and Kendall's circle product in Step-along; P: (Step-across) Williamson (1978), (Step-along) Williamson (1983), L, MT (but progs are quite short); see also prog. 13 above.

48. SIMCA; S. Wold, Research Group of Chemometrics, Institute of Chemistry, Umeå University, S-901 87 Umeå, Sweden; (i) BASIC on ABC-80 personal computer, Laxor-Scania Metric, Stockholm, Sweden, (ii) FORTRAN on larger computers; $t \times n$; groups; qn; PCA, measuring variation in the OTUs and testing for outliers among the OTUs of each group, by an F-test (object validation method). Elegant graphical output including also for comparing the groups; P: Söderström et al. (1982).

F. Programs for analysing protein and nucleotide sequences

See also Table I, under proteins/nucleotides, for more programs.

49. HAN7, GEOMAS; G. E. Schulz, Institut für organische Chemie und

Biochemie der Universität, 7800 Freiburg i. Br., Albertstraße 21, FRG; NORD-100; FORTRAN; (prog. HAN7) machine dependence very slight; amino-acid sequence pair; slides segments of one of the sequences along the other sequences and tries to find positions of insertions and deletions according to the values of certain input parameters. Similar method is used by Staden (1982)—see prog. 50 below; P: Wieland *et al.* (1984); (prog. GEOMAS) machine dependence slight; aligns secondary structure of two proteins by translation and rotation to best least-squares fit and measures their chain-fold similarity according to a measure of area between the two chains. Uses a Monte Carlo method to assess significance; P: Schulz (1983).

50. Various programs for computer analysis of biological sequences; enq A. W. F. Coulson, Department of Molecular Biology, University of Edinburgh, King's Buildings, Mayfield Road, Edinburgh, EH9 3JR, UK; DEC VAX, but accessible by all UK universities and elsewhere via JANET network; the system allows access to (i) program package written by the University of Wisconsin Genetics Computer Group for the analysis of nucleic-acid and protein sequences, including restriction mapping, sequence translation, homology searching, secondary structure analysis, sequence composition analysis,and hypothetical sequence manipulation. For details see Devereux *et al.* (1984), (ii) programs written by R. Staden, Laboratory of Molecular Biology, MRC Centre, University Medical School, Hills Road, Cambridge CB2 2QH, UK for data management in DNA sequencing projects. These progs allow gel readings to be entered, edited, reconciled into "contigs", stored and displayed. For details see Staden (1982), (iii) US (Genbank) and European (EMBL) nucleic-acid-sequence databases and the NBRF protein-sequence database, including PSQ system of searching the NBRF database, (iv) other users; P, as above, W as letter of 22 November 1984 from Dr Coulson giving a succinct outline of the facilities and how to gain access to them.

G.   Programs for evolutionary trees

See also Table I, under evolutionary/Wagner trees, for other progs that contain these options.

51. PAUP—Phylogenetic Analysis Using Parsimony; D. L. Swofford, Section of Economic Entomology, State Natural History Survey Division, 607 East Peabody Drive, Champaign, IL 61820, USA; IBM under MVS and VM/CMS, CDC under NOS 1 and 2, DEC VAX under VMS (*not* UNIX), UNIVAC 1100, Honeywell; FTN77 with optional assembler for greater speed; machine dependence otherwise very slight; er chk: extensive; $t \times n$;

NC; bin, ql, qn, but qn chs must be non-negative integers. The ql chs here are chs whose interstate relationships are unknown before the analysis; interactive prog. for evolutionary tree by maximum parsimony criteria, trying to minimize the total length of a Manh metric on the tree. Many options. Tree is Wagner if there are no ql chs. Evaluates tree by measure of homoplasy (parallel and reverse evolution); W, MT (by special arrangement); see prog. 42 for data transformation from DELTA format to PAUP format.

52.   DNAPEQ, DNAJEQ; M. J. Bishop, Department of Zoology, University of Cambridge, Downing Street, Cambridge CB2 3HU, UK; IBM 3081 under MVT and MVS; FTN77; machine dependence slight; er chk: some; estimates phylogeny from DNA sequences by the method of maximum likelihood under the exponential failure model. Calculates a "support ratio" to compare maximum-likelihood hypotheses with competing hypotheses; P: Bishop and Friday (1985), MT; cost of MT plus handling charge.

53.   PHYLIP—Phylogeny Inference Package; J. Felsenstein and colleagues, Department of Genetics SK-50, University of Washington, Seattle, WA 98195, USA; almost all computers, including microcomputers; PASCAL; machine dependence minimal; er chk: minimal; $t \times n$; (bin or qn chs), gene frequencies, immunological or DNA hybridization distances, DNA and protein sequences; NC (most progs); 19 progs for estimating phylogeny by various parsimony methods, maximum likelihood method, Fitch–Margoliash and least-squares methods, evolutionary compatibility methods; tree comparisons based on strict consensus trees (Day, 1985); W, MT, FD; has been implemented on many different computers.

H.   Programs for multidimensional scaling

See also Table I for other programs that contain these options.

54.   MVAR—Multivariate Analysis Routines; D. J. Puckey, Meat Research Institute, Langford, Bristol BS18 7DY, UK; Data General 3 under IDOS (Finnigan Mat Ltd); FORTRAN; machine dependence moderate; er chk: via IDOS; includes $t \times n$; no NC: qn; MVAR is a package for analysing bacterial samples that have been subjected to direct-probe mass spectroscopy. Options include MDSCAL on proportional sim coeffs; W, MT, hard disc.

I.   Programs for evaluating the quality of taxonomic data

See Table I, under "Data quality evaluation," for other progs in this area.

55. Various progs; P. H. A. Sneath, Department of Microbiology, University of Leicester, Leicester LE1 7RH, UK; DEC VAX under VMS; BASIC; machine dependence minimal; er chk: little; (prog. OVCLUST) calculates the overlap between pairs of cls and for each pair of cls tests whether the observed overlap is significantly less than an arbitrarily chosen expected, or critical, overlap (Sneath, 1979b). The prog. allows several starting points: (a) $t \times n$ (no NC) and group membership, (b) intercentroid distances, distances of each OTU from each cluster centroid, and group membership, or (c) intercentroid distances and standard deviations of distances from their own centroids of projections of OTUs along intercentroid axis. Assumes cls are multivariate normal. Published prog. (PHS7B19) allows only one pair of cls in a run. Versions MJS8B19 and MJS9B19 (M. J. Sackin, same address) allow all pairs, with starting points (c), (a) respectively. Starting point (c) may be produced by TAXPAK (prog. 15 above); (prog. TESTDEN) as OVCLUST but with a dendrogram as starting point. Prog. considers the pairs of cls emanating from each branch point (Sneath, 1979a). Assumes cls are hyperspherical; (prog. KOLCLUS) non-parametric, conservative analogue of OVCLUST, with starting points (a) and (b) above (Sneath, 1979c); (prog. OVERMAT) as OVCLUST but with id mx as starting point (Sneath, 1980c). Assumes cls are hyperspherical; (prog. INTGROV) as OVCLUST but with mean inter- and intragroup sims as starting point. Assumes cls are hyperspherical; (prog. CHARSEP) from id mx computes various measures of ch separation, to assess their usefulness in identification (Sneath, 1979e); (prog. DIACHAR) from id mx finds the most diagnostic chs in each group (Sneath, 1980a); (progs PHS3B01 to PHS3B05) progs to examine the effect of test errors on an id mx; (prog. MOSTTYP) from id mx forms the most typical hypothetical member of each cl (the HMO, hypothetical median organism) and performs identification on the HMOs by methods (i), (ii), (iii) and (iv) of MATIDEN (prog. 39 above). For evaluating the quality of an id mx (Sneath, 1980b); (prog. MATHIST) gives histogram summaries of 10 properties of an id mx, including those calculated by OVERMAT, CHARSEP, DIACHAR and MOSTTYP; (prog. DENBRAN) from a dendrogram, tests whether the OTUs could be samples from multivariate normal distributions and estimates the "effective" number of dimensions (Sneath, 1985); W, P as above, L, MT; id mx may be generated by prog. TAXPAK (prog. 15 above). For corresponding identification progs see progs 39 above.

J. Taxonomy based on similarity to reference OTUs only

See also Hubálek (1981, 1982).

56. REFOTUS; P. H. A. Sneath, Department of Microbiology, University of Leicester, Leicester LE1 7RH, UK; DEC VAX under VMS; BASIC; machine dependence minimal; er chk: little; from the similarities between the OTUs and a subset of them (the reference OTUs), i.e. a "strip" of the sim mx, estimates the remaining entries in the mx and uses it for clustering. Allows d, r, semichord of r, and clustering by SL, CL, UPGMA, WPGMA, WPGMC, Ward. Also allows PCD. The similarities among the reference OTUs need not be symmetrical, but the output matrix is symmetrical. The prog. is of use, for example, for serological cross-reactions; W, P; Sneath (1980d, 1983), L, MT.

K. Miscellaneous programs to display taxomonic data

See also the ordination and MDSCAL options in Table I.

57. Program for faces; H. Chernoff, Department of Statistics, Stanford University, Stanford, CA 94305, USA; versions at Stanford, on Bell Laboratories S, and on MIT Center for Computational Research in Economics and Management Science system TROLL; FORTRAN; machine dependence high; $t \times n$; no NC; qn; plots multivariate data in the form of human faces, where each OTU becomes a face and the chs become the facial features; P: Chernoff (1973).

L. Programs for comparing classifications

See also Table I for other progs containing options for comparing classifications. For entry into this fast-moving field see Sackin (1985) and Day and McMorris (1985).

58. CONTREE; D. L. Swofford, Section of Economic Entomology, State Natural History Survey Division, 607 East Peabody Drive, Champaign, IL 61820 USA; FTN77; forms Adams (Adams, 1972) and strict (Sokal and Rohlf, 1981, p. 312) consensus trees plus associated congruence statistics.

59. CMTREE, FSTREE; progr C. Finden, Mathematical Institute, University of St Andrews, North Haugh, St Andrews, KY16 9SS, UK; enq A. D. Gordon, same address; DEC VAX 11/780 under VMS; FTN77; machine dependence: programs incorporate a few VAX-11 FORTRAN extensions; er ch: yes; from two dendrograms (trees), attempts to prune the trees down to the largest topologically identical (i.e. local order equivalent— Sibson, 1972) subtrees common to both trees. The two progs differ in detail only. P: Gordon (1979, 1980), W, L, MT; progs free via JANET network (see prog. 50) or at media and postage cost on MT.

Acknowledgements

I am most grateful to the following for program information: F. A. Bisby, M. J. Bishop, R. K. Blashfield, P. D. Bridge, Y. Brun, T. N. Bryant, J. W. Carmichael, H. Chernoff, D. H. Colless, T. J. Crovello, M. J. Dallwitz, W. H. E. Day, G. F. Eastbrook, B. S. Everitt, J. Felsenstein, F. Gavini, D. W. Goodall, A. D. Gordon, A. V. Hall, R. A. Hellenthal, M. A. Holder-Franklin, Z. Hubálek, R. B. Ivmey-Cook, P. J. H. Jackman, M. Jambu, K. K. Kersters, L. P. Lefkovitch, P. Legendre, I. C. Lerman, J. McNeill, G. W. Milligan, G. Ohmayer, R. J. Pankhurst, R. W. Payne, D. J. Puckey, F. J. Rohlf, D. Ross, G. J. S. Ross, E. W. Rypka, S. Sakai, J. Schindler, G. E. Schulz, H. Seiler, S. S. Shaukat, G. L. Smith, D. L. Swofford, S. T. C. Weatherup, G. Wieten, M. F. Willemse-Collinet and M. H. Williamson.

TABLE I

Program features and the programs that contain them. Programs are referred to by numbers given in Section III. This table gives the most common features. An entry such as ?11 means that the corresponding feature is *probably* present in program 11. An entry such as (33) means that the corresponding feature is expected to be implemented soon

$t \times n$ matrix	
NC	2, 4, 5, 7, 8, 11, 12, 13, 14, 15, 18, 19, 21, (22), 26, 27, 28, 29, 31, 51, 52, 53
bin	1, 2, 3, 4, 5, 6, 7, 8, 9, 10, 11, 12, 13, 14, 15, 18, 19, 21, 22, 23, 24, 25, 26, 27, 28, 29, 31, 32, 47, 51, 53
ql	2, 3, 5, 7, 8, 9, 13, 14, 15, 18, 19, 20, 21, ?27, 28, ?29, 34, 51
qn	1, 2, 3, 5, 6, 7, 8, 9, 10, 11, 12, 13, 14, 15, 16, 17, 18, 19, 20, 21, 22, 23, 24, 25, 26, 27, 28, 29, 30, 45, 46, 51, 53, 54, 56, 57
Trace data	1, 24, 33, 34
Proteins/nucleotides	49, 50, 52, 53
ch trsfns	2, 3, 5, 6, 8, 10, 11, 12, 14, 15, 19, 20, 22, 26, 28, 33, 57
S_{SM}	1, ?2, 4, 5, 6, 7, 8, 11, ?12, 13, 14, 15, ?18, 21, 22, 24, 29, 32
S_J	1, ?2, 4, 5, 6, 7, 8, 11, ?12, 13, 14, 15, ?18, 21, 22, 24, 29, 31, 32
Other assoc. coeffs	?2, 5, 6, 7, 8, 9, 10, 11, ?12, 15, 22, 33, 56
D_P	1, 5, 15, 22
S_G	?1, 3, 5, 7, 8, 13, 14, 15, 18, 21, 27, 29

TABLE I *continued*

d	1, 2, 3, 5, 6, 8, 9, 10, 11, 12, 13, 14, 15, 16, 17, 19, 20, 21, 22, 25, 29, 30
Manh	1, 2, 3, 5, 8, 11, 13, 14, 15, 17, 18, 20, 21, 27
Mink	2, 3, 8, 17, 20
cos θ	1, 5, 15, 22, 24
Canberra metric	2, 8, 13, 29
r	2, 5, 8, 10, 11, 12, 15, 16, 20, 22, 24, 29, 33
Information statistic	6, 8, 13, 22
D (see also: CVA and DA, identification: other)	8, 12, 16, 18, 20, 21, 46
Other sim	2, 3, 5, 6, 8, 10, 13, 15, 19, 20, 22, 23, 24, 28, 34, 56
Compare sim mces (see also: Compare 2 classifications)	2
SL	1, 2, 3, 4, 5, 6, 7, 8, 10, 11, 12, 13, 14, 15, 16, 17, 18, 19, 20, 21, 22, 24, 25, 30, 56
CL	1, 2, 3, 4, 6, 7, 8, 10, ?11, 12, 13, 14, (15), 16, 17, 18, 19, 20, 21, 22, 24, 30, 56
UPGMA	1, 2, 3, 4, 5, 6, 7, 8, 10, 11, 12, 13, 15, 16, 18, 20, 21, 22, 24, 30, 31, 32, 33, 34, 56
WPGMA	2, 3, 5, 7, 8, 10, 11, 12, 13, 15, 16, 18, 22, 30, 34, 56
UPGMC	2, 3, 6, 7, 8, 10, ?11, ?12, 13, 14, (15), 17, 18, 19, 20, 21, 22, 30
WPGMC	2, 3, 6, 7, 8, 10, ?11, ?12, 13, 14, (15), 17, 18, 21, 22, 30, 56
av. l.	10, 14, 17, 25
L. & W. gen. sorting	2, 3, 7, 8
L. & W. flex. sorting	2, 3, 7, 8, 11, 13, 18, 22, 30
Ward/incremental sum of squares	6, 7, 10, 13, (15), 16, 17, 18, 22, 30, 56
Other hier. agglom. clustering	2, 6, 7, 8, 12, 13, 17, 20, 28
B_k	?12, 22
MST	6, 7, 11, 13, 14, (15), 19, 21, 22
it. rel.	3, 6, 7, 9, 13, 14, 20, 21, 22, 30
Other non-hier. clustering	7, 8, 11, 12, 13, 22, 23, 27

Divisive clustering	7, 8, 13, 22, 23
coph. corr.	1, 8, ?9, 10, 11, 12, 15, 18, 22, 34
Other goodness of clustering	3, 6, 7, 8, 9, 10, 16, 22, 30, 34, 55
Inter- and intra-group sims	1, 4, 5, 13, 14, 15, 21, 24, 27
PCA	5, 6, 8, 10, 11, ?12, 13, 15, 18, 19, 21, 22, 23, 26, 48
PCD	5, 7, 8, 10, 11, ?12, 13, 14, 15, 18, 21, 26, 47, 56
CVA and DA (see also identification: other, D)	10, 12, 18, 19, 20, 21, 22, 28, 45, 46
FA	5, 6, 12, 20
ADDPT	14, 21
Willcox identification	1, 26, 32, 35, 36, 37, 38, 39
Key generation	28, 41, 42, 43
Identification: other (see also D, CVA and DA)	6, 10, 14, 22, 25, (33), 39, 40, 41, 42, 43, 44, 45
id mx and cl evaluation (see also next entry)	2, 7, 26, 55
Data-quality evaluation, e.g., reproducibility (see also preceding entry)	3, 6, 18, (33), 55
Time-related behaviour of cls	8
Evolutionary/Wagner trees	2, 11, 34, 51, 52, 53
MDSCAL	6, 17, 19, 22, 27, 54
Compare classifications	2, 6, 10, 13, 14, (15), 22, 58, 59
FTN4	3, 5, 6, 9, 10, 14, 17, 19, 22, 23, 24, 26, 27, 29, 30, 31, 40, 41, 42, 43, 44, 47
FTN77	2, 13, 15, 18, 19, 22, 34, 37, (42), 44, 47, 51, 52, 58, 59
WATFIV	4
FORTRAN G	4
FORTRAN (unspecified)	7, 9, 11, 12, 20, 21, 25, 28, 35, 36, 45, 48, 54, 57
ALGOL 60	15
BASIC	1, 10, 25, 26, 33, 36, 38, 39, 44, 47, 48, 55

TABLE I *continued*

PASCAL	8, 33, 47, 53
APL	46
Assembly	38
Programming language unknown or not applicable	16, 32, 50

Table II

Roughly synonymous terms used in numerical taxonomy. This table could be much extended, but has been restricted to the terms relevant to features in the programs described in this chapter. Terms in italics are those used consistently throughout this chapter; in a few cases several terms are used interchangeably, e.g. taxon, cluster, group (terms 26 below). Equivalent, though not necessarily identical, terms are shown in roman type. These terms are all to be found in program write-ups and in the literature generally

---

Taxonomic data (See also Groups—terms 26)

1. *OTU* (operational taxonomic unit), *point*, individual, sample, observation, case (especially in prog. 20), object, unit, sampling unit, element, specimen, taxon (this can be confusing; see Groups—terms 26 below), population (also see Groups), base point (prog. 59), terminal OTU, quadrat (in plant ecology), site (likewise), species (see also Groups), EU (evolutionary unit—some of progs 3), ETU (evolutionary taxonomic unit), unknown (for identification)
2. *character, variable, test*, attribute, descriptor, property, variate, feature, response (on an unknown), question (on an unknown)
3. *character state, character value, test result*, character (confusing; see 2), attribute value

Taxonomic character types

4. *binary*, qualitative (see also 5), nominal 2-state, presence–absence, categorical, logical (prog. 6), (0, 1), incidence
5. *qualitative*, disordered multistate, nominal
6. *quantitative* (integer values), ordered multistate, ordinal (i.e. ranked), interval (i.e. equal intervals)
7. *quantitative* (real values), numeric, metric, continuous, absolute

Preliminary processing

8. *delete*, mask

Similarity: general

9. *similarity, resemblance*, dissimilarity, proximity

10. *matching zeros*, matching negatives, double zeros (Legendre and Legendre, 1983)

Similarity: actual coefficients

11. van der Maarel's coefficient (Wildi and Orlóci, 1983), Similarity Ratio (prog. 22)
12. *mean character difference (MCD)*, Czekanowski's coefficient, durchschnittliche Differenz
13. *Manhattan metric* (= MCD/number of characters), city block metric

Clustering: general

14. *clustering*, cluster analysis, sorting (especially Lance and Williams)
15. hierarchical (Sneath and Sokal, 1973), stratified (Jardine and Sibson, 1971)
16. hierarchical and non-overlapping (Sneath and Sokal, 1973), hierarchical (Jardine and Sibson, 1971)
17. *agglomerative hierarchical clustering*, ascending hierarchical clustering (prog. 6)
18. *divisive hierarchical clustering*, descending hierarchical clustering (prog. 6)

Clustering: actual methods

19. *single linkage*, nearest-neighbour sorting, linkage analysis (L. L. McQuitty)
20. *complete linkage*, furthest-neighbour sorting, diameter method, maximum distance, homostat production
21. *UPGMA* (unweighted pair-group method using arithmetic averages), *unweighted average linkage*, group average (Lance and Williams), average linkage (in prog. 22), McQuitty differential sorting scheme (in prog. 22)
22. *WPGMA* (weighted pair-group method using arithmetic averages), *weighted average linkage*, McQuitty similarity analysis (in prog. 22), simple average.
23. *UPGMC* (unweighted pair-group centroid method), centroid, unweighted centroid
24. *WPGMC* (weighted pair-group centroid method), median, weighted centroid, Gower
25. *minimum spanning tree (MST)*, shortest spanning tree, minimum-length tree, shortest connection network, Prim network

Groups (see also terms 1 above)

26. *group, taxon, cluster*, population, species, class, subset, object (sometimes in progs 42)

Identification

27. *score*, probability, likelihood

Dendrograms

28. *dendrogram*, tree, phenogram

Multidimensional scaling
29. *multidimensional scaling (MDSCAL)*, non-linear mapping

References

Adams, E. N. (1972). *Syst. Zool.* **21**, 390–397.

Aldenderfer, M. S. (1977). A consumer report on cluster analysis software. (2) Hierarchical methods. Unpublished report.

Alderson, G. (1985). In *Computer-assisted Bacterial Systematics* (M. Goodfellow, D. Jones and F. G. Priest, eds.), pp. 227–263. Academic Press, London.

Anderberg, M. R. (1973). *Cluster Analysis for Applications.* Academic Press, London.

Bishop, M. J. and Friday, A. K. (1985). *Proc. R. Soc. Lond.* **226**, 271–302.

Blashfield, R. K. (1976a). *Classification Soc. Bull.* **3**, (4), 25–42.

Blashfield, R. K. (1976b). A consumer report on the versatility and user manuals of cluster analysis software. Unpublished report.

Blashfield, R. K. (1977a). A consumer report on cluster analysis software. (3) Iterative partitioning methods. Unpublished Report.

Blashfield, R. K. (1977b). A consumer report on cluster analysis software. (4) Useability. Unpublished Report.

Blashfield, R. K. and Aldenderfer, M. S. (1977). A consumer report on cluster analysis software. (1) Cluster analysis methods and their literature. Unpublished report.

Bryant, T. N. and J. E. Smith (1979). *J. Biol. Educ.* **13** (1), 58–66.

Burr, E. J. (1970). *Aust. Comput. J.* **2**, 98–103.

Carmichael, J. W., Julius, R. S. and Martin, P. M. D. (1965). *Nature (London)* **208**, 544–547.

Carmichael, J. W., George, J. A. and Julius, R. S. (1968). *Syst. Zool.* **17**, 144–150.

Carmichael, J. W. and Sneath, P. H. A. (1969). *Syst. Zool.* **18**, 402–415.

Chernoff, H. (1973). *J. Am. Statist. Assoc.* **68**, 361–368.

Chernoff, H. (1979). *Sequential Analysis and Optimal Design*, 2nd printing, pp. 50–52. SIAM, Philadelphia.

Colless, D. H. (1984). *Syst. Zool.* **33**, 64–68.

Dallwitz, M. J. (1974). *Syst. Zool.* **23**, 50–57.

Dallwitz, M. J. (1980). *Taxon* **29**, 41–46.

Day, W. H. E. (1985). *J. Classification* **2**, 8–30.

Day, W. H. E. and McMorris, F. R. (1985). *Bull. Math. Biol.* **47**, 215–229.

Devereux, J., Haeberli, P. and Smithies, O. (1984). *Nucl. Acids Res.* **12**, 387–395.

Estabrook, G. F. (1971). *Math. Geol.* **3**, 203–207.

Estabrook, G. F. and Rogers, D. J. (1966). *BioScience* **16**, 789–793.

Feltham, R. K. A. and Sneath, P. H. A. (1979). *Comput. Biomed. Res.* **12**, 247–263.

Friedman, R. B., Bruce, D., MacLowry, J. and Brenner, V. (1973). *Am. J. Clin. Pathol.* **60**, 395–403.

Goodall, D. W. (1964). *Nature (London)* **203**, 1098.

Goodall, D. W. (1966). *Biometrics* **22**, 882–907.

Gordon, A. D. (1979). *Biometrika* **66**, 7–15.

Gordon, A. D. (1980). In *Analyse de Données et Informatique* (R. Tomassone, ed.), pp. 149–160. INRIA, Le Chesnay.

Gower, J. C. (1968). *Biometrika* **55**, 582–585.

Gower, J. C. (1971). *Biometrics* **27**, 857–871.

Gutteridge, C. S. (1987). Characterization of microorganisms by pyrolysis mass spectrometry. *Meth. Microbiol.* **19**, 000–000 (this volume).

Gutteridge, C. S. and Puckey, D. J. (1982). *J. Gen. Microbiol.* **128**, 721–730.

Gyllenberg, H. G. (1963). *Ann. Acad. Sci. Fenn., Ser A, IV Biol.* No. 69, 1–23.

Hall, A. V. (1965). *Nature (London)* **206**, 952.

Hall, A. V. (1973). *Contrib. Bolus Herbarium* **6**, 1–110.

Hill, M. O. and Gauch, H. G. (1980). *Vegetatio* **42**, 47–58.
Hoogerbrugge, R., Willig, S. J. and Kistemaker, P. G. (1983). *Anal. Chem.* **55**, 1711–1712.
Hubálek, Z. (1981). *Biologické listy* **46**, (4), 272–285.
Hubálek, Z. (1982). *J. Appl. Bacteriol.* **52**, 307–318.
Jackman, P. J. H. (1983). *Microbios Lett.* **23**, 119–124.
Jackman, P. J. H. (1985). In *Chemical Methods in Bacterial Systematics* pp. 115–129 (M. Goodfellow and D. Minnikin, eds.). Academic Press, London.
Jackman, P. J. H., Feltham, R. K. A. and Sneath, P. H. A. (1983). *Microbios Lett.* **23**, 87–98.
Jambu, M. and Lebeaux, M.-O. (1983). *Cluster Analysis and Data Analysis*. North-Holland, Amsterdam.
Jardine, N. and Sibson, R. (1968). *Comput. J.* **11**, 177–184.
Jardine, N. and Sibson, R. (1971). *Mathematical Taxonomy*. Wiley-Interscience, Chichester.
Lambert, J. M., Meacock, S. E., Barrs, J., and Smartt, P. F. M. (1973). *Taxon* **22**, 173–176.
Lance, G. N. and Williams, W. T. (1966). *Nature* **212**, 218.
Lance, G. N. and Williams, W. T. (1967a). *Comput. J.* **9**, 373–380.
Lance, G. N. and Williams, W. T. (1967b). *Aust. Comput. J.* **1**, 15–20.
Legendre, L. and Legendre, P. (1983). *Numerical Ecology*. Elsevier, Amsterdam.
Legendre, P., Dallot, S. and Legendre, L. (1985). *Am. Naturalist* **125**, 257–288.
Leredde, H. (1979). La méthode des poles d'attraction—la méthode des poles d'agrégation. Thesis, Université Paris-6.
Lerman, I. C. (1981). *Classification et Analyse Ordinale des Données*. Dunod, Paris.
Lerman, I. C. (1982). Programmes d'analyse des résultats d'une classification automatique. Rapport de Recherche No. 168, INRIA, Le Chesnay.
Lu, S.-Y. and Fu, K. S. (1978). *IEEE Trans. Syst. Man Cyber.* **8**, 381–389.
Milligan, G. W. and Sokol, L. M. (1980). *Educ. Psychol. Meas.* **40**, 755–759.
Norris, J. R. (1980). In *Microbiol Classification and Identification*, (M. Goodfellow and R. Board, eds.), pp. 1–10. Academic Press, London.
Ohmayer, G., Precht, M., Seiler, H. and Busse, M. (1980). *Zbl. Bakt. II. Abt.* **135**, 22–37.
Orlóci, L. (1978). *Multivariate Analysis in Vegetation Research*, 2nd edn. Junk, The Hague.
Orlóci, L. and Kenkel, N. C. (1983). *Introduction to Data Analysis*. University of Western Ontario, London, Ontario.
Pankhurst, R. J. (1978). *Biological Identification, the Principles and Practice of Identification Methods in Biology*. Edward Arnold, London.
Pankhurst, R. J. (1983). *Math. Biosci.* **65**, 209–218.
Payne, R. W. (1978). GENKEY: a program for constructing and printing identification keys and diagnostic tables. Rothamsted Experimental Station, Harpenden, Herts.
Payne, R. W., Yarrow, D. and Barnett, J. A. (1982). *J. Gen. Microbiol.* **128**, 1265–1277.
Prager, E. M. and Wilson, A. C. (1978). *J. Mol. Evol.* **11**, 129–142.
Rohlf, F. J. (1974). *Ann. Rev. Ecol. Syst.* **5**, 101–113.
Rypka, E. W., Fletcher, E. R. and Babb, R. G. (1982a). *J. Clin. Lab. Autom.* **2**, 191–200.
Rypka, E. W., Fletcher, E. R. and Babb, R. G. (1982b). *J. Clin. Lab. Autom.* **2**, 266–280.
Sackin, M. J. (1981). *J. Gen. Microbiol.* **122**, 247–254.

Sackin, M. J. (1985). In *Computer-assisted Bacterial Systematics* (M. Goodfellow, D. Jones and F. G. Priest, eds.) pp. 21–36. Academic Press, London.
Schindler, Z. and Schindler, J. (1983). *Int. J. Biomed. Comput.* **14**, 17–22.
Schulz, G. E. (1983). In *Numerical Taxonomy* (J. Felsenstein, ed.), pp. 484–488. Springer-Verlag, New York.
Shute, L. A., Gutteridge, C. S., Norris, J. R. and Berkeley, R. C. W. (1984). *J. Gen. Microbiol.* **130**, 343–355.
Sibson, R. (1972). *J. R. Statist. Soc.* **B34**, 311–349.
Sneath, P. H. A. (1968). *J. Gen. Microbiol.* **54**, 1–11.
Sneath, P. H. A. (1979a). *Comput. Geosci.* **5**, 127–137.
Sneath, P. H. A. (1979b). *Comput. Geosci.* **5**, 143–155.
Sneath, P. H. A. (1979c). *Comput. Geosci.* **5**, 173–188.
Sneath, P. H. A. (1979d). *Comput. Geosci.* **5**, 195–213.
Sneath, P. H. A. (1979e). *Comput. Geosci.* **5**, 349–357.
Sneath, P. H. A. (1980a). *Comput. Geosci.* **6**, 21–26.
Sneath, P. H. A. (1980b). *Comput. Geosci.* **6**, 27–34.
Sneath, P. H. A. (1980c). *Comput. Geosci.* **6**, 267–278.
Sneath, P. H. A. (1980d). *Classification Soc. Bull.* **4** (4), 22–43.
Sneath, P. H. A. (1983). *J. Gen. Microbiol.* **129**, 1045–1073.
Sneath, P. H. A. (1985). *Comput. Geosci.* **11**, 767–785.
Sneath, P. H. A. and Sokal, R. R. (1973). *Numerical Taxonomy*. Freeman, San Francisco.
Söderström, B., Wold, S., and Blomquist, G. (1982). *J. Gen. Microbiol.* **128**, 1773–1784.
Sokal, R. R. and Rohlf, F. J. (1981). *Syst. Zool.* **30**, 309–325.
Staden, R. (1982). *Nucl. Acids Res.* **10**, 4731–4751.
Stern, N. J. (1982). *J. Food Protection* **45**, 229–233.
Swofford, D. L. and Selander, R. B. (1981). *J. Hered.* **72**, 281–283.
Ward, J. H. (1963). *J. Am. Statist. Assoc.* **58**, 236–244.
Weatherup, S. T. C. (1980). *J. Agric. Sci. (Camb.)* **94**, 31–46.
Wieland, B., Tomasselli, A. G., Noda, L. H., Frank, R., and Schulz, G. E. (1984). *Eur. J. Biochem.* **143**, 331–339.
Wieten, G. (1983). Studies on classification and identification of Mycobacteria by pyrolysis mass spectrometry. Thesis, FOM Institute, Amsterdam.
Wieten, G., Haverkamp, J., Groothuis, D. G., Berwald, L. G. and David, H. L. (1983). *J. Gen. Microbiol.* **129**, 3679–3688.
Wildi, O. and Orlóci, L. (1983). Management and multivariate analysis of vegetation data. *Eidg. Anst. forstl. Versuchswes.* Ber. No. 215, pp. 1–139.
Willcox, W. R., Lapage, S. P., Bascomb, S. and Curtis, W. A. (1973). *J. Gen. Microbiol.* **77**, 317–330.
Willemse-Collinet, M. F., Tromp, Th. F. J. and Huizinga, T. (1980). *J. Appl. Bacteriol.* **49**, 385–393.
Williamson, M. H. (1978). *J. Ecol.* **66**, 911–920.
Williamson, M. H. (1983). *Oikos* **41**, 378–384.
Wishart, D. (1969). *Biometrics* **22**, 165–170.

INDEX

Contents of Previous Volumes